Mike Holt's Illustrated Guide to

Understanding NEC® Requirements for
SOLAR PHOTOVOLTAIC SYSTEMS

Includes Related Code Changes and Analysis

Based on the 2014 NEC®

D1616546

Mike Holt Enterprises, Inc.
888.NEC.CODE (632.2633) • www.MikeHolt.com

NOTICE TO THE READER

Mike Holt's Illustrated Guide to Understanding NEC® Requirements for Solar Photovoltaic Systems,
based on the 2014 NEC®

First Printing: January 2014

Author: Mike Holt
Technical Illustrator: Mike Culbreath
Cover Design: Madalina Iordache-Levay
Layout Design and Typesetting: Cathleen Kwas

COPYRIGHT © 2014 Charles Michael Holt
ISBN 978-1-932685-77-0

Produced and Printed in the USA

For more information, call 888.NEC.CODE (632.2633), or e-mail Info@MikeHolt.com.

 This logo is a registered trademark of Mike Holt Enterprises, Inc.

If you are an instructor and would like to request an examination copy of this or other Mike Holt Publications:

Call: 888.NEC.CODE (632.2633) • Fax: 352.360.0983
E-mail: Info@MikeHolt.com • Visit: www.MikeHolt.com

You can download a sample PDF of all our publications by visiting www.MikeHolt.com

*I dedicate this book to the
Lord Jesus Christ, my mentor and teacher*

Niko Holst

Our Commitment

We are committed to serving the electrical industry with integrity and respect by always searching for the most accurate interpretation of the *NEC*® and creating the highest quality instructional material that makes learning easy.

We are invested in the idea of changing lives, and build our products with the goal of not only helping you meet your licensing requirements, but also with the goal that this knowledge will improve your expertise in the field and help you throughout your career.

We are committed to building a life-long relationship with you, and to helping you in each stage of your electrical career. Whether you are an apprentice just getting started in the industry, or an electrician preparing to take an exam, we are here to help you. When you need Continuing Education credits to renew your license, we will do everything we can to get our online courses and seminars approved in your state. Or if you are a contractor looking to train your team, we have a solution for you. And if you have advanced to the point where you are now teaching others, we are here to help you build your program and provide tools to make that task easier.

We genuinely care about providing quality electrical training that will help you take your skills to the next level.

Thanks for choosing Mike Holt Enterprises for your electrical training needs. We are here to help you every step of the way and encourage you to contact us so we can be a part of your success.

God bless,

TABLE OF CONTENTS

About This Textbook xi

About the *National Electrical Code* xv

About the Author xx

About the Illustrator xxi

About the Team xxii

Article 90—Introduction to the *National Electrical Code* 1
90.1   Purpose of the *NEC* 2
90.2   Scope of the *NEC* 3
90.3   *Code* Arrangement 4
90.4   Enforcement 5
90.5   Mandatory Requirements and Explanatory Material ... 6
90.6   Formal Interpretations 7
90.7   Examination of Equipment for Product Safety 7
90.9   Units of Measurement 7

Article 90 Practice Questions 8

CHAPTER 1—GENERAL 11

Article 100—Definitions 13

Article 110—Requirements for Electrical Installations 33
110.1   Scope 33
110.2   Approval of Conductors and Equipment 33
110.3   Examination, Identification, Installation, and Use of Equipment 34
110.5   Copper Conductors 35
110.6   Conductor Sizes 35
110.7   Wiring Integrity 35
110.8   Suitable Wiring Methods 36
110.9   Interrupting Protection Rating 36
110.10   Circuit Impedance, Short-Circuit Current Rating, and Other Characteristics 37

110.11   Deteriorating Agents 38
110.12   Mechanical Execution of Work 38
110.13   Mounting and Cooling of Equipment 40
110.14   Conductor Termination and Splicing 40
110.16   Arc-Flash Hazard Warning 46
110.21   Markings 46
110.22   Identification of Disconnecting Means 47
110.25   Lockable Disconnecting Means 47
110.26   Spaces About Electrical Equipment 48
110.27   Guarding 56
110.28   Enclosure Types 57

Chapter 1 Practice Questions 58

CHAPTER 2—WIRING AND PROTECTION 71

Article 200—Use and Identification of Grounded and Neutral Conductors 73
200.1   Scope 73
200.6   Grounded and Neutral Conductor Identification 73

Article 230—Services 77
230.1   Scope 78
230.40   Number of Service-Entrance Conductor Sets 78
230.43   Wiring Methods 78
230.46   Spliced Conductors 79
230.66   Listed as Suitable for Service Equipment 79
230.70   Disconnect Requirements 80
230.71   Number of Disconnects 81
230.72   Grouping of Disconnects 82
230.76   Manual or Power Operated 82
230.77   Indicating 83
230.81   Connection to Terminals 83
230.82   Connected on Supply Side of the Service Disconnect 83
230.90   Overload Protection Required 84
230.91   Location of Overcurrent Protection 84

Article 240—Overcurrent Protection 85
240.1   Scope 86
240.2   Definitions 86
240.4   Protection of Conductors 87
240.6   Standard Ampere Ratings 88
240.10 Supplementary Overcurrent Protection 89
240.15 Ungrounded Conductors 89
240.21 Overcurrent Protection Location in Circuit 89
240.24 Location of Overcurrent Devices 92
240.32 Damp or Wet Locations 95
240.33 Vertical Position 95
240.60 General 95
240.61 Classification 96
240.80 Method of Operation 96
240.81 Indicating 96
240.82 Nontamperable 97
240.83 Markings 97

Article 250—Grounding and Bonding 99
Part I. General 99
250.1   Scope 99
250.4   General Requirements for Grounding and Bonding ... 99
250.8   Termination of Grounding and Bonding
        Conductors 102
250.10 Protection of Fittings 103
250.12 Clean Surfaces 103
Part II. System Grounding and Bonding 104
250.24 Service Equipment—Grounding and Bonding 104
250.30 Separately Derived Systems (Transformers)—
        Grounding and Bonding 108
**Part III. Grounding Electrode System and Grounding
Electrode Conductor** 113
250.50 Grounding Electrode System 113
250.52 Grounding Electrode Types 114
250.53 Grounding Electrode Installation Requirements 117
250.54 Auxiliary Grounding Electrodes 121
250.62 Grounding Electrode Conductor 121
250.64 Grounding Electrode Conductor Installation 122
250.66 Sizing AC Grounding Electrode Conductor 125
250.68 Termination to the Grounding Electrode 126
250.70 Grounding Electrode Conductor Termination
        Fittings 128

**Part IV. Grounding Enclosure, Raceway, and Service
Cable Connections** 128
250.86 Other Enclosures 128
Part V. Bonding 128
250.90 General 128
250.92 Bonding Equipment for Services 128
250.96 Bonding Other Enclosures 131
250.97 Bonding Metal Parts Containing Circuits over
        150V to Ground 131
250.102 Bonding Conductors and Jumpers 132
**Part VI. Equipment Grounding and Equipment
Grounding Conductors** 134
250.112 Specific Equipment Fastened in Place or
        Connected by Permanent Wiring Methods 134
250.114 Cord-and-Plug-Connected Equipment 134
250.118 Types of Equipment Grounding Conductors 134
250.119 Identification of Equipment Grounding
        Conductors 138
250.120 Equipment Grounding Conductor Installation 139
250.122 Sizing Equipment Grounding Conductor 140
Part VII. Methods of Equipment Grounding 141
250.134 Equipment Connected by Permanent Wiring
        Methods 141
250.136 Equipment Considered Grounded 141
250.138 Cord-and-Plug-Connected Equipment 142
250.142 Use of Neutral Conductor for Equipment
        Grounding 142
250.148 Continuity and Attachment of Equipment
        Grounding Conductors in Metal Boxes 142
Part VIII. Direct-Current Systems 143
250.166 Sizing Grounding Electrode Conductor 143

Chapter 2 Practice Questions 144

CHAPTER 3—WIRING METHODS AND MATERIALS 163
**Article 300—General Requirements for Wiring
Methods and Materials** 167
300.1   Scope 167
300.3   Conductors 168
300.4   Protection Against Physical Damage 169

300.5 Underground Installations 172
300.6 Protection Against Corrosion and Deterioration 177
300.7 Raceways Exposed to Different Temperatures 179
300.8 Not Permitted in Raceways 180
300.9 Raceways in Wet Locations Above Grade 180
300.10 Electrical Continuity 181
300.12 Mechanical Continuity 181
300.13 Splices and Pigtails 182
300.14 Length of Free Conductors 182
300.15 Boxes or Conduit Bodies 183
300.17 Raceway Sizing 184
300.18 Inserting Conductors in Raceways 186
300.19 Supporting Conductors in Vertical Raceways 186
300.20 Induced Currents in Ferrous Metal Enclosures
and Raceways 187
300.21 Spread of Fire or Products of Combustion 188
300.22 Wiring in Ducts Not for Air Handling, Fabricated
Ducts for Environmental Air, and Other Spaces
for Environmental Air (Plenums) 189
300.23 Panels Designed to Allow Access 191

Article 310—Conductors for General Wiring 193
310.1 Scope 194
310.10 Uses Permitted 194
310.15 Conductor Ampacity 197
310.104 Conductor Construction and Application 202
310.106 Conductors 203
310.110 Conductor Identification 203

Article 312—Cabinets 205
312.1 Scope 205
312.2 Damp or Wet Locations 206
312.3 Installed in Walls 206
312.4 Repairing Gaps 206
312.5 Enclosures 206
312.6 Deflection of Conductors 208
312.8 Cabinets With Splices, Taps, and Feed-Through
Conductors 208

**Article 314—Outlet, Device, Pull and Junction
Boxes; Conduit Bodies; and Handhole Enclosures** ... 211
314.1 Scope 211
314.3 Nonmetallic Boxes 211

314.4 Metal Boxes 212
314.15 Damp or Wet Locations 212
314.17 Conductors That Enter Boxes or Conduit Bodies 212
314.23 Support of Boxes and Conduit Bodies 213
314.28 Boxes and Conduit Bodies for Conductors 4 AWG
and Larger 214
314.29 Wiring to be Accessible 217
314.30 Handhole Enclosures 218

Article 320—Armored Cable (Type AC) 219
320.1 Scope 219
320.2 Definition 219
320.10 Uses Permitted 220
320.12 Uses Not Permitted 220
320.15 Exposed Work 220
320.17 Through or Parallel to Framing Members 220
320.23 In Accessible Attics or Roof Spaces 221
320.24 Bends 221
320.30 Securing and Supporting 221
320.40 Boxes and Fittings 222
320.80 Conductor Ampacity 222
320.100 Construction 223
320.108 Equipment Grounding Conductor 223

Article 330—Metal-Clad Cable (Type MC) 225
330.1 Scope 225
330.2 Definition 225
330.10 Uses Permitted 226
330.12 Uses Not Permitted 227
330.17 Through or Parallel to Framing Members 227
330.23 In Accessible Attics or Roof Spaces 227
330.24 Bends 227
330.30 Securing and Supporting 228
330.40 Fittings 228
330.80 Conductor Ampacities 229
330.108 Equipment Grounding Conductor 229

**Article 338—Service-Entrance Cable
(Types SE and USE)** 231
338.1 Scope 231
338.2 Definitions 231
338.10 Uses Permitted 232
338.12 Uses Not Permitted 232
338.24 Bends 233

Table of Contents

Article 340—Underground Feeder and Branch-Circuit Cable (Type UF) 235

340.1 Scope 235
340.2 Definition 235
340.6 Listing Requirements 236
340.10 Uses Permitted 236
340.12 Uses Not Permitted 236
340.24 Bends 236
340.80 Ampacity 236
340.112 Insulation 236

Article 342—Intermediate Metal Conduit (Type IMC) 237

342.1 Scope 237
342.2 Definition 237
342.6 Listing Requirements 237
342.10 Uses Permitted 238
342.14 Dissimilar Metals 238
342.20 Trade Size 238
342.22 Number of Conductors 238
342.24 Bends 239
342.26 Number of Bends (360°) 239
342.28 Reaming 239
342.30 Securing and Supporting 239
342.42 Couplings and Connectors 241
342.46 Bushings 241

Article 344—Rigid Metal Conduit (Type RMC) 243

344.1 Scope 243
344.2 Definition 243
344.6 Listing Requirements 244
344.10 Uses Permitted 244
344.14 Dissimilar Metals 244
344.20 Trade Size 244
344.22 Number of Conductors 245
344.24 Bends 245
344.26 Number of Bends (360°) 245
344.28 Reaming 245
344.30 Securing and Supporting 246
344.42 Couplings and Connectors 247
344.46 Bushings 248
344.100 Construction 248
344.130 Standard Lengths 248

Article 348—Flexible Metal Conduit (Type FMC) 249

348.1 Scope 249
348.2 Definition 249
348.6 Listing Requirements 249
348.10 Uses Permitted 249
348.12 Uses Not Permitted 250
348.20 Trade Size 250
348.22 Number of Conductors 250
348.24 Bends 251
348.26 Number of Bends (360°) 251
348.28 Trimming 251
348.30 Securing and Supporting 251
348.42 Fittings 252
348.60 Grounding and Bonding 252

Article 350—Liquidtight Flexible Metal Conduit (Type LFMC) 253

350.1 Scope 253
350.2 Definition 253
350.6 Listing Requirements 253
350.10 Uses Permitted 253
350.12 Uses Not Permitted 254
350.20 Trade Size 254
350.22 Number of Conductors 254
350.24 Bends 255
350.26 Number of Bends (360°) 255
350.30 Securing and Supporting 255
350.42 Fittings 256
350.60 Grounding and Bonding 256

Article 352—Rigid Polyvinyl Chloride Conduit (Type PVC) 257

352.1 Scope 257
352.2 Definition 257
352.10 Uses Permitted 258
352.12 Uses Not Permitted 259
352.20 Trade Size 259
352.22 Number of Conductors 259
352.24 Bends 260
352.26 Number of Bends (360°) 260
352.28 Trimming 260
352.30 Securing and Supporting 260
352.44 Expansion Fittings 261

352.46 Bushings 262
352.48 Joints 263
352.60 Equipment Grounding Conductor 263

Article 358—Electrical Metallic Tubing (Type EMT) 265

358.1   Scope 265
358.2   Definition 265
358.6   Listing Requirement 265
358.10 Uses Permitted 265
358.12 Uses Not Permitted 266
358.20 Trade Size 266
358.22 Number of Conductors 266
358.24 Bends 267
358.26 Number of Bends (360°) 267
358.28 Reaming and Threading 267
358.30 Securing and Supporting 268
358.42 Couplings and Connectors 268
358.60 Grounding 269

Article 376—Metal Wireways 271

376.1   Scope 271
376.2   Definition 271
376.10 Uses Permitted 272
376.12 Uses Not Permitted 272
376.21 Conductors—Maximum Size 272
376.22 Number of Conductors and Ampacity ... 272
376.23 Wireway Sizing 273
376.30 Supports 273
376.56 Splices, Taps, and Power Distribution Blocks 273

Article 392—Cable Trays 275

392.1   Scope 275
392.2   Definition 275
392.10 Uses Permitted 276
392.12 Uses Not Permitted 277
392.18 Cable Tray Installations 277
392.20 Cable and Conductor Installation 278
392.22 Number of Conductors or Cables 278
392.30 Securing and Supporting 278
392.46 Bushed Raceway 278
392.56 Cable Splices 278
392.60 Equipment Grounding Conductor 278

392.80 Ampacity of Conductors 279
Chapter 3 Practice Questions 280

CHAPTER 4—EQUIPMENT FOR GENERAL USE 305

Article 404—Switches 307

404.1   Scope 307
404.3   Switch Enclosures 307
404.4   Damp or Wet Locations 307
404.6   Position of Knife Switches 308
404.7   Indicating 308
404.8   Accessibility and Grouping 308
404.11 Circuit Breakers Used as Switches 309
404.12 Grounding of Enclosures 309
404.15 Switch Marking 309

Article 408—Switchboards and Panelboards 311

408.1   Scope 311
408.4   Field Identification 311
408.5   Clearance for Conductors Entering Bus Enclosures 312
408.7   Unused Openings 312
408.36 Overcurrent Protection of Panelboards .. 313
408.37 Panelboards in Damp or Wet Locations .. 314
408.40 Equipment Grounding Conductor 314
408.41 Neutral Conductor Terminations 314

Article 450—Transformers 315

450.1   Scope 315
450.3   Overcurrent Protection 315
450.9   Ventilation 316
450.10 Grounding and Bonding 316
450.11 Marking 317
450.13 Transformer Accessibility 317
450.14 Disconnecting Means 318

Article 480—Storage Batteries 319

480.1   Scope 319
480.2   Definitions 320
480.3   Battery and Cell Terminations 321
480.4   Wiring and Equipment Supplied from Batteries 321

Table of Contents

| 480.8 | Racks and Trays | 321 |
| 480.9 | Battery Locations | 322 |

Chapter 4 Practice Questions ... 324

CHAPTER 6—SPECIAL EQUIPMENT ... 329

Article 690—Solar Photovoltaic (PV) Systems ... 331

Part I. General ... 331
690.1	Scope	331
690.2	Definitions	332
690.3	Other Articles	338
690.4	General Requirements	338
690.5	Ground-Fault Protection	339
690.6	Alternating-Current Modules	341

Part II. Circuit Requirements ... 341
690.7	Maximum Voltage	341
690.8	Circuit Current and Circuit Sizing	344
690.9	Overcurrent Protection	350
690.10	Stand-Alone Systems	354
690.11	Arc-Fault Circuit Protection (Direct Current)	355
690.12	Rapid Shutdown of PV Systems on Buildings	355

Part III. Disconnecting Means ... 356
690.13	Building Supplied by a PV System	356
690.15	PV Equipment Disconnect	358
690.16	Disconnecting Means for Fuses	359
690.17	Disconnect Type (dc)	360
690.18	Installation and Service	362

Part IV. Wiring Methods ... 363
690.31	Wiring Methods	363
690.33	Connectors	367
690.34	Access to Boxes	368
690.35	Ungrounded Systems	368

Part V. Grounding ... 369
690.41	System Grounding	369
690.42	Point of Grounding Connection	370
690.43	Equipment Grounding (Bonding)	370
690.45	Size of Equipment Grounding Conductors	372
690.46	Array Equipment Grounding Conductors	373
690.47	Grounding Electrode System	373
690.48	Continuity of Equipment Grounding	377
690.49	Continuity of System Grounding	377

Part VI. Marking ... 377
690.53	PV dc Power Source Label	377
690.54	Interactive System	378
690.55	PV Systems with Energy Storage	378
690.56	Identification of Power Sources	378

Part VII. Connection to Other Sources ... 380
690.60	Interactive Systems	380
690.61	Loss of Interactive System Power	380
690.63	Unbalanced Interconnections	380
690.64	Point of Connection	380

Part VIII. Storage Batteries ... 381
690.71	Storage Battery Installation	381
690.72	Charge Control	382
690.74	Battery Interconnections	382

Part X. Electric Vehicle Charging ... 382
| 690.90 | General | 382 |
| 690.91 | Charging Equipment | 382 |

Chapter 6 Practice Questions ... 383

CHAPTER 7—SPECIAL CONDITIONS ... 395

Article 705—Interconnected Electric Power Production Sources ... 397
705.1	Scope	397
705.2	Definitions	398
705.6	Qualified Persons	398
705.10	Directory of Power Sources	398
705.12	Point of Connection	399
705.31	Location of Overcurrent Protection	407
705.32	Ground-Fault Protection	408
705.40	Loss of Primary Source	408
705.100	Voltage Unbalanced (Imbalanced) Interconnections	408

Chapter 7 Practice Questions ... 410

FINAL EXAM A FOR SOLAR PHOTOVOLTAIC SYSTEMS ... 413

FINAL EXAM B FOR SOLAR PHOTOVOLTAIC SYSTEMS ... 423

INDEX ... 433

Mike Holt's Illustrated Guide to Understanding NEC Requirements for Solar Photovoltaic Systems

ABOUT THIS TEXTBOOK

Mike Holt's Illustrated Guide to Understanding NEC® Requirements for Solar Photovoltaic Systems

This textbook covers the *National Electrical Code®* requirements as they relate to Solar Photovoltaic (PV) systems. The *NEC®* rules that govern PV systems are very comprehensive and complicated, and as a result could be easily misinterpreted. The intent of this textbook is to help you better understand how the *NEC* safety requirements should be applied, and as additional explanation we include the reasons and impact for a rule change that occurred between the 2011 *NEC* and 2014 *NEC*.

The writing style of this textbook is meant to be informative, practical, useful, easy to read, and applicable for everyday use. Just like all of Mike Holt's textbooks, this one contains hundreds of full-color illustrations showing the safety requirements of the *National Electrical Code* in practical use, helping you visualize the *Code* in today's electrical installations.

This illustrated textbook contains cautions regarding possible conflicts or confusing *NEC* requirements, tips on proper electrical installations, and warnings of dangers related to improper electrical installations. In spite of this effort, some rules may still seem unclear or need additional editorial improvement.

We can't eliminate confusing, conflicting, or controversial *Code* requirements, but we do try to put them into sharper focus to help you understand their intended purpose. Sometimes a requirement is confusing and it might be hard to understand its actual application. When this occurs, this textbook will point the situation out in an upfront and straightforward manner. We apologize in advance if that ever seems disrespectful, but our intention is to help the industry understand the current *NEC* as best as possible, point out areas that need refinement, and encourage *Code* users to be a part of the change process that creates a better *NEC* for the future.

The Scope of this Textbook

This textbook, *Mike Holt's Illustrated Guide to Understanding NEC Requirements for Solar Photovoltaic Systems*, covers the important *NEC* rules that apply to Solar PV systems. The scope of the textbook covers the general requirements contained in Articles 90 through 480, as well as the specific rules relating to Solar PV systems Articles 690 and 705. It is based on the following conditions:

1. **Power Systems and Voltage.** All power-supply systems are assumed to be one of the following, unless identified otherwise:

   - 2-wire, single-phase, 120V
   - 3-wire, single-phase, 120/240V
   - 4-wire, three-phase, 120/240V Delta
   - 4-wire, three-phase, 120/208V or 277/480V Wye

2. **Electrical Calculations.** Unless the questions or examples specifies three-phase, they're based on a single-phase power supply. In addition, all amperage calculations are rounded to the nearest ampere in accordance with Section 220.5(B).

3. **Conductor Material.** Conductors are assumed to be copper, unless aluminum is identified or specified.

4. **Conductor Sizing.** Conductors are sized based on a THHN/THWN-2 copper conductor terminating on a 75°C terminal in accordance with 110.14(C), unless the question or example indicates otherwise.

5. **Overcurrent Device.** The term "overcurrent device" refers to a molded-case circuit breaker, unless specified otherwise. Where a fuse is specified, it's a single-element type fuse, also known as a "one-time fuse," unless the text specifies otherwise.

This textbook is to be used along with the *NEC*, not as a replacement for it. Be sure to have a copy of the 2014 *National Electrical Code* handy. Compare what's being explained in this textbook to what the *Code* book says, and discuss any topics that you find difficult to understand with others.

You'll notice that we've paraphrased a great deal of the *NEC* wording, and some of the article and section titles appear different from the text in the actual *Code* book. We believe doing so makes it easier to understand the content of the rule, so keep this in mind when comparing this textbook to the actual *NEC*.

This textbook follows the *NEC* format, but it doesn't cover every *Code* requirement. For example, it doesn't include every article,

section, subsection, exception, or Informational Note. So don't be concerned if you see that the textbook contains Exception 1 and Exception 3, but not Exception 2.

We hope that as you read through this textbook, you'll allow sufficient time to review the text along with the outstanding graphics and examples, which are invaluable to your understanding.

How to Use This Textbook

The layout of this textbook incorporates special features designed not only to help you navigate easily through the material but to enhance your understanding as well.

Color coding and a modular format make it easy to navigate through each section of the textbook.

Framed white notes contain examples and practical application questions and answers. **Formulas** are easily identifiable in green text in the gray bar.

Graphics with an icon and green border contain a 2014 *Code* change, with *NEC* text changes underlined in green. Green-bordered graphics with no green underlined text most likely indicate that the change is the removal of some text. Graphics without a colored border support the concept being discussed, but nothing in the graphic was affected by a change for 2014.

Bolded Author's Comments are intended to help you understand the *NEC* material and background information.

Yellow "sticky notes" contain an an analysis of the *Code* change for the 2014 *NEC*.

A QR code under the article number can be scanned with a smartphone app to take you to a sample video clip so you can watch Mike and the DVD panel discuss this topic.

Text that's underlined in the chapter color denotes a change in the *Code* for 2014.

Danger, Caution, and Warning icons highlight areas of concern.

Light gray sections with a border in the chapter color contain additional background information.

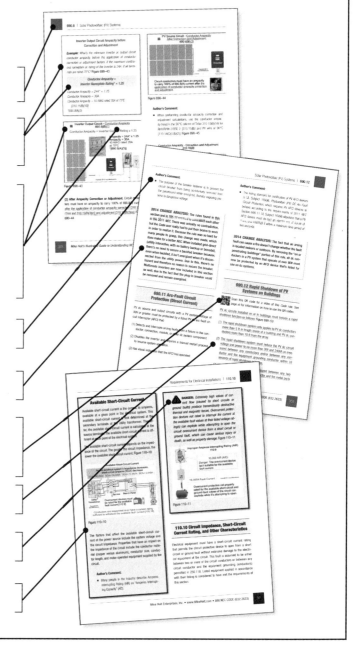

Cross-References, Notes, and Exceptions

Cross-References. This textbook contains several *NEC* cross-references to other related *Code* requirements to help you develop a better understanding of how the *NEC* rules relate to one another. These cross-references are indicated by *Code* section numbers in brackets, an example of which is "[90.4]."

Informational Notes. Informational Notes contained in the *NEC* will be identified in this textbook as "Note," except when that phrase is used in the change summary (gray background) or analysis (yellow background).

Exceptions. Exceptions contained in this textbook will be identified as "Ex" and not spelled out.

Textbook Corrections

We're committed to providing you the finest product with the fewest errors. We take great care in researching the *NEC* requirements to ensure this textbook is correct, but we're realistic and know that there'll be errors found and reported after this textbook is printed. This can occur because the *NEC* is dramatically changed each *Code* cycle; new articles are added, some are deleted, some are relocated, and many are renumbered.

The last thing we want is for you to have problems finding, communicating, or accessing this information. Any errors found after printing are listed on our website, so if you find an error, first check to see if it's already been corrected by going to www.MikeHolt.com, click on "Books," and then click on "Corrections" (www.MikeHolt.com/bookcorrections.htm).

If you believe that there's an error of any kind (typographical, grammatical, technical, or anything else) in this textbook or in the Answer Key and it isn't already listed on the website, e-mail Corrections@MikeHolt.com. Be sure to include the textbook title, page number, and any other pertinent information.

If you have adopted Mike Holt textbooks for use in your classroom you can register for up-to-date answer keys that can be downloaded from our website. To register and receive a log-in password, go to our website www.MikeHolt.com, click on

"Instructors" in the sidebar of links, and then click on "Answer Keys." On this same page you'll also find instructions for accessing and downloading these answer keys. Please note that this feature will only work after you've received a log-in password.

Technical Questions

As you progress through this textbook, you might find that you don't understand every explanation, example, calculation, or comment. Don't become frustrated, and don't get down on yourself. Remember, this is the *National Electrical Code*, and sometimes the best attempt to explain a concept isn't enough to make it perfectly clear. If you're still confused, visit www.MikeHolt.com, and post your question on our free Code Forum for help. The forum is a moderated community of electrical professionals where you can exchange ideas and post technical questions that will be answered by your peers.

QR Codes

What's this symbol? It's a QR code and gives you the ability to use your smartphone to scan the image (using a barcode reader app) and be directed to a website. For example, the QR code to the right (when captured) will direct your smartphone to the Mike Holt Enterprises website. We've included these in various places in our textbook to make it easier for you to go directly to the website page referenced.

Follow the QR Code! When you see a QR code next to a section in the text, scan it with your smartphone to bring it to life. You will be able to watch a video clip that shows Mike and his panel of experts discussing this section!

These video clips are samples from the DVDs that were created for this book. Whether you're a visual or an auditory learner, watching the DVDs will enhance your knowledge and understanding of Solar PV Systems.

If you haven't already ordered the Solar Photovoltaic DVDs, you can order them at a discounted price by calling 888.632.2633.

Additional Products to Help You Learn

Understanding NEC Requirements for Solar Photovoltaic Systems DVDs, based on the 2014 NEC

One of the best ways to get the most out of this textbook is to use it in conjunction with the corresponding DVDs. Mike Holt's DVDs provide a 360° view of each topic with specialized commentary from Mike and his panel of industry experts.

To order your copy of the DVDs at a discounted price, call our office at 888.632.2633.

Detailed *Code* Library

When you really need to understand the *NEC*, there's no better way to learn it than with Mike's Detailed *Code* Library. It takes you step-by-step through the *NEC*, in *Code* order with detailed illustrations, great practice questions, and in-depth DVD analysis. This library is perfect for engineers, electricians, contractors, and electrical inspectors.

- *Understanding the National Electrical Code—Volume 1*
- *Understanding the National Electrical Code—Volume 2*
- *NEC Exam Practice Questions* workbook
- *General Requirements* DVDs (2)
- *Grounding versus Bonding* DVDs (2)
- *Wiring Methods* DVDs (2)
- *Equipment for General Use* DVD
- *Special Occupancies* DVD
- *Special Equipment* DVD
- *Limited Energy and Communications Systems* DVD

Order Mike Holt's Detailed *Code* Library by calling 888.NEC.CODE (632.2633) or going to our website at www.MikeHolt.com/14DECO.

2014 Ultimate Solar PV Library

As the market for Solar PV systems and businesses continues to grow, the challenges for the designer, installer, contractor, instructor or inspector continue to evolve. But don't be intimidated—Mike's Ultimate Solar PV Library will give you the edge. Take your PV skills to the next level and build a successful business.

Program includes these great Solar Resources:

- *Mike Holt's Understanding NEC Requirements for Solar Photovoltaic Systems* textbook plus 2 DVDs
- *Photovoltaic Systems* textbook with CD Rom, Jim Dunlop
- OSEIA Solar Construction Safety PDF
- Bill Brook's Field inspection Guidelines PDF

Plus these additional libraries to round out your education:

- *Mike Holt's Basic Electrical Theory* textbook and 3 DVDs
- *Mike Holt's Electrical Estimating* textbook and 4 DVDs
- *Mike Holt's Business Management Skills* workbook and DVD

For more information visit www.MikeHolt.com/solar.

2014 *Code* Book

Whether you prefer the softbound, spiral bound or the loose-leaf version, everyone should have an updated *Code* book for accurate reference.

To order, visit www.MikeHolt.com/14code.

Tabs

To navigate your *Code* book correctly, it helps to have it tabbed. Mike's best-selling tabs make this easy.

To order, visit www.MikeHolt.com/14tabs.

ABOUT THE
NATIONAL ELECTRICAL CODE

The *National Electrical Code* is written for persons who understand electrical terms, theory, safety procedures, and electrical trade practices. These individuals include electricians, electrical contractors, electrical inspectors, electrical engineers, designers, and other qualified persons. The *Code* isn't written to serve as an instructional or teaching manual for untrained individuals [90.1(A)].

Learning to use the *NEC* can be likened to learning the strategy needed to play the game of chess well; it's a great game if you enjoy mental warfare. When learning to play chess, you must first learn the names of the game pieces, how they're placed on the board, and how each one is moved.

Once you understand the fundamentals, you're ready to start playing the game. Unfortunately, at this point all you can do is make crude moves, because you really don't understand how all the information works together. To play chess well, you'll need to learn how to use your knowledge by working on subtle strategies before you can work your way up to the more intriguing and complicated moves.

The *Code* is updated every three years to accommodate new electrical products and materials, changing technologies, improved installation techniques, and to make editorial refinements to improve readability and application. While the uniform adoption of each new edition of the *NEC* is the best approach for all involved in the electrical industry, many inspection jurisdictions modify the *Code* when it's adopted. To further complicate this situation, the *NEC* allows the authority having jurisdiction, typically the "Electrical Inspector," the flexibility to waive specific *Code* requirements, and to permit alternative methods. This is only allowed when he or she is assured the completed electrical installation is equivalent in establishing and maintaining effective safety [90.4].

Keeping up with requirements of the *Code* should be the goal of everyone involved in the safety of electrical installations. This includes electrical installers, contractors, owners, inspectors,

engineers, instructors, and others concerned with electrical installations.

About the 2014 *NEC*

The actual process of changing the *Code* takes about two years, and it involves hundreds of individuals making an effort to have the *NEC* as current and accurate as possible. Let's review how this process works:

Step 1. Proposals—November, 2011. Anybody can submit a proposal to change the *Code* before the proposal closing date. Thousands of proposals were submitted to modify the 2011 *NEC* and create the 2014 *Code*. Of these proposals, several hundred rules were revised that significantly affect the electrical industry. Some changes were editorial revisions, while others were more significant, such as new articles, sections, exceptions, and Informational Notes.

Step 2. *Code*-Making Panel(s) Review Proposals—January, 2012. All *Code* change proposals were reviewed by *Code*-Making Panels. There were 19 panels in the 2014 revision process who voted to accept, reject, or modify proposals.

Step 3. Report on Proposals (ROP)—July, 2012. The voting of the *Code*-Making Panels on the proposals was published for public review in a document called the "Report on Proposals," frequently referred to as the "ROP."

Step 4. Public Comments—October, 2012. Once the ROP was available, public comments were submitted asking the *Code*-Making Panel members to revise their earlier actions on change proposals, based on new information. The closing date for "Comments" was October, 2012.

Step 5. Comments Reviewed by *Code* Panels—December, 2012. The *Code*-Making Panels met again to review, discuss, and vote on public comments.

Step 6. Report on Comments (ROC)—March, 2013. The voting on the "Comments" was published for public review in a document called the "Report on Comments," frequently referred to as the "ROC."

Step 7. Electrical Section—June, 2013. The NFPA Electrical Section discussed and reviewed the work of the *Code*-Making Panels. The Electrical Section developed recommendations on last-minute motions to revise the proposed *NEC* draft that would be presented at the NFPA's annual meeting.

Step 8. NFPA Annual Meeting—June, 2013. The 2014 *NEC* was voted by the NFPA members to approve the action of the *Code*-Making Panels at the annual meeting, after a number of motions (often called "floor actions" or "NITMAMs") were voted on.

Step 9. Standards Council Review Appeals and Approves the 2014 *NEC*—July, 2013. The NFPA Standards Council reviewed the record of the *Code*-making process and approved publication of the 2014 *NEC*.

Step 10. 2014 *NEC* Published—September, 2013. The 2014 *National Electrical Code* was published, following the NFPA Board of Directors review of appeals.

> **Author's Comment:** Proposals and comments can be submitted online at the NFPA website (www.nfpa.org). From the homepage, click on "Codes and Standards", then find NFPA 70 (*National Electrical Code*). From there, follow the on screen instructions to download the proposal form. The deadline for proposals to create the 2017 *National Electrical Code* will be around November of 2014. If you would like to see something changed in the *Code*, you're encouraged to participate in the process.

Not a Game

Electrical work isn't a game, and it must be taken very seriously. Learning the basics of electricity, important terms and concepts, as well as the basic layout of the *NEC* gives you just enough knowledge to be dangerous. There are thousands of specific and unique applications of electrical installations, and the *Code* doesn't cover every one of them. To safely apply the *NEC*, you must understand the purpose of a rule and how it affects the safety aspects of the installation.

NEC Terms and Concepts

The *NEC* contains many technical terms, so it's crucial for *Code* users to understand their meanings and their applications. If you don't understand a term used in a *Code* rule, it will be impossible to properly apply the *NEC* requirement. Be sure you understand that Article 100 defines the terms that apply to two or more *Code* articles. For example, the term "Dwelling Unit" is found in many articles; if you don't know what a dwelling unit is, how can you apply the requirements for it?

In addition, many articles have terms unique for that specific article and definitions of those terms are only applicable for that given article. For example, Section 250.2 contains the definitions of terms that only apply to Article 250—Grounding and Bonding.

Small Words, Grammar, and Punctuation

It's not only the technical words that require close attention, because even the simplest of words can make a big difference to the application of a rule. The word "or" can imply alternate choices for wiring methods, while "and" can mean an additional requirement. Let's not forget about grammar and punctuation. The location of a comma can dramatically change the requirement of a rule.

Slang Terms or Technical Jargon

Electricians, engineers, and other trade-related professionals use slang terms or technical jargon that isn't shared by all. This makes it very difficult to communicate because not everybody understands the intent or application of those slang terms. So where possible, be sure you use the proper word, and don't use a word if you don't understand its definition and application. For example, lots of electricians use the term "pigtail" when describing the short conductor for the connection of a receptacle, switch, luminaire, or equipment. Although they may understand it, not everyone does.

NEC Style and Layout

Before we get into the details of the *NEC*, we need to take a few moments to understand its style and layout. Understanding the structure and writing style of the *Code* is very important before it can be used and applied effectively. The *National Electrical Code* is organized into ten major components.

1. Table of Contents
2. Article 90 (Introduction to the *Code*)
3. Chapters 1 through 9 (major categories)
4. Articles 90 through 840 (individual subjects)
5. Parts (divisions of an article)
6. Sections and Tables (*NEC* requirements)
7. Exceptions (*Code* permissions)
8. Informational Notes (explanatory material)
9. Annexes (information)
10. Index

1. Table of Contents. The Table of Contents displays the layout of the chapters, articles, and parts as well as the page numbers. It's an excellent resource and should be referred to periodically to observe the interrelationship of the various *NEC* components. When attempting to locate the rules for a particular situation, knowledgeable *Code* users often go first to the Table of Contents to quickly find the specific *NEC* Part that applies.

2. Introduction. The *NEC* begins with Article 90, the introduction to the *Code*. It contains the purpose of the *NEC*, what's covered and what isn't covered along with how the *Code* is arranged. It also gives information on enforcement and how mandatory and permissive rules are written as well as how explanatory material is included. Article 90 also includes information on formal interpretations, examination of equipment for safety, wiring planning, and information about formatting units of measurement.

3. Chapters. There are nine chapters, each of which is divided into articles. The articles fall into one of four groupings: General Requirements (Chapters 1 through 4), Specific Requirements (Chapters 5 through 7), Communications Systems (Chapter 8), and Tables (Chapter 9).

Chapter 1—General
Chapter 2—Wiring and Protection

Chapter 3—Wiring Methods and Materials
Chapter 4—Equipment for General Use
Chapter 5—Special Occupancies
Chapter 6—Special Equipment
Chapter 7—Special Conditions
Chapter 8—Communications Systems (Telephone, Data, Satellite, Cable TV and Broadband)
Chapter 9—Tables–Conductor and Raceway Specifications

4. Articles. The *NEC* contains approximately 140 articles, each of which covers a specific subject. For example:

Article 110—General Requirements
Article 250—Grounding and Bonding
Article 300—General Requirements for Wiring Methods and Materials
Article 430—Motors and Motor Controllers
Article 500—Hazardous (Classified) Locations
Article 680—Swimming Pools, Fountains, and Similar Installations
Article 725—Remote-Control, Signaling, and Power-Limited Circuits
Article 800—Communications Circuits

5. Parts. Larger articles are subdivided into parts. Because the parts of a *Code* article aren't included in the section numbers, we have a tendency to forget what "part" the *NEC* rule is relating to. For example, Table 110.34(A) contains working space clearances for electrical equipment. If we aren't careful, we might think this table applies to all electrical installations, but Table 110.34(A) is located in Part III, which only contains requirements for "Over 600 Volts, Nominal" installations. The rules for working clearances for electrical equipment for systems 600V, nominal, or less are contained in Table 110.26(A)(1), which is located in Part II—600 Volts, Nominal, or Less.

6. Sections and Tables.

Sections. Each *NEC* rule is called a "*Code* Section." A *Code* section may be broken down into subsections by letters in parentheses (A), (B), and so on. Numbers in parentheses (1), (2), and so forth, may further break down a subsection, and lower-case letters (a), (b), and so on, further break the rule down to the third level. For example, the rule requiring all receptacles in a dwelling unit bathroom to be GFCI protected is contained in

Section 210.8(A)(1). Section 210.8(A)(1) is located in Chapter 2, Article 210, Section 8, Subsection (A), Sub-subsection (1).

Many in the industry incorrectly use the term "Article" when referring to a *Code* section. For example, they say "Article 210.8," when they should say "Section 210.8." Section numbers in this textbook are shown without the word "Section," unless they begin a sentence. For example, Section 210.8(A) is shown as simply 210.8(A).

Tables. Many *NEC* requirements are contained within tables, which are lists of *Code* rules placed in a systematic arrangement. The titles of the tables are extremely important; you must read them carefully in order to understand the contents, applications, limitations, and so forth, of each table in the *NEC*. Many times notes are provided in or below a table; be sure to read them as well since they're also part of the requirement. For example, Note 1 for Table 300.5 explains how to measure the cover when burying cables and raceways, and Note 5 explains what to do if solid rock is encountered.

7. Exceptions. Exceptions are *Code* requirements or permissions that provide an alternative method to a specific rule. There are two types of exceptions—mandatory and permissive. When a rule has several exceptions, those exceptions with mandatory requirements are listed before the permissive exceptions.

Mandatory Exceptions. A mandatory exception uses the words "shall" or "shall not." The word "shall" in an exception means that if you're using the exception, you're required to do it in a particular way. The phrase "shall not" means it isn't permitted.

Permissive Exceptions. A permissive exception uses words such as "shall be permitted," which means it's acceptable (but not mandatory) to do it in this way.

8. Informational Notes. An Informational Note contains explanatory material intended to clarify a rule or give assistance, but it isn't a *Code* requirement.

9. Annexes. Annexes aren't a part of the *NEC* requirements, and are included in the *Code* for informational purposes only.

Annex A. Product Safety Standards
Annex B. Application Information for Ampacity Calculation
Annex C. Raceway Fill Tables for Conductors and Fixture Wires of the Same Size

Annex D. Examples
Annex E. Types of Construction
Annex F. Critical Operations Power Systems (COPS)
Annex G. Supervisory Control and Data Acquisition (SCADA)
Annex H. Administration and Enforcement
Annex I. Recommended Tightening Torques
Annex J. ADA Standards for Accessible Design

10. Index. The Index at the back of the *Code* book is helpful in locating a specific rule.

Changes to the *NEC* since the previous edition(s), are identified by shading, but rules that have been relocated aren't identified as a change. A bullet symbol "•" is located on the margin to indicate the location of a rule that was deleted from a previous edition. New articles contain a vertical line in the margin of the page.

Different Interpretations

Some electricians, contractors, instructors, inspectors, engineers, and others enjoy the challenge of discussing the *NEC* requirements, hopefully in a positive and productive manner. This give-and-take is important to the process of better understanding the *Code* requirements and application(s). However, if you're going to participate in an *NEC* discussion, please don't spout out what you think without having the actual *Code* book in your hand. The professional way of discussing an *NEC* requirement is by referring to a specific section, rather than talking in vague generalities.

How to Locate a Specific Requirement

How to go about finding what you're looking for in the *Code* book depends, to some degree, on your experience with the *NEC*. *Code* experts typically know the requirements so well they just go to the correct rule without any outside assistance. The Table of Contents might be the only thing very experienced *NEC* users need to locate the requirement they're looking for. On the other hand, average *Code* users should use all of the tools at their disposal, including the Table of Contents and the Index.

Table of Contents. Let's work out a simple example: What *NEC* rule specifies the maximum number of disconnects permitted for a service? If you're an experienced *Code* user, you'll know Article 230 applies to "Services," and because this article is so large, it's divided up into multiple parts (actually eight parts). With this knowledge, you can quickly go to the Table of Contents and see it lists the Service Equipment Disconnecting Means requirements in Part VI.

> **Author's Comment:** The number 70 precedes all page numbers because the *NEC* is NFPA Standard Number 70.

Index. If you use the Index, which lists subjects in alphabetical order, to look up the term "service disconnect," you'll see there's no listing. If you try "disconnecting means," then "services," you'll find that the Index indicates that the rule is located in Article 230, Part VI. Because the *NEC* doesn't give a page number in the Index, you'll need to use the Table of Contents to find it, or flip through the *Code* book to Article 230, then continue to flip through pages until you find Part VI.

Many people complain that the *NEC* only confuses them by taking them in circles. As you gain experience in using the *Code* and deepen your understanding of words, terms, principles, and practices, you'll find the *NEC* much easier to understand and use than you originally thought.

Customizing Your *Code* Book

One way to increase your comfort level with the *Code* book is to customize it to meet your needs. You can do this by highlighting and underlining important *NEC* requirements, and by attaching tabs to important pages. Be aware that if you're using your *Code* book to take an exam, some exam centers don't allow markings of any type.

Highlighting. As you read through this textbook, be sure you highlight those requirements in the *Code* that are the most important or relevant to you. Use one color for general interest and a different one for important requirements you want to find quickly. Be sure to highlight terms in the Index and the Table of Contents as you use them.

Underlining. Underline or circle key words and phrases in the *NEC* with a red pen (not a lead pencil) and use a short ruler or other straightedge to keep lines straight and neat. This is a very handy way to make important requirements stand out. A short ruler or other straightedge also comes in handy for locating specific information in the many *Code* tables.

Tab Your *Code* Book

Placing tabs on *Code* articles, sections, and tables will make it easier for you to use the *NEC*. However, too many tabs will defeat the purpose. You can order a set of *Code* book tabs designed by Mike Holt online at www.MikeHolt.com/14code, or by calling 1.888.NEC.CODE (632.2633).

ABOUT THE AUTHOR

Mike Holt—Author

Founder and President
Mike Holt Enterprises
Groveland, FL
www.MikeHolt.com

Mike Holt worked his way up through the electrical trade. He began as an apprentice electrician and became one of the most recognized experts in the world as it relates to electrical power installations. He's worked as a journeyman electrician, master electrician, and electrical contractor. Mike's experience in the real world gives him a unique understanding of how the *NEC* relates to electrical installations from a practical standpoint. You'll find his writing style to be direct, nontechnical, and powerful.

Did you know Mike didn't finish high school? So if you struggled in high school or didn't finish at all, don't let it get you down. However, realizing that success depends on one's continuing pursuit of education, Mike immediately attained his GED, and ultimately attended the University of Miami's Graduate School for a Master's degree in Business Administration.

Mike resides in Central Florida, is the father of seven children, has five grandchildren, and enjoys many outside interests and activities. He's a nine-time National Barefoot Water-Ski Champion (1988, 1999, 2005–2009, 2012–2013). He's set many national records and continues to train year-round at a World competition level (www.barefootwaterskier.com).

What sets him apart from some is his commitment to living a balanced lifestyle; placing God first, family, career, then self.

Special Acknowledgments—First, I want to thank God for my godly wife who's always by my side and my children, Belynda, Melissa, Autumn, Steven, Michael, Meghan, and Brittney.

A special thank you must be sent to the staff at the National Fire Protection Association (NFPA), publishers of the *NEC*—in particular Jeff Sargent for his assistance in answering my many *Code* questions over the years. Jeff, you're a "first class" guy, and I admire your dedication and commitment to helping others understand the *NEC*. Other former NFPA staff members I would like to thank include John Caloggero, Joe Ross, and Dick Murray for their help in the past.

A personal thank you goes to Sarina, my long-time friend and office manager. It's been wonderful working side-by-side with you for over 25 years nurturing this company's growth from its small beginnings.

ABOUT THE ILLUSTRATOR

Mike Culbreath—Illustrator

Graphic Illustrator
Alden, MI
www.MikeHolt.com

Mike Culbreath devoted his career to the electrical industry and worked his way up from an apprentice electrician to master electrician. He started in the electrical field doing residential and light commercial construction. He later did service work and custom electrical installations. While working as a journeyman electrician, he suffered a serious on-the-job knee injury. As part of his rehabilitation, Mike completed courses at Mike Holt Enterprises. and then passed the exam to receive his Master Electrician's license. In 1986, with a keen interest in continuing education for electricians, he joined the staff to update material and began illustrating Mike Holt's textbooks and magazine articles.

He started with simple hand-drawn diagrams and cut-and-paste graphics. When frustrated by the limitations of that style of illustrating, he took a company computer home to learn to how operate some basic computer graphic software. Becoming aware that computer graphics offered a lot of flexibility for creating illustrations, Mike took every computer graphics class and seminar he could to help develop his computer graphic skills. He's now worked as an illustrator and editor with the company for over 25 years and, as Mike Holt has proudly acknowledged, has helped to transform his words and visions into lifelike graphics.

Originally from South Florida, Mike now lives in northern lower Michigan where he enjoys kayaking, photography, and cooking, but his real passion is his horses.

Mike loves spending time with his children Dawn and Mac and his grandchildren Jonah and Kieley.

Special Acknowledgments—I would like to thank Ryan Jackson, an outstanding and very knowledgeable *Code* guy, and Eric Stromberg, an electrical engineer and super geek (and I mean that in the most complimentary manner, this guy is brilliant), for helping me keep our graphics as technically correct as possible.

I also want to give a special thank you to Cathleen Kwas for making me look good with her outstanding layout design and typesetting skills and Toni Culbreath who proofreads all of my material. I would also like to acknowledge Belynda Holt Pinto, our Chief Operations Officer and the rest of the outstanding staff at Mike Holt Enterprises, for all the hard work they do to help produce and distribute these outstanding products.

And last but not least, I need to give a special thank you to Mike Holt for not firing me over 25 years ago when I "borrowed" one of his computers and took it home to begin the process of learning how to do computer illustrations. He gave me the opportunity and time needed to develop my computer graphic skills. He's been an amazing friend and mentor since I met him as a student many years ago. Thanks for believing in me and allowing me to be part of the Mike Holt Enterprises family.

ABOUT THE TEAM

Editorial and Production Team

 A special thanks goes to **Toni Culbreath** for her outstanding contribution to this project. She worked tirelessly to proofread and edit this publication. Her attention to detail and dedication is irreplaceable.

Many thanks to **Cathleen Kwas** who did the design, layout, and production of this book. Her desire to create the best possible product for our customers is greatly appreciated.

Also, thanks to **Paula Birchfield** who was the Production Coordinator of the textbook. She helped keep everything flowing and tied up all the loose ends.

Thanks to **Bruce Marcho** for doing such an excellent job recording, editing, and producing our DVDs. Bruce has played a vital role in the production of our products for over 25 years.

Video Team Members

Ryan Jackson and **Eric Stromberg** deserve special acknowledgment for their contribution to this product. They both provided outstanding technical advice as they served in the background during the recording of these DVDs.

Ryan is co-author of *Mike Holt's Illustrated Guide to Changes to the NEC 2014.* He devoted his time to attending this recording to interpret and write all of the analysis of *Code* changes relating to Solar PV Systems that appear in this textbook.

Eric's support during this process was invaluable. He kept the entire team on track and managed the questions and feedback from the viewers who participated in the live streaming of the recording.

Video Team

Bill Brooks, PE

 Principal Engineer
Vacaville, CA
www.BrookSolar.com

Bill Brooks has over 25 years of experience designing, installing, and evaluating grid-connected PV systems. More than 12,000 installers and inspectors have attended his courses throughout the U.S. and abroad. His field troubleshooting skills have been valuable in determining where problems occur to focus training on those issues of greatest need. He has written several important technical manuals for the industry that are now widely used throughout the United States and beyond. His recent publications include the *Expedited Permit Process for PV Systems*, the *Field Inspection Guidelines for PV Systems*, and *Understanding the CalFire Solar PV Installation Guidelines*, as well as articles in *Photon* and *SolarPro* magazines.

He is actively involved in the developments of PV codes and standards including IEEE-929 and IEEE1547 (PV Utility Interconnection), the *National Electrical Code (NEC)* Article 690 (Solar Photovoltaic Systems), and IEC TC82 (international PV standards). Mr. Brooks is an active participant on many codes and standards panels including *Code*-Making Panel 4 of the *National Electrical Code*, UL1703 and UL1741 Standards Technical Panels, and IEC TC82 Working Group 3 and 6. Mr. Brooks was a member of the California Office of the State Fire Marshal's (Cal Fire) PV Task force that developed the Solar Photovoltaic Installation Guideline, which became the model for national fire regulation. He holds B.S. and M.S. degrees in Mechanical Engineering from North Carolina State University and is a registered Professional Mechanical and Electrical Engineer.

Bill enjoys helping people make progress in reaching their God-given potential. His interests include sailing, motorcycle riding, performance automobiles, home theater, and all types of music.

Dave Click, PE

Program Director, PV Project Engineering
Florida Solar Energy Center
Cocoa, FL
www.floridaenergycenter.org

Dave Click became involved in solar energy through the Department of Energy's first Solar Decathlon, serving as project manager for the engineering team behind the University of Virginia's entry. After receiving his BS and MS degrees in electrical engineering from UVA, he joined Solar Design Associates in Massachusetts from 2004 to 2007, managing and designing PV projects from 3-600 kWdc.

Since 2007, Dave's been working at the Florida Solar Energy Center in Cocoa, Florida with projects including training prospective PV installers, educating code officials on proper PV design and installation, and analyzing the impacts of widespread PV on power systems. He serves as a volunteer for the North American Board of Certified Energy Practitioners (NABCEP) and he is coordinator for a 7-university team aiming to expand power systems education.

Dave and his family live beneath their 5.4 kW PV system in Orlando; over the last four years, their total electric bill was $81.99.

Jason Fisher

Founder, Solar Technical Consulting
Charlottesville, Virginia
www.solartechconsulting.com

Jason Fisher has been earning his living in the PV industry for more than 16 years. From 1996 to 2006, he owned and operated the first fully licensed PV contracting firm in Maryland, where he designed and installed many of the DC region's earliest utility-interconnected PV systems including systems for the Pentagon, the Department of State, and the White House. For six years Jason was the Senior Director for Technical Training for a global manufacturer of PV systems. As an independent consultant, Jason provides technical services to many clients in the PV industry including technical training, design review, performance modeling and validation, system optimization, commissioning, troubleshooting, and owner's agent.

Jason is a licensed master electrician, a NABCEP™ Certified PV Installation Professional, and a UL Certified PV System Installer. He has over 7 years of experience training thousands of engineers, installers, and inspectors in PV applications and the *NEC*. He is also the author of several technical articles on PV and is the co-author of a textbook on PV design and installation for a PV system manufacturer.

Jason lives in Charlottesville Virginia with his wife and two kids. He enjoys hiking, sea kayaking, mountain biking, and wood oven cooking.

Ryan Mayfield

State Licensed PV Installer/PV Instructor
Renewable Energy Associates
Corvallis, OR
www.renewableassociates.com

Ryan Mayfield has been working in the renewable energy field since 1999 and currently focuses on commercial photovoltaic (PV) system design and education. As the President at Renewable Energy Associates, he provides design, support and educational services for contractors, architectural and engineering firms, manufacturers and government agencies. Typical projects include commercial and residential PV system designs and training PV system designers and installers. Ryan also works directly with manufacturers of PV-specific products to help gain market acceptance and develop products that directly help the implementation and use of their products.

Ryan serves as Photovoltaic Systems Technical Editor for *SolarPro* magazine, regularly writing feature articles in *SolarPro* and *Home Power* magazines; he is also the author of *PV Design and Installation for Dummies* (published in 2010). He is an Affiliated Certified Master Trainer (from the Institute for Sustainable Power Quality) for the PV course he teaches

About the Team

at Lane Community College. Ryan also teaches various PV courses across the nation for electricians, existing solar professionals, code officials, inspectors and individuals looking to join the solar industry. Ryan holds a Limited Renewable Energy Technician (LRT) license in Oregon and chairs Oregon's LRT apprenticeship committee.

Ryan lives in Corvallis, OR with his wife, Amy, and three children, A.J., Lauren and Kai. They enjoy getting outdoors as much as possible, especially when they get the opportunity to get in the canoe for a few days.

Richard Stovall

LEED AP BD+C
CEO, SolPowerPeople, Inc.
Austin, Texas

Richard Stovall has been actively involved in the Solar Industry since 2008 motivated by his belief that solar technology will be an engine for economic growth for at least the next century. He has worked in 2 different accredited and industry recognized solar training organizations. Richard has been involved in developing state of the art hands-on training labs for on-site and mobile education, developing curriculum, and training thousands of electricians, firefighters, solar installers, and utility workers. His company, SolPowerPeople, is known for the SolarMOOC Academy, which features free live lectures by industry experts (Mike Holt being the very first) that have been viewed by over 50,000 people globally. Richard says about his work as a solar instructor: "What's most satisfying is when I have the opportunity to dispel the myths and misconceptions that most people have about solar energy, and leave them with the knowledge that solar is a viable, affordable, and inevitable solution."

Richard's professional experience includes: CEO and owner of SolPowerPeople, Inc. (since 2011); Director of Operations and Lead Instructor for a leading solar training organization (2009 to 2011); Certified IREC ISPQ Master Trainer in Photovoltaics;

Certified NABCEP PV Installation Professional; Certified NABCEP PV Technical Sales Professional; Certified NABCEP Solar Thermal Installer; Participant on NABCEP's Solar PV Installer Technical Committee; LEED AP BD+C (Building Design and Construction); M.B.A. with a focus in Technology Management, University of Phoenix; B.A. Business Administration, Saint Edwards University; Certificate in Renewable Energy, Austin Community College.

Richard lives with his wife, Leanne, and two children, Piper and Levi, on a ranch just outside of Austin, Texas.

Sean White

PV Professor and Solar Entrepreneur
Orinda CA and Manila Philippines
www.pvstudent.com

Sean White is an Interstate Renewable Energy Council (IREC/ISPQ) Certified PV Independent Master Trainer, is NABCEP PV Installation Professional Certified, NABCEP PV Technical Sales Certified, a NABCEP PV Entry Level Program Provider, a California Licensed Electrician, a California Licensed Solar Contractor, a professor at Diablo Valley College and PV instructor who has taught thousands of students in the USA, Canada, China, Philippines, Mongolia and Qatar.

Sean excels at making difficult concepts easy to understand. He is a fun and entertaining speaker. Sean is always working on many projects. Whatever time it is, there is always a PV system that is producing power that Sean has worked on around the world. The latest solar company he has co-founded is a solar services and installation company, White House Solar in the USA with a division in the Philippines.

Sean has a big commute and spends his time living with his wife in the Philippines, with his awesome mother in California or often at a solar event somewhere in between. He is currently installing a 0.0001 MW (do the math) PV system on his sailboat "Stella" in the San Francisco Bay.

ARTICLE 90

INTRODUCTION TO THE *NATIONAL ELECTRICAL CODE*

Introduction to Article 90—Introduction to the *National Electrical Code*

Many NEC violations and misunderstandings wouldn't occur if people doing the work simply understood Article 90. For example, many people see *Code* requirements as performance standards. In fact, the *NEC* requirements are bare minimums for safety. This is exactly the stance electrical inspectors, insurance companies, and courts take when making a decision regarding electrical design or installation.

Article 90 opens by saying the *NEC* isn't intended as a design specification or instruction manual. The *National Electrical Code* has one purpose only, and that's the "practical safeguarding of persons and property from hazards arising from the use of electricity." The necessity of carefully studying the *NEC* rules can't be overemphasized, and the role of textbooks such as this one is to help in that undertaking. Understanding where to find the rules in the *Code* that apply to the installation is invaluable. Rules in several different articles often apply to even a simple installation.

Article 90 then describes the scope and arrangement of the *NEC*. The balance of this article provides the reader with information essential to understanding the *Code* rules.

Typically, electrical work requires you to understand the first four chapters of the *NEC* which apply generally, plus have a working knowledge of the Chapter 9 tables. That understanding begins with Article 90. Chapters 5, 6, and 7 make up a large portion of the *Code*, but they apply to special occupancies, special equipment, or other special conditions. They build on, modify, or amend the rules in the first four chapters. Chapter 8 contains the requirements for communications systems, such as telephone systems, antenna wiring, CATV, and network-powered broadband systems. Communications systems aren't subject to the general requirements of Chapters 1 through 4, or the special requirements of Chapters 5 through 7, unless there's a specific reference in Chapter 8 to a rule in Chapters 1 through 7.

Because understanding this article is important to properly applying *NEC* rules, many of its sections are covered in this textbook.

90.1 Purpose of the *NEC*

(A) Practical Safeguarding. The purpose of the *NEC* is to ensure that electrical systems are installed in a manner that protects people and property by minimizing the risks associated with the use of electricity.

It isn't a design specification standard or instruction manual for the untrained and unqualified. Figure 90–1

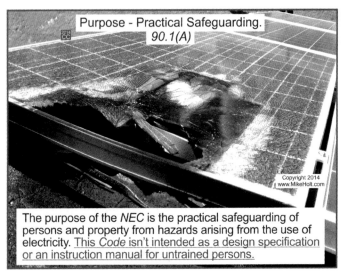

Purpose - Practical Safeguarding.
90.1(A)

The purpose of the *NEC* is the practical safeguarding of persons and property from hazards arising from the use of electricity. This *Code* isn't intended as a design specification or an instruction manual for untrained persons.

Figure 90–1

Author's Comment:

- The *Code* is intended to be used by those skilled and knowledgeable in electrical theory, electrical systems, construction, and the installation and operation of electrical equipment.

(B) Adequacy. The *Code* contains requirements considered necessary for a safe electrical installation. If an electrical system is installed in compliance with the *NEC*, it will be essentially free from electrical hazards. The *Code* is a safety standard, not a design guide.

NEC requirements aren't intended to ensure the electrical installation will be efficient, convenient, adequate for good service, or suitable for future expansion. Specific items of concern, such as electrical energy management, maintenance, and power quality issues aren't within the scope of the *Code*. Figure 90–2

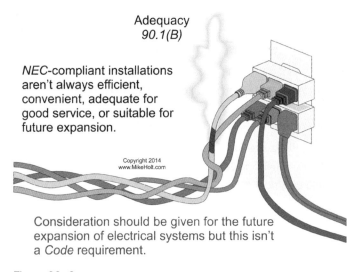

Adequacy
90.1(B)

NEC-compliant installations aren't always efficient, convenient, adequate for good service, or suitable for future expansion.

Consideration should be given for the future expansion of electrical systems but this isn't a *Code* requirement.

Figure 90–2

Note: Hazards in electrical systems often occur because circuits are overloaded or not properly installed in accordance with the *NEC*. These often occur if the initial wiring didn't provide reasonable provisions for system changes or for the increase in the use of electricity. Figure 90–3

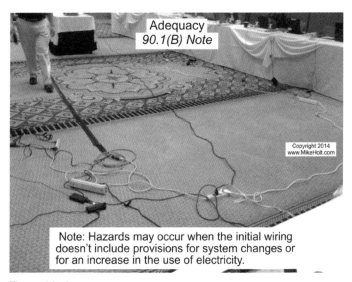

Adequacy
90.1(B) Note

Note: Hazards may occur when the initial wiring doesn't include provisions for system changes or for an increase in the use of electricity.

Figure 90–3

Author's Comment:

■ See the definition of "Overload" in Article 100.

■ The *NEC* doesn't require electrical systems to be designed or installed to accommodate future loads. However, the electrical designer (typically an electrical engineer) is concerned with not only ensuring electrical safety (*Code* compliance), but also with ensuring the system meets the customers' needs, both of today and in the foreseeable future. To satisfy customers' needs, electrical systems are often designed and installed above the minimum requirements contained in the *NEC*. But just remember, if you're taking an exam, licensing exams are based on your understanding of the minimum *Code* requirements.

(C) Relation to International Standards. The requirements of the *NEC* address the fundamental safety principles contained in the International Electrotechnical Commission (IEC) standards, including protection against electric shock, adverse thermal effects, overcurrent, fault currents, and overvoltage. Figure 90–4

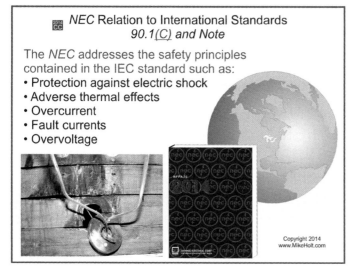

NEC Relation to International Standards
90.1(C) and Note

The *NEC* addresses the safety principles contained in the IEC standard such as:
• Protection against electric shock
• Adverse thermal effects
• Overcurrent
• Fault currents
• Overvoltage

Copyright 2014
www.MikeHolt.com

Figure 90–4

Author's Comment:

■ The *NEC* is used in Chile, Ecuador, Peru, and the Philippines. It's also the Electrical *Code* for Colombia, Costa Rica, Mexico, Panama, Puerto Rico, and Venezuela. Because of these adoptions, it's available in Spanish from the National Fire Protection Association, 617.770.3000, or www.NFPA.Org.

2014 CHANGE ANALYSIS: 90.1 is the first statement in the *NEC*, and it's an important one. Quite often *Code* users need to determine whether or not what they're installing, inspecting, or specifying meets the intent of the *NEC*, and this section tells them what that intent is.

90.1(C) was deleted from the *Code* and moved into the last sentence of subsection (A). This sentence can be a bit intimidating for newer *NEC* users, but it's important to remember that the *Code* is intended to be used by people who understand the electrical industry. The *NEC* doesn't use slang terms, it doesn't dance around a subject, and it doesn't sugar coat difficult topics. A person reading the *Code* needs to have a good understanding of the principals involved or they'll find themselves confused, frustrated, and angry.

The remainder of the section was renumbered due to the removal of 90.1(C).

90.2 Scope of the *NEC*

(A) What Is Covered. The *NEC* contains requirements necessary for the proper installation of electrical conductors, equipment, cables, and raceways for power, signaling, fire alarm, optical cable, and communications systems for: Figure 90–5

(1) Public and private premises, including buildings, mobile homes, recreational vehicles, and floating buildings.

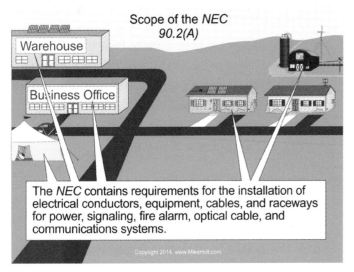

Figure 90–5

(2) Yards, lots, parking lots, carnivals, and industrial substations.

(3) Conductors and equipment connected to the utility supply.

(4) Installations used by an electric utility, such as office buildings, warehouses, garages, machine shops, recreational buildings, and other electric utility buildings that aren't an integral part of a utility's generating plant, substation, or control center. Figure 90–6

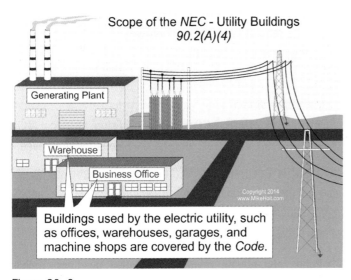

Figure 90–6

90.3 *Code* Arrangement

The *Code* is divided into an introduction, nine chapters, and informational annexes. Figure 90–7

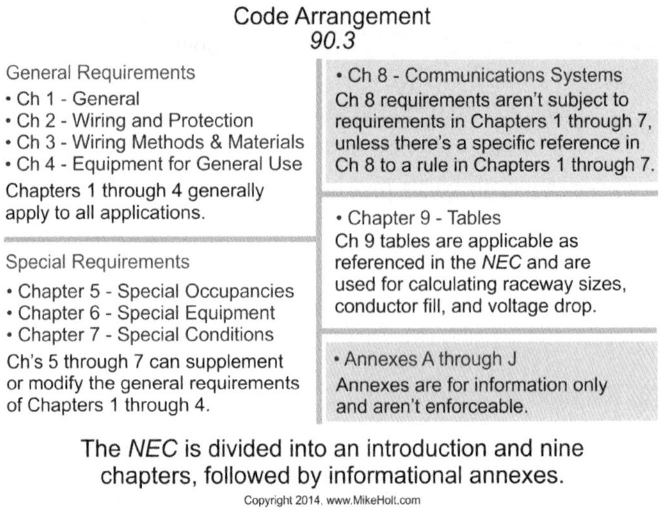

Code Arrangement
90.3

General Requirements
• Ch 1 - General
• Ch 2 - Wiring and Protection
• Ch 3 - Wiring Methods & Materials
• Ch 4 - Equipment for General Use
Chapters 1 through 4 generally apply to all applications.

Special Requirements
• Chapter 5 - Special Occupancies
• Chapter 6 - Special Equipment
• Chapter 7 - Special Conditions
Ch's 5 through 7 can supplement or modify the general requirements of Chapters 1 through 4.

• Ch 8 - Communications Systems
Ch 8 requirements aren't subject to requirements in Chapters 1 through 7, unless there's a specific reference in Ch 8 to a rule in Chapters 1 through 7.

• Chapter 9 - Tables
Ch 9 tables are applicable as referenced in the *NEC* and are used for calculating raceway sizes, conductor fill, and voltage drop.

• Annexes A through J
Annexes are for information only and aren't enforceable.

The *NEC* is divided into an introduction and nine chapters, followed by informational annexes.
Copyright 2014. www.MikeHolt.com

Figure 90–7

General Requirements. The requirements contained in Chapters 1, 2, 3, and 4 apply to all installations.

Author's Comment:

■ These first four chapters may be thought of as the foundation for the rest of the *Code*.

Special Requirements. The requirements contained in Chapters 5, 6, and 7 apply to special occupancies, special equipment, or other special conditions. These chapters can supplement or modify the requirements in Chapters 1 through 4.

Communications Systems. Chapter 8 contains the requirements for communications systems, such as telephone systems, antenna wiring, CATV, and network-powered broadband systems. Communications systems aren't subject to the general requirements of Chapters 1 through 4, or the special requirements of Chapters 5 through 7, unless there's a specific reference in Chapter 8 to a rule in Chapters 1 through 7.

Author's Comment:

- An example of how Chapter 8 works is in the rules for working space about equipment. The typical 3-foot working space isn't required in front of communications equipment, because Table 110.26(A)(1) isn't referenced in Chapter 8.

Tables. Chapter 9 consists of tables applicable as referenced in the *NEC*. The tables are used to calculate raceway sizing, conductor fill, the radius of raceway bends, and conductor voltage drop.

Annexes. Annexes aren't part of the *Code*, but are included for informational purposes. There are two annexes that are important for PV systems:

- Annex C. Raceway Fill Tables for Conductors and Fixture Wires of the Same Size
- Annex I. Recommended Tightening Torques

90.4 Enforcement

The *Code* is intended to be suitable for enforcement by governmental bodies that exercise legal jurisdiction over electrical installations for power, lighting, signaling circuits, and communications systems. Figure 90–8

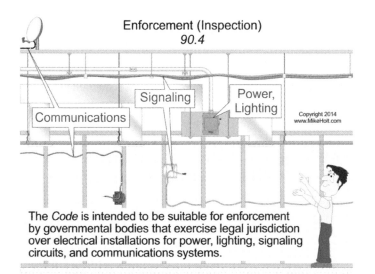

Enforcement (Inspection)
90.4

Signaling

Power, Lighting

Communications

Copyright 2014
www.MikeHolt.com

The *Code* is intended to be suitable for enforcement by governmental bodies that exercise legal jurisdiction over electrical installations for power, lighting, signaling circuits, and communications systems.

Figure 90–8

The enforcement of the *NEC* is the responsibility of the authority having jurisdiction (AHJ), who is responsible for interpreting requirements, approving equipment and materials, waiving *Code* requirements, and ensuring equipment is installed in accordance with listing instructions.

Author's Comment:

- See the definition of "Authority Having Jurisdiction" in Article 100.

Interpretation of the Requirements. The authority having jurisdiction is responsible for interpreting the *NEC*, but his or her decisions must be based on a specific *Code* requirement. If an installation is rejected, the authority having jurisdiction is legally responsible for informing the installer of the specific *NEC* rule that was violated.

Author's Comment:

- The art of getting along with the authority having jurisdiction consists of doing good work and knowing what the *Code* actually says (as opposed to what you only think it says). It's also useful to know how to choose your battles when the inevitable disagreement does occur.

Approval of Equipment and Materials. Only the authority having jurisdiction has authority to approve the installation of equipment and materials. Typically, the authority having jurisdiction will approve equipment listed by a product testing organization, such as Underwriters Laboratories, Inc. (UL). The *NEC* doesn't require all equipment to be listed, but many state and local AHJs do. See 90.7, 110.2, 110.3, and the definitions for "Approved," "Identified," "Labeled," and "Listed" in Article 100. Figure 90–9

Author's Comment:

- According to the *NEC*, the authority having jurisdiction determines the approval of equipment. This means he or she can reject an installation of listed equipment and can approve the use of unlisted equipment. Given our highly litigious society, approval of unlisted equipment is becoming increasingly difficult to obtain.

Interpretation of the Requirements
90.4

The AHJ is responsible for interpreting the *NEC*, but the decision must be based on a specific *Code* requirement. The AHJ is responsible to inform the installer of the specific *NEC* rule that was violated.

Figure 90–9

Approval of Alternate Means. By special permission, the authority having jurisdiction may approve alternate methods where it's assured equivalent safety can be achieved and maintained.

Author's Comment:

- Special permission is defined in Article 100 as the written consent of the authority having jurisdiction.

Waiver of New Product Requirements. If the current *NEC* requires products that aren't yet available at the time the *Code* is adopted, the authority having jurisdiction can allow products that were acceptable in the previous *Code* to continue to be used.

Author's Comment:

- Sometimes it takes years before testing laboratories establish product standards for new *NEC* requirements, and then it takes time before manufacturers can design, manufacture, and distribute those products to the marketplace.

90.5 Mandatory Requirements and Explanatory Material

(A) Mandatory Requirements. In the *NEC* the words "shall" or "shall not," indicate a mandatory requirement.

Author's Comment:

- For the ease of reading this textbook, the word "shall" has been replaced with the word "must," and the words "shall not" have been replaced with "must not." Remember that in many places, we'll paraphrase the *Code* instead of providing exact quotes, to make it easier to read and understand.

(B) Permissive Requirements. When the *Code* uses "shall be permitted" it means the identified actions are permitted but not required, and the authority having jurisdiction isn't permitted to restrict an installation from being completed in that manner. A permissive rule is often an exception to a general requirement.

Author's Comment:

- For ease of reading, the phrase "shall be permitted," as used in the *Code*, has been replaced in this textbook with the phrase "is permitted" or "are permitted."

(C) Explanatory Material. References to other standards or sections of the *NEC*, or information related to a *Code* rule, are included in the form of Informational Notes. Such notes are for information only and aren't enforceable as requirements of the *NEC*.

For example, Informational Note 4 in 210.19(A)(1) recommends that the voltage drop of a circuit not exceed 3 percent. This isn't a requirement; it's just a recommendation.

Author's Comment:

- For convenience and ease of reading in this textbook, Informational Notes will simply be identified as "Note."

- Informational Notes aren't enforceable, but Table Notes are. This textbook will call notes found in a table "Table Notes."

(D) Informative Annexes. Nonmandatory information annexes contained in the back of the *Code* book are for information only and aren't enforceable as requirements of the *NEC*.

90.6 Formal Interpretations

To promote uniformity of interpretation and application of the provisions of the *NEC*, formal interpretation procedures have been established and are found in the NFPA Regulations Governing Committee Projects.

Author's Comment:

- Formal interpretations from the NFPA are rarely done because it's a very time-consuming process and aren't binding on the authority having jurisdiction.

90.7 Examination of Equipment for Product Safety

Product evaluation for safety is typically performed by a testing laboratory, which publishes a list of equipment that meets a nationally recognized test standard. Except to detect alterations or damage, listed factory-installed internal wiring and construction of equipment need not be inspected at the time of installation [300.1(B)]. Figure 90–10

Examination of Equipment
90.7

Listed, factory-installed, internal wiring and construction of equipment need not be inspected at the time of installation, except to detect alterations or damage.

Copyright 2014, www.MikeHolt.com

Figure 90–10

90.9 Units of Measurement

(B) Dual Systems of Units. Both the metric and inch-pound measurement systems are shown in the *NEC*, with the metric units (International System of Units (SI)) appearing first and the inch-pound system immediately following in parentheses.

Author's Comment:

- This "dual system of units" is the format used in all NFPA standards, even though the U.S. construction industry uses inch-pound units of measurement. You'll need to be cautious when using the tables in the *Code* because the additional units can make the tables more complex and more difficult to read.

(D) Compliance. Installing electrical systems in accordance with the metric system or the inch-pound system is considered to comply with the *Code*.

Author's Comment:

- Since the use of either the metric or the inch-pound system of measurement constitutes compliance with the *NEC*, this textbook uses only inch-pound units.

ARTICLE 90 PRACTICE QUESTIONS

Please use the 2014 *Code* book to answer the following questions.

1. The *NEC* is _____.

   (a) intended to be a design manual
   (b) meant to be used as an instruction guide for untrained persons
   (c) for the practical safeguarding of persons and property
   (d) published by the Bureau of Standards

2. The *Code* isn't intended as a design specification standard or instruction manual for untrained persons.

   (a) True
   (b) False

3. Compliance with the provisions of the *NEC* will result in _____.

   (a) good electrical service
   (b) an efficient electrical system
   (c) an electrical system essentially free from hazard
   (d) all of these

4. The *Code* contains provisions considered necessary for safety, which will not necessarily result in _____.

   (a) efficient use
   (b) convenience
   (c) good service or future expansion of electrical use
   (d) all of these

5. Hazards often occur because of _____.

   (a) overloading of wiring systems by methods or usage not in conformity with the *NEC*
   (b) initial wiring not providing for increases in the use of electricity
   (c) a and b
   (d) none of these

6. The following systems shall be installed in accordance with the *NEC* requirements:

   (a) signaling conductors, equipment, and raceways
   (b) communications conductors, equipment, and raceways
   (c) electrical conductors, equipment, and raceways
   (d) all of these

7. The *NEC* applies to the installation of _____.

   (a) electrical conductors and equipment within or on public and private buildings
   (b) outside conductors and equipment on the premises
   (c) optical fiber cables and raceways
   (d) all of these

8. This *Code* covers the installation of _____ for public and private premises, including buildings, structures, mobile homes, recreational vehicles, and floating buildings.

   (a) optical fiber cables
   (b) electrical equipment
   (c) raceways
   (d) all of these

9. The *NEC* does not cover electrical installations in ships, watercraft, railway rolling stock, aircraft, or automotive vehicles.

    (a) True
    (b) False

10. The *Code* covers underground mine installations and self-propelled mobile surface mining machinery and its attendant electrical trailing cable.

    (a) True
    (b) False

11. Installations of communications equipment that are under the exclusive control of communications utilities, and located outdoors or in building spaces used exclusively for such installations _____ covered by the *NEC*.

    (a) are
    (b) are sometimes
    (c) are not
    (d) may be

12. Electric utilities may include entities that install, operate, and maintain _____.

    (a) communications systems (telephone, CATV, Internet, satellite, or data services)
    (b) electric supply systems (generation, transmission, or distribution systems)
    (c) local area network wiring on the premises
    (d) a or b

13. Utilities may be subject to compliance with codes and standards covering their regulated activities as adopted under governmental law or regulation.

    (a) True
    (b) False

14. Utilities may include entities that are designated or recognized by governmental law or regulation by public service/utility commissions.

    (a) True
    (b) False

15. The *NEC* does not apply to electric utility-owned wiring and equipment _____.

    (a) installed by an electrical contractor
    (b) installed on public property
    (c) consisting of service drops or service laterals
    (d) in a utility office building

16. Chapters 1 through 4 of the *NEC* apply _____.

    (a) generally to all electrical installations
    (b) only to special occupancies and conditions
    (c) only to special equipment and material
    (d) all of these

17. Communications wiring such as telephone, antenna, and CATV wiring within a building shall not be required to comply with the installation requirements of Chapters 1 through 7, except where specifically referenced in Chapter 8.

    (a) True
    (b) False

18. The material located in the *NEC* Annexes are part of the requirements of the *Code* and shall be complied with.

    (a) True
    (b) False

19. The authority having jurisdiction shall not be allowed to enforce any requirements of Chapter 7 (Special Conditions) or Chapter 8 (Communications Systems).

    (a) True
    (b) False

20. The _____ has the responsibility for deciding on the approval of equipment and materials.

    (a) manufacturer
    (b) authority having jurisdiction
    (c) testing agency
    (d) none of these

21. By special permission, the authority having jurisdiction may waive specific requirements in this *Code* where it is assured that equivalent objectives can be achieved by establishing and maintaining effective safety.

    (a) True
    (b) False

22. The authority having jurisdiction has the responsibility for _____.

    (a) making interpretations of rules
    (b) deciding upon the approval of equipment and materials
    (c) waiving specific requirements in the *Code* and permitting alternate methods and material if safety is maintained
    (d) all of these

23. If the *NEC* requires new products that are not yet available at the time a new edition is adopted, the _____ may permit the use of the products that comply with the most recent previous edition of the *Code* adopted by that jurisdiction.

    (a) electrical engineer
    (b) master electrician
    (c) authority having jurisdiction
    (d) permit holder

24. In the *NEC*, the words "_____" indicate a mandatory requirement.

    (a) shall
    (b) shall not
    (c) shall be permitted
    (d) a or b

25. When the *Code* uses "_____," it means the identified actions are allowed but not required, and they may be options or alternative methods.

    (a) shall
    (b) shall not
    (c) shall be permitted
    (d) a or b

26. Explanatory material, such as references to other standards, references to related sections of the *NEC*, or information related to a *Code* rule, are included in the form of Informational Notes.

    (a) True
    (b) False

27. Nonmandatory Informative Annexes contained in the back of the *Code* book _____.

    (a) are for information only
    (b) aren't enforceable as a requirement of the *Code*
    (c) are enforceable as a requirement of the *Code*
    (d) a and b

28. Factory-installed _____ wiring of listed equipment need not be inspected at the time of installation of the equipment, except to detect alterations or damage.

    (a) external
    (b) associated
    (c) internal
    (d) all of these

29. Compliance with either the SI or the inch-pound unit of measurement system shall be permitted.

    (a) True
    (b) False

CHAPTER 1 GENERAL

Introduction to Chapter 1—General

Before you can make sense of the *Code*, you must become familiar with a few basic rules, concepts, definitions, and requirements. As you study the *NEC*, you'll see that these are the foundation for a proper understanding of the *Code*.

Chapter 1 consists of two topics. Article 100 provides definitions so people can understand one another when trying to communicate about *Code*-related matters and Article 110 provides the general requirements needed to correctly apply the rest of the *NEC*.

Time spent learning this general material is a great investment. After understanding Chapter 1, some of the *Code* requirements that seem confusing to other people will become increasingly clear to you. They'll begin to make sense because you'll have the foundation from which to understand and apply them. When you read the *NEC* requirements in later chapters, you'll understand the principles upon which many of them are based, and not be surprised that they're included. You'll read the rules and feel like you already know them.

- **Article 100—Definitions.** Part I of Article 100 contains the definitions of terms used throughout the *Code* for systems that operate at 600V, nominal, or less. The definitions of terms in Part II apply to systems that operate at over 600V, nominal.

Definitions of standard terms, such as volt, voltage drop, ampere, impedance, and resistance, aren't listed in Article 100. If the *NEC* doesn't define a term, then a dictionary suitable to the authority having jurisdiction should be consulted. A building code glossary might provide better definitions than a dictionary found at your home or school.

Definitions located at the beginning of an article apply only to that specific article. For example, the definition of a swimming "Pool" is contained in 680.2, because this term applies only to the requirements contained in Article 680—Swimming Pools, Fountains, and Similar Installations. As soon as a defined term is used in two or more articles, its definition should be included in Article 100.

■ **Article 110—Requirements for Electrical Installations.** This article contains general requirements for electrical installations for the following:

- Part I. General
- Part II. 600V, Nominal, Or Less

Many of the requirements for PV systems are contained in Chapters 1 through 4 of the *NEC* and this textbook will address rules pertinent to those systems—beginning here in Chapter 1.

ARTICLE 100

DEFINITIONS

Introduction to Article 100—Definitions

Have you ever had a conversation with someone, only to discover that what you said and what he or she heard were completely different? This often happens when people in a conversation don't understand the definitions of the words being used, and that's why the definitions of key terms are located right at the beginning of the *NEC* (Article 100), or at the beginning of each article. If we can all agree on important definitions, then we speak the same language and avoid misunderstandings. Because the *Code* exists to protect people and property, and because clear communication is essential, it's very important to know the definitions of the terms presented in Article 100.

Here are a few tips for learning the many definitions in the *Code*:

- Break the task down. Study a few words at a time, rather than trying to learn them all at one sitting.
- Review the graphics in the textbook. These will help you see how a term is applied.
- Relate the definitions to your work. As you read a word, think about how it applies to the work you're doing. This will provide a natural reinforcement to the learning process.

Definitions

Accessible (as it applies to equipment). Admitting close approach and not guarded by locked doors, elevation, or other effective means. Figure 100–1

Accessible (as it applies to wiring methods). Not permanently closed in by the building structure or finish and capable of being removed or exposed without damaging the building structure or finish. Figure 100–2

Author's Comment:

- Conductors in a concealed raceway are considered concealed, even though they may become accessible by withdrawing them from the raceway. See the Note to the definition of "Concealed" in this article.

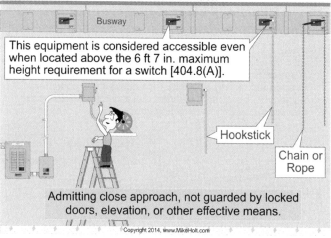

Accessible, Equipment
Article 100 Definition

This equipment is considered accessible even when located above the 6 ft 7 in. maximum height requirement for a switch [404.8(A)].

Hookstick

Chain or Rope

Admitting close approach, not guarded by locked doors, elevation, or other effective means.

Copyright 2014, www.MikeHolt.com

Figure 100–1

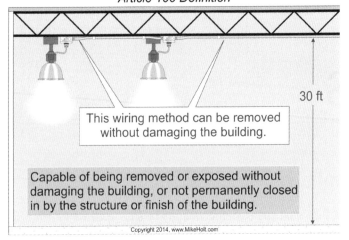

Figure 100–2

- Raceways, cables, and enclosures installed above a suspended ceiling or within a raised floor are considered accessible, because the wiring methods can be accessed without damaging the building structure. See the definitions of "Concealed" and "Exposed" in this article. Figure 100–3

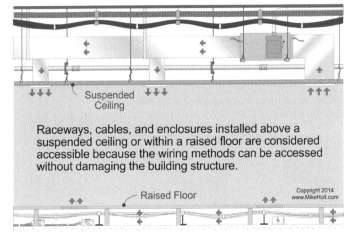

Figure 100–3

Accessible, Readily (Readily Accessible). Capable of being reached quickly without having to climb over or remove obstacles, resort to portable ladders, <u>or use tools</u>. Figures 100–4 and 100–5

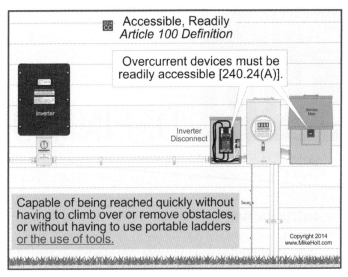

Figure 100–4

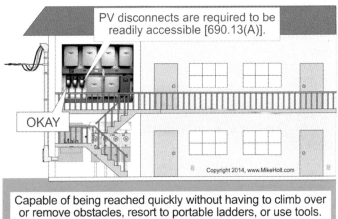

Figure 100–5

2014 CHANGE ANALYSIS: Many items in the *Code* are required to be readily accessible, including GFCI devices [210.8], building and service disconnects [225.32 and 230.70(A)(1)], and overcurrent devices [240.24(A)]. These are required to be readily accessible so they can be reached quickly, such as in an emergency. In an emergency, a person shouldn't have to run to the garage and drag out a ladder so that he or she can shut power off to their house. The same idea holds true as it relates to the use of tools. Do you really want to dig through the toolbox and find a ⁵⁄₁₆" socket to open your service disconnect to shut it off?

Is a key a tool? A literal analysis of the word "tool" would indicate that yes, a key is a tool. If that approach is taken, the *Code* will be unusable. Would that mean panels can't have locks on them? What about doors to equipment rooms that require a key? For that matter, what if your panel is in your house? Does that mean that your front door can't have a lock on it? This change is going to have unintended consequences, and I would implore anyone reading this to not consider a key to be a tool.

Ampacity. The maximum current, in amperes, a conductor can carry continuously, under the conditions of use without exceeding its temperature rating. Figure 100–6

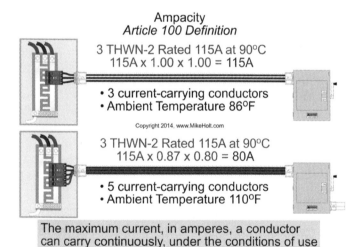

Ampacity
Article 100 Definition

3 THWN-2 Rated 115A at 90°C
115A x 1.00 x 1.00 = 115A

• 3 current-carrying conductors
• Ambient Temperature 86°F

Copyright 2014, www.MikeHolt.com

3 THWN-2 Rated 115A at 90°C
115A x 0.87 x 0.80 = 80A

• 5 current-carrying conductors
• Ambient Temperature 110°F

The maximum current, in amperes, a conductor can carry continuously, under the conditions of use [310.15] without exceeding its temperature rating.

Figure 100–6

Approved. Acceptable to the authority having jurisdiction, usually the electrical inspector. Figure 100–7

Author's Comment:

■ Product listing doesn't mean the product is approved, but it can be a basis for approval. See 90.4, 90.7, 110.2, and the definitions in this article for "Authority Having Jurisdiction," "Identified," "Labeled," and "Listed."

Approved
Article 100 Definition

Okay

Acceptable to the authority having jurisdiction (AHJ).

Copyright 2014, www.MikeHolt.com

Figure 100–7

Arc-Fault Circuit Interrupter (AFCI). An arc-fault circuit interrupter is a device intended to de-energize a circuit when it detects the current waveform characteristics unique to an arcing fault.

Authority Having Jurisdiction (AHJ). The organization, office, or individual responsible for approving equipment, materials, an installation, or a procedure. See 90.4 and 90.7 for more information.

Note: The authority having jurisdiction may be a federal, state, or local government department or an individual, such as a fire chief, fire marshal, chief of a fire prevention bureau or labor department or health department, a building official or electrical inspector, or others having statutory authority. In some circumstances, the property owner or his/her agent assumes the role, and at government installations, the commanding officer, or departmental official may be the authority having jurisdiction.

Author's Comment:

■ Typically, the authority having jurisdiction is the electrical inspector who has legal statutory authority. In the absence of federal, state, or local regulations, the operator of the facility or his or her agent, such as an architect or engineer of the facility, can assume the role.

- Some believe the AHJ should have a strong background in the electrical field, such as having studied electrical engineering or having obtained an electrical contractor's license, and in a few states this is a legal requirement. Memberships, certifications, and active participation in electrical organizations, such as the International Association of Electrical Inspectors (IAEI), speak to an individual's qualifications. Visit www.IAEI.org for more information about that organization.

Battery System. An interconnection of one or more storage batteries and their chargers. It can also include converters, inverters, and other associated equipment. Figure 100–8

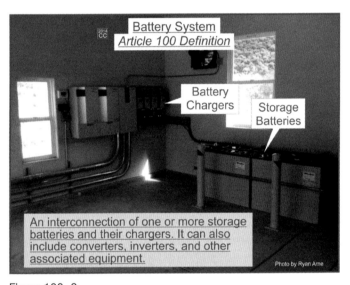

Figure 100–8

2014 CHANGE ANALYSIS: The term "battery system" is found throughout the *NEC*, such as in Articles 480 (storage batteries), 517 (health care facilities), 690 (PV systems), 700 (emergency systems), and 701 (legally required standby systems). Although the term is used mainly in Article 480, which covers batteries, the definition needs to be in Article 100 so that the term applies consistently throughout the *Code*.

Bonded (Bonding). Connected to establish electrical continuity and conductivity.

Author's Comment:

- The purpose of bonding is to connect two or more conductive objects together to ensure the electrical continuity of the fault current path, provide the capacity and ability to conduct safely any fault current likely to be imposed, and to minimize potential differences (voltage) between conductive components. Figure 100–9

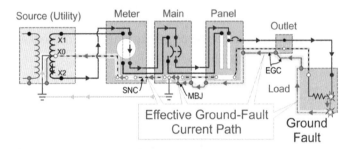

Figure 100–9

Bonding Conductor or Jumper. A conductor that ensures electrical conductivity between metal parts of the electrical installation. Figure 100–10

Bonding Jumper, Main. A conductor, screw, or strap that connects the circuit equipment grounding conductor to the neutral conductor at service equipment in accordance with 250.24(B) [250.24(A)(4), 250.28, and 408.3(C)]. Figure 100–11

Branch Circuit [Article 210]. The conductors between the final overcurrent device and the receptacle outlets, lighting outlets, or other outlets as defined in this article. Figure 100–12

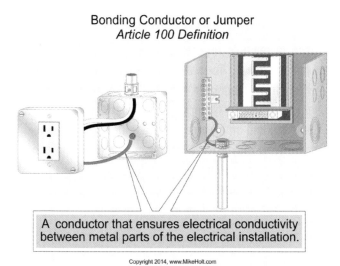

Bonding Conductor or Jumper
Article 100 Definition

A conductor that ensures electrical conductivity between metal parts of the electrical installation.

Copyright 2014, www.MikeHolt.com

Figure 100–10

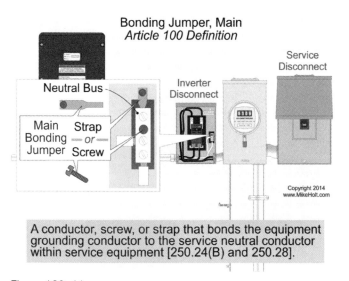

Bonding Jumper, Main
Article 100 Definition

A conductor, screw, or strap that bonds the equipment grounding conductor to the service neutral conductor within service equipment [250.24(B) and 250.28].

Figure 100–11

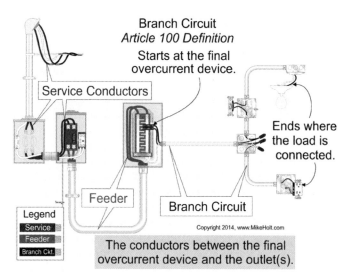

Branch Circuit
Article 100 Definition

Starts at the final overcurrent device.

Ends where the load is connected.

The conductors between the final overcurrent device and the outlet(s).

Copyright 2014, www.MikeHolt.com

Figure 100–12

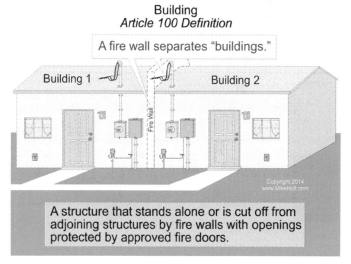

Building
Article 100 Definition

A fire wall separates "buildings."

A structure that stands alone or is cut off from adjoining structures by fire walls with openings protected by approved fire doors.

Copyright 2014 www.MikeHolt.com

Figure 100–13

Building. A structure that stands alone or is cut off from other structures by fire walls with all openings protected by fire doors approved by the authority having jurisdiction. Figure 100–13

Author's Comment:

- Not all fire-rated walls are fire walls. Building codes describe fire barriers, fire partitions and other fire-rated walls, in addition to fire walls. Check with your local building inspector to determine if a rated wall creates a separate building (fire wall).

Cabinet [Article 312]. An enclosure designed for either surface mounting or flush mounting provided with a frame in which a door can be hung. Figure 100–14

Author's Comment:

- Cabinets are used to enclose panelboards. See the definition of "Panelboard" in this article.

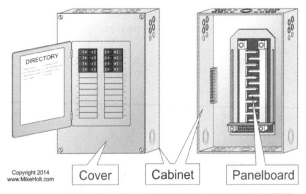

Cabinet
Article 100 Definition

| Cover | Cabinet | Panelboard |

A surface- or flush-mounted enclosure provided with a frame in which a door can be hung.

Figure 100–14

Charge Controller. Equipment that controls dc voltage, dc current, or both, and is used to charge a battery or other energy storage device. Figure 100–15

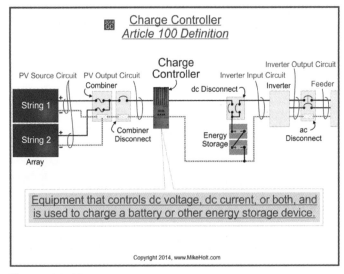

Charge Controller
Article 100 Definition

Equipment that controls dc voltage, dc current, or both, and is used to charge a battery or other energy storage device.

Figure 100–15

Author's Comment:

- A charge controller's primary function is to protect the battery bank from over-charging. As a battery becomes charged, the controller moderates the flow of electricity from the PV modules. The intent of the charge controller is to maximize battery life by avoiding overcharging or undercharging.

2014 CHANGE ANALYSIS: This term is not only used in multiple articles, it was defined in multiple articles as well! To make matters worse, it had two different definitions! In Article 690, a charge controller only charged batteries. In Article 694, it charged batteries and other energy storage devices. While the same term may have different meanings in the context of two different articles, this isn't the case with this type of equipment. One definition in one location seems to be the solution to this problem.

Circuit Breaker. A device designed to be opened and closed manually, and which opens automatically on a predetermined overcurrent without damage to itself. Circuit breakers are available in different configurations, such as inverse time, adjustable trip (electronically controlled), and instantaneous trip/motor-circuit protectors. Figure 100–16

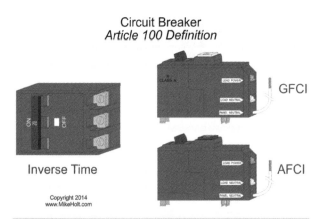

Circuit Breaker
Article 100 Definition

Inverse Time

GFCI

AFCI

A device designed to be opened and closed manually, and which opens automatically on a predetermined overcurrent without damage to itself.

Figure 100–16

Inverse Time. Inverse time breakers operate on the principle that as the current increases, the time it takes for the devices to open decreases. This type of breaker provides overcurrent protection (overload, short circuit, and ground fault). This is the most common type of circuit breaker that you'll buy over-the-counter.

Adjustable Trip. Adjustable trip breakers permit the thermal trip setting to be adjusted. The adjustment is often necessary to coordinate the operation of the circuit breakers with other overcurrent devices.

Author's Comment:

■ Coordination means that the devices with the lowest ratings, closest to the fault, operate and isolate the fault and minimize disruption so the rest of the system can remain energized and functional. This sounds simple, but large systems (especially emergency systems) may require an expensive engineering study to ensure they'll work properly. If you're responsible for bidding a project, be aware of this requirement.

Instantaneous Trip. Instantaneous trip breakers operate on the principle of electromagnetism only and are used for motors. Sometimes these devices are called motor-circuit protectors. This type of overcurrent device doesn't provide overload protection. It only provides short-circuit and ground-fault protection; overload protection must be provided separately.

Author's Comment:

■ Instantaneous trip circuit breakers have no intentional time delay and are sensitive to current inrush, and to vibration and shock. Consequently, they shouldn't be used where these factors are known to exist.

Conduit Body. A fitting that's installed in a conduit or tubing system and provides access to conductors through a removable cover. Figure 100–17

Connector, Pressure (Solderless). A device that establishes a conductive connection between conductors or between a conductor and a terminal by the means of mechanical pressure.

Disconnecting Means. A device that opens all of the ungrounded circuit conductors from their power source. This includes devices such as switches, attachment plugs and receptacles, and circuit breakers. Figure 100–18

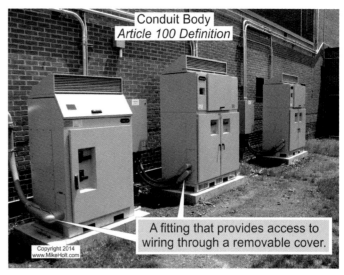

Figure 100–17

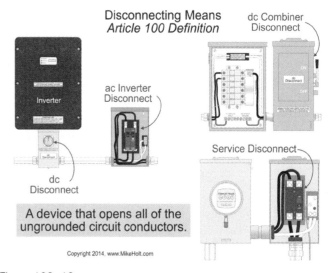

Figure 100–18

Dwelling Unit. A single space that provides independent living facilities, with space for eating, living, and sleeping; as well as permanent facilities for cooking and sanitation. Figure 100–19

Effective Ground-Fault Current Path. An intentionally constructed low-impedance conductive path designed to carry fault current from the point of a ground fault to the source for the purpose of opening the circuit overcurrent protective device. Figure 100–20

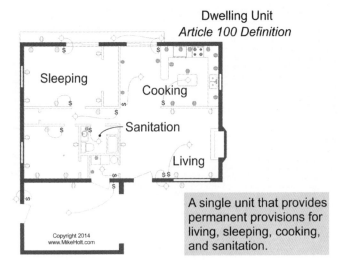

Dwelling Unit
Article 100 Definition

A single unit that provides permanent provisions for living, sleeping, cooking, and sanitation.

Figure 100–19

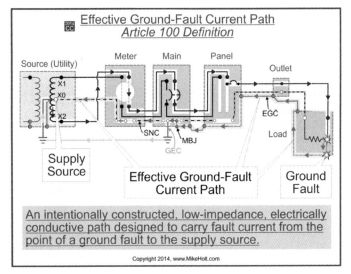

Effective Ground-Fault Current Path
Article 100 Definition

An intentionally constructed, low-impedance, electrically conductive path designed to carry fault current from the point of a ground fault to the supply source.

Figure 100–20

Author's Comment:

■ In Figure 100–20, "EGC" represents the equipment grounding conductor [259.118], "MBJ" represents the main bonding jumper, "SNC" represents the service neutral conductor (grounded service conductor), and "GEC" represents the grounding electrode conductor.

The current path shown between the supply source grounding electrode and the grounding electrode at the service main shows that some current will flow through the earth but the earth isn't part of the effective ground-fault current path.

The effective ground-fault current path is intended to help remove dangerous voltage from a ground fault by opening the circuit overcurrent device. Figure 100– 21

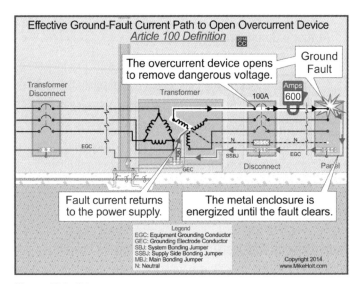

Figure 100–21

2014 CHANGE ANALYSIS: Terms used in more than one Article are supposed to be defined in Article 100. Although this one is mainly used in Article 250, it's used in other locations as well. By moving the definition here, the layout of the *NEC* becomes more consistent.

In addition to be being relocated, the language regarding high-impedance grounded systems was deleted from the definition. Previous editions of the *Code* stated that the effective ground-fault current path works to operate the ground-fault detectors on a high-impedance system. While that's true, it can be said of ungrounded systems as well. Should the *NEC* discuss both systems in the definition, or should it just remove the one example? The *Code*-Making panel opted to remove the example altogether.

Exposed (as applied to wiring methods). On or attached to the surface of a building, or behind panels designed to allow access.

Author's Comment:

- An example is wiring located in the space above a suspended ceiling or below a raised floor. Figure 100–22

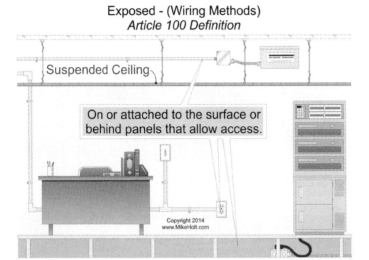

Exposed - (Wiring Methods)
Article 100 Definition

Suspended Ceiling

On or attached to the surface or behind panels that allow access.

Copyright 2014
www.MikeHolt.com

Figure 100–22

Feeder [Article 215]. The conductors between the service equipment, a separately derived system, or other power supply and the final branch-circuit overcurrent device. Figure 100–23

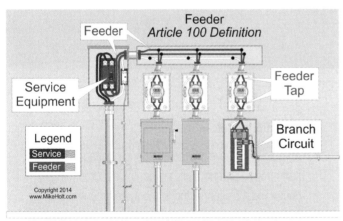

Feeder
Article 100 Definition

Feeder

Service Equipment

Feeder Tap

Branch Circuit

Legend
Service
Feeder

Copyright 2014
www.MikeHolt.com

Conductors between service equipment, a separately derived system, or other power supply, and the final branch-circuit overcurrent device.

Figure 100–23

Author's Comment:

- An "other power source" includes Solar Photovoltaic (PV)) systems.

Ground. The earth. Figure 100–24

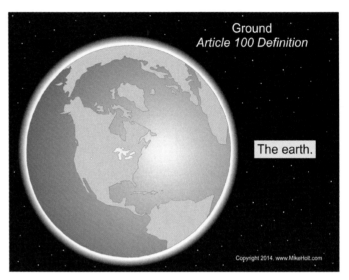

Ground
Article 100 Definition

The earth.

Copyright 2014, www.MikeHolt.com

Figure 100–24

Ground Fault. An unintentional electrically <u>conductive</u> connection between an ungrounded conductor and the metal parts of enclosures, raceways, or equipment. Figure 100–25

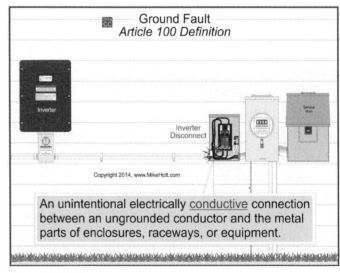

Ground Fault
Article 100 Definition

Inverter

Inverter Disconnect

Service Main

Copyright 2014, www.MikeHolt.com

An unintentional electrically <u>conductive</u> connection between an ungrounded conductor and the metal parts of enclosures, raceways, or equipment.

Figure 100–25

Grounded (Grounding). Connected to ground or to a conductive body that extends the ground connection.

Author's Comment:

■ An example of a "body that extends the ground (earth) connection" is the termination to structural steel that's connected to the earth either directly or by the termination to another grounding electrode in accordance with 250.52. Figure 100–26

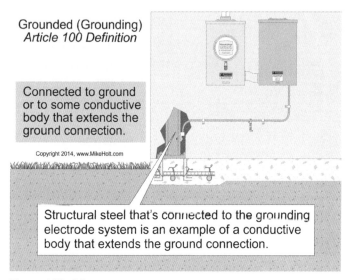

Figure 100–26

Grounded Conductor [Article 200]. The system or circuit conductor that's intentionally grounded (connected to the earth). Figure 100–27

Grounding Conductor, Equipment (EGC). The conductive path(s) that provides a ground-fault current path and connects metal parts of equipment to the system neutral conductor, to the grounding electrode conductor, or both [250.110 through 250.126]. Figure 100–28

> **Note 1:** The circuit equipment grounding conductor also performs bonding.

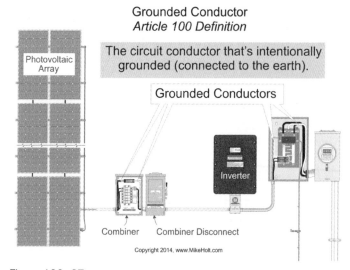

Figure 100–27

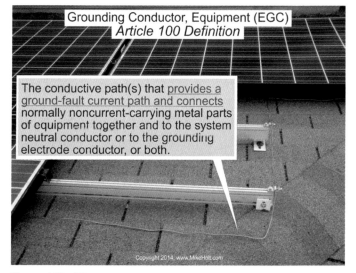

Figure 100–28

Author's Comment:

■ To quickly remove dangerous touch voltage on metal parts from a ground fault, the equipment grounding conductor must be connected to the system neutral conductor at the source, and have low enough impedance so that fault current will quickly rise to a level that will open the circuit's overcurrent device [250.2 and 250.4(A)(3)].

> **Note 2:** An equipment grounding conductor can be any one or a combination of the types listed in 250.118. Figure 100–29

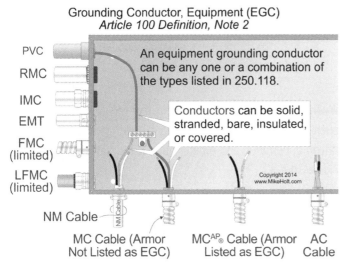

Figure 100–29

Author's Comment:

■ Equipment grounding conductors include:

- □ A bare or insulated conductor
- □ Rigid Metal Conduit
- □ Intermediate Metal Conduit
- □ Electrical Metallic Tubing
- □ Listed Flexible Metal Conduit as limited by 250.118(5)
- □ Listed Liquidtight Flexible Metal Conduit as limited by 250.118(6)
- □ Armored Cable
- □ Copper metal sheath of Mineral Insulated Cable
- □ Metal-Clad Cable as limited by 250.118(10)
- □ Metallic cable trays as limited by 250.118(11) and 392.60
- □ Electrically continuous metal raceways listed for grounding
- □ Surface Metal Raceways listed for grounding

2014 CHANGE ANALYSIS: Anyone who has used a *Code* book for more than ten years or so will certainly agree that the *NEC* deals with grounding and bonding better now than it ever has before. As a continuation of the effort to solidify the concepts, this definition was revised to more fully describe the role of an equipment grounding conductor. Despite its name, this conductor serves much more of a bonding role than a grounding role, and this change shows that. The main function of this conductor is to create a ground-fault current path that will be a major component of the effective ground-fault current path. The effective ground-fault current path is a system of ground-fault current paths, including the EGCs, the system or main bonding jumper, the utility neutral conductor, and even small things like raceway fittings and terminations that, when installed correctly, come together to create a low-impedance fault current path that's capable of opening the circuit's overcurrent device.

Grounding Electrode. A conducting object used to make a direct electrical connection to the earth [250.50 through 250.70]. Figure 100–30

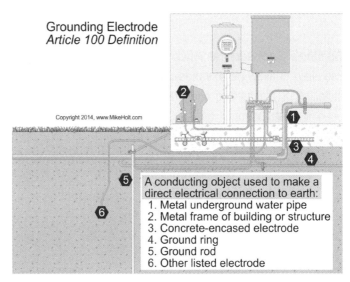

Figure 100–30

Grounding Electrode Conductor (GEC). The conductor used to connect the system grounded (neutral) conductor to a grounding electrode. Figure 100–31

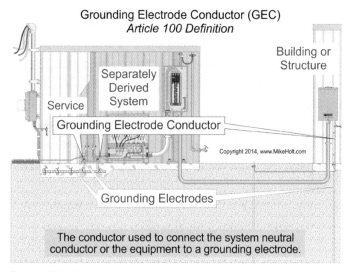

Figure 100–31

Author's Comment:

■ For services see 250.24(A), for separately derived systems see 250.30(A), and for buildings supplied by a feeder see 250.32(A).

Handhole Enclosure. An enclosure for underground system use sized to allow personnel to reach into it for the purpose of installing or maintaining equipment or wiring. It may have an open or closed bottom. Figure 100–32

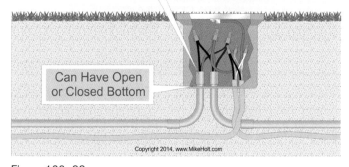

Figure 100–32

Author's Comment:

■ See 314.30 for the installation requirements for hand-hole enclosures.

Hybrid System. A system comprised of multiple power sources, such as photovoltaic, wind, micro-hydro generators, engine-driven generators, and others, but not the utility power system. Figure 100–33

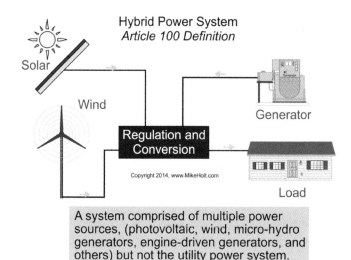

Figure 100–33

Identified Equipment. Recognized as suitable for a specific purpose, function, or environment by listing, labeling, or other means approved by the authority having jurisdiction.

Author's Comment:

■ See 90.4, 90.7, 110.3(A)(1), and the definitions for "Approved," "Labeled," and "Listed" in this article.

In Sight From (Within Sight). Visible and not more than 50 ft away from the equipment. Figure 100–34

Interrupting Rating. The highest short-circuit current at rated voltage a device is identified to interrupt under standard test conditions.

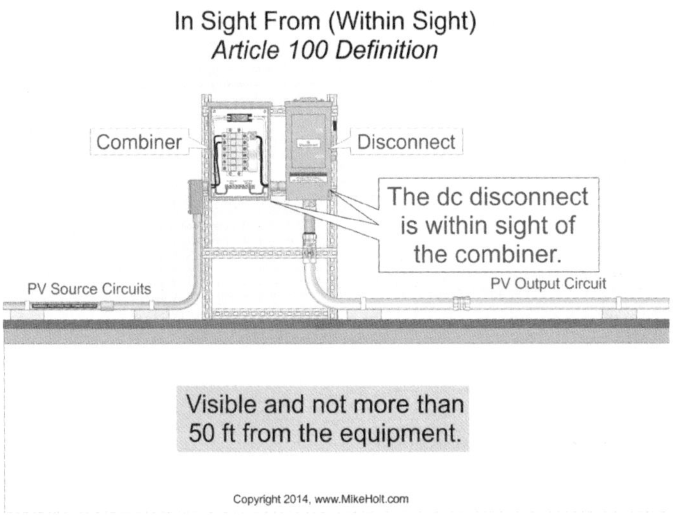

In Sight From (Within Sight)
Article 100 Definition

Combiner   Disconnect

The dc disconnect is within sight of the combiner.

PV Source Circuits   PV Output Circuit

Visible and not more than 50 ft from the equipment.

Copyright 2014, www.MikeHolt.com

Figure 100–34

Author's Comment:

- For more information, see 110.9 in this textbook.

Labeled. Equipment or materials that have a label, symbol, or other identifying mark in the form of a sticker, decal, printed label, or molded or stamped into the product by a testing laboratory acceptable to the authority having jurisdiction. Figure 100–35

Labeled
Article 100 Definition

Equipment or materials that have a label, symbol, or mark by an acceptable testing organization.
Copyright 2014 www.MikeHolt.com

Figure 100–35

Author's Comment:

- Labeling and listing of equipment typically provides the basis for equipment approval by the AHJ [90.4, 90.7, 110.2, and 110.3].

Listed. Equipment or materials included in a list published by a testing laboratory acceptable to the authority having jurisdiction. The listing organization must periodically inspect the production of listed equipment or material to ensure the equipment or material meets appropriate designated standards and is suitable for a specified purpose.

Author's Comment:

- The *NEC* doesn't require all electrical equipment to be listed, but some *Code* rules do specifically require product listing. Organizations such as OSHA increasingly require that listed equipment be used when such equipment is available [90.7, 110.2, and 110.3].

Location, Damp. Locations protected from weather and not subject to saturation with water or other liquids.

Note: This includes locations partially protected under canopies, marquees, roofed open porches, and interior locations subject to moderate degrees of moisture, such as some basements, barns, and cold-storage warehouses. Figure 100–36

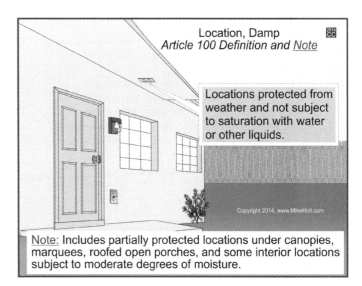

Location, Damp
Article 100 Definition and Note

Locations protected from weather and not subject to saturation with water or other liquids.

Copyright 2014, www.MikeHolt.com

Note: Includes partially protected locations under canopies, marquees, roofed open porches, and some interior locations subject to moderate degrees of moisture.

Figure 100–36

2014 CHANGE ANALYSIS: Definitions seem to work better when they're short and to the point. This definition has always been a rather lengthy one, but necessarily so. A damp location is somewhere between a dry location and a wet location, and some explanatory material in the *Code* helps to point that out. By removing the explanatory material from the actual definition, however, some *NEC* users may ignore it. Informational Notes aren't enforceable [90.5(C)], which means some *Code* users don't read them, don't care about them, and see no value in them.

Location, Dry. An area not normally subjected to dampness or wetness, but which may temporarily be subjected to dampness or wetness, such as a building under construction.

Location, Wet. An installation underground, in concrete slabs in direct contact with the earth, as well as locations subject to saturation with water, and unprotected locations exposed to weather. Figures 100-37 and 100-38

Figure 100–38

Overcurrent. Current, in amperes, greater than the rated current of the equipment or conductors resulting from an overload, short circuit, or ground fault. Figure 100–39

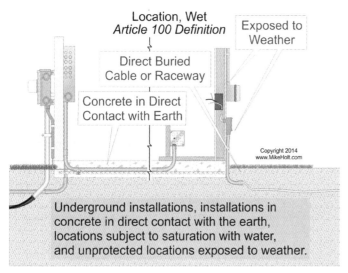

Figure 100–37

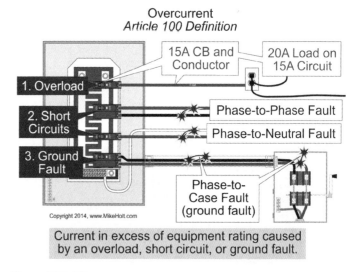

Figure 100–39

Author's Comment:

- The interior of a raceway installed in wet locations is considered a wet location, therefore any conductors used within it must be suitable for wet locations [300.5(B) and 300.9].

Author's Comment:

- See the definitions of "Ground Fault" in 250.2 and "Overload" in this article.

Overcurrent Protective Device, Supplementary. A device intended to provide limited overcurrent protection for specific applications and utilization equipment. This limited protection is in addition to the required protection provided in the branch circuit by the branch-circuit overcurrent device. Figure 100–40

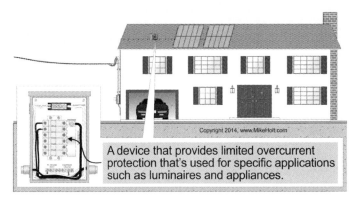

Overcurrent Protective Device, Supplementary
Article 100 Definition

A device that provides limited overcurrent protection that's used for specific applications such as luminaires and appliances.

Figure 100–40

Overload. The operation of equipment above its current rating, or current in excess of conductor ampacity. When an overload condition persists for a sufficient length of time, it can result in equipment failure or in a fire from damaging or dangerous overheating. A fault, such as a short circuit or ground fault, isn't an overload.

Panelboard [Article 408]. A distribution point containing overcurrent devices and designed to be installed in a cabinet. Figure 100–41

Author's Comment:

- See the definition of "Cabinet" in this article.

- The slang term in the electrical field for a panelboard is "the guts." This is the interior of the panelboard assembly and is covered by Article 408, while the cabinet is covered by Article 312.

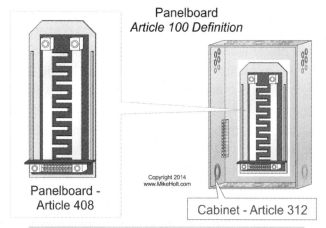

Panelboard
Article 100 Definition

Panelboard - Article 408

Cabinet - Article 312

A distribution point containing overcurrent devices which is designed to be placed in a cabinet.

Figure 100–41

Photovoltaic (PV) System. The combination of all components and subsystems that convert solar energy into electrical energy. Figure 100–42

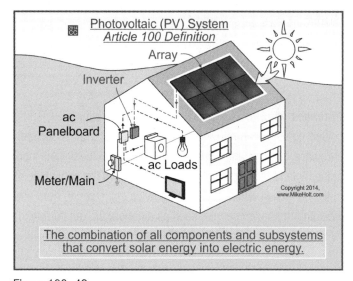

Photovoltaic (PV) System
Article 100 Definition

Array

Inverter

ac Panelboard

ac Loads

Meter/Main

The combination of all components and subsystems that convert solar energy into electric energy.

Figure 100–42

2014 CHANGE ANALYSIS: This term was defined in two different articles in previous editions of the *NEC*, which is obviously one more than needed. Having the term defined in both Article 100 and Article 690 may seem like a fine approach, but problems often come up when two portions of the *Code* talk about the same thing.

Take the rules for AFCIs for example. For years the rules in 550.25 (AFCI protection for manufactured homes) were three years behind the rules in 210.12 (AFCI protection for dwelling units), because people would make changes to 210.12 but not 550.25. Three years later 550.25 would be changed to catch up with 210.12, but in the meantime 210.12 was also being changed (again) so they still didn't match! With this term being defined in two locations it opened the door for similar problems.

The word "solar" has been removed from the term, as that seems to be the preferred nomenclature in the PV industry. Interestingly, the term "PV system" was used more often in the 2011 *NEC* than the (at that time) correct term "solar photovoltaic system."

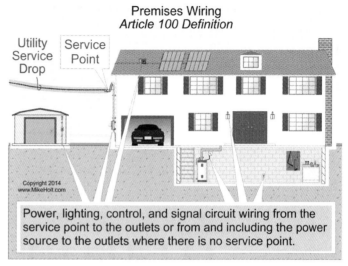

Figure 100–43

Premises Wiring. The interior and exterior wiring, including power, lighting, control, and signal circuits, and all associated hardware, fittings, and wiring devices. This includes both permanently and temporarily installed wiring from the service point to the outlets, or where there's no service point, wiring from and including the power source, such as a generator, transformer, or PV system to the outlets. Figure 100–43

Premises wiring doesn't include the internal wiring of electrical equipment and appliances, such as luminaires, dishwashers, water heaters, motors, controllers, motor control centers, air-conditioning equipment, and so on [90.7 and 300.1(B)]. Figure 100–44

Note: Power sources include, but aren't limited to, interconnected or stand-alone batteries, PV systems, other distributed generation systems, or generators.

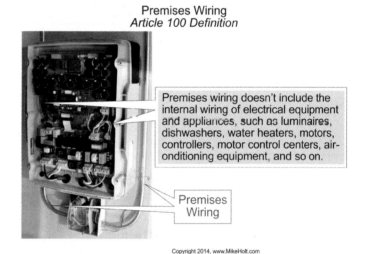

Figure 100–44

2014 CHANGE ANALYSIS: The more things change the more they stay the same. Experienced *Code* users might be asking themselves "didn't we just delete this last *Code* cycle?" A list similar to this used to be in the Article 100 definitions of "premises wiring system" and "separately derived system," but was removed because it was becoming so long it was no longer manageable. Time will only tell how long this Informational Note is left alone before people want to start adding all of the stuff that was deleted from the definition in 2005, like wind, fuel cells, and converter windings.

Qualified Person. A person who has the skill and knowledge related to the construction and operation of electrical equipment and its installation. This person must have received safety training to recognize and avoid the hazards involved with electrical systems. Figure 100–45

Figure 100–45

Note: NFPA 70E, *Standard for Electrical Safety in the Workplace*, provides information on safety training requirements expected of a "qualified person."

Author's Comment:

- Examples of this safety training include, but aren't limited to, training in the use of special precautionary techniques, of personal protective equipment (PPE), of insulating and shielding materials, and of using insulated tools and test equipment when working on or near exposed conductors or circuit parts that can become energized.

- In many parts of the United States, electricians, electrical contractors, electrical inspectors, and electrical engineers must complete from 6 to 24 hours of *NEC* review each year as a requirement to maintain licensing. This in itself doesn't make one qualified to deal with the specific hazards involved with electrical systems.

Service [Article 230]. The conductors from the electric utility that deliver electric energy to the wiring system of the premises. Figure 100–46

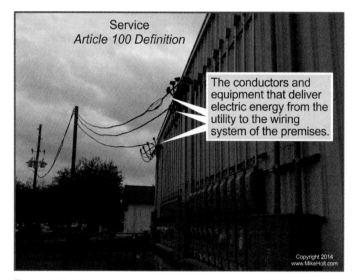

Figure 100–46

Author's Comment:

- Conductors from a UPS system, solar PV system, generator, or transformer aren't service conductors. See the definitions of "Feeder," "Service Conductors," and "Service Point" in this article.

Service Conductors. The conductors from the service point to the service disconnecting means. Figure 100–47

Author's Comment:

- These conductors fall within the requirements of Article 230, since they're owned by the customer.

- "Service Conductors" is a term that can include service lateral and service-entrance conductors.

Service Equipment [Article 230]. Circuit breaker(s) or switch(es) connected to the load end of service conductors, intended to control and cut off the service supply to the buildings. Figure 100–48

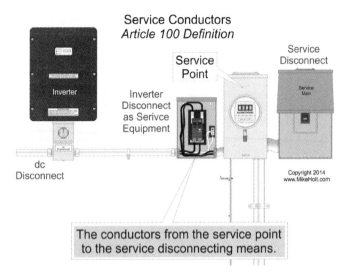

Figure 100–47

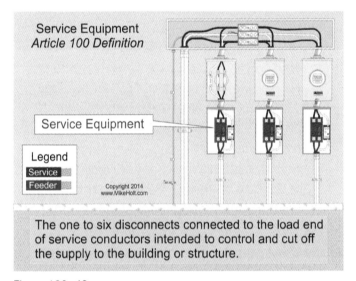

Figure 100–48

Author's Comment:

- It's important to know where a service begins and where it ends in order to properly apply the *NEC* requirements. Sometimes the service ends before the metering equipment. Figure 100–49

- Service equipment is often referred to as the "service disconnect" or "service disconnecting means."

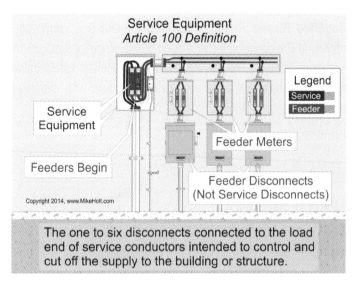

Figure 100–49

Service Point [Article 230]. The point where the electrical utility conductors make contact with premises wiring. Figure 100–50

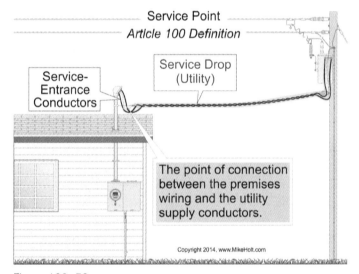

Figure 100–50

Note: The service point is the point where the serving utility ends and the premises wiring begins.

Short-Circuit Current Rating. The prospective symmetrical fault current at a nominal voltage to which electrical equipment is able to be connected without sustaining damage that exceeds defined acceptance criteria.

Special Permission. Written consent from the authority having jurisdiction.

Author's Comment:

- See the definition of "Authority Having Jurisdiction."

Ungrounded System. An electrical power system that isn't connected to the ground (earth) or a conductive body that extends the ground (earth) connection. Figure 100–51

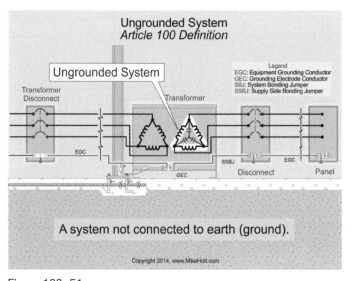

Figure 100–51

Voltage (of a circuit). The greatest effective root-mean-square difference of potential between any two conductors of the circuit.

Voltage, Nominal. A value assigned for the purpose of conveniently designating voltage classes, such as 120/240V, 120/208V, or 277/480V [220.5(A)].

Note 1: The actual voltage at which a circuit operates can vary from the nominal within a range that permits satisfactory operation of equipment. Figure 100–52

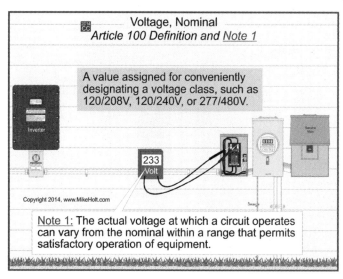

Figure 100–52

Author's Comment:

- Common voltage ratings of electrical equipment are 115V, 200V, 208V, 230V, and 460V. The electrical power supplied might be at the 240V, nominal voltage, but the voltage at the equipment will be less. Therefore, electrical equipment is rated at a value less than the nominal system voltage.

2014 CHANGE ANALYSIS: In an effort to make this definition one sentence, a portion of it was cut and pasted into a new Informational Note. This information may be useful, so it wasn't removed from the *Code* altogether, but it's not really part of the definition either.

Voltage to Ground. For grounded circuits, the voltage between a conductor and a conductor that's grounded; for ungrounded circuits, the greatest voltage between a conductor and any other conductor of the circuit. Figure 100–53

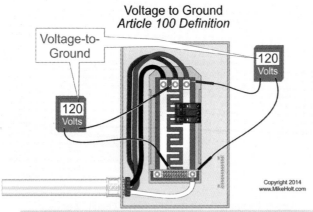

The greatest difference of potential (RMS) between an ungrounded conductor and the neutral point of the circuit that's grounded.

Figure 100–53

ARTICLE 110

REQUIREMENTS FOR ELECTRICAL INSTALLATIONS

Introduction to Article 110—Requirements for Electrical Installations

Article 110 sets the stage for how you'll implement the rest of the *NEC*. This article contains a few of the most important and yet neglected parts of the *Code*. For example:

- How should conductors be terminated?
- What kinds of warnings, markings, and identification does a given installation require?
- What's the right working clearance for a given installation?
- What do the temperature limitations at terminals mean?
- What are the *NEC* requirements for dealing with flash protection?

As you read this article, you're building your foundation for correctly applying the *NEC*. In fact, this article itself is a foundation for much of the *Code*. The purpose for the *National Electrical Code* is to provide a safe installation overall, but Article 110 is perhaps a little more focused on providing an installation that's safe for those who install and maintain it, so time spent in this article is time well spent.

Part I. General Requirements

110.1 Scope

Article 110 covers the general requirements for the examination and approval of, installation and use of, and access to and spaces about, electrical equipment; as well as general requirements for enclosures intended for personnel entry (manholes, vaults, and tunnels).

110.2 Approval of Conductors and Equipment

The authority having jurisdiction must approve all electrical conductors and equipment. Figure 110–1

Author's Comment:

- For a better understanding of product approval, review 90.4, 90.7, 110.3 and the definitions for "Approved," "Identified," "Labeled," and "Listed" in Article 100.

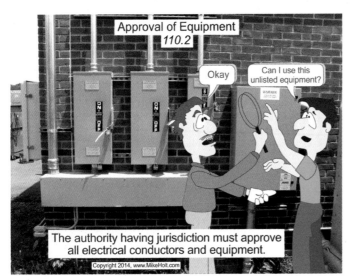

Figure 110-1

110.3 Examination, Identification, Installation, and Use of Equipment

(A) Guidelines for Approval. The AHJ must approve equipment. In doing so, consideration must be given to the following:

(1) Suitability for installation and use in accordance with the *NEC*

> **Note:** Suitability of equipment use may be identified by a description marked on or provided with a product to identify the suitability of the product for a specific purpose, environment, or application. Special conditions of use or other limitations may be marked on the equipment, in the product instructions, or appropriate listing and labeling information. Suitability of equipment may be evidenced by listing or labeling.

(2) Mechanical strength and durability

(3) Wire-bending and connection space

(4) Electrical insulation

(5) Heating effects under all conditions of use

(6) Arcing effects

(7) Classification by type, size, voltage, current capacity, and specific use

(8) Other factors contributing to the practical safeguarding of persons using or in contact with the equipment

(B) Installation and Use. Equipment must be installed and used in accordance with any instructions included in the listing or labeling requirements. Figures 110–2 and 110–3

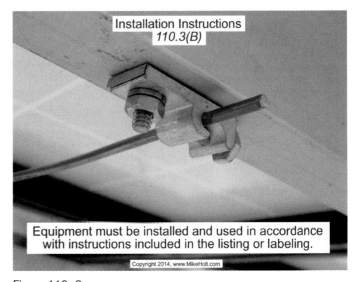

Figure 110-2

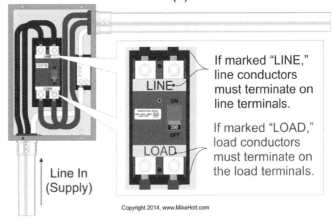

Figure 110-3

Author's Comment:

- See the definitions of "Labeling" and "Listing" in Article 100.

- Failure to follow product listing instructions, such as the torquing of terminals and the sizing of conductors, is a violation of this *Code* rule. Figure 110–4

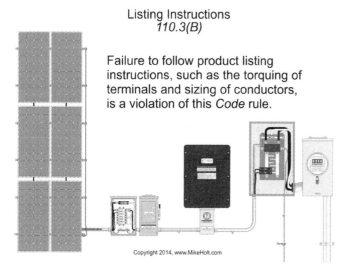

Listing Instructions
110.3(B)

Failure to follow product listing instructions, such as the torquing of terminals and sizing of conductors, is a violation of this *Code* rule.

Figure 110–4

110.5 Copper Conductors

When the conductor material (copper/aluminum) isn't specified in a rule, the material and sizes are based on a copper conductor.

110.6 Conductor Sizes

Conductor sizes are expressed in American Wire Gage (AWG), typically from 18 AWG up to 4/0 AWG. Conductor sizes larger than 4/0 AWG are expressed in kcmil (thousand circular mils). Figure 110–5

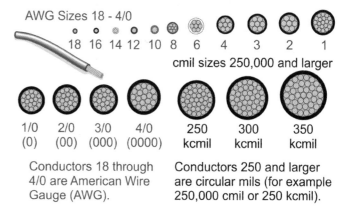

Conductor Sizes - AWG or Cmils
110.6

AWG Sizes 18 - 4/0
18 16 14 12 10 8 6 4 3 2 1

cmil sizes 250,000 and larger

1/0   2/0   3/0   4/0   250   300   350
(0)   (00) (000) (0000) kcmil kcmil kcmil

Conductors 18 through 4/0 are American Wire Gauge (AWG).

Conductors 250 and larger are circular mils (for example 250,000 cmil or 250 kcmil).

Copyright 2014, www.MikeHolt.com

Figure 110–5

110.7 Wiring Integrity

Completed installations must be free from short circuits, ground faults, or any connections to ground unless required or permitted by the *Code*. Figure 110–6

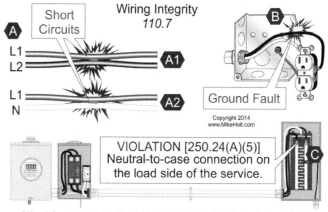

Wiring Integrity
110.7

Short Circuits

Ground Fault

VIOLATION [250.24(A)(5)]
Neutral-to-case connection on the load side of the service.

Copyright 2014
www.MikeHolt.com

All wiring must be installed so as to be free from short circuits, ground faults, and any connection to ground unless required or permitted by the *NEC*.

Figure 110–6

110.8 Suitable Wiring Methods

Only wiring methods recognized as suitable are included in the *NEC*, and they must be installed in accordance with the *Code*. Figure 110–7

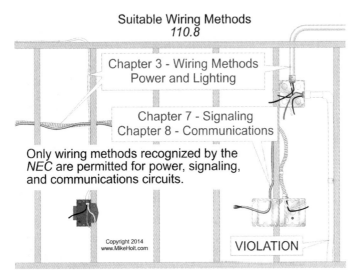

Figure 110–7

Author's Comment:

■ See Chapter 3 for power and lighting wiring methods, Article 480 for Storage Batteries, Article 690 for Solar Photovoltaic (PV) Systems, and Article 705 for Interconnected Electric Power Production Sources.

110.9 Interrupting Protection Rating

Overcurrent devices such as circuit breakers and fuses are intended to interrupt the circuit, and they must have an interrupting rating at nominal circuit voltage sufficient for the current that's available at the line terminals of the equipment. Figure 110–8

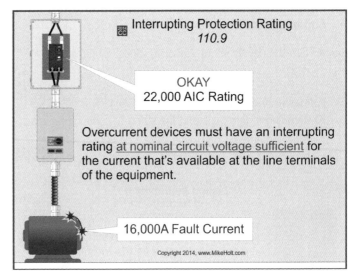

Figure 110–8

Author's Comment:

■ See the definition of "Interrupting Rating" in Article 100.

■ Unless marked otherwise, the ampere interrupting rating for circuit breakers is 5,000A [240.83(C)], and for fuses it's 10,000A [240.60(C)(3)]. Figure 110–9

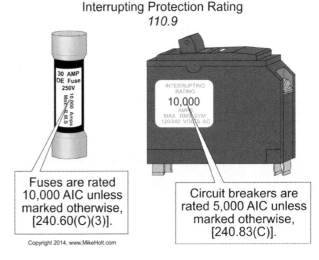

Figure 110–9

Available Short-Circuit Current

Available short-circuit current is the current, in amperes, available at a given point in the electrical system. This available short-circuit current is first determined at the secondary terminals of the utility transformer. Thereafter, the available short-circuit current is calculated at the source terminals. The available short-circuit current is different at each point of the electrical system.

The available short-circuit current depends on the impedance of the circuit. The greater the circuit impedance, the lower the available short-circuit current. Figure 110–10

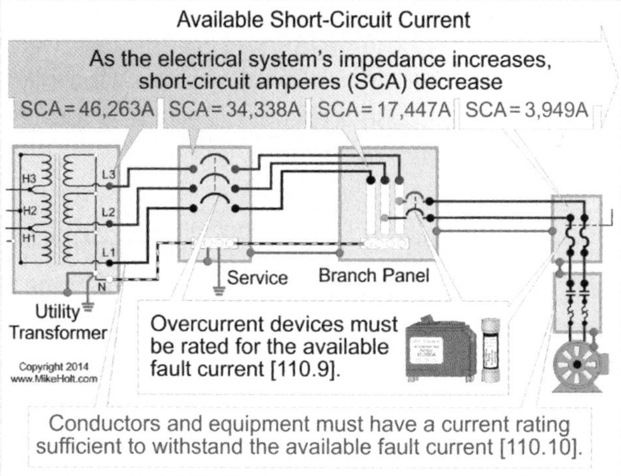

Figure 110–10

The factors that affect the available short-circuit current at the power source include the system voltage and the circuit impedance. Properties that have an impact on the impedance of the circuit include the conductor material (copper versus aluminum), conductor size, conductor length, and motor-operated equipment supplied by the circuit.

Author's Comment:

- Many people in the industry describe Amperes Interrupting Rating (AIR) as "Amperes Interrupting Capacity" (AIC).

DANGER: *Extremely high values of current flow (caused by short circuits or ground faults) produce tremendously destructive thermal and magnetic forces. Overcurrent protection devices not rated to interrupt the current at the available fault values at their listed voltage rating(s) can explode while attempting to open the circuit overcurrent device from a short circuit or ground fault, which can cause serious injury or death, as well as property damage.* Figure 110–11

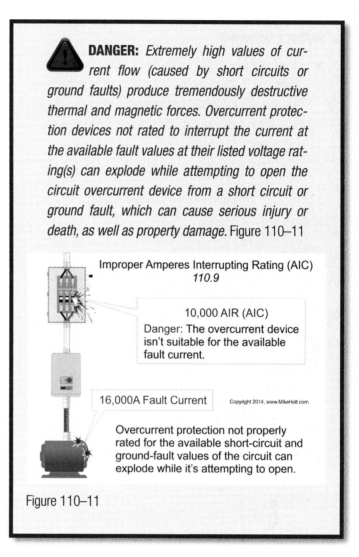

Figure 110–11

110.10 Circuit Impedance, Short-Circuit Current Rating, and Other Characteristics

Electrical equipment must have a short-circuit current rating that permits the circuit protective device to open from a short circuit or ground fault without extensive damage to the electrical equipment of the circuit. This fault is assumed to be either between two or more of the circuit conductors or between any circuit conductor and the equipment grounding conductor(s) permitted in 250.118. Listed equipment applied in accordance with their listing is considered to have met the requirements of this section.

Author's Comment:

- For example, a motor controller must have a sufficient short-circuit rating for the available fault current. If the fault current exceeds the controller's short-circuit current rating, it can explode thereby endangering persons and property. Figure 110–12

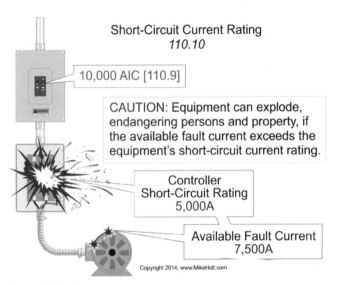

Figure 110–12

110.11 Deteriorating Agents

Electrical equipment and conductors must be suitable for the environment and conditions of use. Consideration must also be given to the presence of corrosive gases, fumes, vapors, liquids, or other substances that can have a deteriorating effect on the conductors or equipment. Figure 110–13

Author's Comment:

- Conductors must not be exposed to ultraviolet rays from the sun unless identified for the purpose [310.10(D)].

Note 1: Raceways, cable trays, cablebus, cable armor, boxes, cable sheathing, cabinets, elbows, couplings, fittings, supports, and support hardware must be of materials that are suitable for the environment in which they're to be installed, in accordance with 300.6.

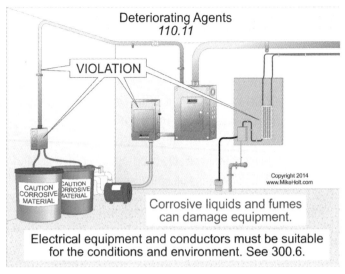

Figure 110–13

Note 2: Some cleaning and lubricating compounds contain chemicals that can cause deterioration of the plastic used for insulating and structural applications in equipment.

Equipment not identified for outdoor use and equipment identified only for indoor use must be protected against damage from the weather during construction.

Note 3: See *NEC* Table 110.28 for appropriate enclosure-type designations.

110.12 Mechanical Execution of Work

Electrical equipment must be installed in a neat and workmanlike manner. Figure 110–14

Note: Accepted industry practices are described in ANSI/NECA 1, Standard *Practice of* Good Workmanship in Electrical *Construction.* Figure 110–15

Figure 110–14

Figure 110–15

Author's Comment:

■ The National Electrical Contractors Association (NECA) created a series of *National Electrical Installation Standards (NEIS®)* that established the industry's first quality guidelines for electrical installations. These standards define a benchmark or baseline of quality and workmanship for installing electrical products and systems. They explain what installing electrical products and systems in a "neat and workmanlike manner" means. For more information about these standards, visit www.neca-neis.org/.

(A) Unused Openings. Unused openings, other than those intended for the operation of equipment or for mounting purposes, or those that are part of the design for listed products, must be closed by fittings that provide protection substantially equivalent to the wall of the equipment. Figure 110–16

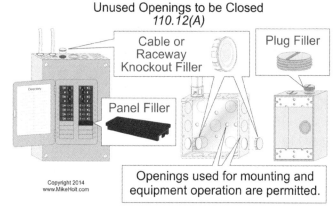

Unused openings, other than those for equipment operation or mounting purposes, must be effectively closed with a fitting that provides equivalent protection.

Figure 110–16

(B) Integrity of Electrical Equipment. Internal parts of electrical equipment must not be damaged or contaminated by foreign material, such as paint, plaster, cleaners, and so forth.

Author's Comment:

■ Precautions must be taken to provide protection from contamination of the internal parts of panelboards and receptacles during building construction. Make sure that electrical equipment is properly masked and protected before painting or before other phases of the project take place that can cause damage. Figure 110–17

Electrical equipment that contains damaged parts may adversely affect safe operation or mechanical strength of the equipment and must not be installed. This includes parts that are broken, bent, cut, or deteriorated by corrosion, chemical action, or overheating. Figure 110–18

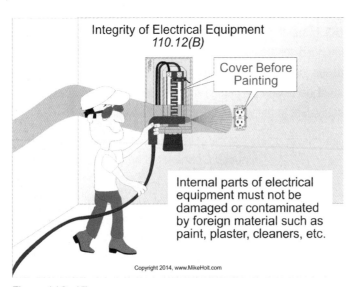

Figure 110–17

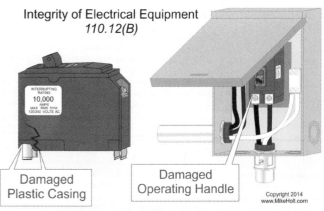

Figure 110–19

Figure 110–18

Author's Comment:

- Damaged parts include cracked insulators, arc shields not in place, overheated fuse clips, and damaged or missing switch handles or circuit-breaker handles. Figure 110–19

110.13 Mounting and Cooling of Equipment

(A) Mounting. Electrical equipment must be firmly secured to the surface on which it's mounted. Figure 110–20

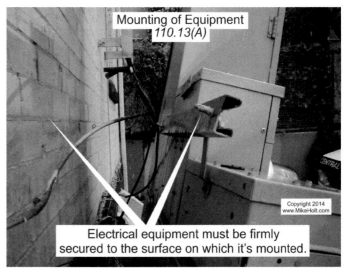

Figure 110–20

Author's Comment:

- See 314.23 for similar requirements for boxes.

110.14 Conductor Termination and Splicing

Conductor terminal and splicing devices must be identified for the conductor material and they must be properly installed and used. Figure 110–21

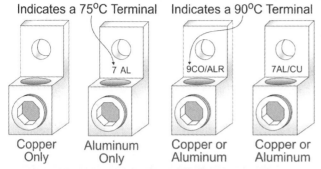

Conductor Termination - Terminal Conductor Marking
110.14

Indicates a 75°C Terminal | Indicates a 90°C Terminal

Copper Only | Aluminum Only | Copper or Aluminum | Copper or Aluminum

Terminals that are suitable only for aluminum must be marked AL. Terminals suitable for both copper and aluminum must be marked CO/ALR or AL/CU.

Copyright 2014, www.MikeHolt.com

Figure 110–21

Finely Stranded Flexible Conductor Termination
110.14

Copyright 2014. www.MikeHolt.com

Connectors and terminations for conductors more finely stranded than Class B and Class C stranding must be identified for the conductor class [Chapter 9, Table 10].

Figure 110–22

Copper and Aluminum Mixed. Copper and aluminum conductors must not make contact with each other in a device unless the device is listed and identified for this purpose.

Author's Comment:

■ Few terminations are listed for the mixing of aluminum and copper conductors, but if they are, that will be marked on the product package or terminal device. The reason copper and aluminum shouldn't be in contact with each other is because corrosion develops between the two different metals due to galvanic action, resulting in increased contact resistance at the splicing device. This increased resistance can cause the splice to overheat and cause a fire.

■ Switches and receptacles marked CO/ALR are designed to ensure a good connection through the use of a larger contact area and compatible materials. The terminal screws are plated with the element called "Indium." Indium is an extremely soft metal that forms a gas-sealed connection with the aluminum conductor.

Connectors and terminals for conductors more finely stranded than Class B and Class C, as shown in Table 10 of Chapter 9, must be identified for the use of finely stranded conductors. Figure 110–22

Author's Comment:

■ According to UL Standard 486 A-B, a terminal/lug/ connector must be listed and marked for use with other than Class B stranded conductors. With no marking or factory literature/instructions to the contrary, terminals may only be used with Class B stranded conductors.

■ See the definition of "Identified" in Article 100.

■ Conductor terminations must comply with the manufacturer's instructions as required by 110.3(B). For example, if the instructions for the device state "Suitable for 18-12 AWG Stranded," then only stranded conductors can be used with the terminating device. If the instructions state "Suitable for 18-12 AWG Solid," then only solid conductors are permitted, and if the instructions state "Suitable for 18-12 AWG," then either solid or stranded conductors can be used with the terminating device.

Note: Many terminations and equipment are either marked with a tightening torque or have the torque values included in the product's instructions. Figure 110–23

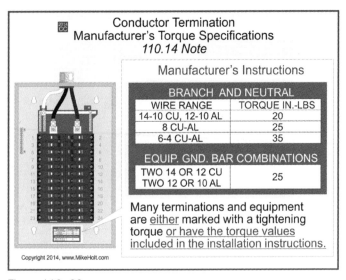

Figure 110–23

Author's Comment:

- Conductors must terminate in devices that have been properly tightened in accordance with the manufacturer's torque specifications included with equipment instructions. Failure to torque terminals can result in excessive heating of terminals or splicing devices due to a loose connection. A loose connection can also lead to arcing which increases the heating effect and may also lead to a short circuit or ground fault. Any of these can result in a fire or other failure, including an arc-flash event. In addition, this is a violation of 110.3(B), which requires all equipment to be installed in accordance with listing or labeling instructions.

Question: What do you do if the torque value isn't provided with the device?

Answer: In the absence of connector or equipment manufacturer's recommended torque values, Table I.1, Table I.2, and Table I.3 contained in Annex I may be used to correctly tighten screw-type connections for power and lighting circuits.

Author's Comment:

- Terminating conductors without a torque tool can result in an improper and unsafe installation. If a torque screwdriver isn't used, there's a good chance the conductors aren't properly terminated.

2014 CHANGE ANALYSIS: Many pieces of equipment are, in fact, marked with their tightening torque. This isn't, however, the only place that one might expect to find this information. The instructions that come with the product may contain this information as well, and, if it's listed equipment, these instructions must be followed [110.3(B)]. Although it wouldn't be a *Code* violation to ignore torque values on equipment that isn't listed, it probably wouldn't be a good idea to do so. Most electrical fires don't start in the middle of a raceway; they start at a termination of some sort. The importance of properly torquing terminations can't possibly be overstated.

(A) Terminations. Conductor terminals must ensure a good connection without damaging the conductors and must be made by pressure connectors (including set screw type) or splices to flexible leads. Figure 110–24

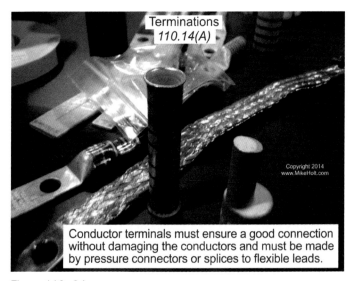

Figure 110–24

Author's Comment:

- See the definition of "Connector, Pressure" in Article 100.

> **Question:** What if the conductor is larger than the terminal device?
>
> **Answer:** This condition needs to be anticipated in advance, and the equipment should be ordered with terminals that will accommodate the larger conductor. However, if you're in the field, you should:
>
> - Contact the manufacturer and have the proper terminals, bolts, washers, and nuts express delivered you, or
> - Order a terminal device that crimps on the end of the larger conductor and reduces the termination size.

Terminals for more than one conductor and terminals used for aluminum conductors must be identified for this purpose, either within the equipment instructions or on the terminal itself.

Author's Comment:

- Split-bolt connectors are commonly listed for only two conductors, although some are listed for three conductors. However, it's a common industry practice to terminate as many conductors as possible within a split-bolt connector, even though this violates the *NEC.* Figure 110–25

(B) Conductor Splices. Conductors must be spliced by a splicing device identified for the purpose or by exothermic welding.

Author's Comment:

- Conductors aren't required to be twisted together prior to the installation of a twist-on wire connector, unless specifically required in the installation instructions. Figure 110–26

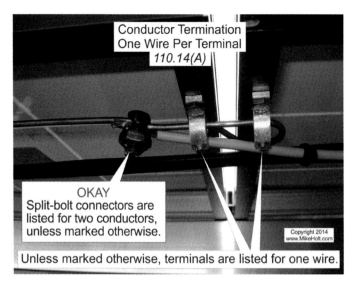
Figure 110–25

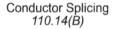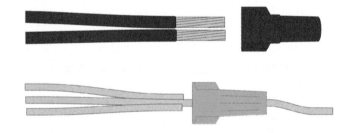

Conductors must be spliced by an identified splicing device and they aren't required to be twisted together prior to the installation of a twist-on wire connector.
Copyright 2014, www.MikeHolt.com

Figure 110–26

The free ends of the conductors must be insulated to prevent the exposed end of the conductor from touching energized parts. This requirement can be met by the use of an insulated twist-on or push-on wire connector. Figure 110–27

Author's Comment:

- See the definition of "Energized" in Article 100.

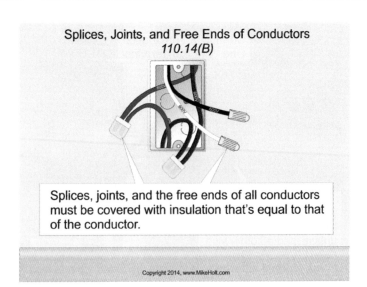

Figure 110–27

Single or multiconductor direct burial conductors of types UF or USE can be spliced underground without a junction box, but the conductors must be spliced with a device listed for direct burial [300.5(E) and 300.15(G)]. Figure 110–28

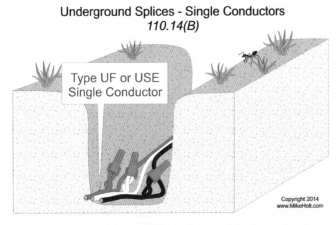

Figure 110–28

(C) Temperature Limitations (Conductor Size). Conductors are to be sized using their ampacity from the insulation temperature rating column of Table 310.15(B)(16) that corresponds to the lowest temperature rating of any terminal, device, or conductor of the circuit.

Conductors with insulation temperature ratings higher than the termination's temperature rating are permitted for ampacity adjustment, correction, or both. Figure 110–29

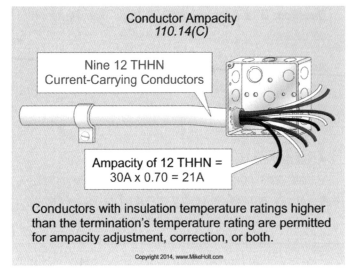

Figure 110–29

(1) Equipment Temperature Rating Provisions. Unless the equipment is listed and marked otherwise, conductor sizing for equipment terminations must be based on Table 310.15(B)(16) in accordance with (a) or (b):

(a) Equipment Rated 100A or Less.

(1) Conductors must be sized using the 60°C temperature column of Table 310.15(B)(16). Figure 110–30

(3) Conductors terminating on terminals rated 75°C are sized in accordance with the ampacities listed in the 75°C temperature column of Table 310.15(B)(16). Figure 110–31

(b) Equipment Rated Over 100A.

(1) Conductors must be sized using the 75°C temperature column of Table 310.15(B)(16). Figure 110–32

(2) Separate Connector Provisions. Conductors can be sized to the 90°C column of Table 310.15(B)(16) if the conductors and pressure connectors are rated at least 90°C. Figure 110–33

Note: Equipment markings or listing information may restrict the sizing and temperature ratings of connected conductors.

Conductor Sizing - Equipment Rated 100A or Less
110.14(C)(1)(a)(1)

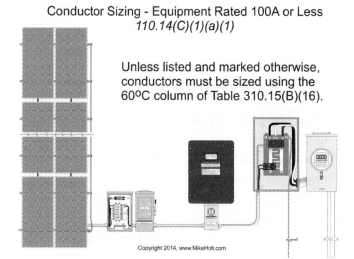

Unless listed and marked otherwise, conductors must be sized using the 60ºC column of Table 310.15(B)(16).

Copyright 2014, www.MikeHolt.com

Figure 110–30

Conductor Sizing - Equipment Over 100A
110.14(C)(1)(b)(1)

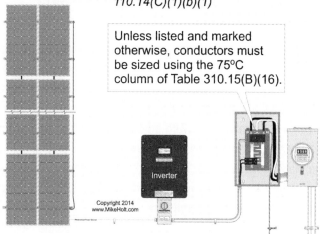

Unless listed and marked otherwise, conductors must be sized using the 75ºC column of Table 310.15(B)(16).

Inverter

Copyright 2014
www.MikeHolt.com

Figure 110–32

Conductor Sizing - Equipment Rated 100A or Less
110.14(C)(1)(a)(3)

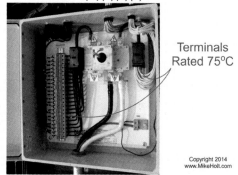

Terminals Rated 75ºC

Copyright 2014
www.MikeHolt.com

Conductors terminating on equipment rated 75ºC are sized in accordance with the ampacities listed in the 75ºC temperature column of Table 310.15(B)(16), provided the conductors have an insulation rating of at least 75ºC.

Figure 110–31

Separately Installed Connectors
110.14(C)(2)

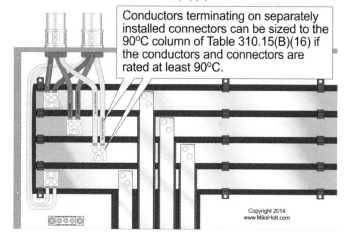

Conductors terminating on separately installed connectors can be sized to the 90ºC column of Table 310.15(B)(16) if the conductors and connectors are rated at least 90ºC.

Copyright 2014
www.MikeHolt.com

Figure 110–33

110.16 Arc-Flash Hazard Warning

Electrical equipment such as switchboards, panelboards, industrial control panels, meter socket enclosures, and motor control centers in other than dwelling units that are likely to require examination, adjustment, servicing, or maintenance while energized must be marked to warn qualified persons of the danger associated with an arc flash from short circuits or ground faults. The marking can be made in the field or the factory, must not be handwritten, must be permanently affixed, be of sufficient durability to withstand the environment involved [110.21(B)], and be clearly visible to qualified persons before they examine, adjust, service, or perform maintenance on the equipment. Figure 110–34

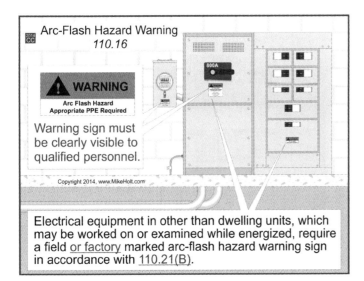

Arc-Flash Hazard Warning
110.16

⚠ **WARNING**
Arc Flash Hazard
Appropriate PPE Required

Warning sign must be clearly visible to qualified personnel.

Copyright 2014, www.MikeHolt.com

Electrical equipment in other than dwelling units, which may be worked on or examined while energized, require a field or factory marked arc-flash hazard warning sign in accordance with 110.21(B).

Figure 110–34

Author's Comment:

- See the definition of "Qualified Person" in Article 100.

- This rule is meant to warn qualified persons who work on energized electrical systems that an arc-flash hazard exists so they'll select proper personal protective equipment (PPE) in accordance with industry accepted safe work practice standards.

Note 1: NFPA 70E, *Standard for Electrical Safety in the Workplace*, provides assistance in determining the severity of potential exposure, planning safe work practices, arc-flash labeling, and selecting personal protective equipment.

2014 CHANGE ANALYSIS: Since the introduction of this section in 2002, it's been changed every single *Code* cycle. The upside is that it seems to improve every three years.

The requirement for the marking to take place in the field has been removed. It seems a bit silly that an installation can pass or fail an inspection based on who put the sticker on the equipment. If the sticker is present, and it provides the necessary information, why should it be noncompliant?

A reference to the new 110.21(B) has also been added. This new requirement contains information about signage in general, and will be discussed further in that section of this textbook.

Lastly, Informational Note 1 has been revised to make the *Code* user aware of the fact NFPA 70E contains requirements for arc-flash labeling as well.

110.21 Markings

(A) Manufacturer's Markings. The manufacturer's name, trademark, or other descriptive marking must be placed on all electrical equipment and, where required by the *Code*, markings such as voltage, current, wattage, or other ratings must be provided. All marking must have sufficient durability to withstand the environment involved.

(B) Field-Applied Hazard Markings. Where caution, warning, or danger signs or labels are required, the labels must meet the following:

(1) The markings must use words, colors, or symbols that effectively warn personnel. Figure 110–35

Note: ANSI Z535.4, Product Safety Signs and Labels, provides guidelines for the design and durability of signs and labels.

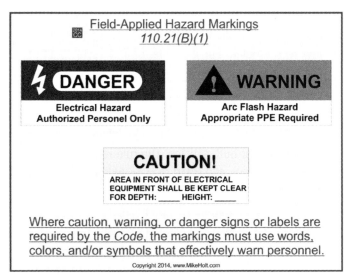

Figure 110–35

(2) The label can't be handwritten, and it must be permanently affixed to the equipment. Figure 110–36

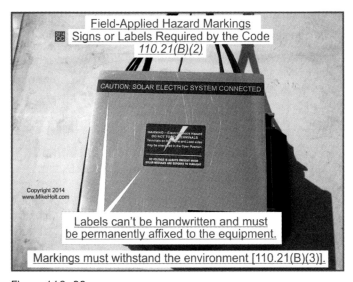

Figure 110–36

Ex to (2): Labels that contain information that's likely to change can be handwritten if legible.

Author's Comment:

- A permanently affixed sign includes a sticker, but not a piece of paper taped to the equipment.

(3) The marking must be of sufficient durability to withstand the environment involved.

2014 CHANGE ANALYSIS: In an effort to standardize the marking requirements found in the *NEC*, this requirement has been added. Certainly most will agree that a typed sign is better than a handwritten one.

There are several changes to the *Code* that require compliance with this section, but even without those changes this rule still applies. For example, 110.16 includes a statement requiring compliance with this section. If that statement weren't in 110.16, it wouldn't make this rule optional.

Some of the locations in which this rule applies are 110.16, 110.22, 250.20 (although there's no reference in that section) 312.8, 404.6, 408.3, and many, many others.

110.22 Identification of Disconnecting Means

(A) General. Each disconnecting means must be legibly marked to indicate its purpose unless located and arranged so the purpose is evident. The marking must be of sufficient durability to withstand the environment involved. Figure 110–37

110.25 Lockable Disconnecting Means

Where the *Code* requires that a disconnecting means be lockable in the open position, the provisions for locking must remain in place whether or not the lock is installed. Figure 110–38

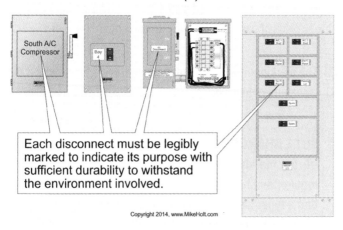

Figure 110–37

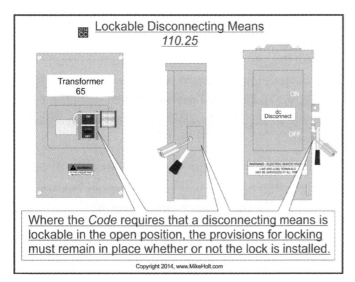

Figure 110–38

Ex: Locking provisions for cord-and-plug-connected equipment don't need to remain in place without the lock installed.

2014 CHANGE ANALYSIS: When different *Code* articles have the same requirements it's nearly impossible to make them all say the same thing. This is due to the fact that there isn't just one group of a bunch of guys smoking cigars in a dark room choosing which *NEC* change proposals pass and which fail. They're groups of professionals in 19 different *Code*-Making

Panels (CMPs), each of which is responsible for a few *NEC* articles. For example, CMP-4 reviews all of the proposals for Articles 225 and 230, while CMP-9 covers 312, 314, 404, 408, 450, and 490. It makes sense that the rules in Part II of Article 225 are almost identical to those in Article 230—the same people are responsible for both articles. The rule requiring a disconnect in Article 450 (CMP-9) is probably not going to say the same thing as the rule in Article 210 (CMP-2). The rules for equipment requiring a disconnect run the entire gamut of the *Code*-Making Panels. In order for all of the rules to say the same thing, you have to have one rule, and it has to cover everything. This new rule will hopefully satisfy this goal.

The exception to this rule is a rather obvious one, but I guess the *NEC* has to include it. A lock installed over the end of a cord is an effective way to ensure worker safety. It obviously can't remain in place at all times, unless you never want to use the equipment again!

Part II. 600V, Nominal, or Less

110.26 Spaces About Electrical Equipment

For the purpose of safe operation and maintenance of equipment, access and working space must be provided about all electrical equipment.

(A) Working Space. Equipment that may need examination, adjustment, servicing, or maintenance while energized must have working space provided in accordance with (1), (2), and (3):

Author's Comment:

- The phrase "while energized" is the root of many debates. As always, check with the AHJ to see what equipment he or she believes needs a clear working space.

(1) Depth of Working Space. The working space, which is measured from the enclosure front, must not be less than the distances contained in Table 110.26(A)(1). Figure 110–39

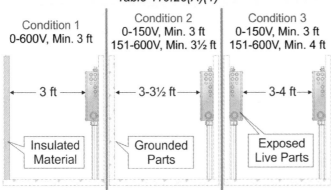

Figure 110–39

	Condition 1	Condition 2	Condition 3
Voltage-to-Ground			
0–150V	3 ft	3 ft	3 ft
151–600V	3 ft	3½ft	4 ft

Table 110.26(A)(1) Working Space

- **Condition 1:** *Exposed live parts on one side of the working space and no live or grounded parts, including concrete, brick, or tile walls are on the other side of the working space.*

- **Condition 2:** *Exposed live parts on one side of the working space and grounded parts, including concrete, brick, or tile walls are on the other side of the working space.*

- **Condition 3:** *Exposed live parts on both sides of the working space.*

(a) Rear and Sides. Working space isn't required for the back or sides of assemblies where all connections and all renewable or adjustable parts are accessible from the front. Figure 110–40

(b) Low Voltage. If special permission is granted in accordance with 90.4, working space for equipment that operates at not more than 30V ac or 60V dc can be less than the distance in Table 110.26(A)(1). Figure 110–41

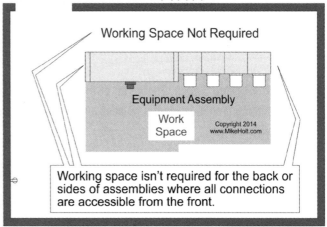

Figure 110–40

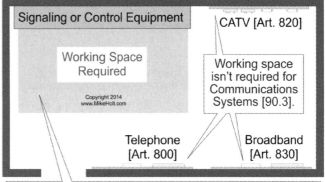

Figure 110–41

Author's Comment:

- See the definition of "Special Permission" in Article 100.

(c) Existing Buildings. If electrical equipment is being replaced, Condition 2 working space is permitted between dead-front switchboards, panelboards, or motor control centers located across the aisle from each other where conditions of maintenance and supervision ensure that written procedures have been adopted to prohibit equipment on both sides of the aisle from being open at the same time, and only authorized, qualified persons will service the installation.

Author's Comment:

■ The working space requirements of 110.26 don't apply to equipment included in Chapter 8—Communications Circuits [90.3].

(2) Width of Working Space. The width of the working space must be a minimum of 30 in., but in no case less than the width of the equipment. Figure 110–42

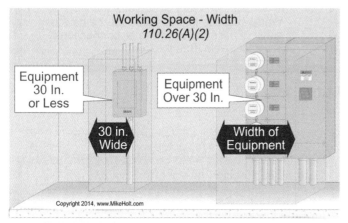

The width of the working space must be a minimum of 30 in., but in no case less than the width of the equipment, whichever is greater.

Figure 110–42

Author's Comment:

■ The width of the working space can be measured from left-to-right, from right-to-left, or simply centered on the equipment, and the working space can overlap the working space for other electrical equipment. Figure 110–43

In all cases, the working space must be of sufficient width, depth, and height to permit all equipment doors to open 90 degrees. Figure 110–44

(3) Height of Working Space (Headroom). The height of the working space in front of equipment must not be less than 6½ ft, measured from the grade, floor, platform, or the equipment height, whichever is greater. Figure 110–45

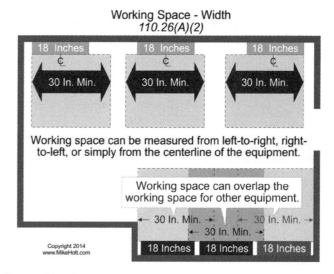

Figure 110–43

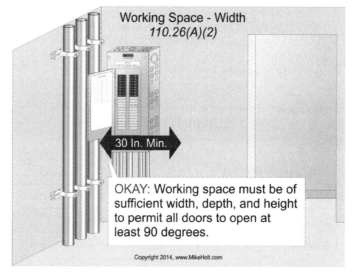

Figure 110–44

Equipment such as raceways, cables, wireways, or cabinets can be located above or below electrical equipment, but must not extend more than 6 in. into the equipment's working space. Figure 110–46

Ex 1: The minimum headroom requirement doesn't apply to service equipment or panelboards rated 200A or less located in an existing dwelling unit.

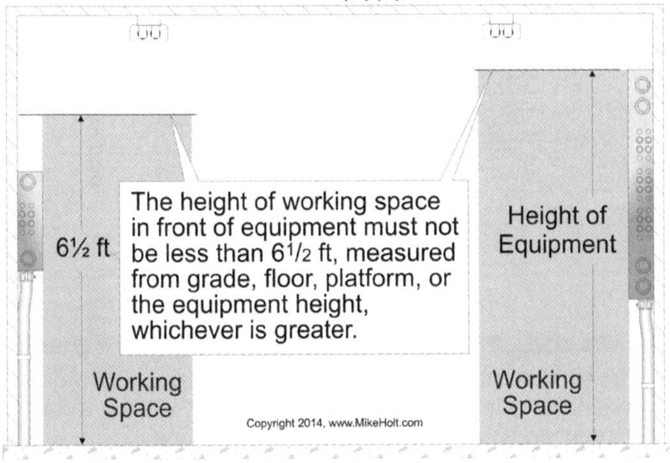

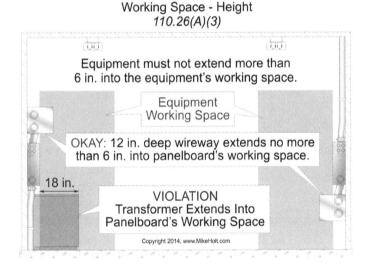

Working Space - Height
110.26(A)(3)

6½ ft

The height of working space in front of equipment must not be less than 6½ ft, measured from grade, floor, platform, or the equipment height, whichever is greater.

Height of Equipment

Working Space

Working Space

Copyright 2014, www.MikeHolt.com

Figure 110–45

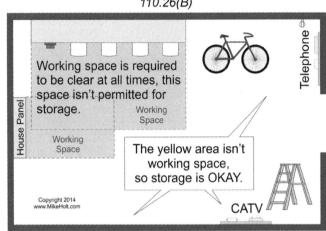

Working Space - No Storage
110.26(B)

Telephone

House Panel

Working space is required to be clear at all times, this space isn't permitted for storage.

Working Space

Working Space

The yellow area isn't working space, so storage is OKAY.

Copyright 2014 www.MikeHolt.com

CATV

Figure 110–47

Working Space - Height
110.26(A)(3)

Equipment must not extend more than 6 in. into the equipment's working space.

Equipment Working Space

OKAY: 12 in. deep wireway extends no more than 6 in. into panelboard's working space.

18 in.

VIOLATION
Transformer Extends Into Panelboard's Working Space

Copyright 2014, www.MikeHolt.com

Figure 110–46

Author's Comment:

■ See the definition of "Dwelling Unit" in Article 100.

Ex 2: Meters installed in meter sockets are permitted to extend beyond the other equipment.

(B) Clear Working Space. The working space required by this section must be clear at all times. Therefore, this space isn't permitted for storage. Figure 110–47

When normally enclosed live parts are exposed for inspection or servicing, the working space, if in a passageway or general open space, must be suitably guarded.

Author's Comment:

■ When working in a passageway, the working space must be guarded from occupants using it. When working on electrical equipment in a passageway one must be mindful of a fire alarm evacuation with numerous occupants congregated and moving through the area.

⚠ **CAUTION:** *It's very dangerous to service energized parts in the first place, and it's unacceptable to be subjected to additional dangers by working around bicycles, boxes, crates, appliances, and other impediments.*

Author's Comment:

■ Signaling and communications equipment must not be installed in a manner that encroaches on the working space of the electrical equipment. Figure 110–48

(C) Entrance to and Egress from Working Space.

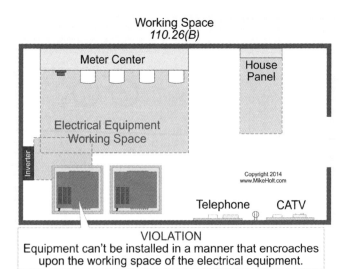

Figure 110–48

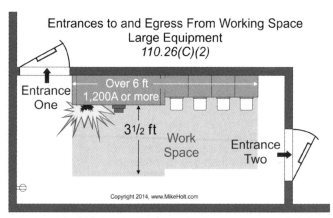

For equipment rated 1,200A or more and over 6 ft wide, an entrance to and egress from (2 ft wide x 6 ½ ft wide) is required at each end of the working space.

Figure 110–49

(1) Minimum Required. At least one entrance of sufficient area must provide access to and egress from the working space.

Author's Comment:

- Check to see what the authority having jurisdiction considers "Sufficient Area." Building codes contain minimum dimensions for doors and openings for personnel travel.

(2) Large Equipment. An entrance to and egress from each end of the working space of electrical equipment rated 1,200A or more that's over 6 ft wide is required. The opening must be a minimum of 24 in. wide and 6½ ft high. Figure 110–49

A single entrance to and egress from the required working space is permitted where either of the following conditions is met:

(a) Unobstructed Egress. Only one entrance is required where the location permits a continuous and unobstructed way of egress travel. Figure 110–50

(b) Double Workspace. Only one entrance is required where the required working space depth is doubled, and the equipment is located so the edge of the entrance is no closer than the required working space distance. Figure 110–51

(3) Personnel Doors. If equipment with overcurrent or switching devices rated <u>800A</u> or more is installed, personnel door(s)

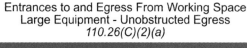
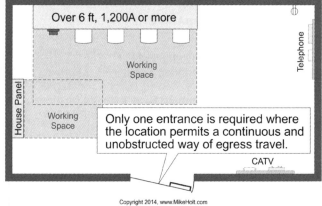

Figure 110–50

for entrance to and egress from the working space located less than 25 ft from the nearest edge of the working space must have the door(s) open in the direction of egress and be equipped with <u>listed panic hardware</u>. Figure 110–52

Author's Comment:

- History has shown that electricians who suffer burns on their hands in electrical arc-flash or arc-blast events often can't open doors equipped with knobs that must be turned.

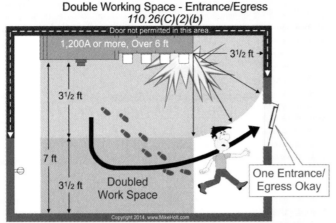

Double Working Space - Entrance/Egress
110.26(C)(2)(b)

One entrance/egress is permitted where the required working space is doubled, and equipment is located so the edge of the entrance is no closer than the required working space distance.

Figure 110–51

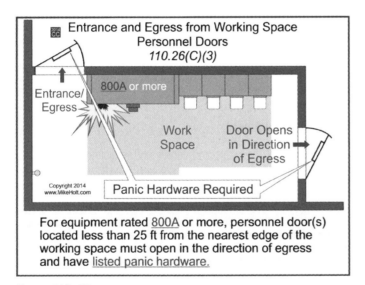

Entrance and Egress from Working Space
Personnel Doors
110.26(C)(3)

For equipment rated 800A or more, personnel door(s) located less than 25 ft from the nearest edge of the working space must open in the direction of egress and have listed panic hardware.

Figure 110–52

- Since this requirement is in the *NEC*, the electrical contractor is responsible for ensuring that panic hardware is installed where required. Some electrical contractors are offended at being held liable for nonelectrical responsibilities, but this rule is designed to save the lives of electricians. For this and other reasons, many construction professionals routinely hold "pre-construction" or "pre-con" meetings to review potential opportunities for miscommunication—before the work begins.

2014 CHANGE ANALYSIS: The requirements for door swings and hardware in equipment rooms containing large equipment are among the most important safety provisions for electricians in the entire *NEC*. When an electrical accident occurs, particularly an arc flash or arc blast, the victim is rendered incapable of opening a door if the door swings in or has hardware that must be operated. Because the victim's hands and eyes are the two parts of the body most often affected, this issue is even more important. These incidents occur at currents much, much less than 1,200A. By decreasing the current threshold of this requirement to 800A, more electrical rooms will be equipped with outward swinging doors with panic hardware.

The requirements for the door hardware itself have also changed. Since the inception of this rule in 2002, the hardware requirements for the outward swinging door have allowed for panic hardware or similar devices that open without the victim having to manipulate a knob or similar hardware. In this new edition of the *Code*, there's no longer any option. Panic hardware must be used, and it must be listed. Most people will agree that a safety feature like panic hardware probably should be a listed piece of equipment, but now that's the only option. Hardware like a push/pull plate is no longer allowed, despite the fact that it's even easier to use than the required panic hardware.

(D) Illumination. Service equipment, switchboards, and panelboards, as well as motor control centers located indoors must have illumination located indoors and must not be controlled solely by automatic means. Figure 110–53

Author's Comment:

- The *Code* doesn't provide the minimum foot-candles required to provide proper illumination. Proper illumination of electrical equipment rooms is essential for the safety of those qualified to work on such equipment.

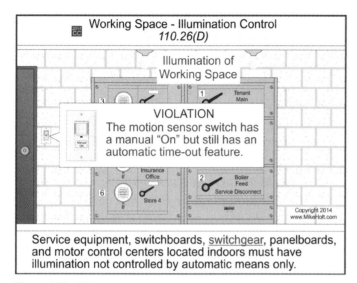

Figure 110–53

(E) Dedicated Equipment Space. Switchboards, panelboards, and motor control centers must have dedicated equipment space as follows:

(1) Indoors.

(a) Dedicated Electrical Space. The footprint space (width and depth of the equipment) extending from the floor to a height of 6 ft above the equipment or to the structural ceiling, whichever is lower, must be dedicated for the electrical installation. Figure 110–54

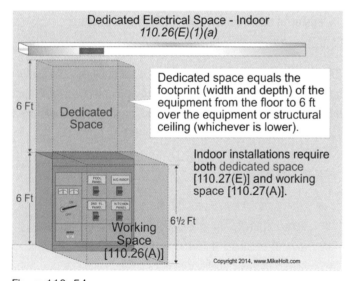

Figure 110–54

No piping, ducts, or other equipment foreign to the electrical installation can be installed in this dedicated footprint space. Figure 110–55

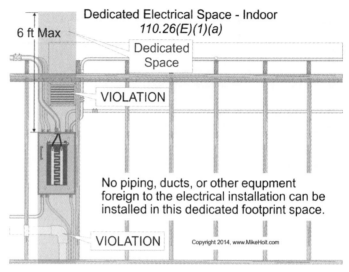

Figure 110–55

Author's Comment:

■ Electrical raceways and cables not associated with the dedicated space can be within the dedicated space. These aren't considered "other equipment foreign to the electrical installation." Figure 110–56

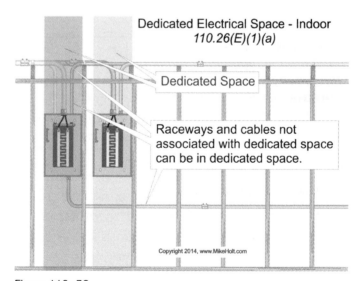

Figure 110–56

Ex: Suspended ceilings with removable panels can be within the dedicated footprint space [110.26(E)(1)(d)].

(b) Foreign Systems. Foreign systems can be located above the dedicated space if protection is installed to prevent damage to the electrical equipment from condensation, leaks, or breaks in the foreign systems, which can be as simple as a drip-pan. Figure 110–57

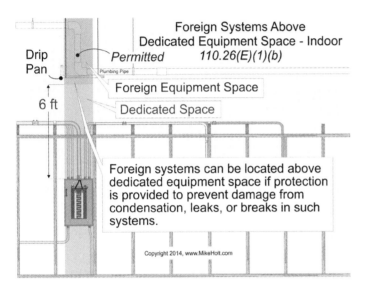

Figure 110–57

(c) Sprinkler Protection. Sprinkler protection piping is permitted in the dedicated space where the piping complies with this section.

(d) Suspended Ceilings. A dropped, suspended, or similar ceiling isn't considered a structural ceiling. Figure 110–58

(2) Outdoor. Outdoor installations must comply with 110.26(E) (2)(a) and (b).

(a) Installation Requirements. Outdoor electrical equipment must be installed in suitable enclosures and be protected from accidental contact by unauthorized personnel, vehicular traffic, or by accidental spillage or leakage from piping systems.

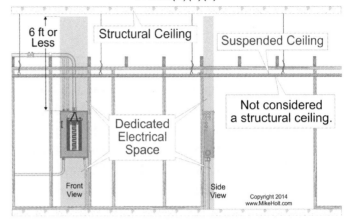

Figure 110–58

(b) Dedicated Electrical Space. The footprint space (width and depth of the equipment) extending from the floor to a height of 6 ft above the equipment must be dedicated for the electrical installation. No piping, ducts, or other equipment foreign to the electrical installation can be installed in this dedicated footprint space. Figure 110–59

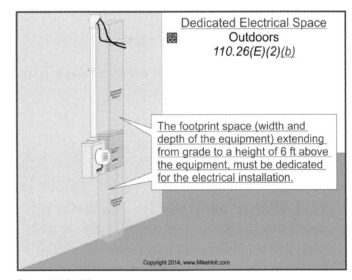

Figure 110–59

Author's Comment:

- See the definition of "Accessible as it applies to equipment" in Article 100.

2014 CHANGE ANALYSIS: New to this edition of the *NEC* is a requirement for outdoor equipment to have dedicated space above and below it, similar to the requirements for indoor installations. The intent of the dedicated space rule for indoor equipment is to allow the installer enough space to install raceways and cables. This is just as important outdoors as it is indoors.

110.27 Guarding

(A) Guarding Live Parts. Live parts of electrical equipment operating at 50V or more must be guarded against accidental contact. This can be done by:

(1) Locating them in a separate room, vault, or enclosure.

(2) Guarding with a substantial partition or screen.

(3) Locating them on a balcony or platform.

(4) Elevating them above the floor or working surface, in accordance with the following:

(a) 8 ft for 50V through 300V.

(b) 8½ ft for 301V through 600V.

2014 CHANGE ANALYSIS: The requirements for guarding live parts have been revised in order to correlate with the *National Electrical Safety Code (NESC)*. It's typically used by utility companies as the document that regulates their installations. In many instances there's no need to correlate the *NEC* and the *NESC*, since they're intended to have different rules. In this case, however, it was determined that the *NESC* has the better rule for elevation requirements, so it's been copied and pasted here.

(B) Prevent Physical Damage. Electrical equipment must not be installed where subject to physical damage, unless enclosures or guards are so arranged and of sufficient strength to prevent damage. Figures 110–60 and 110–61

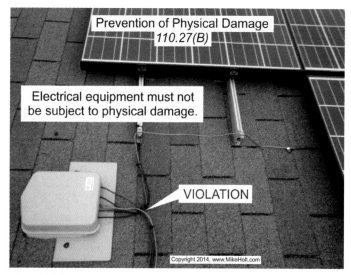

Figure 110–60

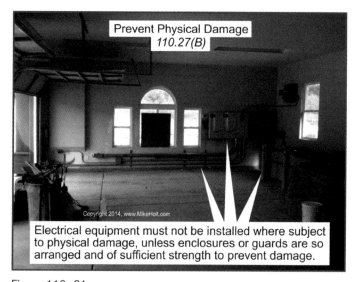

Figure 110–61

(C) Warning Signs. Entrances to rooms and other guarded locations containing exposed live parts must be marked with conspicuous signs forbidding unqualified persons from entering. Such signs must meet the requirements of 110.21(B).

2014 CHANGE ANALYSIS: The requirements for guarding live parts have been revised in order to correlate with the *National Electrical Safety Code* (*NESC*). It's typically used by utility companies as the document that regulates their installations. In many instances there's no need to correlate the *NEC* and the *NESC*, since they're intended to have different rules. In this case, however, it was determined that the *NESC* has the better rule for elevation requirements, so it's been copied and pasted here.

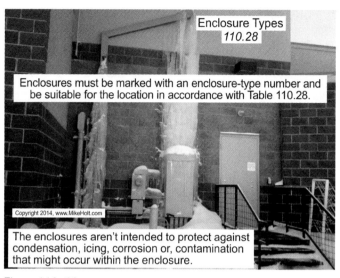

Figure 110–62

110.28 Enclosure Types

Enclosures must be marked with an enclosure-type number and be suitable for the location in accordance with Table 110.28.

The enclosures aren't intended to protect against condensation, icing, corrosion, or contamination that might occur within the enclosure or that enters via the raceway or unsealed openings. Figure 110–62

> **Note:** Raintight enclosures include Types 3, 3S, 3SX, 3X, 4, 4X, 6, and 6P; rainproof enclosures are Types 3R, and 3RX; watertight enclosures are Types 4, 4X, 6, and 6P; driptight enclosures are Types 2, 5, 12, 12K, and 13; and dusttight enclosures are Types 3, 3S, 3SX, 3X, 5, 12, 12K, and 13.

CHAPTER 1 PRACTICE QUESTIONS

Please use the 2014 *Code* book to answer the following questions.

Article 100. Definitions

1. Admitting close approach not guarded by locked doors, elevation, or other effective means, is referred to as _____.

    (a) accessible (as applied to equipment)
    (b) accessible (as applied to wiring methods)
    (c) accessible, readily
    (d) all of these

2. Capable of being removed or exposed without damaging the building structure or finish, or not permanently closed in by the structure or finish of the building is known as _____.

    (a) accessible (as applied to equipment)
    (b) accessible (as applied to wiring methods)
    (c) accessible, readily
    (d) all of these

3. Capable of being reached quickly for operation, renewal, or inspections without resorting to portable ladders or the use of tools is known as _____.

    (a) accessible (as applied to equipment)
    (b) accessible (as applied to wiring methods)
    (c) accessible, readily
    (d) all of these

4. The maximum current, in amperes, that a conductor can carry continuously, where the temperature will not be raised in excess of the conductor's insulation temperature rating is called its "_____."

    (a) short-circuit rating
    (b) ground-fault rating
    (c) ampacity
    (d) all of these

5. "_____" means acceptable to the authority having jurisdiction.

    (a) Identified
    (b) Listed
    (c) Approved
    (d) Labeled

6. An arc-fault circuit interrupter is a device intended to de-energize the circuit when it recognizes characteristics unique to _____.

    (a) overcurrent
    (b) arcing
    (c) ground fault
    (d) harmonic fundamental

7. Where no statutory requirement exists, the authority having jurisdiction can be a property owner or his/her agent, such as an architect or engineer.

    (a) True
    (b) False

8. A battery system includes storage batteries and battery chargers, and can include inverters, converters, and associated electrical equipment.

    (a) True
    (b) False

9. "Bonded" can be described as _____ to establish electrical continuity and conductivity.

    (a) isolated
    (b) guarded
    (c) connected
    (d) separated

10. A reliable conductor that ensures electrical conductivity between metal parts of the electrical installation that are required to be electrically connected is called a "_____."

    (a) grounding electrode
    (b) auxiliary ground
    (c) bonding conductor or jumper
    (d) tap conductor

11. The connection between the grounded circuit conductor and the equipment grounding conductor at the service is accomplished by installing a(n) _____ bonding jumper.

    (a) main
    (b) system
    (c) equipment
    (d) circuit

12. The connection between the grounded circuit conductor and the supply-side bonding jumper or equipment grounding conductor, or both, at a _____ is called a "system bonding jumper."

    (a) service disconnect
    (b) separately derived system
    (c) motor control center
    (d) separate building or structure disconnect

13. The circuit conductors between the final overcurrent device protecting the circuit and the outlet(s) are known as "_____ conductors."

    (a) feeder
    (b) branch-circuit
    (c) home run
    (d) none of these

14. The *NEC* defines a(n) "_____" as a structure that stands alone or that is cut off from adjoining structures by fire walls or fire barriers, with all openings therein protected by approved fire doors.

    (a) unit
    (b) apartment
    (c) building
    (d) utility

15. An enclosure for either surface mounting or flush mounting provided with a frame in which a door can be hung is called a(n) "_____."

    (a) enclosure
    (b) outlet box
    (c) cutout box
    (d) cabinet

16. A circuit breaker is a device designed to _____ the circuit automatically on a predetermined overcurrent without damage to itself when properly applied within its rating.

    (a) energize
    (b) reset
    (c) connect
    (d) open

17. _____ is a term indicating that there is an intentional delay in the tripping action of the circuit breaker, which decreases as the magnitude of the current increases.

    (a) Adverse time
    (b) Inverse time
    (c) Time delay
    (d) Timed unit

18. A separate portion of a raceway system that provides access through a removable cover(s) to the interior of the system, defines the term _____.

    (a) junction box
    (b) accessible raceway
    (c) conduit body
    (d) cutout box

19. A solderless pressure connector is a device that _____ between two or more conductors or between one or more conductors and a terminal by means of mechanical pressure and without the use of solder.

    (a) provides access
    (b) protects the wiring
    (c) is never needed
    (d) establishes a connection

20. A(n) _____ is a device, or group of devices, by which the conductors of a circuit can be disconnected from their source of supply.

    (a) feeder
    (b) enclosure
    (c) disconnecting means
    (d) conductor interrupter

21. A _____ is a single unit that provides independent living facilities for one or more persons, including permanent provisions for living, sleeping, cooking, and sanitation.

    (a) one-family dwelling
    (b) two-family dwelling
    (c) dwelling unit
    (d) multifamily dwelling

22. An effective ground-fault current path is an intentionally constructed, low-impedance electrically conductive path designed and intended to carry current under ground-fault conditions from the point of a ground fault on a wiring system to _____.

    (a) ground
    (b) earth
    (c) the electrical supply source
    (d) none of these

23. For wiring methods, "on or attached to the surface, or behind access panels designed to allow access" is known as _____.

    (a) open
    (b) uncovered
    (c) exposed
    (d) bare

24. The *NEC* defines a "_____" as all circuit conductors between the service equipment, the source of a separately derived system, or other power supply source and the final branch-circuit overcurrent device.

    (a) service
    (b) feeder
    (c) branch circuit
    (d) all of these

25. The word "Earth" best describes what *NEC* term?

    (a) Bonded
    (b) Ground
    (c) Effective ground-fault current path
    (d) Guarded

26. A(n) _____ is an unintentional, electrically conductive connection between an ungrounded conductor of an electrical circuit, and the normally noncurrent-carrying conductors, metallic enclosures, metallic raceways, metallic equipment, or earth.

    (a) grounded conductor
    (b) ground fault
    (c) equipment ground
    (d) bonding jumper

27. Connected to ground or to a conductive body that extends the ground connection is called "_____."

    (a) equipment grounding
    (b) bonded
    (c) grounded
    (d) all of these

28. A system or circuit conductor that is intentionally grounded is called a(n) "_____."

    (a) grounding conductor
    (b) unidentified conductor
    (c) grounded conductor
    (d) grounding electrode conductor

29. The installed conductive path(s) that provide(s) a ground-fault current path and connects normally noncurrent-carrying metal parts of equipment together and to the system grounded conductor or to the grounding electrode conductor, or both, is known as a(n) _____.

    (a) grounding electrode conductor
    (b) grounding conductor
    (c) equipment grounding conductor
    (d) none of these

30. A conducting object through which a direct connection to earth is established is a "_____."

    (a) bonding conductor
    (b) grounding conductor
    (c) grounding electrode
    (d) grounded conductor

31. A conductor used to connect the system grounded conductor or the equipment to a grounding electrode or to a point on the grounding electrode system is called the "_____ conductor."

    (a) main grounding
    (b) common main
    (c) equipment grounding
    (d) grounding electrode

32. A handhole enclosure is an enclosure for use in underground systems, provided with an open or closed bottom, and sized to allow personnel to _____.

    (a) enter and exit freely
    (b) reach into but not enter
    (c) have full working space
    (d) examine it visually

33. A hybrid system is comprised of multiple power sources, such as _____, but not the utility power system.

    (a) photovoltaic
    (b) wind
    (c) micro-hydro generators
    (d) all of these

34. A hybrid system includes the utility power system.

    (a) True
    (b) False

35. A hybrid system includes _____.

    (a) storage batteries
    (b) flywheel storage equipment
    (c) superconducting magnetic storage equipment
    (d) none of these

36. Recognized as suitable for the specific purpose, function, use, environment, and application is the definition of "_____."

    (a) labeled
    (b) identified (as applied to equipment)
    (c) listed
    (d) approved

37. Within sight means visible and not more than _____ ft distant from the equipment.

    (a) 10
    (b) 20
    (c) 25
    (d) 50

38. The highest current at rated voltage that a device is identified to interrupt under standard test conditions is the _____.

    (a) interrupting rating
    (b) manufacturer's rating
    (c) interrupting capacity
    (d) withstand rating

39. Equipment or materials to which a label, symbol, or other identifying mark of a product evaluation organization that is acceptable to the authority having jurisdiction has been attached is known as "_____."

    (a) listed
    (b) labeled
    (c) approved
    (d) identified

40. Equipment or materials included in a list published by a testing laboratory acceptable to the authority having jurisdiction is said to be "_____."

    (a) book
    (b) digest
    (c) manifest
    (d) listed

41. A _____ location is protected from weather and not subject to saturation with water or other liquids.

    (a) dry
    (b) damp
    (c) wet
    (d) moist

42. A _____ location may be temporarily subject to dampness and wetness.

    (a) dry
    (b) damp
    (c) moist
    (d) wet

43. Conduit installed underground or encased in concrete slabs that are in direct contact with the earth is considered a _____ location.

    (a) dry
    (b) damp
    (c) wet
    (d) moist

44. Any current in excess of the rated current of equipment or the ampacity of a conductor is called "_____."

    (a) trip current
    (b) fault current
    (c) overcurrent
    (d) a short circuit

45. A(n) _____ is intended to provide limited overcurrent protection for specific applications and utilization equipment such as luminaires and appliances. This limited protection is in addition to the protection provided by the required branch-circuit overcurrent protective device.

    (a) supplementary overcurrent device
    (b) surge protection device
    (c) arc-fault circuit interrupter
    (d) Class A GFCI

46. An overload is the same as a short circuit or ground fault.

    (a) True
    (b) False

47. A panel, including buses and automatic overcurrent devices, designed to be placed in a cabinet or cutout box and accessible only from the front is known as a "_____."

    (a) switchboard
    (b) disconnect
    (c) panelboard
    (d) switch

48. A _____ is the total components and subsystem that, in combination, convert solar energy into electric energy suitable for connection to a utilization load.

    (a) photovoltaic system
    (b) solar array
    (c) a and b
    (d) neither a nor b

49. Premises wiring includes _____ wiring from the service point or power source to the outlets.

    (a) interior
    (b) exterior
    (c) underground
    (d) a and b

50. The *NEC* defines a(n) "_____" as one who has skills and knowledge related to the construction and operation of the electrical equipment and installations and has received safety training to recognize and avoid the hazards involved.

    (a) inspector
    (b) master electrician
    (c) journeyman electrician
    (d) qualified person

51. NFPA 70E—*Standard for Electrical Safety in the Workplace*, provides information to help determine the electrical safety training requirements expected of a qualified person.

    (a) True
    (b) False

52. The conductors and equipment from the electric utility that deliver electric energy to the wiring system of the premises is called a "_____."

    (a) branch circuit
    (b) feeder
    (c) service
    (d) none of these

53. Service conductors originate at the service point and terminate at the service disconnecting means.

    (a) True
    (b) False

54. The _____ is the necessary equipment, usually consisting of a circuit breaker(s) or switch(es) and fuse(s) and their accessories, connected to the load end of service conductors, and intended to constitute the main control and cutoff of the supply.

    (a) service equipment
    (b) service
    (c) service disconnect
    (d) service overcurrent device

55. The _____ is the point of connection between the facilities of the serving utility and the premises wiring.

    (a) service entrance
    (b) service point
    (c) overcurrent protection
    (d) beginning of the wiring system

56. The prospective symmetrical fault current at a nominal voltage to which an apparatus or system is able to be connected without sustaining damage exceeding defined acceptance criteria is known as the "_____."

    (a) short-circuit current rating
    (b) arc flash rating
    (c) overcurrent rating
    (d) available fault current

57. Special permission is the written consent from the _____.

    (a) testing laboratory
    (b) manufacturer
    (c) owner
    (d) authority having jurisdiction

58. "Ungrounded" means not connected to ground or to a conductive body that extends the ground connection.

    (a) True
    (b) False

59. The voltage of a circuit is defined by the *Code* as the _____ root-mean-square (effective) difference of potential between any two conductors of the circuit concerned.

    (a) lowest
    (b) greatest
    (c) average
    (d) nominal

60. A value assigned to a circuit or system for the purpose of conveniently designating its voltage class, such as 120/240V, is called "_____ voltage."

    (a) root-mean-square
    (b) circuit
    (c) nominal
    (d) source

Article 110. Requirements for Electrical Installations

1. In judging equipment for approval, considerations such as the following shall be evaluated:

    (a) mechanical strength
    (b) wire-bending space
    (c) arcing effects
    (d) all of these

2. Listed or labeled equipment shall be installed and used in accordance with any instructions included in the listing or labeling.

    (a) True
    (b) False

3. Conductors normally used to carry current shall be _____ unless otherwise provided in this *Code*.

    (a) bare
    (b) stranded
    (c) of copper
    (d) of aluminum

4. Conductor sizes are expressed in American Wire Gage (AWG) or in _____.

    (a) inches
    (b) circular mils
    (c) square inches
    (d) cubic inches

5. Wiring shall be installed so that the completed system will be free from _____, other than as required or permitted elsewhere in the *Code*.

    (a) short circuits
    (b) ground faults
    (c) connections to the earth
    (d) all of these

6. Only wiring methods recognized as _____ are included in this *Code*.

    (a) expensive
    (b) efficient
    (c) suitable
    (d) cost-effective

7. Equipment intended to interrupt current at fault levels shall have an interrupting rating at nominal circuit voltage sufficient for the current that is available at the line terminals of the equipment.

    (a) True
    (b) False

8. The _____ of a circuit shall be selected and coordinated to permit the circuit protective devices to clear a fault without extensive damage to the electrical equipment of the circuit.

   (a) overcurrent devices
   (b) total circuit impedance
   (c) equipment short-circuit current ratings
   (d) all of these

9. Unless identified for use in the operating environment, no conductors or equipment shall be _____ having a deteriorating effect on the conductors or equipment.

   (a) located in damp or wet locations
   (b) exposed to fumes, vapors, liquids, or gases
   (c) exposed to excessive temperatures
   (d) all of these

10. Some cleaning and lubricating compounds can cause severe deterioration of many plastic materials used for insulating and structural applications in equipment.

    (a) True
    (b) False

11. The *NEC* requires that electrical equipment be _____.

    (a) installed in a neat and workmanlike manner
    (b) installed under the supervision of a licensed person
    (c) completed before being inspected
    (d) all of these

12. Accepted industry workmanship practices are described in ANSI/NECA 1-2010, *Standard Practice of Good Workmanship in Electrical Construction*, and other ANSI-approved installation standards.

    (a) True
    (b) False

13. Unused openings other than those intended for the operation of equipment, intended for mounting purposes, or permitted as part of the design for listed equipment shall be _____.

    (a) filled with cable clamps or connectors only
    (b) taped over with electrical tape
    (c) repaired only by welding or brazing in a metal slug
    (d) closed to afford protection substantially equivalent to the wall of the equipment

14. Internal parts of electrical equipment, including _____, shall not be damaged or contaminated by foreign materials such as paint, plaster, cleaners, abrasives, or corrosive residues.

    (a) busbars
    (b) wiring terminals
    (c) insulators
    (d) all of these

15. Wooden plugs driven into holes in _____ or similar materials shall not be used for securing electrical equipment.

    (a) masonry
    (b) concrete
    (c) plaster
    (d) all of these

16. Conductor terminal and splicing devices must be _____ for the conductor material and they must be properly installed and used.

    (a) listed
    (b) approved
    (c) identified
    (d) all of these

17. Connectors and terminals for conductors more finely stranded than Class B and Class C, as shown in Table 10 of Chapter 9, must be _____ for the specific conductor class or classes.

    (a) listed
    (b) approved
    (c) identified
    (d) all of these

18. Many terminations and equipment are either marked with _____, or have that information included in the product's installation instructions.

    (a) an etching tool
    (b) a removable label
    (c) a tightening torque
    (d) the manufacturer's initials

19. Connection of conductors to terminal parts shall ensure a thoroughly good connection without damaging the conductors and shall be made by means of _____.

    (a) solder lugs
    (b) pressure connectors
    (c) splices to flexible leads
    (d) any of these

20. Connection by means of wire-binding screws, studs, or nuts having upturned lugs or the equivalent shall be permitted for _____ or smaller conductors.

    (a) 12 AWG
    (b) 10 AWG
    (c) 8 AWG
    (d) 6 AWG

21. Soldered splices shall first be spliced or joined so as to be mechanically and electrically secure without solder and then be soldered.

    (a) True
    (b) False

22. The temperature rating associated with the ampacity of a _____ shall be selected and coordinated so as not to exceed the lowest temperature rating of any connected termination, conductor, or device.

    (a) terminal
    (b) conductor
    (c) device
    (d) all of these

23. Conductor ampacity shall be determined using the _____ column of Table 310.15(B)(16) for circuits rated 100A or less or marked for 14 AWG through 1 AWG conductors, unless the equipment terminals are listed for use with conductors that have higher temperature ratings.

    (a) 30°C
    (b) 60°C
    (c) 75°C
    (d) 90°C

24. For circuits rated 100A or less, when the equipment terminals are listed for use with 75°C conductors, the _____ column of Table 310.15(B)(16) shall be used to determine the ampacity of THHN conductors.

    (a) 30°C
    (b) 60°C
    (c) 75°C
    (d) 90°C

25. Conductors shall have their ampacity determined using the _____ column of Table 310.15(B)(16) for circuits rated over 100A, or marked for conductors larger than 1 AWG, unless the equipment terminals are listed for use with higher temperature-rated conductors.

    (a) 30°C
    (b) 60°C
    (c) 75°C
    (d) 90°C

26. Separately installed pressure connectors shall be used with conductors at the _____ not exceeding the ampacity at the listed and identified temperature rating of the connector.

    (a) voltages
    (b) temperatures
    (c) listings
    (d) ampacities

27. Electrical equipment such as switchboards, switchgear, panelboards, industrial control panels, meter socket enclosures, and motor control centers, that are in other than dwelling units, and are likely to require _____ while energized, shall be field or factory marked to warn qualified persons of potential electric arc flash hazards.

    (a) examination
    (b) adjustment
    (c) servicing or maintenance
    (d) any of these

28. Each disconnecting means shall be legibly marked to indicate its purpose unless located and arranged so _____.

    (a) that it can be locked out and tagged
    (b) it is not readily accessible
    (c) the purpose is evident
    (d) that it operates at less than 300 volts-to-ground

29. Access and _____ shall be provided and maintained about all electrical equipment to permit ready and safe operation and maintenance of such equipment.

    (a) ventilation
    (b) cleanliness
    (c) circulation
    (d) working space

30. A minimum working space depth of _____ to live parts operating at 277 volts-to-ground is required where there are exposed live parts on one side and no live or grounded parts on the other side.

    (a) 2 ft
    (b) 3 ft
    (c) 4 ft
    (d) 6 ft

31. The minimum working space on a circuit that is 120 volts-to-ground, with exposed live parts on one side and no live or grounded parts on the other side of the working space, is _____.

    (a) 1 ft
    (b) 3 ft
    (c) 4 ft
    (d) 6 ft

32. Concrete, brick, or tile walls are considered _____, as applied to working space requirements.

    (a) inconsequential
    (b) in the way
    (c) grounded
    (d) none of these

33. The required working space for access to live parts operating at 300 volts-to-ground, where there are exposed live parts on one side and grounded parts on the other side, is _____.

    (a) 3 ft
    (b) 3½ ft
    (c) 4 ft
    (d) 4½ ft

34. The required working space for access to live parts operating at 300 volts-to-ground, where there are exposed live parts on both sides of the workspace is _____.

    (a) 3 ft
    (b) 3½ ft
    (c) 4 ft
    (d) 4½ ft

35. Working space distances for enclosed live parts shall be measured from the _____ of equipment or apparatus, if the live parts are enclosed.

    (a) enclosure
    (b) opening
    (c) a or b
    (d) none of these

36. The working space in front of the electric equipment shall not be less than _____ wide, or the width of the equipment, whichever is greater.

    (a) 15 in.
    (b) 30 in.
    (c) 40 in.
    (d) 60 in.

37. Equipment associated with the electrical installation can be located above or below other electrical equipment within their working space when the associated equipment does not extend more than _____ from the front of the electrical equipment.

    (a) 3 in.
    (b) 6 in.
    (c) 12 in.
    (d) 30 in.

38. The minimum height of working spaces about electrical equipment, switchboards, panelboards, or motor control centers operating at 600V, nominal, or less and likely to require examination, adjustment, servicing, or maintenance while energized shall be 6½ ft or the height of the equipment, whichever is greater, except for service equipment or panelboards in existing dwelling units that do not exceed 200A.

    (a) True
    (b) False

39. Working space shall not be used for _____.

    (a) storage
    (b) raceways
    (c) lighting
    (d) accessibility

40. When normally enclosed live parts are exposed for inspection or servicing, the working space, if in a passageway or general open space, shall be suitably _____.

    (a) accessible
    (b) guarded
    (c) open
    (d) enclosed

41. For equipment rated 1,200A or more and over 6 ft wide that contains overcurrent devices, switching devices, or control devices, there shall be one entrance to and egress from the required working space not less than 24 in. wide and _____ high at each end of the working space.

    (a) 5½ ft
    (b) 6 ft
    (c) 6½ ft
    (d) any of these

42. For equipment rated 800A or more that contains overcurrent devices, switching devices, or control devices; and where the entrance to the working space has a personnel door less than 25 ft from the working space, the door shall _____.

    (a) open either in or out with simple pressure and shall not have any lock
    (b) open in the direction of egress and be equipped with listed panic hardware
    (c) be equipped with a locking means
    (d) be equipped with an electronic opener

43. Illumination shall be provided for all working spaces about service equipment, switchboards, switchgear, panelboards, and motor control centers _____.

    (a) over 600V
    (b) located indoors
    (c) rated 1,200A or more
    (d) using automatic means of control

44. All switchboards, panelboards, and motor control centers shall be _____.

    (a) located in dedicated spaces
    (b) protected from damage
    (c) in weatherproof enclosures
    (d) a and b

45. The minimum height of dedicated equipment space for motor control centers installed indoors is _____ above the enclosure, or to the structural ceiling, whichever is lower.

    (a) 3 ft
    (b) 5 ft
    (c) 6 ft
    (d) 6½ ft

46. For indoor installations, heating, cooling, or ventilating equipment shall not be installed in the dedicated space above a panelboard or switchboard.

    (a) True
    (b) False

47. The dedicated equipment space for electrical equipment that is required for panelboards installed indoors is measured from the floor to a height of _____ above the equipment, or to the structural ceiling, whichever is lower.

    (a) 3 ft
    (b) 6 ft
    (c) 12 ft
    (d) 30 ft

48. The dedicated space above a panelboard extends to a dropped or suspended ceiling, which is considered a structural ceiling.

    (a) True
    (b) False

49. Electrical equipment rooms or enclosures housing electrical apparatus that are controlled by a lock(s) shall be considered _____ to qualified persons.

    (a) readily accessible
    (b) accessible
    (c) available
    (d) none of these

50. To guard live parts operating at 50V must be guarded by being _____.

    (a) located in a room accessible only to qualified persons
    (b) located on a balcony accessible only to qualified persons
    (c) elevated 8 ft or more above the floor or other working surface for 50V to 300V
    (d) any of these

51. Live parts of electrical equipment operating at _____ or more shall be guarded against accidental contact by approved enclosures or by suitable permanent, substantial partitions or screens arranged so that only qualified persons have access to the space within reach of the live parts.

    (a) 20V
    (b) 30V
    (c) 50V
    (d) 100V

52. In locations where electrical equipment is likely to be exposed to _____, enclosures or guards shall be so arranged and of such strength as to prevent such damage.

    (a) corrosion
    (b) physical damage
    (c) magnetic fields
    (d) weather

53. Entrances to rooms and other guarded locations containing exposed live parts shall be marked with conspicuous _____ forbidding unqualified persons to enter.

    (a) warning signs
    (b) alarms
    (c) a and b
    (d) neither a nor b

54. The term "rainproof" is typically used in conjunction with Enclosure-Type Number _____.

    (a) 3
    (b) 3R
    (c) 3RX
    (d) b and c

WIRING AND PROTECTION

Introduction to Chapter 2—Wiring and Protection

Chapter 2 provides general rules for wiring and for the protection of conductors. The rules in this chapter apply to all electrical installations covered by the *NEC*—except as modified in Chapters 5, 6, and 7 [90.3].

Communications systems (Chapter 8 systems) aren't subject to the general requirements of Chapters 1 through 4, or the special requirements of Chapters 5 through 7, unless there's a specific reference in Chapter 8 to a rule in Chapters 1 through 7 [90.3].

As you go through Chapter 2, remember its purpose. It's primarily concerned with correctly sizing and protecting circuits. Every article in this chapter deals with a different aspect of this purpose. This differs from the purpose of Chapter 3, which is to correctly install the conductors that make up those circuits.

Chapter 1 introduced you to the *NEC* and provided a solid foundation for understanding the *Code*. Chapters 2 (Wiring and Protection) and 3 (Wiring Methods and Materials) continue building the foundation for applying the *NEC*. Chapter 4 applies the preceding chapters to general equipment. It's beneficial to learn the first four chapters of the *Code* in a sequential manner because each of the first four chapters builds on the one before it. Once you've become familiar with the first four chapters, you can learn the next four in any order you wish.

While understanding Chapter 2 of the *NEC* is important, this textbook includes only the requirements that are especially meaningful to the proper installation of Solar PV systems. They're located in the following articles:

- **Article 200—Use and Identification of Grounded Conductors.** This article contains the requirements for the use and identification of the grounded conductor and its terminals.

Author's Comment:

- Throughout this textbook, we'll use the term "neutral" when referring to the grounded conductor when the application isn't related to PV systems or corner-grounded delta-connected systems.

- **Article 230—Services.** Article 230 covers the installation requirements for service conductors and equipment. It's very important to know where the service begins and ends when applying Article 230.

Author's Comment:

- Conductors from a battery, uninterruptible power supply, PV system, generator, or transformer aren't service conductors; they're feeder conductors.

- **Article 240—Overcurrent Protection.** This article provides the requirements for overcurrent protection and overcurrent devices. Overcurrent protection for conductors and equipment is provided to open the circuit if the current reaches a value that will cause an excessive or dangerous temperature on the conductors or conductor insulation.

- **Article 250—Grounding and Bonding.** Article 250 covers the grounding requirements for providing a path to the earth to reduce overvoltage from lightning, and the bonding requirements for a low-impedance fault current path necessary to facilitate the operation of overcurrent devices in the event of a ground fault.

USE AND IDENTIFICATION OF GROUNDED AND NEUTRAL CONDUCTORS

Introduction to Article 200—Use and Identification of Grounded and Neutral Conductors

This article contains the requirements for the identification of the grounded and neutral conductor and its terminals. Figure 200–1

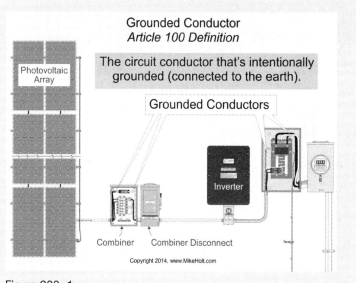

Grounded Conductor
Article 100 Definition

The circuit conductor that's intentionally grounded (connected to the earth).

Grounded Conductors

Photovoltaic Array

Inverter

Combiner   Combiner Disconnect

Copyright 2014, www.MikeHolt.com

Figure 200–1

Part I. General

200.1 Scope

Article 200 contains requirements for the use and identification of grounded and neutral conductors and terminals.

200.6 Grounded and Neutral Conductor Identification

(A) Size 6 AWG or Smaller. Grounded and Neutral conductors 6 AWG and smaller must be identified by one of the following means: Figures 200–2 and 200–3

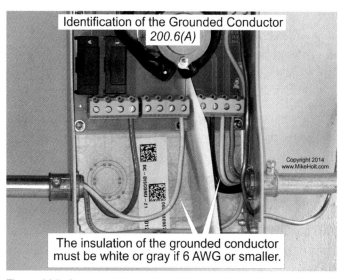

Identification of the Grounded Conductor
200.6(A)

The insulation of the grounded conductor must be white or gray if 6 AWG or smaller.

Copyright 2014
www.MikeHolt.com

Figure 200–2

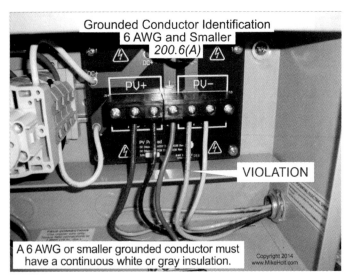

Figure 200–3

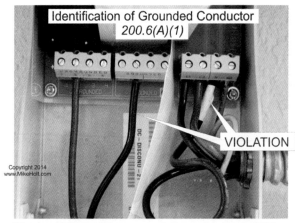

The insulation of the grounded conductor 6 AWG or smaller must be white or gray, reidentification is not permitted unless it complies with 200.6(A)(6).

Figure 200–4

(1) A continuous white outer finish.

(2) A continuous gray outer finish.

(3) Three continuous white or gray stripes along its entire length on other than green insulation.

(4) Wires that have their outer covering finished to show a white or gray color but have colored tracer threads in the braid identifying the source of manufacture are considered to meet the provisions of this section.

Author's Comment:

- The use of white tape, paint, or other methods of identification aren't permitted for grounded conductors 6 AWG and smaller. Figure 200–4

(6) A single-conductor, sunlight-resistant, outdoor-rated cable used as the grounded conductor in PV power systems as permitted by 690.31(B) must be identified by distinctive white marking at all terminations. Figure 200–5

(B) Size 4 AWG or Larger. Grounded and neutral conductors 4 AWG or larger must be identified by one of the following means: Figure 200–6

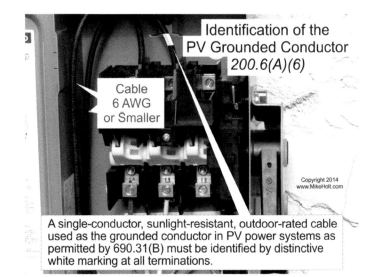

A single-conductor, sunlight-resistant, outdoor-rated cable used as the grounded conductor in PV power systems as permitted by 690.31(B) must be identified by distinctive white marking at all terminations.

Figure 200–5

(1) A continuous white outer finish along its entire length.

(2) A continuous gray outer finish along its entire length.

(3) Three continuous white or gray stripes along its length.

(4) White or gray tape or markings at the terminations.

Grounded Conductor Identification
Sizes 4 AWG and Larger
200.6(B)

Grounded conductors 4 AWG or larger must be identified by one of the following means:
(1) A continuous white outer finish along its entire length.
(2) A continuous gray outer finish along its entire length.
(3) Three continuous white <u>or gray</u> stripes along its length.
(4) White or gray tape or markings at the terminations.

Copyright 2014, www.MikeHolt.com

Figure 200–6

2014 CHANGE ANALYSIS: It's interesting that the *NEC* can have an obvious error in it that nobody catches for several *Code* cycles. Neutral conductors have long been required to be either white or gray in color or to have white stripes on them (or the other methods discussed here). It seems that the *NEC* never intended to prohibit gray stripes, but interestingly that practice wasn't recognized in the *Code*. Since most people never noticed the omission, most people won't consider this a substantial change.

A similar change has been made to 200.7.

Mike Holt's Illustrated Guide to Understanding NEC Requirements for Solar Photovoltaic Systems

ARTICLE
230

SERVICES

Introduction to Article 230—Services

This article covers the installation requirements for service conductors and service equipment. The requirements for service conductors differ from those for other conductors. For one thing, service conductors for one building can't pass through the interior of another building or structure [230.3], and you apply different rules depending on whether a service conductor is inside or outside a building. When are they "outside" as opposed to "inside?" The answer may seem obvious, but 230.6 should be consulted before making this decision.

Let's review the following definitions in Article 100 to understand when the requirements of Article 230 apply:

- **Service Point.** The point of connection between the serving utility and the premises wiring.

- **Service Conductors.** The conductors from the service point to the service disconnecting means. Service-entrance conductors can either be overhead or underground.

- **Service Equipment.** The necessary equipment, usually consisting of circuit breakers or switches and fuses and their accessories, connected to the load end of service conductors at a building or other structure, and intended to constitute the main control and cutoff of the electrical supply. Service equipment doesn't include individual meter socket enclosures [230.66].

After reviewing these definitions, you should understand that service conductors originate at the serving utility (service point) and terminate on the line side of the service disconnecting means. Conductors and equipment on the load side of service equipment are considered feeder conductors or branch circuits, and must be installed in accordance with Articles 210 and 215. They must also comply with Article 225 if they're outside branch circuits and feeders, such as the supply to a building. Feeder conductors include: Figures 230–1 and 230–2

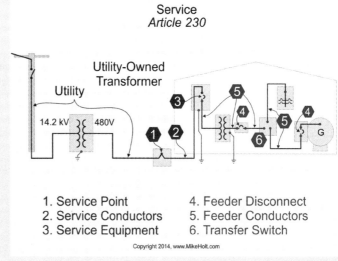

Service
Article 230

1. Service Point
2. Service Conductors
3. Service Equipment
4. Feeder Disconnect
5. Feeder Conductors
6. Transfer Switch

Copyright 2014, www.MikeHolt.com

Figure 230–1

- Secondary conductors from customer-owned transformers,
- Conductors from generators, UPS systems, or PV systems, and
- Conductors to remote buildings

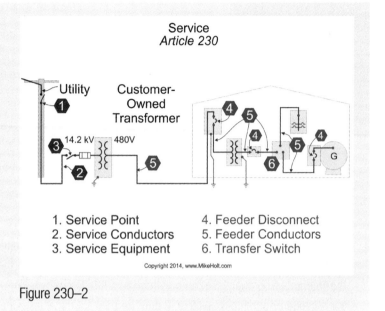

Service
Article 230

1. Service Point
2. Service Conductors
3. Service Equipment
4. Feeder Disconnect
5. Feeder Conductors
6. Transfer Switch

Copyright 2014, www.MikeHolt.com

Figure 230–2

Part I. General

230.1 Scope

Article 230 covers the installation requirements for service conductors and service equipment.

Part IV. Service-Entrance Conductors

230.40 Number of Service-Entrance Conductor Sets

Each service drop, service lateral, or set of underground or overhead service conductors may only supply one set of service-entrance conductors.

Ex 5: One set of service-entrance conductors connected to the supply side of the normal service disconnecting means can supply standby power systems, fire pump equipment, and fire and sprinkler alarms [230.82(5)] as well as Solar PV systems [230.82(6)]. Figure 230–3

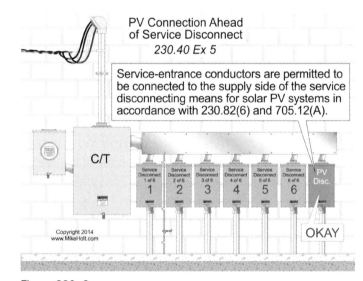

PV Connection Ahead
of Service Disconnect
230.40 Ex 5

Service-entrance conductors are permitted to be connected to the supply side of the service disconnecting means for solar PV systems in accordance with 230.82(6) and 705.12(A).

Copyright 2014
www.MikeHolt.com

Figure 230–3

230.43 Wiring Methods

Service-entrance conductors must be installed using one of the following wiring methods:

(1) Open wiring on insulators

(3) Rigid metal conduit (RMC)

(4) Intermediate metal conduit (IMC)

(5) Electrical metallic tubing (EMT)

(6) Electrical nonmetallic tubing (ENT)

(7) Service-entrance cables

(8) Wireways

(9) Busways

(11) PVC Conduit

(13) Type MC Cable

(15) Flexible metal conduit (FMC) or liquidtight flexible metal conduit (LFMC) not longer than 6 ft

(16) Liquidtight flexible nonmetallic conduit (LFNC)

(17) High-Density Polyethylene Conduit (HDPE)

(18) Nonmetallic Underground Conduit with Conductors (NUCC)

(19) Reinforced Thermosetting Resin Conduit (RTRC)

230.46 Spliced Conductors

Service-entrance conductors can be spliced or tapped in accordance with 110.14, 300.5(E), 300.13, and 300.15. Figure 230–4

Part V. Service Equipment—General

230.66 Listed as Suitable for Service Equipment

The service disconnecting means must be listed as suitable for use as service equipment. Figure 230–5

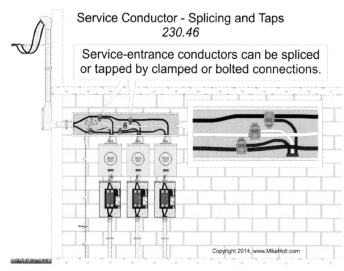

Figure 230–4

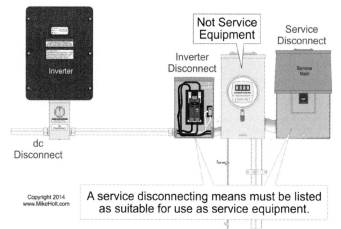

Figure 230–5

Author's Comment:

■ "Suitable for use as service equipment" means, among other things, that the service disconnecting means is supplied with a main bonding jumper so a neutral-to-case connection can be made, as required in 250.24(C) and 250.142(A).

Part VI. Service Equipment—Disconnecting Means

230.70 Disconnect Requirements

The service disconnecting means must open all service-entrance conductors from the building premises wiring.

(A) Location.

(1) Readily Accessible. The service disconnecting means must be placed at a readily accessible location either outside the building, or inside nearest the point of service conductor entry. Figure 230–6

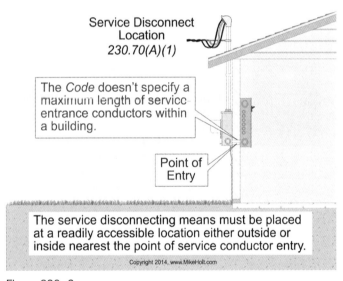

Figure 230–6

⚠️ **WARNING:** *Because service-entrance conductors don't have short-circuit or ground-fault protection, they must be limited in length when installed inside a building. Some local jurisdictions have a specific requirement as to the maximum length permitted within a building.*

(2) Bathrooms. The service disconnecting means isn't permitted to be installed in a bathroom. Figure 230–7

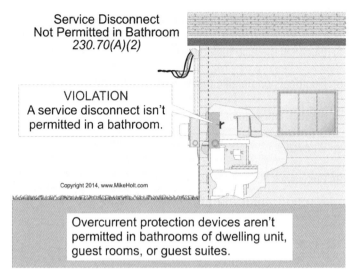

Figure 230–7

Author's Comment:

■ Overcurrent devices must not be located in the bathrooms of dwelling units, or guest rooms or guest suites of hotels or motels [240.24(E)].

(3) Remote Control. If a remote-control device (such as a pushbutton for a shunt-trip breaker) is used to actuate the service disconnecting means, the service disconnecting means must still be at a readily accessible location either outside the building, or nearest the point of entry of the service conductors in accordance with 230.70(A)(1). Figure 230–8

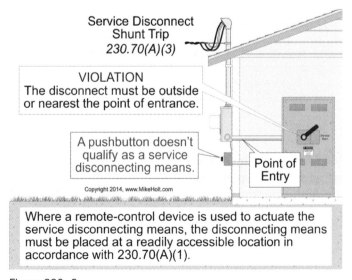

Figure 230–8

Author's Comment:

- See the definition of "Remote Control" in Article 100.

- The service disconnecting means must consist of a manually operated switch, a power-operated switch, or a circuit breaker that's also capable of being operated manually [230.76].

(B) Disconnect Identification. Each service disconnecting means must be permanently marked to identify it as a service disconnecting means. Figure 230–9

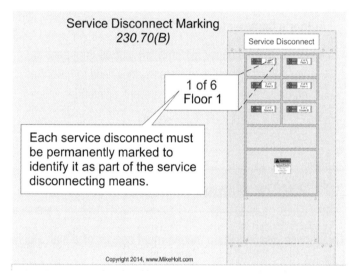

Figure 230–9

Author's Comment:

- When a building has multiple services and/or feeders, a plaque is required at each service or feeder disconnect location to show the location of the other service or feeder disconnect locations. See 230.2(E).

(C) Suitable for Use. Each service disconnecting means must be suitable for the prevailing conditions.

230.71 Number of Disconnects

(A) Maximum. There must be no more than six service disconnects for each service permitted by 230.2, or each set of service-entrance conductors permitted by 230.40 Ex 5 for PV systems.

The service disconnecting means for each service grouped in one location [230.72(A)] can consist of up to six switches or six circuit breakers mounted in a single enclosure, in a group of separate enclosures, or in or on a switchboard. Figure 230–10

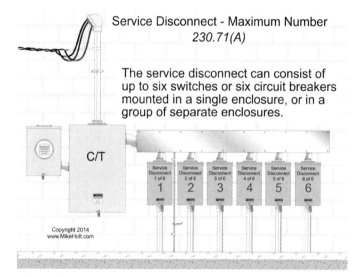

Figure 230–10

⚠ CAUTION: *The rule is six disconnecting means for each service, not for each building. If the building has two services, then there can be a total of 12 service disconnects (six disconnects per service).* Figure 230–11

Disconnecting means used for the following aren't considered a service disconnecting means:

(1) Power monitoring equipment

(2) Surge-protective device(s).

Service Disconnect - Maximum Number
230.71(A)

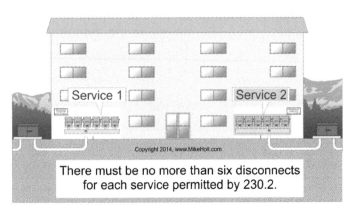

Figure 230–11

(3) Control circuit of the ground-fault protection system

(4) Power-operable service disconnecting means

Author's Comment:

■ A PV system connected to the supply-side of service equipment as permitted by 230.40 Ex. 2, 230.82(6), and 705.12(A) isn't considered a service disconnecting means. Figure 230–12

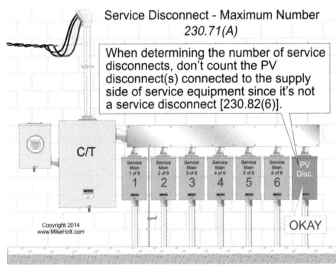

Figure 230–12

230.72 Grouping of Disconnects

(A) Two to Six Disconnects. The service disconnecting means for each service must be grouped.

(B) Additional Service Disconnecting Means. To minimize the possibility of simultaneous interruption of power, the disconnecting means for fire pumps [Article 695], emergency [Article 700], legally required standby [Article 701], or optional standby [Article 702] systems must be located remote from the one to six service disconnects for normal service.

Author's Comment:

■ Because emergency systems are just as important as fire pumps and standby systems, they need to have the same safety precautions to prevent unintended interruption of the supply of electricity.

230.76 Manual or Power Operated

The service disconnecting means must consist of either: Figure 230–13

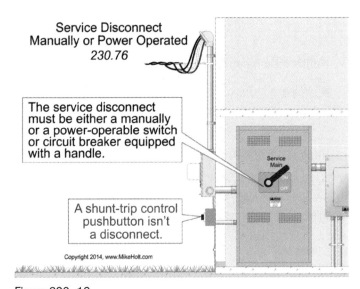

Figure 230–13

(1) A manually operable switch or circuit breaker equipped with a handle or other suitable operating means.

(2) A power-operated switch or circuit breaker, provided it can be opened by hand in the event of a power supply failure.

230.77 Indicating

The service disconnecting means must indicate whether it's in the off (open) or (closed) position.

230.81 Connection to Terminals

The service conductors must be connected to the service disconnecting means by pressure connectors, clamps, or other means approved by the authority having jurisdiction. Connections must not be made using solder.

230.82 Connected on Supply Side of the Service Disconnect

Electrical equipment must not be connected to the supply side of the service disconnect enclosure, except for the following:

(2) Meters and meter sockets can be connected to the supply side of the service disconnect enclosure.

(3) Meter disconnect switches. Figure 230–14

Author's Comment:

■ Electric utilities often require a meter disconnect switch for 277/480V services to enhance safety for utility personnel when they install or remove a meter.

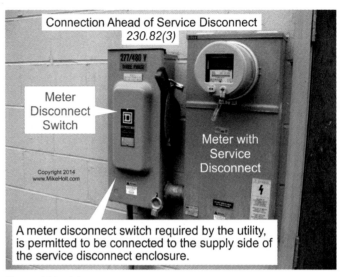

Figure 230–14

(5) Taps used to supply legally required and optional standby power systems, fire pump equipment, fire and sprinkler alarms, and load (energy) management devices can be connected to the supply side of the service disconnect enclosure.

(6) Solar PV systems can be connected to the supply side of the service disconnect enclosure in accordance with 705.12(A). Figure 230–15

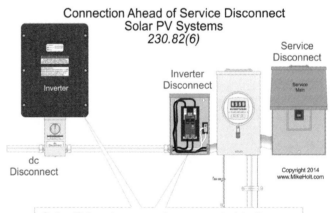

Figure 230–15

Part VII. Service Equipment Overcurrent Protection

Author's Comment:

- The *NEC* doesn't require service conductors to be provided with short-circuit or ground-fault protection, but the feeder overcurrent device provides overload protection for the service conductors.

230.90 Overload Protection Required

Each ungrounded service conductor must have overload protection at the point where the service conductors terminate [240.21(D)]. Figure 230–16

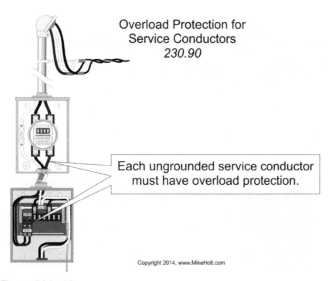

Overload Protection for Service Conductors
230.90

Each ungrounded service conductor must have overload protection.

Copyright 2014, www.MikeHolt.com

Figure 230–16

(A) Overcurrent Device Rating. The rating of the overcurrent device must not be more than the ampacity of the conductors.

Ex 2: If the ampacity of the ungrounded conductors doesn't correspond with the standard rating of overcurrent devices as listed in 240.6(A), the next higher overcurrent device can be used, if it doesn't exceed 800A [240.4(B)].

> **Example:** *Two sets of parallel 500 kcmil THHN conductors (each rated 380A at 75°C) can be protected by an 800A overcurrent device.* Figure 230–17

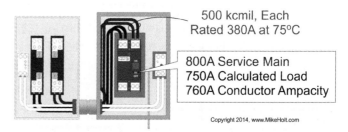

Overload Protection for Service Conductors
Next Size Up
230.90(A) Ex 2

500 kcmil, Each
Rated 380A at 75°C

800A Service Main
750A Calculated Load
760A Conductor Ampacity

Copyright 2014, www.MikeHolt.com

Where the ampacity of the ungrounded conductors doesn't correspond with the standard rating of the overcurrent device, the next higher overcurrent device can be used, if it doesn't exceed 800A [240.4(B)].

Figure 230–17

230.91 Location of Overcurrent Protection

The service overcurrent device must be an integral part of the service disconnecting means or be located immediately adjacent thereto.

OVERCURRENT PROTECTION

Introduction to Article 240—Overcurrent Protection

This article provides the requirements for selecting and installing overcurrent devices. Overcurrent exists when current exceeds the rating of equipment or the ampacity of a conductor. This can be due to an overload, short circuit, or ground fault [Article 100].

- **Overload.** An overload is a condition where equipment or conductors carry current exceeding their current rating [Article 100]. A fault, such as a short circuit or ground fault, isn't an overload. An example of an overload is plugging two 12.50A (1,500W) hair dryers into a 20A branch circuit.

- **Short Circuit.** A short circuit is the unintentional electrical connection between any two normally current-carrying conductors of an electrical circuit, either line-to-line or line-to-neutral.

- **Ground Fault.** A ground fault is an unintentional, electrically conducting connection between an ungrounded conductor of an electrical circuit and the normally noncurrent-carrying conductors, metallic enclosures, metallic raceways, metallic equipment, or the earth [Article 100]. During the period of a ground fault, dangerous voltages will be present on metal parts until the circuit overcurrent device opens.

Overcurrent devices protect conductors and equipment. Selecting the proper overcurrent protection for a specific circuit can become more complicated than it sounds. The general rule for overcurrent protection is that conductors must be protected in accordance with their ampacities at the point where they receive their supply [240.4 and 240.21]. There are many special cases that deviate from this basic rule, such as the overcurrent protection limitations for small conductors [240.4(D)] and the rules for specific conductor applications found in other articles, as listed in Table 240.4(G). There are also a number of rules allowing tap conductors in specific situations [240.21(B)]. Article 240 even has limits on where overcurrent devices are allowed to be located [240.24].

An overcurrent protection device must be capable of opening a circuit when an overcurrent situation occurs, and must also have an interrupting rating sufficient to avoid damage in fault conditions [110.9]. Carefully study the provisions of this article to be sure you provide sufficient overcurrent protection in the correct location.

Part I. General

240.1 Scope

Article 240 covers the general requirements for overcurrent protection and the installation requirements of overcurrent devices. Figure 240–1

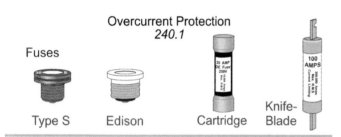

Overcurrent Protection
240.1

Fuses

Type S   Edison   Cartridge   Knife-Blade

Circuit Breakers

GFCI   AFCI

Copyright 2014, www.MikeHolt.com

Article 240 covers the general requirements for overcurrent protection and the installation requirements of overcurrent devices.

Figure 240–1

Author's Comment:

- Overcurrent is a condition where the current exceeds the rating of equipment or ampacity of a conductor due to overload, short circuit, or ground fault [Article 100]. Figure 240–2

Note: An overcurrent device protects the circuit by opening the device when the current reaches a value that will cause excessive or dangerous temperature rise (overheating) in conductors. Overcurrent devices must have an interrupting rating sufficient for the maximum possible fault current available on the line-side terminals of the equipment [110.9]. Electrical equipment must have a short-circuit current rating that permits the circuit's overcurrent device to clear short circuits or ground faults without extensive damage to the circuit's electrical components [110.10].

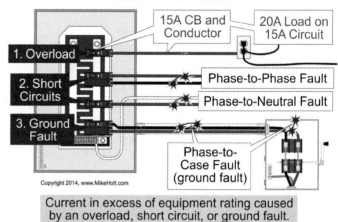

Overcurrent
Article 100 Definition

Current in excess of equipment rating caused by an overload, short circuit, or ground fault.

Figure 240–2

240.2 Definitions

Tap Conductors. A conductor, other than a service conductor, that has overcurrent protection rated more than the ampacity of a conductor. See 240.21(A) and 240.21(B) for details. Figure 240–3

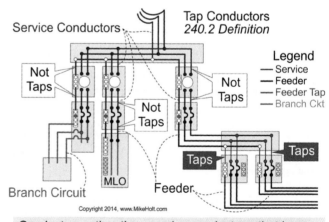

Tap Conductors
240.2 Definition

Conductors, other than service conductors, that have overcurrent protection ahead of the point of supply that exceeds the value permitted for similar conductors.

Figure 240–3

240.4 Protection of Conductors

Except as permitted by (A) through (G), conductors must be protected against overcurrent in accordance with their ampacity after ampacity correction and adjustment as specified in 310.15. Figure 240–4

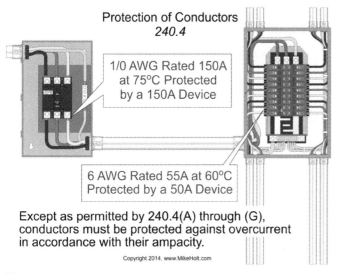

Protection of Conductors
240.4

1/0 AWG Rated 150A at 75°C Protected by a 150A Device

6 AWG Rated 55A at 60°C Protected by a 50A Device

Except as permitted by 240.4(A) through (G), conductors must be protected against overcurrent in accordance with their ampacity.

Copyright 2014, www.MikeHolt.com

Figure 240–4

(A) Power Loss Hazard. Conductor overload protection isn't required, but short-circuit protection is required where the interruption of the circuit will create a hazard; such as in a material-handling electromagnet circuit or fire pump circuit.

(B) Overcurrent Devices Rated 800A or Less. The next higher standard rating of overcurrent device listed in 240.6 (above the ampacity of the ungrounded conductors being protected) is permitted, provided all of the following conditions are met:

(1) The conductors aren't part of a branch circuit supplying more than one receptacle for cord-and-plug-connected loads.

(2) The ampacity of a conductor, after the application of ambient temperature correction [310.15(B)(2)(a)], conductor bundling adjustment [310.15(B)(3)(a)], or both, doesn't correspond with the standard rating of a fuse or circuit breaker in 240.6(A).

(3) The overcurrent device rating doesn't exceed 800A. Figure 240–5

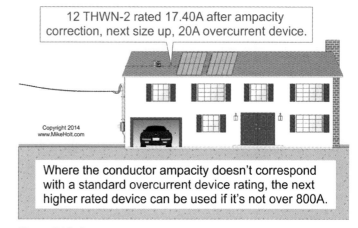

Overcurrent Devices - Not Over 800A - Next Size Up
240.4(B)(3)

12 THWN-2 rated 17.40A after ampacity correction, next size up, 20A overcurrent device.

Copyright 2014
www.MikeHolt.com

Where the conductor ampacity doesn't correspond with a standard overcurrent device rating, the next higher rated device can be used if it's not over 800A.

Figure 240–5

Example: A 400A overcurrent device can protect 500 kcmil conductors, where each conductor has an ampacity of 380A at 75°C, in accordance with Table 310.15(B)(16). Figure 240–6

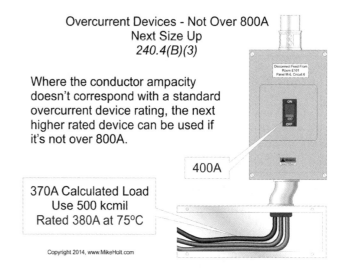

Overcurrent Devices - Not Over 800A
Next Size Up
240.4(B)(3)

Where the conductor ampacity doesn't correspond with a standard overcurrent device rating, the next higher rated device can be used if it's not over 800A.

Disconnect Feed From
Room E101
Panel M-4, Circuit 6

ON
OFF

400A

370A Calculated Load
Use 500 kcmil
Rated 380A at 75°C

Copyright 2014, www.MikeHolt.com

Figure 240–6

Author's Comment:

- This "next size up" rule doesn't apply to feeder tap conductors [240.21(B)] or transformer secondary conductors [240.21(C)].

(C) Overcurrent Devices Rated Over 800A. If the circuit's overcurrent device exceeds 800A, the conductor ampacity (after the application of ambient temperature correction [310.15(B)(2)(a)], conductor bundling adjustment [310.15(B)(3)(a)], or both, must have a rating of not less than the rating of the overcurrent device defined in 240.6.

> **Example:** A 1,200A overcurrent device can protect three sets of 600 kcmil conductors per phase, where each conductor has an ampacity of 420A at 75°C, in accordance with Table 310.15(B)(16). Figure 240–7

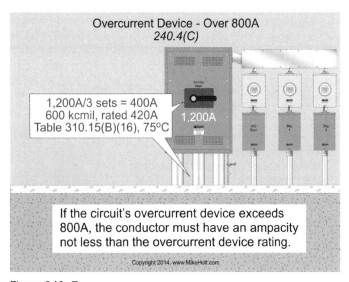

Figure 240–7

(D) Small Conductors. Unless specifically permitted in 240.4(E) or (G), overcurrent protection must not exceed the following: Figure 240–8

(1) 18 AWG Copper—7A

(2) 16 AWG Copper—10A

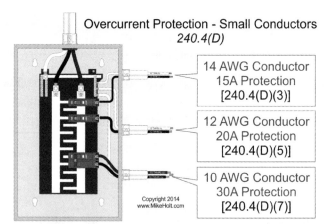

Except as permitted by 240.4(E) or (G), overcurrent protection must not exceed 15A for 14 AWG, 20A for 12 AWG, and 30A for 10 AWG copper.

Figure 240–8

(3) 14 AWG Copper—15A

(4) 12 AWG Aluminum/Copper-Clad Aluminum—15A

(5) 12 AWG Copper—20A

(6) 10 AWG Aluminum/Copper-Clad Aluminum—25A

(7) 10 AWG Copper—30A

240.6 Standard Ampere Ratings

(A) Fuses and Fixed-Trip Circuit Breakers. The standard ratings in amperes for fuses and inverse time breakers are: 15, 20, 25, 30, 35, 40, 45, 50, 60, 70, 80, 90, 100, 110, 125, 150, 175, 200, 225, 250, 300, 350, 400, 450, 500, 600, 700, 800, 1,000, 1,200, 1,600, 2,000, 2,500, 3,000, 4,000, 5,000 and 6,000. Figure 240–9

(B) Adjustable Circuit Breakers. The ampere rating of an adjustable circuit breaker is equal to its maximum long-time pickup current setting.

(C) Restricted Access, Adjustable-Trip Circuit Breakers. The ampere rating of adjustable-trip circuit breakers that have restricted access to the adjusting means is equal to their adjusted long-time pickup current settings.

Standard Overcurrent Device Ratings
240.6(A)

The standard ratings for fuses and inverse-time breakers include: 15, 20, 25, 30, 35, 40, 45, 50, 60, 70, 80, 90, 100, 110, 125, 150, 175, 200, 225, 250, 300, 350, 400, 450, 500, 600, 700, 800, 1,000, 1,200, 1,600, 2,000, 2,500, 3,000, 4,000, 5,000, and 6,000A.

Figure 240–9

240.10 Supplementary Overcurrent Protection

Supplementary overcurrent devices can't be used as the required branch-circuit overcurrent device and aren't required to be readily accessible [240.24(A)(2)]. Figure 240–10

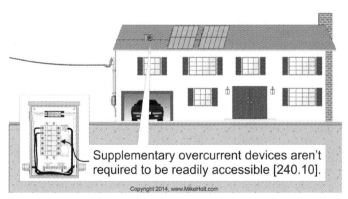

Supplementary Overcurrent Device Not Required to be Readily Accessible
240.24(A)(2)

Supplementary overcurrent devices aren't required to be readily accessible [240.10].

Figure 240–10

Author's Comment:

- Article 100 defines a "Supplementary Overcurrent Device" as a device intended to provide limited overcurrent protection for specific applications and utilization equipment. This limited protection is in addition to the protection provided in the required branch circuit by the branch-circuit overcurrent device.

240.15 Ungrounded Conductors

(A) Overcurrent Device Required. A fuse or circuit breaker must be connected in series with each ungrounded conductor.

Part II. Location

240.21 Overcurrent Protection Location in Circuit

Except as permitted by (A) through (H), overcurrent devices must be placed at the point where the feeder conductors receive their power. Taps and transformer secondary conductors aren't permitted to supply another conductor (tapping a tap isn't permitted). Figure 240–11

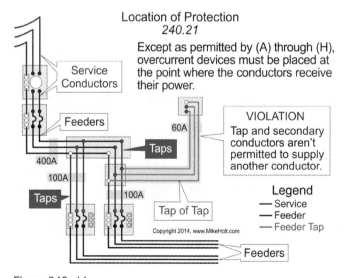

Location of Protection
240.21

Except as permitted by (A) through (H), overcurrent devices must be placed at the point where the conductors receive their power.

Figure 240–11

(B) Feeder Taps. Conductors can be tapped to a feeder as specified in 240.21(B)(1) through (B)(5). The "next size up protection rule" of 240.4(B) isn't permitted for tap conductors. Figure 240–12

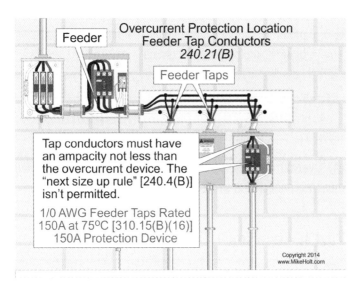

Figure 240–12

(1) 10-Foot Feeder Tap. Feeder tap conductors up to 10 ft long are permitted without overcurrent protection at the tap location if the tap conductors comply with the following:

(1) The ampacity of the tap conductor must not be less than: Figure 240–13

    a. The calculated load in accordance with Article 220, and

    b. The rating of the overcurrent device supplied by the tap conductors.

Ex to b: Listed equipment, such as a surge protection device, can have their conductors sized in accordance with the manufacturer's instructions.

(2) The tap conductors must not extend beyond the equipment they supply.

(3) The tap conductors are installed in a raceway if they leave the enclosure.

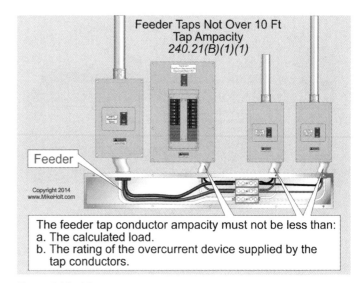

Figure 240–13

(4) If the tap conductors leave the enclosure or vault in which the tap is made, the tap conductors must have an ampacity not less than 10 percent of the rating of the overcurrent device that protects the feeder. Figure 240–14

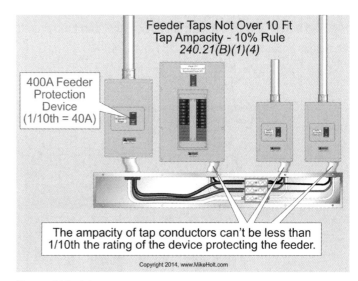

Figure 240–14

Note: See 408.36 for the overcurrent protection requirements for panelboards.

Example: *A 400A breaker protects a set of 500 kcmil feeder conductors. There are three taps fed from the 500 kcmil feeder that supply disconnects with 200A, 150A, and 30A overcurrent devices. What are the minimum size conductors for these taps?* Figure 240–15

- **200A:** *3/0 AWG is rated 200A at 75°, and is greater than 10 percent of the rating of the overcurrent device (400A).*

- **150A:** *1/0 AWG is rated 150A at 75°, and is greater than 10 percent of the rating of the overcurrent device (400A).*

- **30A:** *8 AWG is rated 50A at 75°, and is greater than 10 percent of the rating of the overcurrent device (400A). Anything smaller than 8 AWG can't be used, as it will have an ampacity of less than 10 percent of the rating of the overcurrent device (400A).*

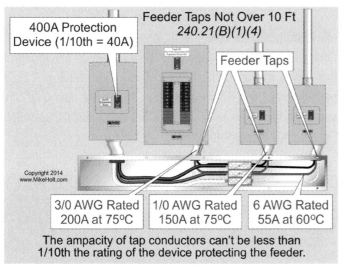

Figure 240–15

2014 CHANGE ANALYSIS: Surge protection devices (SPDs) often have very specific instructions regarding conductor sizing and installation. These instructions frequently include not only what size conductor to use, but the length and bending radius of the conductors as well. These conductor sizes are a result of investigation and engineering by the manufacturer, and are reviewed during the listing process by third parties as well. Due to the unique natures of the different SPDs, it would be nearly impossible to write *Code* language that applies to all of them. By having this exception, the *NEC* defers to the manufacturer and third party listing to ensure safety.

(2) 25-Foot Feeder Tap. Feeder tap conductors up to 25 ft long are permitted without overcurrent protection at the tap location if the tap conductors comply with the following: Figures 240–16 and 240–17

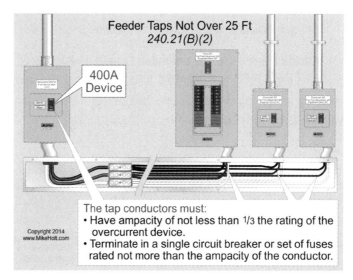

Figure 240–16

(1) The ampacity of the tap conductors must not be less than one-third the rating of the overcurrent device that protects the feeder.

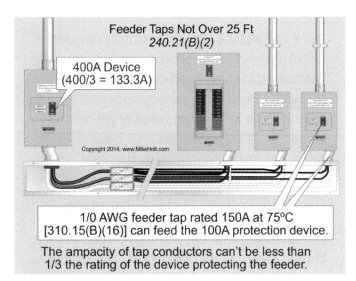

Figure 240–17

(2) The tap conductors terminate in a single circuit breaker, or set of fuses rated no more than the tap conductor ampacity in accordance with 310.15 [Table 310.15(B)(16)].

(3) The tap conductors are protected from physical damage by being enclosed in a manner approved by the authority having jurisdiction, such as within a raceway.

(5) Outside Feeder Taps of Unlimited Length. Outside feeder tap conductors can be of unlimited length, without overcurrent protection at the point they receive their supply, if they comply with the following: Figure 240–18

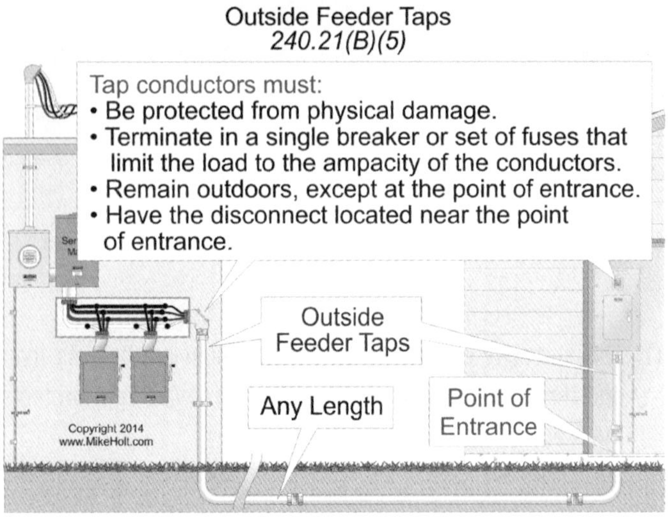

(1) The tap conductors are suitably protected from physical damage in a raceway or manner approved by the authority having jurisdiction.

(2) The tap conductors must terminate at a single circuit breaker or a single set of fuses that limits the load to the ampacity of the tap conductors.

(3) The overcurrent device for the tap conductors is an integral part of the disconnecting means, or it's located immediately adjacent to it.

(4) The disconnecting means is located at a readily accessible location, either outside the building, or nearest the point of entry of the tap conductors.

(H) Battery Conductors. Overcurrent protection can be installed as close as practicable to the storage battery terminals.

240.24 Location of Overcurrent Devices

(A) Readily Accessible. Circuit breakers and fuses must be readily accessible, and they must be installed so the center of the grip of the operating handle of the fuse switch or circuit breaker, when in its highest position, isn't more than 6 ft 7 in. above the floor or working platform, unless the installation is for: Figures 240–19 and 240–20

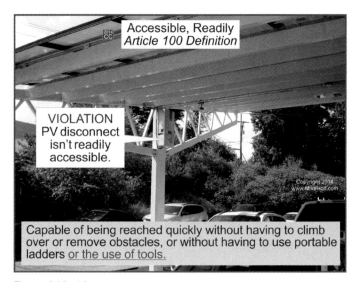

Figure 240–18

Figure 240–19

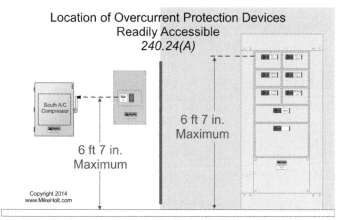

Location of Overcurrent Protection Devices
Readily Accessible
240.24(A)

6 ft 7 in.
Maximum

6 ft 7 in.
Maximum

The center of the grip of the operating handle of a
fusible switch or circuit breaker, when in its highest
position, can't be more than 6 ft 7 in. above the floor.

Figure 240–20

(1) Busways, as provided in 368.17(C).

(2) Supplementary overcurrent devices which aren't required to
be readily accessible [240.10]. Figure 240–21

Supplementary Overcurrent Device
Not Required to be Readily Accessible
240.24(A)(2)

Supplementary overcurrent devices aren't
required to be readily accessible [240.10].

Figure 240–21

(3) Overcurrent devices, as described in 225.40 and 230.92.

(4) Overcurrent devices located next to equipment can be
mounted above 6 ft 7 in., if accessible by portable means
[404.8(A) Ex 2]. Figure 240–22

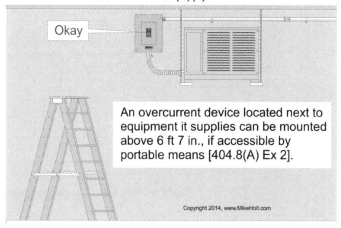

Location of Overcurrent Devices
240.24(A)(4)

Okay

An overcurrent device located next to
equipment it supplies can be mounted
above 6 ft 7 in., if accessible by
portable means [404.8(A) Ex 2].

Figure 240–22

(C) Not Exposed to Physical Damage. Overcurrent devices
must not be exposed to physical damage. Figure 240–23

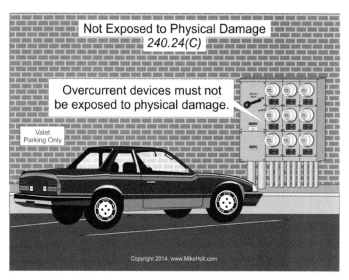

Not Exposed to Physical Damage
240.24(C)

Overcurrent devices must not
be exposed to physical damage.

Valet
Parking Only

Figure 240–23

Note: Electrical equipment must be suitable for the environment,
and consideration must be given to the presence of corrosive
gases, fumes, vapors, liquids, or chemicals that have a deteriorating effect on conductors or equipment [110.11]. Figure 240–24

(D) Not in Vicinity of Easily Ignitible Material. Overcurrent
devices must not be located near easily ignitible material, such
as in clothes closets. Figure 240–25

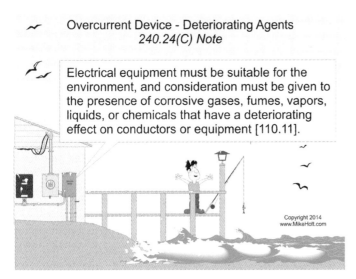

Overcurrent Device - Deteriorating Agents
240.24(C) Note

Electrical equipment must be suitable for the environment, and consideration must be given to the presence of corrosive gases, fumes, vapors, liquids, or chemicals that have a deteriorating effect on conductors or equipment [110.11].

Copyright 2014
www.MikeHolt.com

Figure 240–24

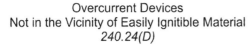

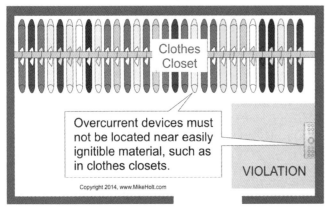

Overcurrent Devices
Not in the Vicinity of Easily Ignitible Material
240.24(D)

Clothes Closet

Overcurrent devices must not be located near easily ignitible material, such as in clothes closets.

VIOLATION

Copyright 2014, www.MikeHolt.com

Figure 240–25

(E) Not in Bathrooms. Overcurrent devices aren't permitted to be located in the bathrooms of dwelling units, dormitories, or guest rooms or guest suites of hotels or motels. Figure 240–26

Author's Comment:

■ The service disconnecting means must not be located in a bathroom, even in commercial or industrial facilities [230.70(A)(2)].

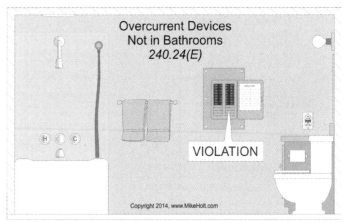

Overcurrent Devices
Not in Bathrooms
240.24(E)

VIOLATION

Copyright 2014, www.MikeHolt.com

Overcurrent devices must not be located in the bathrooms of dwelling units, dormitories, guest rooms, or guest suites.

Figure 240–26

(F) Over Steps. Overcurrent devices must not be located over the steps of a stairway. Figure 240–27

Location of Overcurrent Devices - Not Over Steps
240.24(F)

Okay

VIOLATION
Overcurrent devices must not be located over steps of a stairway.

Copyright 2014, www.MikeHolt.com

Figure 240–27

Author's Comment:

■ Clearly, it's difficult for electricians to safely work on electrical equipment that's located on uneven surfaces such as over stairways.

Part III. Enclosures

240.32 Damp or Wet Locations

In damp or wet locations, enclosures containing overcurrent devices must prevent moisture or water from entering or accumulating within the enclosure. When the enclosure is surface mounted in a wet location, it must be mounted with not less than ¼ in. of air space between it and the mounting surface. See 312.2.

240.33 Vertical Position

Enclosures containing overcurrent devices must be mounted in a vertical position unless this isn't practical. Circuit-breaker enclosures can be mounted horizontally if the circuit breaker is installed in accordance with 240.81. Figure 240–28

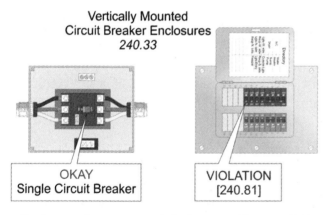

Vertically Mounted
Circuit Breaker Enclosures
240.33

OKAY
Single Circuit Breaker

VIOLATION
[240.81]

Enclosures for overcurrent devices must be mounted in a vertical position, unless this isn't practical.

Copyright 2014, www.MikeHolt.com

Figure 240–28

Author's Comment:

- Section 240.81 specifies that where circuit-breaker handles are operated vertically, the "up" position of the handle must be the "on" position. So, in effect, an enclosure that contains one row of circuit breakers can

be mounted horizontally, but an enclosure that contains a panelboard with multiple circuit breakers on opposite sides of each other will have to be mounted vertically.

Part VI. Cartridge Fuses and Fuseholders

Author's Comment:

- There are two basic designs of cartridge fuses, the ferrule type with a maximum rating of 60A and the knife-blade type rated over 60A. The fuse length and diameter varies with the voltage and current rating. Figure 240–29

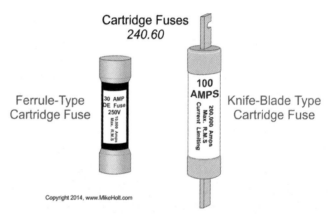

Cartridge Fuses
240.60

Ferrule-Type
Cartridge Fuse

Knife-Blade Type
Cartridge Fuse

Copyright 2014, www.MikeHolt.com

There are two basic designs of cartridge fuses, the ferrule type (maximum 60A) and the knife-blade type. The size of the fuse varies with the fuse voltage and current rating.

Figure 240–29

240.60 General

(B) Noninterchangeable Fuseholders. Fuseholders must be designed to make it difficult to interchange fuses of any given class for different voltages and current ratings.

Fuseholders for current-limiting fuses must be designed so only current-limiting fuses can be inserted.

Author's Comment:

- A current-limiting fuse is a fast-clearing overcurrent device that reduces the fault current to a magnitude substantially lower than that obtainable in the same circuit if the current-limiting device isn't used [240.2].

(C) Marking. Cartridge fuses have an interrupting rating of 10,000A, unless marked otherwise. They must be marked showing the following:

(1) Ampere rating

(2) Voltage rating

(3) Interrupting rating if not 10,000A

(4) Current limiting if applicable

(5) Name or trademark of manufacturer

⚠️ **WARNING:** *Fuses must have an interrupting rating sufficient for the short-circuit current available at the line terminals of the equipment. Using a fuse with an inadequate interrupting current rating can cause equipment to be destroyed from a line-to-line or ground fault, and result in death or serious injury. See 110.9 for more details.* Figure 240–30

240.61 Classification

Cartridge fuses and fuseholders are classified according to voltage and amperage ranges. Fuses rated 1,000V, nominal, or less are permitted for voltages at or below their ratings.

Part VII. Circuit Breakers

240.80 Method of Operation

Circuit breakers must be capable of being opened and closed by hand. Nonmanual means of operating a circuit breaker, such as electrical shunt trip or pneumatic operation, are permitted as long as the circuit breaker can also be manually operated.

240.81 Indicating

Circuit breakers must clearly indicate whether they're in the open "off" or closed "on" position. When the handle of a circuit breaker is operated vertically, the "up" position of the handle must be the "on" position. See 240.33 and 404.6(C). Figure 240–31

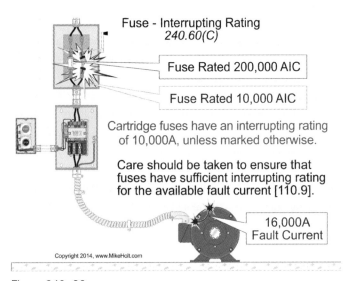

Fuse - Interrupting Rating
240.60(C)

Fuse Rated 200,000 AIC

Fuse Rated 10,000 AIC

Cartridge fuses have an interrupting rating of 10,000A, unless marked otherwise.

Care should be taken to ensure that fuses have sufficient interrupting rating for the available fault current [110.9].

16,000A Fault Current

Copyright 2014, www.MikeHolt.com

Figure 240–30

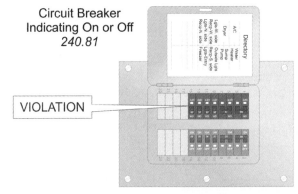

Circuit Breaker
Indicating On or Off
240.81

VIOLATION

Circuit breakers must indicate whether they're in the "off" or "on" position. When the handle is operated vertically, the "up" position of the handle must be the "on" position.

Copyright 2014, www.MikeHolt.com

Figure 240–31

240.82 Nontamperable

A circuit breaker must be designed so that any alteration of its trip point (calibration) or the time required for its operation requires dismantling of the device or the breaking of a seal for other than intended adjustments.

240.83 Markings

(A) Durable and Visible. Circuit breakers must be marked with their ampere rating in a manner that's durable and visible after installation. Such marking is permitted to be made visible by removal of a trim or cover.

(C) Interrupting Rating. Circuit breakers have an interrupting rating of 5,000A unless marked otherwise.

⚠ **WARNING:** *Take care to ensure the circuit breaker has an interrupting rating sufficient for the short-circuit current available at the line terminals of the equipment. Using a circuit breaker with an inadequate interrupting current rating can cause equipment to be destroyed from a line-to-line or ground fault, and result in death or serious injury. See 110.9 for more details.* Figure 240–32

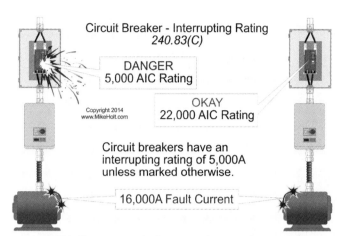

Circuit Breaker - Interrupting Rating
240.83(C)

DANGER
5,000 AIC Rating

OKAY
22,000 AIC Rating

Circuit breakers have an interrupting rating of 5,000A unless marked otherwise.

16,000A Fault Current

Copyright 2014
www.MikeHolt.com

CAUTION: Overcurrent devices must have an interrupting rating not less than the nominal circuit voltage and the current that's available at the line terminals of the equipment [110.9].

Figure 240–32

Notes

Mike Holt's Illustrated Guide to Understanding NEC Requirements for Solar Photovoltaic Systems

ARTICLE 250

GROUNDING AND BONDING

Introduction to Article 250—Grounding and Bonding

No other article can match Article 250 for misapplication, violation, and misinterpretation. Terminology used in this article has been a source for much confusion, but that has improved during the last few *NEC* revisions. It's very important to understand the difference between grounding and bonding in order to correctly apply the provisions of Article 250. Pay careful attention to the definitions that apply to grounding and bonding both here and in Article 100 as you begin the study of this important article. Article 250 covers the grounding requirements for providing a path to the earth to reduce overvoltage from lightning, and the bonding requirements for a low-impedance fault current path back to the source of the electrical supply to facilitate the operation of overcurrent devices in the event of a ground fault.

Over the past several *Code* cycles, this article was extensively revised to organize it better and make it easier to understand and implement. It's arranged in a logical manner, so it's a good idea to just read through Article 250 to get a big picture view—after you review the definitions. Next, study the article closely so you understand the details. The illustrations will help you understand the key points.

Part I. General

250.1 Scope

Article 250 contains the following grounding and bonding requirements:

(1) What systems and equipment are required to be grounded.

(3) Location of grounding connections.

(4) Types and sizes of electrodes, and grounding and bonding conductors.

(5) Methods of grounding and bonding.

250.4 General Requirements for Grounding and Bonding

(A) Solidly Grounded Systems.

(1) Electrical System Grounding. Electrical power systems that are grounded must be connected to the earth in a manner that will limit the voltage induced by lightning, line surges, or unintentional contact by higher-voltage lines. Figure 250–1

Author's Comment:

■ System grounding helps reduce fires in buildings as well as voltage stress on electrical insulation, thereby ensuring longer insulation life for motors, transformers, and other system components. Figure 250–2

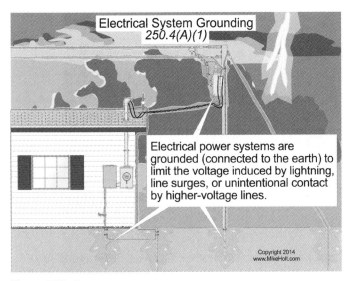

Figure 250–1

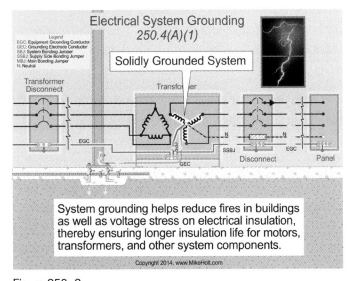

Figure 250–2

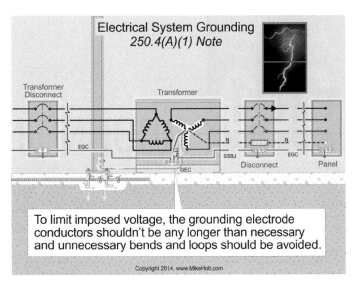

Figure 250–3

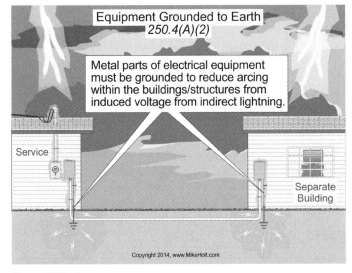

Figure 250–4

Note: To limit imposed voltage, the grounding electrode conductors shouldn't be any longer than necessary and unnecessary bends and loops should be avoided. Figure 250–3

(2) Equipment Grounding. Metal parts of electrical equipment must be grounded to reduce arcing within the buildings/structures from induced voltage from indirect lightning. Figure 250–4

⚠ **DANGER:** *Failure to ground metal parts to earth can result in induced voltage on metal parts from an indirect lightning strike seeking a path to the earth within the building—possibly resulting in a fire and/or electric shock from a sideflash.* Figure 250–5

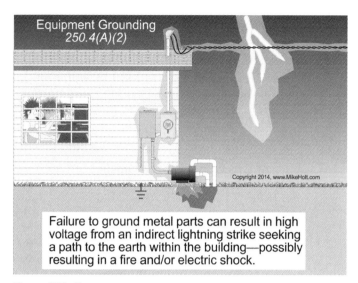

Failure to ground metal parts can result in high voltage from an indirect lightning strike seeking a path to the earth within the building—possibly resulting in a fire and/or electric shock.

Figure 250–5

Author's Comment:

■ Grounding metal parts helps drain off static electricity charges before flashover potential is reached. Static grounding is often used in areas where the discharge (arcing) of the voltage buildup (static) can cause dangerous or undesirable conditions [500.4 Note 3].

(3) Equipment Bonding. Metal parts of electrical raceways, cables, enclosures, and equipment must be connected to the supply source via an effective ground-fault current path. Figure 250–6

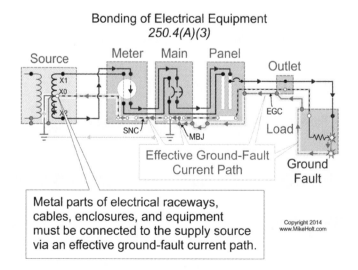

Metal parts of electrical raceways, cables, enclosures, and equipment must be connected to the supply source via an effective ground-fault current path.

Figure 250–6

Author's Comment:

■ To quickly remove dangerous voltage on metal parts from a ground fault, the effective ground-fault current path must have sufficiently low impedance to the source so that fault current will quickly rise to a level that will open the branch-circuit overcurrent device. Figure 250–7

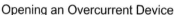
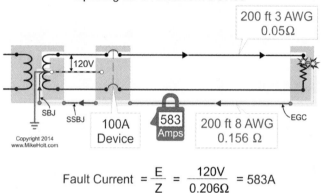

$$\text{Fault Current} = \frac{E}{Z} = \frac{120V}{0.206\Omega} = 583A$$

The 100A overcurrent device quickly opens and removes dangerous voltage from metal parts.

Figure 250–7

■ The time it takes for an overcurrent device to open is inversely proportional to the magnitude of the fault current. This means that the higher the ground-fault current value, the less time it will take for the overcurrent device to open and clear the fault. For example, a 20A circuit with an overload of 40A (two times the 20A rating) takes 25 to 150 seconds to open the circuit overcurrent device. At 100A (five times the 20A rating) the 20A breaker trips in 5 to 20 seconds.

(4) Bonding Conductive Materials. Electrically conductive materials likely to become energized, such as metal water piping systems, metal sprinkler piping, metal gas piping, and other metal-piping systems, as well as exposed structural steel members, must be connected to the supply source via an effective ground-fault current path. Figure 250–8

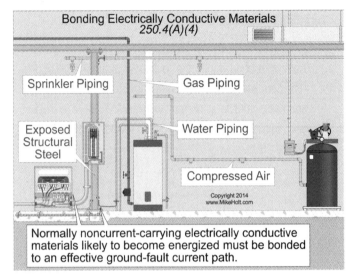

Figure 250–8

Author's Comment:

■ The phrase "likely to become energized" is subject to interpretation by the authority having jurisdiction.

(5) Effective Ground-Fault Current Path. Metal parts of electrical raceways, cables, enclosures, or equipment must be bonded together and to the supply source in a manner that creates a low-impedance path for ground-fault current that facilitates the operation of the circuit overcurrent device. Figure 250–9

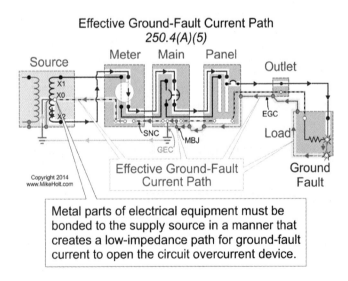

Figure 250–9

Author's Comment:

■ To ensure a low-impedance ground-fault current path, all circuit conductors must be grouped together in the same raceway, cable, or trench [300.3(B), 300.5(I), and 300.20(A)]. Figure 250–10

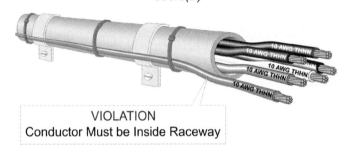

To help ensure a low-impedance effective ground-fault path, all circuit conductors must be grouped together in the same raceway, cable, or trench [300.5(I), 300.20(A)].

Figure 250–10

250.8 Termination of Grounding and Bonding Conductors

(A) Permitted Methods. Equipment grounding conductors, grounding electrode conductors, and bonding jumpers must terminate in one or more of the following methods:

(1) Listed pressure connectors

(2) Terminal bars

(3) Pressure connectors listed for grounding and bonding

(4) Exothermic welding

(5) Machine screws that engage at least two threads or are secured with a nut. Figure 250–11

(6) Self-tapping machine screws that engage at least two threads

(7) Connections that are part of a listed assembly

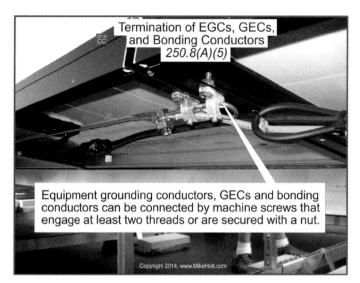

Figure 250–11

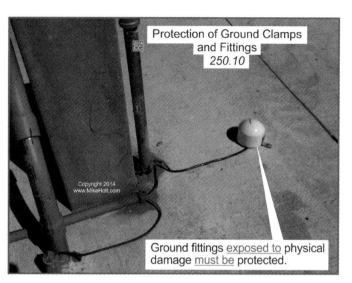

Figure 250–12

(8) Other listed means

(B) Methods Not Permitted. Connection devices or fittings that depend solely on solder aren't allowed.

2014 CHANGE ANALYSIS: While this change is completely obvious, it's an important enough section of the *Code* to make sure that the language is completely accurate. One can argue that in 2011 one (and only one) of the methods discussed could be used. This certainly wasn't the intent of this section, so the text has been changed to eliminate the argument. Connection devices or fittings that depend solely on solder aren't allowed.

250.10 Protection of Fittings

Where exposed to physical damage, grounding and bonding fittings must be protected by enclosing the fittings in metal, wood, or an equivalent protective covering. Figure 250–12

Author's Comment:

■ Grounding and bonding fittings can be buried or encased in concrete if they're installed in accordance with 250.53(G), 250.68(A) Ex 1, and 250.70.

2014 CHANGE ANALYSIS: Over the last few *Code* development cycles there's been a real effort to use lists when there are multiple requirements or options in a paragraph. Most of the time this is a change for the better, but sometimes it doesn't really make any sense. The previous edition of this section had a two-item list that was unnecessary since item one was so incredibly obvious (protecting the equipment from damage by putting it somewhere that it can't be harmed).

250.12 Clean Surfaces

Nonconductive coatings, such as paint, must be removed to ensure good electrical continuity, or the termination fittings must be designed so as to make such removal unnecessary [250.53(A) and 250.96(A)].

Author's Comment:

■ Tarnish on copper water pipe need not be removed before making a termination.

Part II. System Grounding and Bonding

250.24 Service Equipment— Grounding and Bonding

(A) Grounded System. Service equipment supplied from a grounded system must have the grounding electrode conductor terminate in accordance with (1) through (5).

(1) Grounding Location. A grounding electrode conductor must connect the service neutral conductor to the grounding electrode at any accessible location, from the load end of the overhead service conductors, service drop, underground service laterals, or service lateral, up to and including the service disconnecting means. Figure 250–13

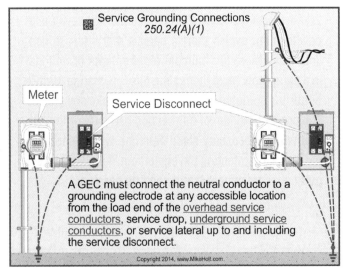

Figure 250–13

Author's Comment:

■ Some inspectors require the service neutral conductor to be grounded (connected to the earth) from the meter socket enclosure, while other inspectors insist that it be

grounded (connected to the earth) only from the service disconnect. Grounding at either location complies with this rule.

2014 CHANGE ANALYSIS: The 2011 *NEC* contained many, many changes in Articles 100 and 230 to "service" related terms (service point, service drop, overhead service conductors, and so on). With that many changes, some instances of incorrect usage are bound to remain, as it's nearly impossible to make that many changes and not miss something. This section has been revised to reflect the fact that service laterals and service drops aren't the only two ways electricity can get to a building that's supplied by a utility.

(4) Grounding Termination. When the service neutral conductor is connected to the service disconnecting means [250.24(B)] by a wire or busbar [250.28], the grounding electrode conductor is permitted to terminate to either the neutral terminal or the equipment grounding terminal within the service disconnect.

(5) Neutral-to-Case Connection. A neutral-to-case connection isn't permitted on the load side of service equipment, except as permitted by 250.142(B). Figure 250–14

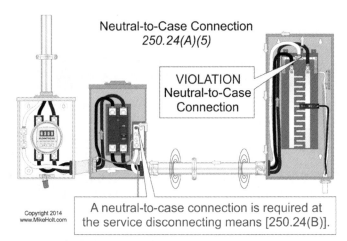

A neutral-to-case connection must not be made on the load side of the service equipment.

Figure 250–14

Author's Comment:

- If a neutral-to-case connection is made on the load side of service equipment, dangerous objectionable neutral current will flow on conductive metal parts of electrical equipment [250.6(A)]. Objectionable neutral current on metal parts of electrical equipment can cause electric shock and even death from ventricular fibrillation, as well as a fire. Figures 250–15 and 250–16

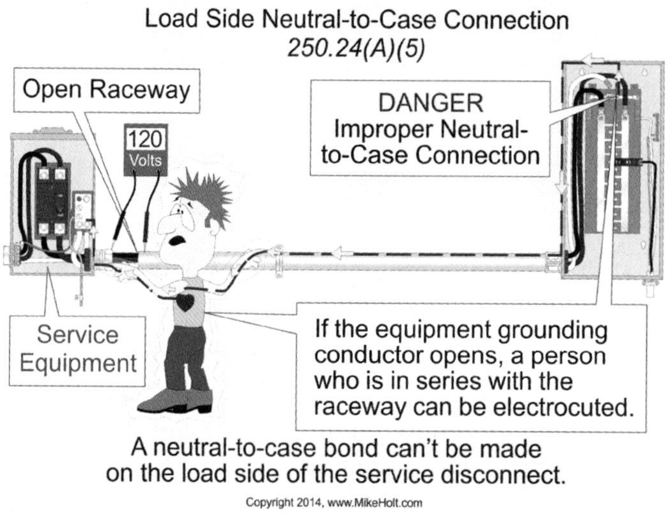

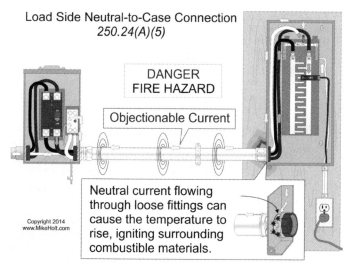

Figure 250–15

Figure 250–16

(B) Main Bonding Jumper. A main bonding jumper [250.28] is required to connect the neutral conductor to the equipment grounding conductor within the service disconnecting means. Figure 250–17

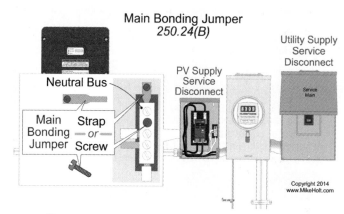

The neutral conductor on the supply-side of service equipment must be bonded to the PV disconnect in accordance with 250.24(C).

Figure 250–17

DANGER: *Dangerous voltage from a ground fault won't be removed from metal parts, metal piping, and structural steel if the main bonding jumper isn't installed in the service disconnecting means. This is because the contact resistance of a grounding electrode to the earth is so great that insufficient fault current returns to the power supply if the earth is the only fault-current return path to open the circuit overcurrent device.* Figure 250–18

(C) Neutral Conductor Brought to Service Equipment. A service neutral conductor must be run from the electric utility supply with the ungrounded conductors and terminate to the service disconnect neutral terminal. Figure 250–19

A main bonding jumper [250.24(B)] must be installed between the service neutral terminal and the service disconnecting means enclosure [250.28]. Figure 250–20

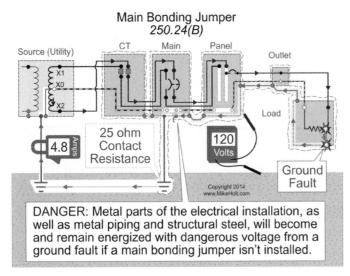

Figure 250–18

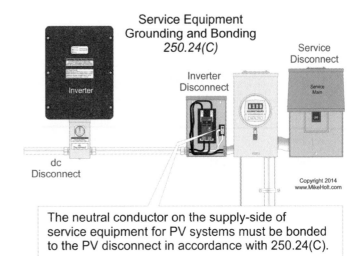

Figure 250–20

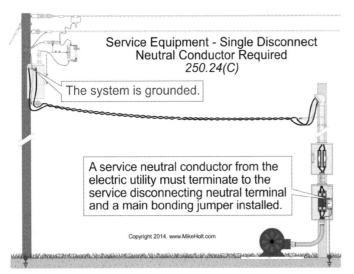

Figure 250–19

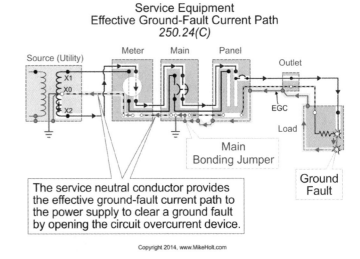

Figure 250–21

Author's Comment:

- The service neutral conductor provides the effective ground-fault current path to the power supply to ensure that dangerous voltage from a ground fault will be quickly removed by opening the overcurrent device [250.4(A)(3) and 250.4(A)(5)]. **Figure 250–21**

- If the neutral conductor is opened, dangerous voltage will be present on metal parts under normal conditions providing the potential for electric shock. If the earth's ground resistance is 25 ohms and the load's resistance is 25 ohms, the voltage drop across each of these resistors will be half the voltage source. Since the neutral is connected to the service disconnect, all metal parts will be elevated to 60V above the earth's potential for a 120/240V system. **Figure 250–22**

- To determine the actual voltage on the metal parts from an open service neutral conductor, you need to do some complex calculations. Visit www.MikeHolt.com and go to the "Free Stuff" link to download a spreadsheet for this purpose.

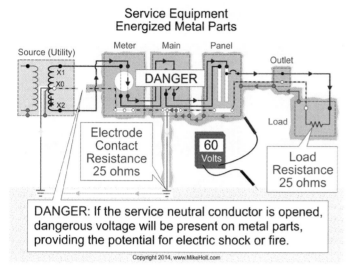

DANGER: If the service neutral conductor is opened, dangerous voltage will be present on metal parts, providing the potential for electric shock or fire.

Figure 250–22

(1) Single Raceway. Because the service neutral conductor serves as the effective ground-fault current path to the source for ground faults, the neutral conductor must be sized so it can safely carry the maximum fault current likely to be imposed on it [110.10 and 250.4(A)(5)]. This is accomplished by sizing the neutral conductor not smaller than specified in Table 250.102(C)(1), based on the cross-sectional area of the largest ungrounded service conductor. Figure 250–23

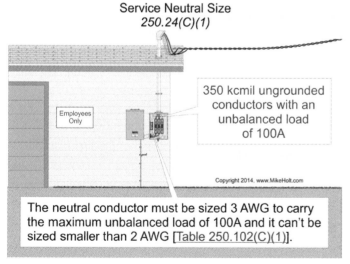

The neutral conductor must be sized 3 AWG to carry the maximum unbalanced load of 100A and it can't be sized smaller than 2 AWG [Table 250.102(C)(1)].

Figure 250–23

Author's Comment:

- In addition, the neutral conductors must have the capacity to carry the maximum unbalanced neutral current in accordance with 220.61.

(2) Parallel Conductors in Two or More Raceways. If service conductors are paralleled in two or more raceways, a neutral conductor must be installed in each of the parallel raceways. The size of the neutral conductor in each raceway must not be smaller than specified in Table 250.102(C)(1), based on the cross-sectional area of the largest ungrounded service conductor in each raceway. In no case can the neutral conductor in each parallel set be sized smaller than 1/0 AWG [310.10(H)(1)].

Author's Comment:

- In addition, the neutral conductors must have the capacity to carry the maximum unbalanced neutral current in accordance with 220.61.

> **Question:** What's the minimum size service neutral conductor required for each of two raceways, where the ungrounded service conductors in each of the raceways are 350 kcmil and the maximum unbalanced load is 100A? Figure 250–24
>
> (a) 3 AWG   (b) 2 AWG   (c) 1 AWG (d) 1/0 AWG
>
> **Answer:** (d) 1/0 AWG per raceway [Table 250.102(C)(1) and 310.10(H)]
>
> The unbalanced load of 50A in each raceway requires an 8 AWG service neutral conductor, which is rated 50A at 75°C in accordance with Table 310.15(B)(16) [220.61]. Also, Table 250.102(C)(1) requires a minimum of 2 AWG in each raceway; however, 1/0 AWG is the smallest conductor permitted to be paralleled [310.10(H) and Table 310.15(B)(16)].

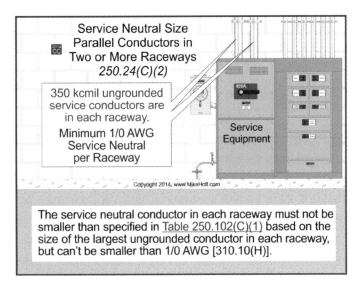

Figure 250–24

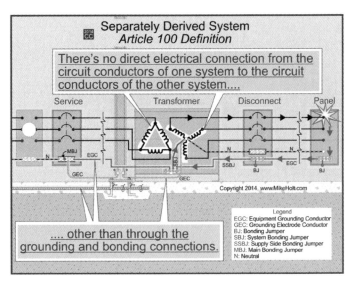

Figure 250–25

(D) Grounding Electrode Conductor. A grounding electrode conductor, sized in accordance with 250.66 based on the area of the ungrounded service conductor, must connect the neutral conductor and metal parts of service equipment enclosures to a grounding electrode in accordance with Part III of Article 250.

250.30 Separately Derived Systems (Transformers)—Grounding and Bonding

Author's Comment:

- According to Article 100, a separately derived system is a wiring system whose power is derived from a source, other than a utility, where there's no direct electrical connection to the supply conductors of another system, other than through grounding and bonding connections.

- Transformers are separately derived when the primary conductors have no direct electrical connection from circuit conductors of one system to circuit conductors of another system, other than connections through grounding and bonding connections. Figure 250–25

(A) Grounded Systems. Separately derived systems (transformers) must be grounded and bonded in accordance with (A)(1) through (A)(8).

A neutral-to-case connection must not be made on the load side of the system bonding jumper, except as permitted by 250.142(B).

(1) System Bonding Jumper. A system bonding jumper must be installed at the same location where the grounding electrode conductor terminates to the neutral terminal of the separately derived system (transformer); either at the separately derived system (transformer) or the system disconnecting means, but not at both locations [250.30(A)(5)].

(a) System Bonding Jumper at Source. Where the system bonding jumper is installed at the source of the separately derived system (transformer), the system bonding jumper must connect the neutral conductor of the derived system to the metal enclosure of the derived system. Figure 250–26

(b) System Bonding Jumper at Disconnecting Means. Where the system bonding jumper is installed at the first disconnecting means of a separately derived system (transformer), the system bonding jumper must connect the neutral conductor of the derived system to the metal disconnecting means enclosure. Figure 250–27

Author's Comment:

- A system bonding jumper is a conductor, screw, or strap that bonds the metal parts of a separately derived

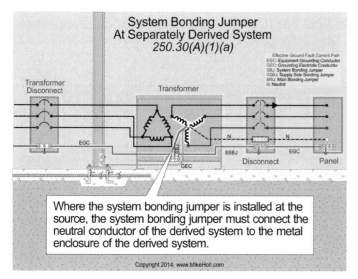

Figure 250–26

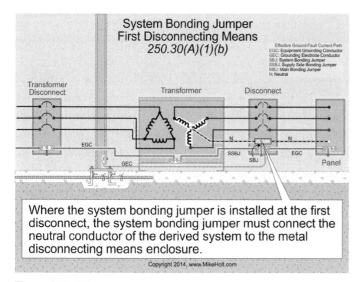

Figure 250–27

system (transformer) to the system neutral point [Article 100 Bonding Jumper, System], and it's sized to Table 250.102(C)(1) in accordance with 250.28(D).

DANGER: *During a ground fault, metal parts of electrical equipment, as well as metal piping and structural steel, will become and remain energized providing the potential for electric shock and fire if the system bonding jumper isn't installed.* Figure 250–28

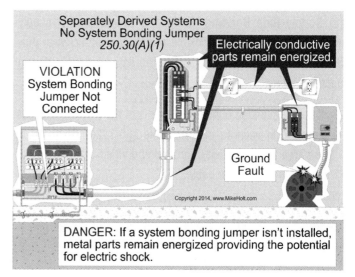

Figure 250–28

CAUTION: *Dangerous objectionable neutral current will flow on conductive metal parts of electrical equipment as well as metal piping and structural steel, in violation of 250.6(A), if more than one system bonding jumper is installed, or if it's not located where the grounding electrode conductor terminates to the neutral conductor.* Figure 250–29

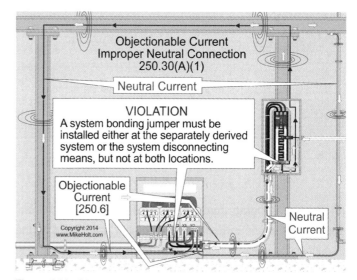

Figure 250–29

(2) Supply-Side Bonding Jumper to Disconnect. A supply-side bonding jumper (nonflexible metal raceway or wire) must be run from the derived system to the derived system disconnecting means.

(a) If the supply-side bonding jumper is of the wire type, it must be sized in accordance with Table 250.102(C)(1), based on the area of the largest ungrounded derived system conductor in the raceway or cable.

Question: *What size supply-side bonding jumper is required for flexible metal conduit containing 300 kcmil secondary conductors?* Figure 250–30

(a) 3 AWG   (b) 2 AWG   (c) 1 AWG   (d) 1/0 AWG

Answer: *(b) 2 AWG [Table 250.102(C)(1)]*

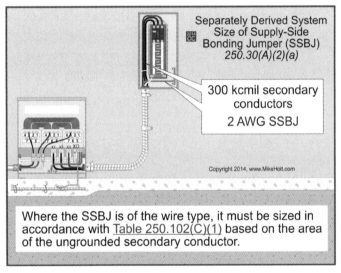

Where the SSBJ is of the wire type, it must be sized in accordance with Table 250.102(C)(1) based on the area of the ungrounded secondary conductor.

Figure 250–30

(3) System Bonding Jumper at Disconnect—Neutral Conductor Size. If the system bonding jumper is installed at the disconnecting means instead of at the source, the following requirements apply:

(a) Sizing for Single Raceway. The neutral conductor must be routed with the ungrounded conductors of the derived system to the disconnecting means and be sized not smaller than specified

in Table 250.102(C)(1), based on the area of the ungrounded conductor of the derived system. Figure 250–31

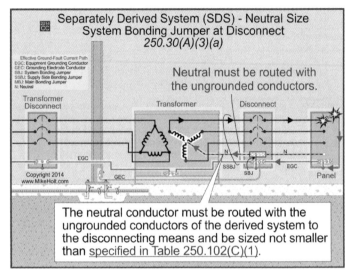

The neutral conductor must be routed with the ungrounded conductors of the derived system to the disconnecting means and be sized not smaller than specified in Table 250.102(C)(1).

Figure 250–31

(b) Parallel Conductors in Two or More Raceways. If the conductors from the derived system are installed in parallel in two or more raceways, the neutral conductor of the derived system in each raceway or cable must be sized not smaller than specified in Table 250.102(C)(1), based on the area of the largest ungrounded conductor of the derived system in the raceway or cable. In no case is the neutral conductor of the derived system permitted to be smaller than 1/0 AWG [310.10(H)].

Author's Comment:

■ If the system bonding jumper is installed at the disconnecting means instead of at the source, a supply-side bonding jumper must connect the metal parts of the separately derived system (transformer) to the neutral conductor at the disconnecting means [250.30(A)(2)].

(4) Grounding Electrode. The grounding electrode for a separately derived system (transformer) must be as near as practicable, and preferably in the same area where the system bonding jumper is installed and be one of the following: Figure 250–32

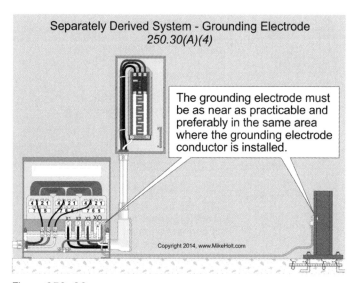

Figure 250–32

(1) Metal water pipe electrode, within 5 ft of the entry to the building [250.52(A)(1)].

(2) Metal building frame electrode [250.52(A)(2)].

Ex 1: If the water pipe or structural metal electrode aren't available, one of the following electrodes can be used:

• *A concrete-encased electrode encased by not less than 2 in. of concrete, located horizontally or vertically, and within that portion of concrete foundation or footing that's in direct contact with the earth [250.52(A)(3)].*

• *A ground ring electrode encircling the building, buried not less than 30 in. below grade, consisting of at least 20 ft of bare copper conductor not smaller than 2 AWG [250.52(A)(4) and 250.53(F)].*

• *A rod electrode having not less than 8 ft of contact with the soil meeting the requirements of 250.52(A)(5) and 250.53(G).*

• *Other metal underground systems, piping systems, or underground tanks [250.52(A)(8)].*

Note 1: Interior metal water piping in the area served by separately derived systems (transformers) must be bonded to the separately derived system (transformer) in accordance with 250.104(D).

(5) Grounding Electrode Conductor, Single Separately Derived System (Transformer). The grounding electrode conductor must be sized in accordance with 250.66, based on the area of the largest ungrounded conductor of the derived system. A grounding electrode conductor must terminate to the neutral at the same point on the separately derived system (transformer) where the system bonding jumper is connected. Figure 250–33

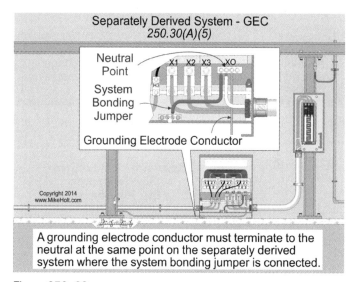

Figure 250–33

Author's Comment:

■ System grounding helps reduce fires in buildings as well as voltage stress on electrical insulation, thereby ensuring longer insulation life for motors, transformers, and other system components. Figure 250–34

■ To prevent objectionable neutral current from flowing [250.6] onto metal parts, the grounding electrode conductor must originate at the same point on the separately derived system (transformer) where the system bonding jumper is connected [250.30(A)(1)].

Ex 1: The grounding electrode conductor is permitted to terminate to the equipment grounding terminal at the derived system or first system disconnecting means in accordance with 250.30(A)(1). Figure 250–35

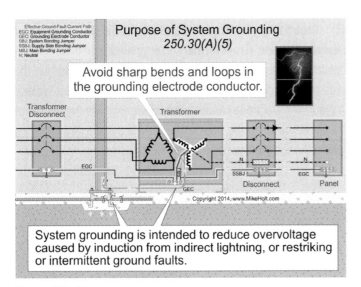

Figure 250–34

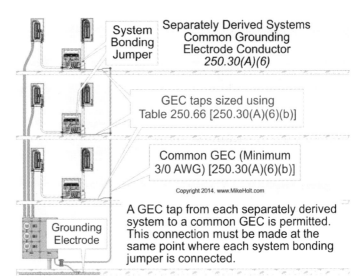

Figure 250–36

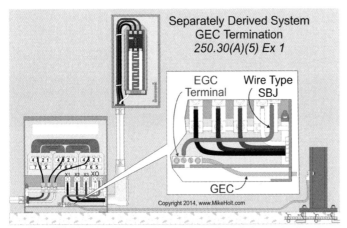

The GEC is permitted to terminate to the equipment grounding terminal at the derived system or first system disconnecting means in accordance with 250.30(A)(1).

Figure 250–35

Ex 3: Separately derived systems (transformers) rated 1 kVA or less aren't required to be grounded (connected to the earth).

(6) Grounding Electrode Conductor, Multiple Separately Derived Systems (Transformers). Where there are multiple separately derived systems (transformers), a grounding electrode conductor tap from each separately derived system (transformer) to a common grounding electrode conductor is permitted. This connection is to be made at the same point on the separately derived system (transformer) where the system bonding jumper is connected [250.30(A)(1)]. Figure 250–36

Ex 1: If the system bonding jumper is a wire or busbar, the grounding electrode conductor tap can terminate to either the neutral terminal or the equipment grounding terminal, bar, or bus in accordance with 250.30(A)(1).

Ex 2: Separately derived systems (transformers) rated 1 kVA or less aren't required to be grounded (connected to the earth).

(a) Common Grounding Electrode Conductor. The common grounding electrode conductor can be one of the following:

(1) A conductor not smaller than 3/0 AWG copper or 250 kcmil aluminum.

(2) The metal frame of the buildings that complies with 250.52(A)(2) or is connected to the grounding electrode system by a conductor not smaller than 3/0 AWG copper or 250 kcmil aluminum.

(b) Tap Conductor Size. Grounding electrode conductor taps must be sized in accordance with Table 250.66, based on the area of the largest ungrounded conductor of the given derived system.

(c) Connections. All tap connections to the common grounding electrode conductor must be made at an accessible location by one of the following methods:

(1) A connector listed as grounding and bonding equipment.

(2) Listed connections to aluminum or copper busbars not less than ¼ in. in depth x 2 in. in width

(3) Exothermic welding.

Grounding electrode conductor taps must be connected to the common grounding electrode conductor so the common grounding electrode conductor isn't spliced.

(7) Installation. The grounding electrode conductor must comply with the following:

- Be of copper where within 18 in. of the earth [250.64(A)].

- Be securely fastened to the surface on which it's carried [250.64(B)].

- Be adequately protected if exposed to physical damage [250.64(B)].

- Metal enclosures enclosing a grounding electrode conductor must be made electrically continuous from the point of attachment to cabinets or equipment to the grounding electrode [250.64(E)].

(8) Structural Steel and Metal Piping. To ensure dangerous voltage from a ground fault is removed quickly, structural steel and metal piping in the area served by a separately derived system (transformer) must be connected to the neutral conductor at the separately derived system (transformer) in accordance with 250.104(D).

(C) Outdoor Source. Separately derived systems located outside the building must have the grounding electrode connection made at the separately derived system (transformer) location. Figure 250–37

Part III. Grounding Electrode System and Grounding Electrode Conductor

250.50 Grounding Electrode System

Any grounding electrode described in 250.52(A)(1) through (A)(7) that's present at a building must be bonded together to form the grounding electrode system. Figure 250–38

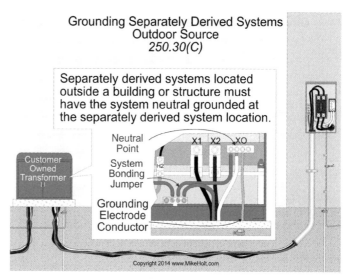

Figure 250–37

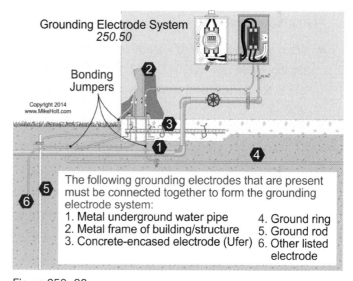

Figure 250–38

- Underground metal water pipe [250.52(A)(1)]
- Metal frame of the buildings [250.52(A)(2)]
- Concrete-encased electrode [250.52(A)(3)]
- Ground ring [250.52(A)(4)]
- Rod [250.52(A)(5)]
- Other listed electrodes [250.52(A)(6)]
- Grounding plate [250.52(A)(7)]

Ex: Concrete-encased electrodes aren't required for existing buildings where the conductive steel reinforcing bars aren't accessible without chipping up the concrete. Figure 250–39

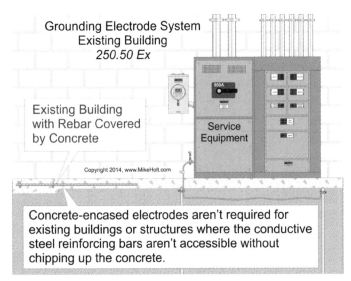

Figure 250–39

Author's Comment:

■ When a concrete-encased electrode is used at a building that doesn't have an underground metal water pipe electrode, no additional electrode is required. **Figure 250–40**

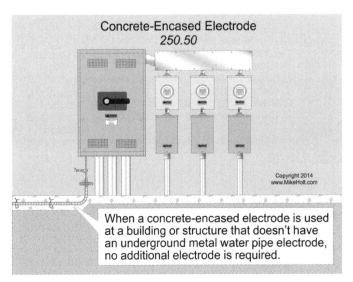

Figure 250–40

250.52 Grounding Electrode Types

(A) Electrodes Permitted for Grounding.

(1) Underground Metal Water Pipe Electrode. Underground metal water pipe in direct contact with the earth for 10 ft or more can serve as a grounding electrode. Figure 250–41

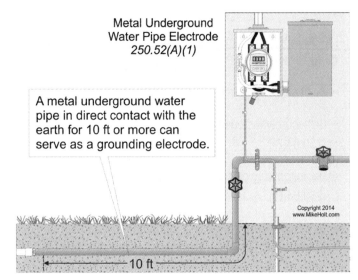

Figure 250–41

(2) Metal Frame Electrode. The metal frame of a building can serve as a grounding electrode when it meets at least one of the following conditions:

(1) At least one structural metal member is in direct contact with the earth for 10 ft or more, with or without concrete encasement.

(2) The hold-down bolts securing the structural steel are connected to a concrete-encased electrode [250.52(A)(3)] by welding, exothermic welding, steel tie wires, or other approved means. Figure 250–42

(3) Concrete-Encased Electrode. Figure 250–43

(1) One or more electrically conductive steel reinforcing bars of not less than ½ in. in diameter, mechanically connected together by steel tie wires, or other effective means to create a 20 ft or greater length can serve as a grounding electrode. Figure 250–44

(2) Bare copper conductor not smaller than 4 AWG of 20 ft or greater length.

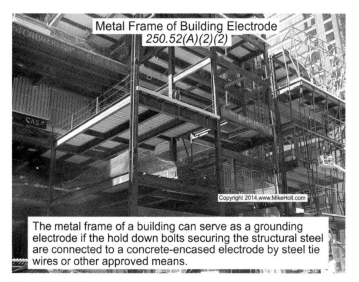

Metal Frame of Building Electrode
250.52(A)(2)(2)

The metal frame of a building can serve as a grounding electrode if the hold down bolts securing the structural steel are connected to a concrete-encased electrode by steel tie wires or other approved means.

Figure 250–42

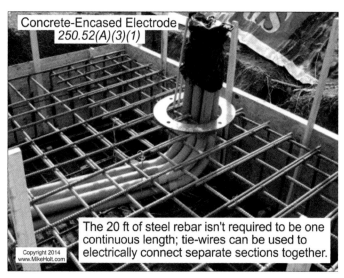

Concrete-Encased Electrode
250.52(A)(3)(1)

The 20 ft of steel rebar isn't required to be one continuous length; tie-wires can be used to electrically connect separate sections together.

Figure 250–44

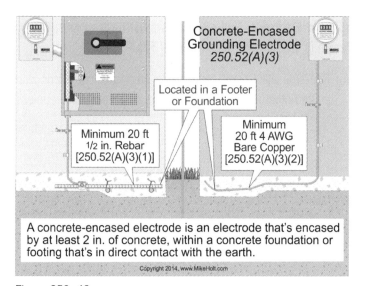

Concrete-Encased
Grounding Electrode
250.52(A)(3)

Located in a Footer or Foundation

Minimum 20 ft
1/2 in. Rebar
[250.52(A)(3)(1)]

Minimum
20 ft 4 AWG
Bare Copper
[250.52(A)(3)(2)]

A concrete-encased electrode is an electrode that's encased by at least 2 in. of concrete, within a concrete foundation or footing that's in direct contact with the earth.

Figure 250–43

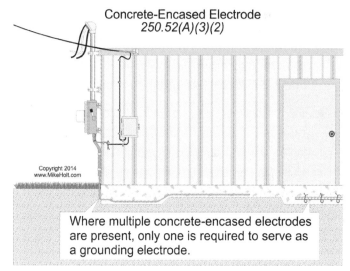

Concrete-Encased Electrode
250.52(A)(3)(2)

Where multiple concrete-encased electrodes are present, only one is required to serve as a grounding electrode.

Figure 250–45

The reinforcing bars or bare copper conductor must be encased by at least 2 in. of concrete located horizontally in a concrete footing or vertically within a concrete foundation that's in direct contact with the earth can serve as a grounding electrode.

Where multiple concrete-encased electrodes are present at a building, only one is required to serve as a grounding electrode. Figure 250–45

Note: Concrete separated from the earth because of insulation, vapor barriers, or similar items isn't considered to be in direct contract with the earth. Figure 250–46

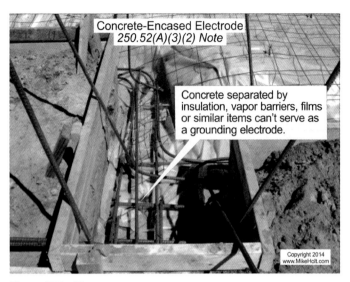

Figure 250–46

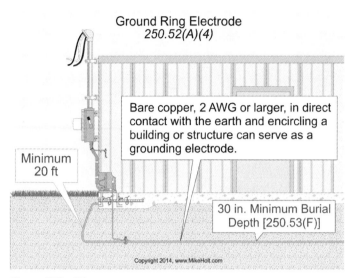

Figure 250–47

Author's Comment:

- The grounding electrode conductor to a concrete-encased grounding electrode isn't required to be larger than 4 AWG copper [250.66(B)].

- The concrete-encased grounding electrode is also called a "Ufer Ground," named after a consultant working for the U.S. Army during World War II. The technique Mr. Ufer came up with was necessary because the site needing grounding had no underground water table and little rainfall. The desert site was the location of a series of bomb storage vaults in the area of Flagstaff, Arizona. This type of grounding electrode generally offers the lowest ground resistance for the cost.

(4) Ground Ring Electrode. A ground ring consisting of at least 20 ft of bare copper conductor not smaller than 2 AWG buried in the earth encircling a building, can serve as a grounding electrode. Figure 250–47

Author's Comment:

- The ground ring must be buried not less than 30 in. [250.53(F)], and the grounding electrode conductor to a ground ring isn't required to be larger than the ground ring conductor size [250.66(C)].

(5) Rod Electrode. Rod electrodes must have at least 8 ft in length in contact with the earth [250.53(G)].

(b) Rod-type electrodes of stainless steel and copper or zinc coated steel must have a diameter of at least ⅝ in., unless listed. Figure 250–48

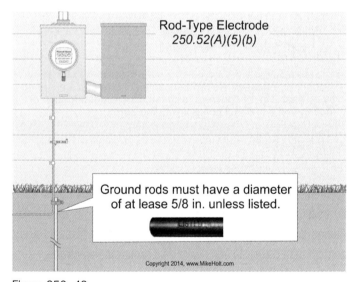

Figure 250–48

Author's Comment:

- The grounding electrode conductor, if it's the sole connection to the rod(s), isn't required to be larger than 6 AWG copper [250.66(A)].

- The diameter of a rod has an insignificant effect on the contact resistance of a rod(s) to the earth. However, larger diameter rods (¾ in. and 1 in.) are sometimes installed where mechanical strength is desired, or to compensate for the loss of the electrode's metal due to corrosion.

(6) Listed Electrode. Other listed grounding electrodes can serve as a grounding electrode.

(7) Ground Plate Electrode. A bare or conductively coated iron or steel plate with not less than ¼ in. of thickness, or a solid uncoated copper metal plate not less than 0.06 in. of thickness, with an exposed surface area of not less than 2 sq ft can serve as a grounding electrode.

(8) Metal Underground Piping Electrode. Metal underground metal piping and well casings can serve as a grounding electrode. Figure 250–49

Figure 250–49

Author's Comment:

- The grounding electrode conductor to the metal underground system must be sized in accordance with Table 250.66.

(B) Not Permitted for Use as a Grounding Electrode.

(1) Underground metal gas-piping systems aren't permitted to be used as a grounding electrode. Figure 250–50

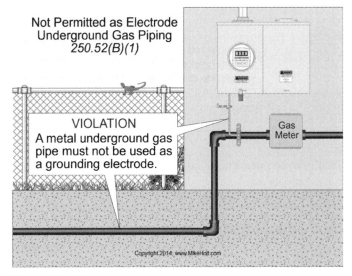

Figure 250–50

250.53 Grounding Electrode Installation Requirements

(A) Rod Electrodes.

(1) Below Permanent Moisture Level. If practicable, pipe electrodes must be embedded below the permanent moisture level and be free from nonconductive coatings such as paint or enamel.

(2) Supplemental Electrode. A rod electrode must be supplemented by an additional electrode that's bonded to: Figure 250–51

(1) Another rod electrode

(2) The grounding electrode conductor

(3) The service neutral conductor

(4) A nonflexible metal service raceway

(5) The service disconnect

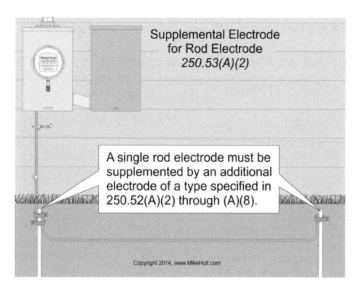

Figure 250–51

Ex: A single rod electrode having a contact resistance to the earth of 25 ohms or less isn't required to have a supplemental electrode. Figure 250–52

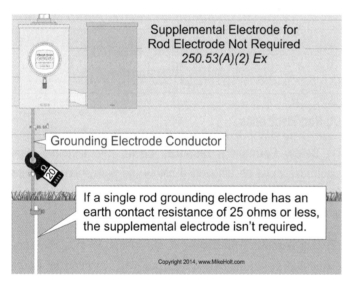

Figure 250–52

(3) Spacing. The supplemental electrode for a rod electrode must be installed not less than 6 ft from the rod electrode. Figure 250–53

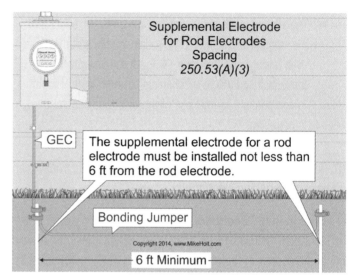

Figure 250–53

(B) Electrode Spacing. Rod electrodes for premises systems must be located no closer than 6 ft from lightning protection system grounding electrodes. Two or more grounding electrodes that are bonded together are considered a single grounding electrode system. Figure 250–54

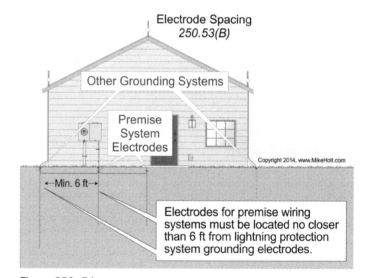

Figure 250–54

(C) Grounding Electrode Bonding Jumper. Grounding electrode bonding jumpers must be copper when within 18 in. of the earth [250.64(A)], be securely fastened to the surface, and be protected from physical damage [250.64(B)]. The bonding jumper to each electrode must be sized in accordance with 250.66. Figure 250–55

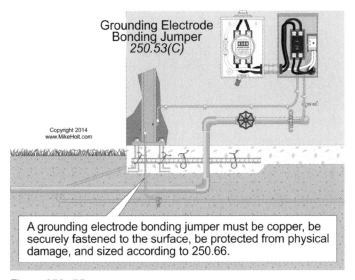

Figure 250–55

Author's Comment:

- The grounding electrode bonding jumpers must terminate by one of the following means in accordance with 250.8(A):

  □ Listed pressure connectors
  □ Terminal bars
  □ Pressure connectors listed as grounding and bonding equipment
  □ Exothermic welding
  □ Machine screw-type fasteners that engage not less than two threads or are secured with a nut
  □ Thread-forming machine screws that engage not less than two threads in the enclosure
  □ Connections that are part of a listed assembly
  □ Other listed means

When the termination is encased in concrete or buried, the termination fittings must be listed for this purpose [250.70].

(D) Underground Metal Water Pipe Electrode.

(1) Interior Metal Water Piping. The bonding connection for the interior metal water piping system, as required by 250.104(A), must not be dependent on water meters, filtering devices, or similar equipment likely to be disconnected for repairs or replacement. When necessary, a bonding jumper must be installed around insulated joints and equipment likely to be disconnected for repairs or replacement. Figure 250–56

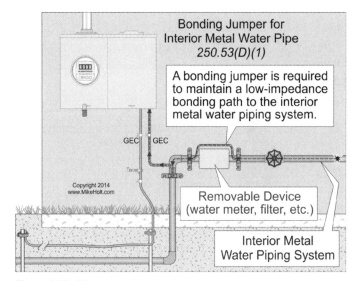

Figure 250–56

(2) Underground Metal Water Pipe Supplemental Electrode. When an underground metal water pipe grounding electrode is present, it must be used as part of the grounding electrode system [250.52(A)(1)], and it must be supplemented by one of the following electrodes:

- Metal frame of the building electrode [250.52(A)(2)]
- Concrete-encased electrode [250.52(A)(3)] Figure 250–57
- Ground ring electrode [250.52(A)(4)]
- Rod electrode [250.52(A)(5)]
- Other listed electrode [250.52(A)(6)]
- Metal underground piping electrode [250.52(A)(8)]

The supplemental grounding electrode conductor must terminate to one of the following: Figure 250–58

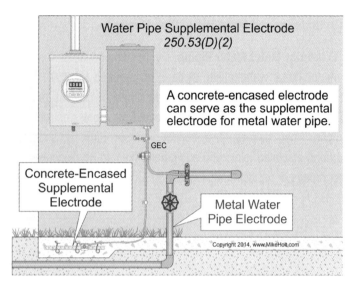

Figure 250–57

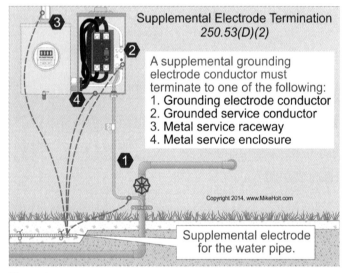

Figure 250–58

(1) Grounding electrode conductor

(2) Service neutral conductor

(3) Metal service raceway

(4) A nonflexible metal service raceway

Ex: The supplemental electrode is permitted to be bonded to interior metal water piping located not more than 5 ft from the point of entrance to the building [250.68(C)(1)].

(E) Supplemental Rod Electrode. The grounding electrode conductor to a rod(s) that serves as a supplemental electrode isn't required to be larger than 6 AWG copper.

(F) Ground Ring. A ground ring electrode (conductor) that encircles the building, consisting of at least 20 ft of bare copper conductor not smaller than 2 AWG, must be buried not less than 30 in. [250.52(A)(4)]. Figure 250–59

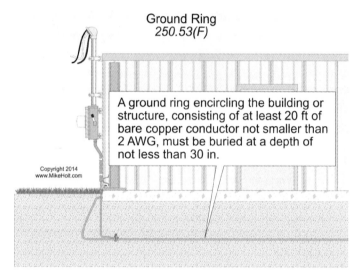

Figure 250–59

(G) Rod Electrodes. Rod electrodes must be installed so that not less than 8 ft of length is in contact with the soil. If rock bottom is encountered, the rod must be driven at an angle not to exceed 45 degrees from vertical. If rock bottom is encountered at an angle up to 45 degrees from vertical, the rod can be buried in a minimum 30 in. deep trench. Figure 250–60

The upper end of the rod must be flush with or underground unless the grounding electrode conductor attachment is protected against physical damage as specified in 250.10.

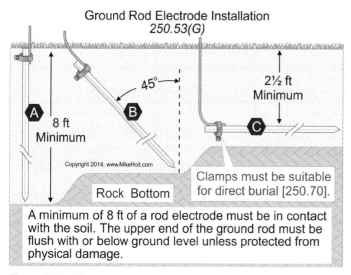

Ground Rod Electrode Installation
250.53(G)

45°

Ⓐ 8 ft Minimum

Ⓑ

2½ ft Minimum

Ⓒ

Copyright 2014, www.MikeHolt.com

Rock Bottom

Clamps must be suitable for direct burial [250.70].

A minimum of 8 ft of a rod electrode must be in contact with the soil. The upper end of the ground rod must be flush with or below ground level unless protected from physical damage.

Figure 250–60

250.54 Auxiliary Grounding Electrodes

Auxiliary electrodes are permitted, but they have no requirements since they serve no useful purpose related to electrical safety addressed by the *NEC*. If an auxiliary electrode is installed, it isn't required to be bonded to the building grounding electrode system, required to have the grounding conductor sized to 250.66, or comply with the 25-ohm requirement of 250.53(A)(2) Ex. Figure 250–61

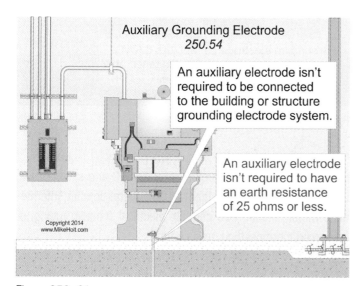

Auxiliary Grounding Electrode
250.54

An auxiliary electrode isn't required to be connected to the building or structure grounding electrode system.

An auxiliary electrode isn't required to have an earth resistance of 25 ohms or less.

Copyright 2014
www.MikeHolt.com

Figure 250–61

⚠ **CAUTION:** *An auxiliary electrode typically serves no useful purpose, and in some cases it may actually cause equipment failures by providing a path for lightning to travel through electronic equipment.* Figure 250–62

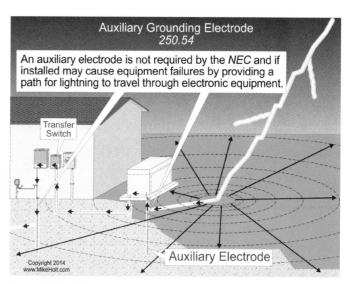

Auxiliary Grounding Electrode
250.54

An auxiliary electrode is not required by the *NEC* and if installed may cause equipment failures by providing a path for lightning to travel through electronic equipment.

Transfer Switch

Auxiliary Electrode

Copyright 2014
www.MikeHolt.com

Figure 250–62

250.62 Grounding Electrode Conductor

Grounding electrode conductors of the wire type must be solid or stranded, insulated or bare, and must be copper if within 18 in. of the earth [250.64(A)]. Figure 250–63

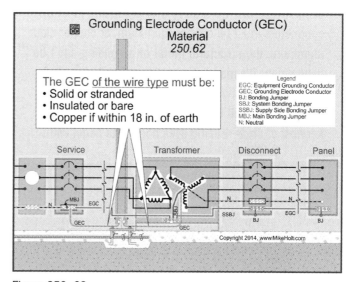

Grounding Electrode Conductor (GEC) Material
250.62

The GEC of the wire type must be:
• Solid or stranded
• Insulated or bare
• Copper if within 18 in. of earth

Legend
EGC: Equipment Grounding Conductor
GEC: Grounding Electrode Conductor
BJ: Bonding Jumper
SBJ: System Bonding Jumper
SSBJ: Supply Side Bonding Jumper
MBJ: Main Bonding Jumper
N: Neutral

Service   Transformer   Disconnect   Panel

MBJ   EGC   SSBJ   BJ   EGC   BJ

GEC   GEC

Copyright 2014, www.MikeHolt.com

Figure 250–63

Author's Comment:

- The metal structural frame of a building can be used as a conductor to interconnect electrodes [250.68(C)] Figure 250–64

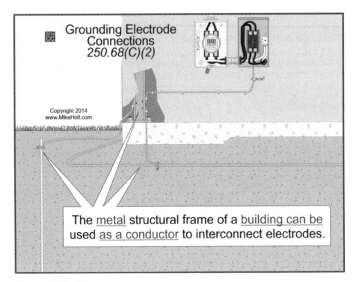

Figure 250–64

2014 CHANGE ANALYSIS: Changes made in the 2011 *NEC* to 250.68 had the ultimate effect of calling interior water pipe and structural metal "grounding electrode conductors" without coming right out and saying it. While there's no problem within the context of 250.68(C), it does create a bit of a conflict with this section (250.62). By stating that grounding electrode conductors must be copper, aluminum, or copper-clad aluminum, the structural metal of a building can't be used unless it's made of one of these materials. Since buildings aren't typically built out of copper, this section was tweaked to resolve the conflict that only the keenest of *Code*-reading eyes noticed to begin with.

250.64 Grounding Electrode Conductor Installation

Grounding electrode conductors must be installed as specified in (A) through (F).

(A) Aluminum Conductors. Aluminum grounding electrode conductors must not be in contact with masonry, subject to corrosive conditions, or within 18 in. of the earth.

(B) Conductor Protection. Where installed exposed, grounding electrode conductors must be protected where subject to physical damage and are permitted to be installed on or through framing members. Grounding electrode conductors 6 AWG and larger can be installed exposed along the surface of the building if securely fastened and not subject to physical damage. Figure 250–65

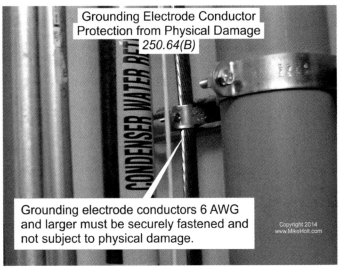

Figure 250–65

Grounding electrode conductors sized 8 AWG and smaller must be protected by installing them in rigid metal conduit, intermediate metal conduit, PVC conduit, electrical metallic tubing, or reinforced thermosetting resin conduit.

Author's Comment:

- A ferrous metal raceway containing a grounding electrode conductor must be made electrically continuous by bonding each end of the raceway to the grounding electrode conductor [250.64(E)], so it's best to use nonmetallic conduit.

Grounding electrode conductors and bonding jumpers located underground, aren't required to comply with the cover requirements of 300.5. Figure 250–66

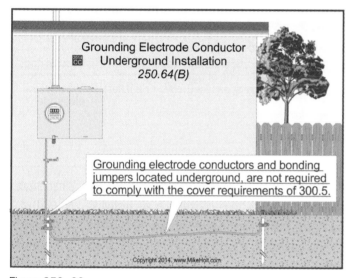

Figure 250–66

2014 CHANGE ANALYSIS: Table 300.5 gives the cover (also known as burial depth) requirements for underground installations. Nothing in that table, or section, indicates whether or not it applies to grounding electrode conductors or bonding jumpers. While it wouldn't be good to hit one of these conductors with a shovel, you probably wouldn't get electrocuted.

(C) Continuous. Grounding electrode conductor(s) must be installed without a splice or joint except by:

(1) Irreversible compression-type connectors or exothermic welding.

(2) Busbars connected together.

(3) Bolted, riveted, or welded connections of structural metal frames of buildings.

(4) Threaded, welded, brazed, soldered or bolted-flange connections of metal water piping.

(E) Ferrous Enclosures and Raceways Containing Grounding Electrode Conductors.

(1) General. To prevent inductive choking of grounding electrode conductors, ferrous raceways and enclosures containing grounding electrode conductors must have each end of the raceway or enclosure bonded to the grounding electrode or grounding electrode conductor. Figure 250–67

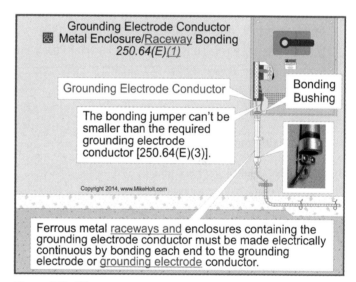

Figure 250–67

(2) Methods. Bonding must be done by one of the methods discussed in 250.92(B)(2) through (B)(4).

(3) Size. Bonding jumpers must be the same size or larger than the required size of the grounding electrode conductor in the raceway or other enclosure.

(4) Wiring Methods. When a raceway is used for a grounding electrode conductor, it must meet all of the requirements for the raceway, such as securing and supporting, number of bends, conductor fill, and so forth.

Author's Comment:

- Nonferrous metal raceways, such as aluminum rigid metal conduit, enclosing the grounding electrode conductor aren't required to meet the "bonding each end of the raceway to the grounding electrode conductor" provisions of this section.

⚠️ **CAUTION:** *The effectiveness of a grounding electrode is significantly reduced if a ferrous metal raceway containing a grounding electrode conductor isn't bonded to the ferrous metal raceway at both ends. This is because a single conductor carrying high-frequency induced lightning current in a ferrous raceway causes the raceway to act as an inductor, which severely limits (chokes) the current flow through the grounding electrode conductor. ANSI/IEEE 142—Recommended Practice for Grounding of Industrial and Commercial Power Systems (Green Book) states: "An inductive choke can reduce the current flow by 97 percent."*

Author's Comment:

- To save a lot of time and effort, install the grounding electrode conductor exposed if it's not subject to physical damage [250.64(B)], or enclose it in nonmetallic conduit suitable for the application [352.10(F)].

2014 CHANGE ANALYSIS: In 2011 250.64(E) was a remarkably long paragraph. When rules are written in overly long paragraphs they tend to be misread, misunderstood, or ignored altogether. While there are no real technical changes to the requirements of bonding these raceways, few will argue that the list format the *NEC* is using more and more often is a better method here.

(F) Termination to Grounding Electrode.

(1) Single Grounding Electrode Conductor. A single grounding electrode conductor is permitted to terminate to any grounding electrode of the grounding electrode system. Figure 250–68

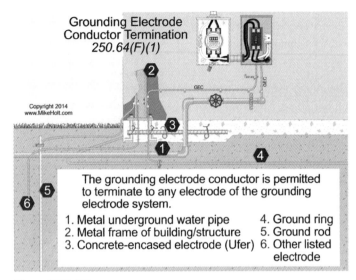

Figure 250–68

(2) Multiple Grounding Electrode Conductors. When multiple grounding electrode conductors are installed [250.64(D)(2)], each grounding electrode conductor is permitted to terminate to any grounding electrode of the grounding electrode system. Figure 250–69

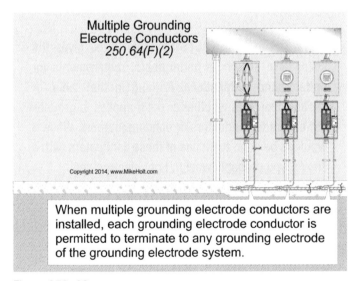

Figure 250–69

(3) Termination to Busbar. Grounding electrode conductors and grounding electrode bonding jumpers are permitted to terminate to a busbar sized not less than ¼ in. × 2 in. that's securely fastened at an accessible location. The terminations to the busbar must be made by a listed connector or by exothermic welding. Figure 250–70

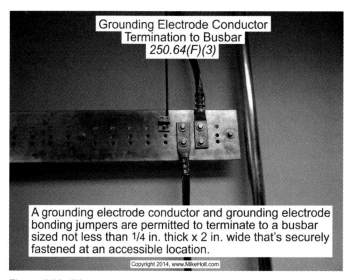

Figure 250–70

250.66 Sizing AC Grounding Electrode Conductor

Except as permitted in (A) through (C), the ac grounding electrode conductor must be sized in accordance with Table 250.66.

(A) Rod. If the grounding electrode conductor is connected to one or more rods, as permitted in 250.52(A)(5), that portion of the grounding electrode conductor that's the sole connection to the rod(s) isn't required to be larger than 6 AWG copper. Figure 250–71

(B) Concrete-Encased Grounding Electrode. If the grounding electrode conductor is connected to one or more concrete-encased electrodes, as permitted in 250.52(A)(3), that portion of the grounding electrode conductor that's the sole connection to the concrete-encased electrode(s) isn't required to be larger than 4 AWG copper. Figure 250–72

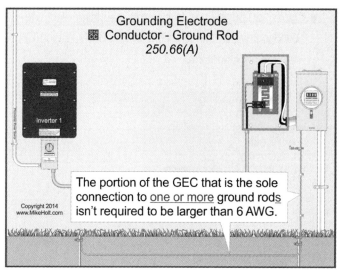

Figure 250–71

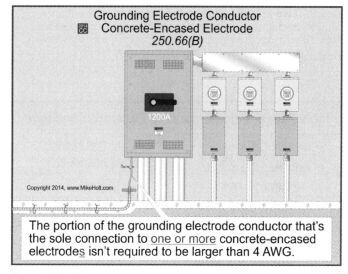

Figure 250–72

(C) Ground Ring. If the grounding electrode conductor is connected to a ground ring, the portion of the conductor that's the sole connection to the ground ring isn't required to be larger than the conductor used for the ground ring.

Author's Comment:

■ A ground ring encircling the building in direct contact with the earth must consist of at least 20 ft of bare copper conductor not smaller than 2 AWG [250.52(A)(4)]. See 250.53(F) for the installation requirements for a ground ring.

- Table 250.66 is used to size the grounding electrode conductor when the conditions of 250.66(A), (B), or (C) don't apply. Figure 250–73

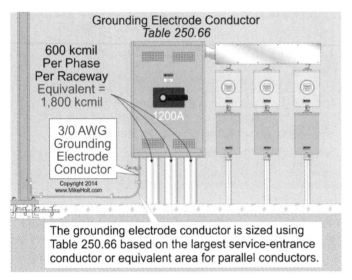

Figure 250–73

Table 250.66 Sizing Grounding Electrode Conductor

Conductor or Area of Parallel Conductors	Copper Grounding Electrode Conductor
12 through 2 AWG	8 AWG
1 or 1/0 AWG	6 AWG
2/0 or 3/0 AWG	4 AWG
Over 3/0 through 350 kcmil	2 AWG
Over 350 through 600 kcmil	1/0 AWG
Over 600 through 1,100 kcmil	2/0 AWG
Over 1,100 kcmil	3/0 AWG

2014 CHANGE ANALYSIS: The *Code* has long allowed for smaller grounding electrode conductors for ground rods and concrete-encased electrodes. Unfortunately, there was a subtle omission that's been addressed by this change. If a person can use 6 AWG to one ground rod, why not allow it for two ground rods that are in parallel? This practice has been used by installers, and allowed by inspectors, who either didn't realize the error in the *NEC* or realized the error and recognized that it was just that—an error.

250.68 Termination to the Grounding Electrode

(A) Accessibility. The mechanical elements used to terminate a grounding electrode conductor or bonding jumper to a grounding electrode must be accessible. Figure 250–74

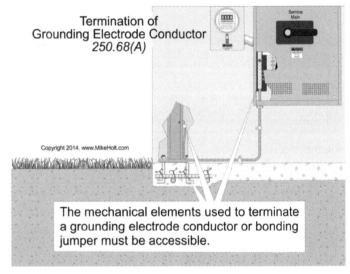

Figure 250–74

Ex 1: The termination isn't required to be accessible if the termination to the electrode is encased in concrete or buried in the earth. Figure 250–75

Author's Comment:

- If the grounding electrode attachment fitting is encased in concrete or buried in the earth, it must be listed for direct soil burial or concrete encasement [250.70].

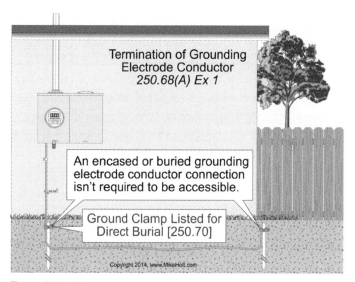

Figure 250–75

Ex 2: Exothermic or irreversible compression connections, together with the mechanical means used to attach to fire-proofed structural metal, aren't required to be accessible.

(C) Grounding Electrode Connections.

(3) A concrete-encased electrode can be extended from the concrete to an accessible location above the concrete. Figure 250–76

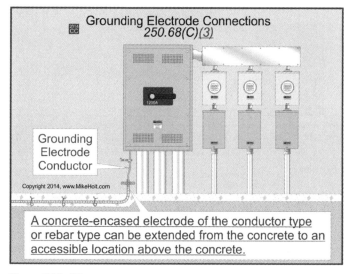

Figure 250–76

2014 CHANGE ANALYSIS: These welcome changes answer many questions that *Code* users have had in the past. It's important to remember that this section isn't telling us when structural metal or water pipe is an electrode…that's handled in 250.52. This section is simply telling us when we can use these items as conductors to connect other items together. The structural metal of a building may or may not be a grounding electrode, but it's certainly conductive, so it can be used to connect different electrodes together.

Consider a metal frame of a building that doesn't meet the definition of a grounding electrode, because it doesn't meet the criteria of 250.52(A)(2). This same building has a water pipe that meets 250.52(A)(1) and therefore must be used as a grounding electrode. The water pipe enters the building three hundred feet away from the service disconnect. Is it okay to use the metal of the building as a conductor to connect the water pipe to the service equipment? This will allow me to use a short piece of wire from the service equipment to the structural metal, then walk three hundred feet to the water pipe and connect the pipe to the structural metal with another short piece of wire. The answer is now clearly yes, as it should be. The structural metal of the building is not only conductive, it has low impedance (probably lower impedance than a copper conductor would be, given the size of the metal). Previous editions of the *Code* only allowed this practice if the structural metal met the criteria of being a grounding electrode.

A new item (3) has also been added to this list, which many people will see as a welcome change. The *NEC* has been silent on the issue of having a piece of rebar (that meets the criteria of a concrete-encased electrode) exit the concrete and enter the building. That piece of steel couldn't be called a grounding electrode, because that portion of the steel wasn't in the concrete and therefore didn't meet the requirements of 250.52(A)(3). This shouldn't matter, and most installers and inspectors have installed and passed it for years, but now the argument can end.

250.70 Grounding Electrode Conductor Termination Fittings

The grounding electrode conductor must terminate to the grounding electrode by exothermic welding, listed lugs, listed pressure connectors, listed clamps, or other listed means. In addition, fittings terminating to a grounding electrode must be listed for the materials of the grounding electrode.

When the termination to a grounding electrode is encased in concrete or buried in the earth, the termination fitting must be listed for direct soil burial or concrete encasement. No more than one conductor can terminate on a single clamp or fitting unless the clamp or fitting is listed for multiple connections. Figure 250–77

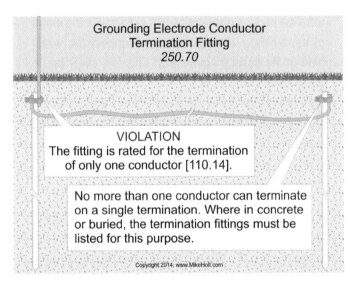

Figure 250–77

Part IV. Grounding Enclosure, Raceway, and Service Cable Connections

250.86 Other Enclosures

Metal raceways and enclosures containing electrical conductors operating at 50V or more [250.20(A)] must be connected to the circuit equipment grounding conductor.

Ex 2: Short sections of metal raceways used for the support or physical protection of cables aren't required to be connected to the circuit equipment grounding conductor.

Ex 3: A metal elbow installed in a run of underground nonmetallic raceway having a minimum of 18 in. of cover or encased in not less than 2 in. of concrete isn't required to be connected to the circuit equipment grounding conductor.

Part V. Bonding

250.90 General

Bonding must be provided to ensure electrical continuity and the capacity to conduct safely any fault current likely to be imposed.

250.92 Bonding Equipment for Services

(A) Bonding Requirements for Equipment for Services. The metal parts of equipment indicated below must be bonded together in accordance with 250.92(B). Figure 250–78

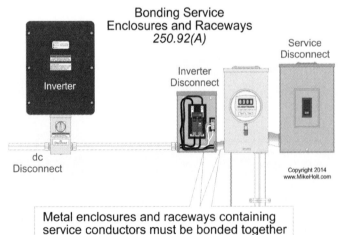

Figure 250–78

(1) Metal raceways containing service conductors.

(2) Metal enclosures containing service conductors.

(B) Methods of Bonding. Bonding jumpers around reducing washers or oversized, concentric, or eccentric knockouts are required. Figure 250–79

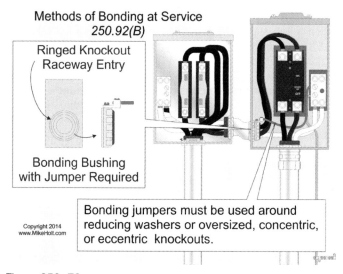

Figure 250–79

Standard locknuts are permitted to make a mechanical connection of the raceway(s), but they can't serve as the bonding means required by this section. Figure 250–80

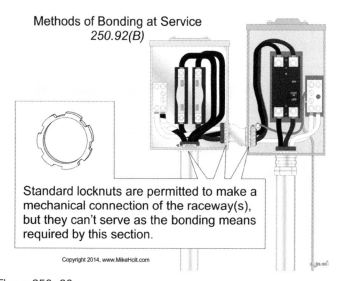

Figure 250–80

Electrical continuity at service equipment, service raceways, and service conductor enclosures must be ensured by one of the following methods:

(1) Bonding the metal parts to the service neutral conductor. Figure 250–81

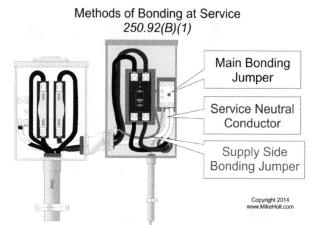

Figure 250–81

Author's Comment:

■ A main bonding jumper is required to bond the service disconnect to the service neutral conductor [250.24(B) and 250.28].

■ At service equipment, the service neutral conductor provides the effective ground-fault current path to the power supply [250.24(C)]; therefore, an equipment grounding conductor isn't required to be installed within PVC conduit containing service-entrance conductors [250.142(A)(1) and 352.60 Ex 2]. Figure 250–82

(2) Terminating metal raceways to metal enclosures by threaded hubs on enclosures if made up wrenchtight. Figure 250–83

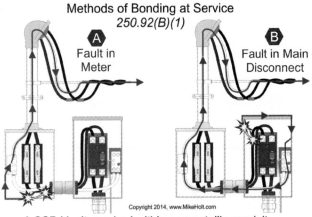

Methods of Bonding at Service
250.92(B)(1)

A — Fault in Meter

B — Fault in Main Disconnect

A SSBJ isn't required within nonmetallic conduit, because the service neutral conductor serves as the effective ground-fault current path [352.60 Ex 2].

Figure 250–82

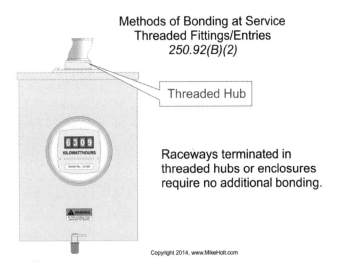

Methods of Bonding at Service
Threaded Fittings/Entries
250.92(B)(2)

Threaded Hub

Raceways terminated in threaded hubs or enclosures require no additional bonding.

Figure 250–83

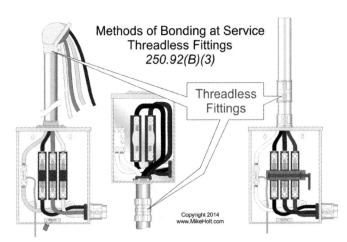

Methods of Bonding at Service
Threadless Fittings
250.92(B)(3)

Threadless Fittings

Raceways are considered suitably bonded by threadless fittings if made up tight.

Figure 250–84

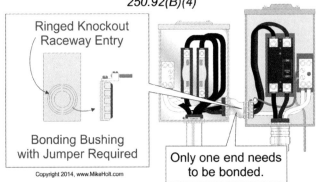

Methods of Bonding at Service - Ringed Knockout Entry
250.92(B)(4)

Ringed Knockout Raceway Entry

Bonding Bushing with Jumper Required

Only one end needs to be bonded.

A listed bonding fitting with a bonding jumper to the service neutral conductor is required when a metal raceway terminates to a ringed knockout.

Figure 250–85

(3) Terminating metal raceways to metal enclosures by threadless fittings if made up tight. Figure 250–84

(4) Other listed devices, such as bonding-type locknuts, bushings, wedges, or bushings with bonding jumpers.

Author's Comment:

■ A listed bonding wedge or bushing with a bonding jumper to the service neutral conductor is required when a metal raceway containing service conductors terminates to a ringed knockout. Figure 250–85

■ The bonding jumper used for this purpose must be sized in accordance with Table 250.102(C)(1), based on the area of the largest ungrounded service conductors within the raceway [250.102(C)].

■ A bonding-type locknut can be used for a metal raceway containing service conductors that terminates to an enclosure without a ringed knockout. Figure 250–86

■ A bonding locknut differs from a standard locknut in that it contains a bonding screw with a sharp point that drives into the metal enclosure to ensure a solid connection.

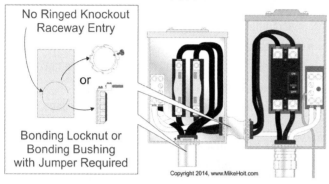

Methods of Bonding at Service
No Ringed Knockout Entry
250.92(B)(4)

No Ringed Knockout
Raceway Entry

or

Bonding Locknut or
Bonding Bushing
with Jumper Required

Copyright 2014, www.MikeHolt.com

A bonding-type locknut can be used for a metal raceway terminating to an enclosure without a ringed knockout.

Figure 250–86

- Bonding one end of a service raceway to the service neutral provides the low-impedance fault current path to the source. Figure 250–87

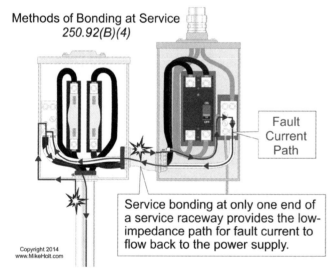

Methods of Bonding at Service
250.92(B)(4)

Fault
Current
Path

Service bonding at only one end of a service raceway provides the low-impedance path for fault current to flow back to the power supply.

Copyright 2014
www.MikeHolt.com

Figure 250–87

250.96 Bonding Other Enclosures

(A) Maintaining Effective Ground-Fault Current Path. Metal parts intended to serve as equipment grounding conductors, including raceways, cables, equipment, and enclosures, must

be bonded together to ensure they have the capacity to conduct safely any fault current likely to be imposed on them [110.10, 250.4(A)(5), and Note to Table 250.122].

Nonconductive coatings such as paint, lacquer, and enamel on equipment must be removed to ensure an effective ground-fault current path, or the termination fittings must be designed so as to make such removal unnecessary [250.12].

Author's Comment:

- The practice of driving a locknut tight with a screwdriver and pliers is considered sufficient in removing paint and other nonconductive finishes to ensure an effective ground-fault current path.

250.97 Bonding Metal Parts Containing Circuits over 150V to Ground

Metal raceways or cables, containing circuits operating at over 150V-to-ground terminating at ringed knockouts must be bonded to the metal enclosure with a bonding jumper sized in accordance with 250.122, based on the rating of the circuit overcurrent device [250.102(D)]. Figures 250–88 and 250–89

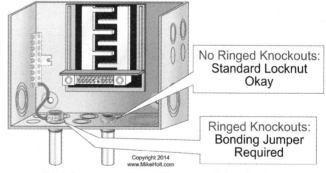

277V/480V Circuit Bonding
250.97

No Ringed Knockouts:
Standard Locknut
Okay

Ringed Knockouts:
Bonding Jumper
Required

Copyright 2014
www.MikeHolt.com

Metal raceways or cables containing 277V or 480V circuits terminating at ringed knockouts must be bonded with a bonding jumper.

Figure 250–88

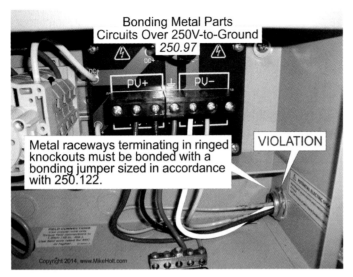

Figure 250–89

Ex: A bonding jumper isn't required where ringed knockouts aren't encountered, knockouts are totally punched out, or where the box is listed to provide a reliable bonding connection. Figure 250–90

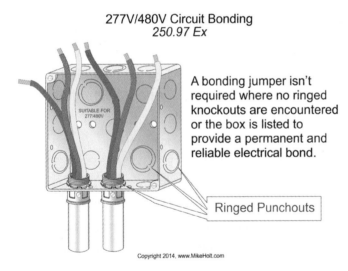

Figure 250–90

250.102 Bonding Conductors and Jumpers

(A) Material. Equipment bonding jumpers must be copper.

(B) Termination. Equipment bonding jumpers must terminate by one of the following means in accordance with 250.8(A):

- Listed pressure connectors
- Terminal bars
- Pressure connectors listed as grounding and bonding equipment
- Exothermic welding
- Machine screw-type fasteners that engage not less than two threads or are secured with a nut
- Thread-forming machine screws that engage not less than two threads in the enclosure
- Connections that are part of a listed assembly
- Other listed means

(C) Supply-Side Bonding Jumper Sizing.

(1) Single Raceway Installations. The supply-side bonding jumper is sized in accordance with Table 250.102(C)(1), based on the largest ungrounded conductor within the raceway. Figure 250–91

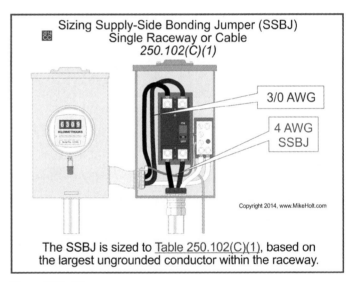

Figure 250–91

(2) Parallel Conductor Installations. If the ungrounded supply conductors are paralleled in two or more raceways or cables, the size of the supply-side bonding jumper for each raceway or cable is sized in accordance with Table 250.102(C)(1), based on the size of the largest ungrounded conductors in each raceway or cable.

Question: *What size single supply-side bonding jumper is required for three metal raceways, each containing 400 kcmil service conductors?* Figure 250– 92

(a) 1 AWG   (b) 1/0 AWG   (c) 2/0 AWG   (d) 300 AWG

Answer: *(b) 1/0 AWG [Table 250.102(C)(1)]*

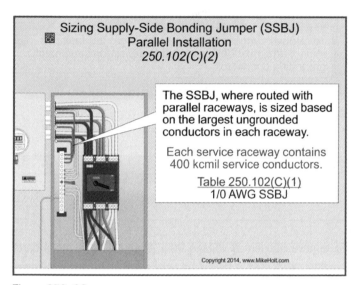

Sizing Supply-Side Bonding Jumper (SSBJ)
Parallel Installation
250.102(C)(2)

The SSBJ, where routed with parallel raceways, is sized based on the largest ungrounded conductors in each raceway.

Each service raceway contains 400 kcmil service conductors.

Table 250.102(C)(1)
1/0 AWG SSBJ

Copyright 2014, www.MikeHolt.com

Figure 250–92

Table 250.102(C)(1). Main Bonding and Supply-Side Bonding Jumpers

Size of Largest Ungrounded Conductor Per Raceway		Size of Conductor or Bonding Jumper	
Copper	Aluminum or Copper-Clad Aluminum	Copper	
2 or smaller	1/0 or smaller	8	
1 or 1/0	2/0 or 3/0	6	
2/0 or 3/0	Over 3/0 250 kcmil	4	
Over 3/0 through 350 kcmil	Over 250 through 500 kcmil	2	
Over 350 through 600 kcmil	Over 500 through 900 kcmil	1/0	

2014 CHANGE ANALYSIS: Experienced *Code* users will recognize this table as a near perfect reproduction of Table 250.66. Despite being named "Grounding Electrode Conductor for AC Systems," Table 250.66 always served many different roles, including sizing the main bonding jumper, system bonding jumper, supply-side bonding jumper, and minimum service neutral conductor. All of these (other than the grounding electrode conductor [GEC]) must carry fault current back to the source, and therefore are very different from the GEC. It makes sense to create a new table for these items, and anyone who has tried to teach Article 250 (especially to a new *Code* user) will almost certainly agree.

(D) Load Side Bonding Jumper Sizing. Bonding jumpers on the load side of feeder and branch-circuit overcurrent devices are sized in accordance with 250.122, based on the rating of the circuit overcurrent device.

Question: *What size equipment bonding jumper is required for each metal raceway where the circuit conductors are protected by a 1,200A overcurrent device?* Figure 250–93

(a) 1 AWG   (b) 1/0 AWG   (c) 2/0 AWG   (d) 3/0 AWG

Answer: *(d) 3/0 AWG [Table 250.122]*

If a single bonding jumper is used to bond two or more raceways, it must be sized in accordance with 250.122, based on the rating of the largest circuit overcurrent device. Figure 250–94

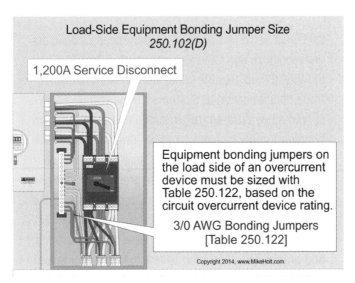

Figure 250–93

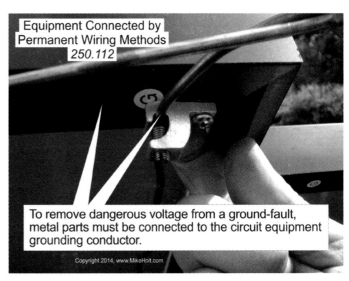

Figure 250–95

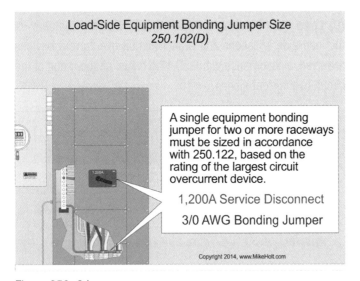

Figure 250–94

Part VI. Equipment Grounding and Equipment Grounding Conductors

250.112 Specific Equipment Fastened in Place or Connected by Permanent Wiring Methods

To remove dangerous voltage from a ground fault, metal parts must be connected to the circuit equipment grounding conductor. Figure 250–95

250.114 Cord-and-Plug-Connected Equipment

To remove dangerous voltage from a ground-fault, metal parts must be connected to the circuit equipment grounding conductor.

Ex: Listed double-insulated equipment isn't required to be connected to the circuit equipment grounding conductor.

250.118 Types of Equipment Grounding Conductors

An equipment grounding conductor can be any one or a combination of the following: Figure 250–96

Author's Comment:

■ The effective ground-fault path is an intentionally constructed low-impedance conductive path designed to carry fault current from the point of a ground fault on a wiring system to the electrical supply source. Its purpose is to quickly remove dangerous voltage from a ground fault by opening the circuit overcurrent device [250.2]. Figure 250–97

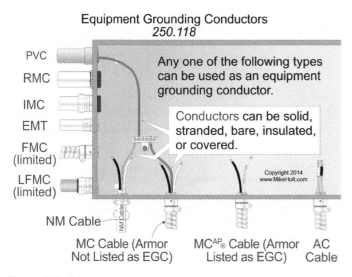

Figure 250–96

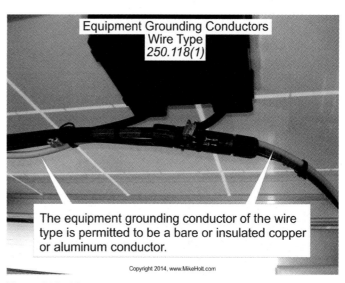

Figure 250–98

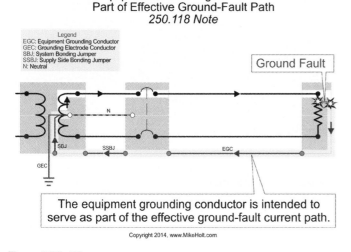

Figure 250–97

(5) Listed flexible metal conduit (FMC) can serve as an equipment grounding conductor where: Figure 250–99

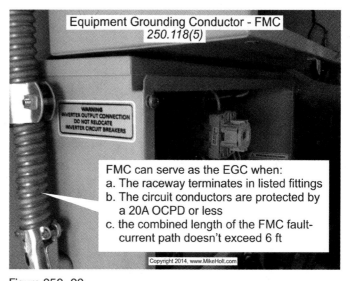

Figure 250–99

(1) An equipment grounding conductor of the wire type is permitted to be a bare or insulated copper or aluminum conductor. Figure 250–98

(2) Rigid metal conduit (RMC) can serve as an equipment grounding conductor.

(3) Intermediate metal conduit (IMC) can serve as an equipment grounding conductor.

(4) Electrical metallic tubing (EMT) can serve as an equipment grounding conductor.

a. The raceway terminates in listed fittings.

b. The circuit conductors are protected by an overcurrent device rated 20A or less.

c. The combined length of the flexible conduit in the same ground-fault current path doesn't exceed 6 ft.

d. If flexibility is required to minimize the transmission of vibration from equipment or to provide flexibility for equipment that requires movement after installation, an equipment grounding conductor of the wire type must be installed with the circuit conductors in accordance with 250.102(E), and it must be sized in accordance with 250.122, based on the rating of the circuit overcurrent device.

(6) Listed liquidtight flexible metal conduit (LFMC) can serve as an equipment grounding conductor where: Figure 250–100

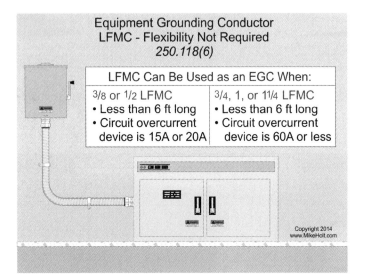

Figure 250–100

a. The raceway terminates in listed fittings.

b. For trade sizes ⅜ through ½, the circuit conductors are protected by an overcurrent device rated 20A or less.

c. For trade sizes ¾ through 1¼, the circuit conductors are protected by an overcurrent device rated 60A or less.

d. The combined length of the flexible conduit in the same ground-fault current path doesn't exceed 6 ft.

e. If flexibility is required to minimize the transmission of vibration from equipment or to provide flexibility for equipment that requires movement after installation, an equipment grounding conductor of the wire type must

be installed with the circuit conductors in accordance with 250.102(E), and it must be sized in accordance with 250.122, based on the rating of the circuit overcurrent device.

(8) The sheath of Type AC cable containing an aluminum bonding strip can serve as an equipment grounding conductor. Figure 250–101

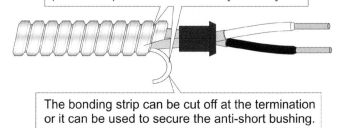

Figure 250–101

Author's Comment:

■ The internal aluminum bonding strip isn't an equipment grounding conductor, but it allows the interlocked armor to serve as an equipment grounding conductor because it reduces the impedance of the armored spirals to ensure that a ground fault will be cleared. It's the aluminum bonding strip in combination with the cable armor that creates the circuit equipment grounding conductor. Once the bonding strip exits the cable, it can be cut off because it no longer serves any purpose.

■ The effective ground-fault current path must be maintained by the use of fittings specifically listed for Type AC cable [320.40]. See 300.12, 300.15, and 320.100.

(9) The copper sheath of Type MI cable can serve as an equipment grounding conductor.

(10) Type MC cable if:

a. The interlock type cable that contains an insulated or uninsulated equipment grounding conductor in compliance with 250.118(1) can serve as an equipment grounding conductor. Figure 250–102

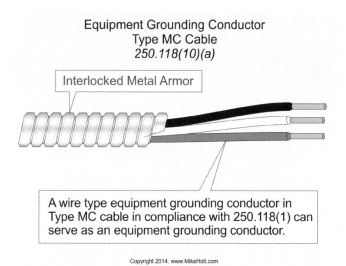

Figure 250–102

b. The combined metallic sheath and uninsulated equipment grounding/bonding conductor of interlocked metal is listed and identified as an equipment grounding conductor can serve as an equipment grounding conductor. Figure 250–103

Author's Comment:

■ Once the bare aluminum grounding/bonding conductor exits the cable, it can be cut off because it no longer serves any purpose. The effective ground-fault current path must be maintained by the use of fittings specifically listed for Type MCAP® cable [330.40]. See 300.12, 300.15, and 330.100. Figure 250–104

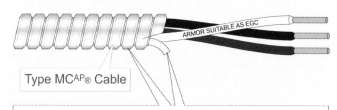

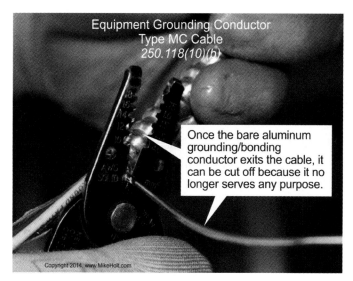

Figure 250–103

Figure 250–104

c. The metallic sheath of the smooth or corrugated tube-type MC cable that's listed and identified as an equipment grounding conductor can serve as an equipment grounding conductor.

(11) Metallic cable trays can serve as an equipment grounding conductor where continuous maintenance and supervision ensure only qualified persons will service the cable tray, with cable tray and fittings identified for grounding and the cable tray, fittings [392.10], and raceways are bonded using bolted mechanical connectors or bonding jumpers sized and installed in accordance with 250.102 [392.60].

(13) Listed electrically continuous metal raceways, such as metal wireways [Article 376] or strut-type channel raceways [384.60] can serve as an equipment grounding conductor. Figure 250–105

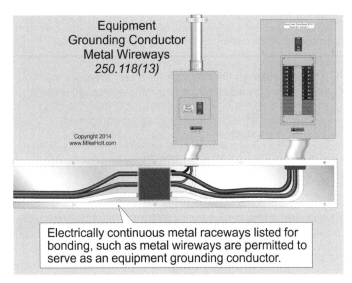

Figure 250–105

(14) Surface metal raceways listed for grounding [Article 386] can serve as an equipment grounding conductor.

250.119 Identification of Equipment Grounding Conductors

Unless required to be insulated, equipment grounding conductors can be bare or covered. Insulated equipment grounding conductors must have a continuous outer finish that's either green or green with one or more yellow stripes. Figure 250–106

Conductors with insulation that's green, or green with one or more yellow stripes, aren't permitted to be used for an ungrounded or neutral conductor. Figure 250–107

Author's Comment:

- The *NEC* neither requires nor prohibits the use of the color green for the identification of grounding electrode conductors.

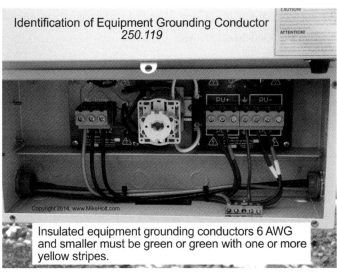

Figure 250–106

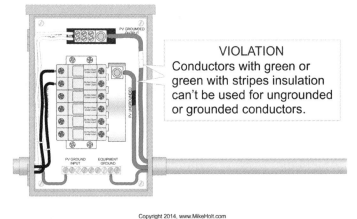

Figure 250–107

(A) Conductors 4 AWG and Larger.

(1) Identified if Accessible. Insulated equipment grounding conductors 4 AWG and larger can be permanently reidentified at the time of installation at every point where the conductor is accessible. Figure 250–108

Ex: Identification of equipment grounding conductors 4 AWG and larger in conduit bodies isn't required.

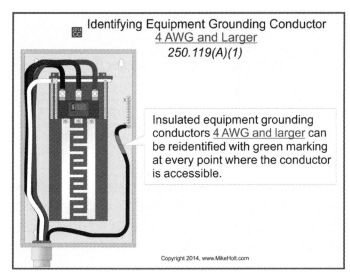

Figure 250–108

(2) Identification Method. Figure 250–109

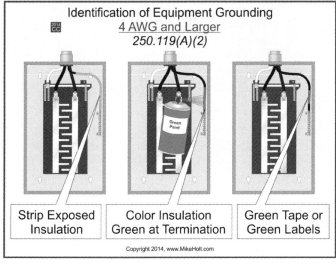

Figure 250–109

a. Removing the insulation from the entire exposed length

b. Coloring the insulation green at termination

c. Marking the insulation at termination with green tape or green adhesive labels

2014 CHANGE ANALYSIS: 250.119(A) was also revised to change the phrase "larger than 6 AWG" to "4 AWG and larger." Although it seems absurd, it really is easier for most people (myself included) to visualize and immediately understand "4 AWG and larger" rather than "larger than 6 AWG."

250.120 Equipment Grounding Conductor Installation

An equipment grounding conductor must be installed as follows:

(A) Raceway, Cable Trays, Cable Armor, Cablebus, or Cable Sheaths. If it consists of a raceway, cable tray, cable armor, cablebus framework, or cable sheath, fittings for joints and terminations must be made tight using suitable tools.

(C) Equipment Grounding Conductors Smaller Than 6 AWG. If not routed with circuit conductors as permitted in 250.130(C) and 250.134(B) Ex 2, equipment grounding conductors smaller than 6 AWG must be installed in a raceway or cable if subject to physical damage. Figure 250–110

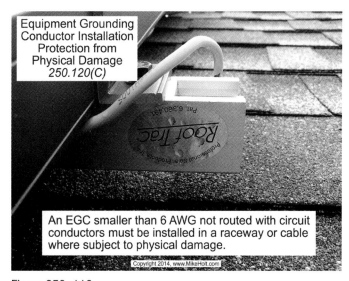

Figure 250–110

250.122 Sizing Equipment Grounding Conductor

(A) General. Equipment grounding conductors of the wire type must be sized not smaller than shown in Table 250.122, based on the rating of the circuit overcurrent device; however, the circuit equipment grounding conductor isn't required to be larger than the circuit conductors. Figure 250–111

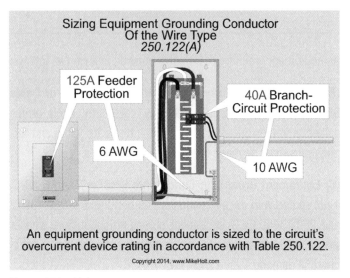

Figure 250–111

Table 250.122 Sizing Equipment Grounding Conductor

Overcurrent Device Rating	Copper Conductor
15A	14 AWG
20A	12 AWG
25A—60A	10 AWG
70A—100A	8 AWG
110A—200A	6 AWG
225A—300A	4 AWG
350A—400A	3 AWG
450A—500A	2 AWG
600A	1 AWG

Table 250.122 Sizing Equipment Grounding Conductor (continued)

Overcurrent Device Rating	Copper Conductor
700A—800A	1/0 AWG
1,000A	2/0 AWG
1,200A	3/0 AWG

(C) Multiple Circuits. When multiple circuits are installed in the same raceway, cable, or cable tray, one equipment grounding conductor sized in accordance with 250.122, based on the rating of the largest circuit overcurrent device is sufficient. Figure 250–112

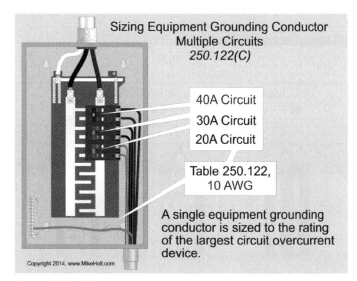

Figure 250–112

(F) Parallel Runs. If circuit conductors are installed in parallel in separate raceways or cable as permitted by 310.10(H), an equipment grounding conductor must be installed for each parallel conductor set. The equipment grounding conductor in each raceway or cable must be sized in accordance with Table 250.122, based on the rating of the circuit overcurrent device, but it's not required to be larger than the circuit conductors [250.122(A)]. Figure 250–113

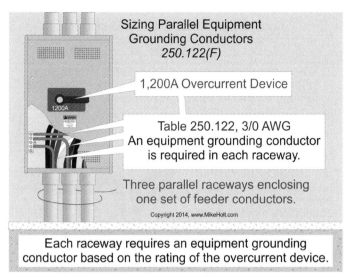

Figure 250–113

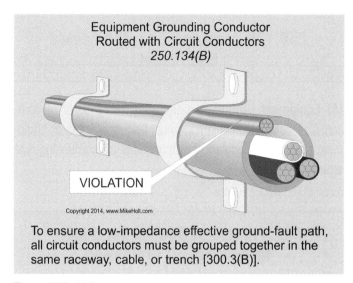

To ensure a low-impedance effective ground-fault path, all circuit conductors must be grouped together in the same raceway, cable, or trench [300.3(B)].

Figure 250–114

Part VII. Methods of Equipment Grounding

250.134 Equipment Connected by Permanent Wiring Methods

Except as permitted for services or separately derived systems (transformers) [250.142(A)], metal parts of equipment, raceways, and enclosures must be connected to an equipment grounding conductor by one of the following methods:

(A) Equipment Grounding Conductor Types. By connecting to one of the equipment grounding conductors identified in 250.118.

(B) With Circuit Conductors. If an equipment grounding conductor of the wire type is installed, it must be in the same raceway, cable tray, trench, cable, or cord with the circuit conductors in accordance with 300.3(B).

Author's Comment:

■ All conductors of a circuit must be installed in the same raceway, cable, trench, cord, or cable tray to minimize induction heating of ferrous metal raceways and enclosures, and to maintain a low-impedance ground-fault current path [250.4(A)(3)]. Figure 250–114

Ex 2: For dc circuits, the equipment grounding conductor is permitted to be run separately from the circuit conductors. Figure 250–115

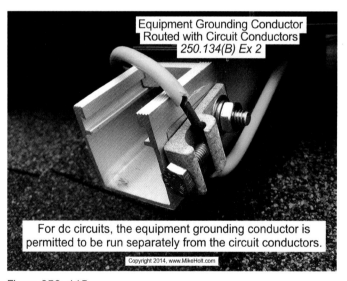

For dc circuits, the equipment grounding conductor is permitted to be run separately from the circuit conductors.

Figure 250–115

250.136 Equipment Considered Grounded

(A) Equipment Secured to Grounded Metal Supports. The structural metal frame of a building must not be used as the required equipment grounding conductor.

250.138 Cord-and-Plug-Connected Equipment

(A) Equipment Grounding Conductor. Metal parts of cord-and-plug-connected equipment must be connected to an equipment grounding conductor that terminates to a grounding-type attachment plug.

250.142 Use of Neutral Conductor for Equipment Grounding

(A) Supply-Side Equipment.

(1) Service Equipment. The neutral conductor can be used as the circuit equipment grounding conductor on the supply side or within the enclosure of the service disconnect in accordance with 250.24(B).

(B) Load-Side Equipment. Except as permitted in 250.30(A)(1) for separately derived systems (transformers) and 250.32(B) Ex, for separate buildings/structures, the neutral conductor isn't permitted to serve as an equipment grounding conductor on the load side of service equipment.

250.148 Continuity and Attachment of Equipment Grounding Conductors in Metal Boxes

If circuit conductors are spliced or terminated on equipment within a metal box, the equipment grounding conductor associated with those circuits must be connected to the box in accordance with the following: Figure 250–116

(A) Splicing. Equipment grounding conductors must be spliced together with a device listed for the purpose [110.14(B)]. Figure 250–117

Continuity and Attachment of Equipment Grounding Conductors to Metal Boxes
250.148

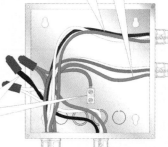

Where circuit conductors aren't spliced or terminated in the box, equipment grounding conductors can pass through without terminating to the box.

Where circuit conductors are spliced or terminated on equipment in the box, equipment grounding conductors must terminate to the box.

Copyright 2014, www.MikeHolt.com

Figure 250–116

Splicing Equipment Grounding Conductors
250.148(A)

Splices for equipment grounding conductors must be made with a splicing device identified for the purpose.

Copyright 2014, www.MikeHolt.com

Figure 250–117

Author's Comment:

■ Wire connectors of any color can be used with equipment grounding conductor splices, but green wire connectors can only be used with equipment grounding conductors since they're only tested for that application.

(B) Grounding Continuity. Equipment grounding conductors must terminate in a manner such that the disconnection or the removal of a receptacle, luminaire, or other device won't interrupt the grounding continuity.

(C) Metal Boxes. Terminating equipment grounding conductors within metal boxes must be with a grounding screw that's not used for any other purpose, a fitting listed for grounding, or a listed grounding device such as a ground clip. Figure 250–118

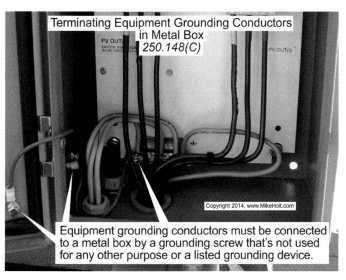

Figure 250–118

Part VIII. Direct-Current Systems

250.166 Sizing Grounding Electrode Conductor

Except as permitted in (C) through (E), the grounding electrode conductor must be sized in accordance with 250.166(A) and (B), but not required to be larger than 3/0 copper or 250 kcmil aluminum.

> **2014 CHANGE ANALYSIS:** In order to coincide with ac systems, the grounding electrode conductor is now never required to be larger than 3/0 copper or 250 kcmil aluminum. This matches the requirements found in 250.66 for ac systems.

(B) Not Smaller Than 8 AWG. The grounding electrode conductor isn't permitted to be smaller than the largest ungrounded dc conductor, and not smaller than 8 AWG copper.

(C) Rod. If the grounding electrode conductor is connected to one or more rods as permitted in 250.52(A)(5), that portion of the grounding electrode conductor that's the sole connection to the rod(s) isn't required to be larger than 6 AWG copper. Figure 250–119

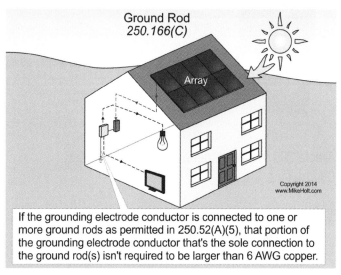

Figure 250–119

(D) Concrete-Encased Grounding Electrode. If the grounding electrode conductor is connected to one or more concrete-encased electrodes as permitted in 250.52(A)(3), that portion of the grounding electrode conductor that's the sole connection to the concrete-encased electrode(s) isn't required to be larger than 4 AWG copper. Figure 250–120

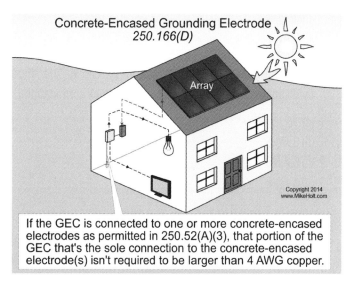

Figure 250–120

CHAPTER 2 PRACTICE QUESTIONS

Please use the 2014 *Code* book to answer the following questions.

Article 200. Use and Identification of Grounded Conductors

1. Article 200 contains the requirements for _____.

   (a) identification of terminals
   (b) grounded conductors in premises wiring systems
   (c) identification of grounded conductors
   (d) all of these

2. An insulated grounded conductor of _____ or smaller shall be identified by a continuous white or gray outer finish, or by three continuous white or gray stripes along its entire length on other than green insulation.

   (a) 8 AWG
   (b) 6 AWG
   (c) 4 AWG
   (d) 3 AWG

3. Grounded conductors _____ and larger can be identified by distinctive white or gray markings at their terminations.

   (a) 10 AWG
   (b) 8 AWG
   (c) 6 AWG
   (d) 4 AWG

Article 230. Services

1. Wiring methods permitted for service-entrance conductors include _____.

   (a) rigid metal conduit
   (b) electrical metallic tubing
   (c) PVC conduit
   (d) all of these

2. Service-entrance conductors can be spliced or tapped by clamped or bolted connections at any time as long as _____.

   (a) the free ends of conductors are covered with an insulation that is equivalent to that of the conductors or with an insulating device identified for the purpose
   (b) wire connectors or other splicing means installed on conductors that are buried in the earth are listed for direct burial
   (c) no splice is made in a raceway
   (d) all of these

3. The service disconnecting means shall be marked as suitable for use as service equipment and shall be _____.

   (a) weatherproof
   (b) listed
   (c) approved
   (d) acceptable

4. A service disconnecting means shall be installed at a(n) _____ location.

   (a) dry
   (b) readily accessible
   (c) outdoor
   (d) indoor

5. A service disconnecting means shall not be installed in bathrooms.

   (a) True
   (b) False

6. Where a remote-control device actuates the service disconnecting means, the service disconnecting means must still be at a readily accessible location either outside the building or structure, or nearest the point of entry of the service conductors.

   (a) True
   (b) False

7. Each service disconnecting means shall be permanently _____ to identify it as a service disconnect.

   (a) identified
   (b) positioned
   (c) marked
   (d) none of these

8. Each service disconnecting means shall be suitable for _____.

   (a) hazardous (classified) locations
   (b) wet locations
   (c) dry locations
   (d) the prevailing conditions

9. There shall be no more than _____ disconnects installed for each service or for each set of service-entrance conductors as permitted in 230.2 and 230.40.

   (a) two
   (b) four
   (c) six
   (d) eight

10. When the service contains two to six service disconnecting means, they shall be _____.

    (a) the same size
    (b) grouped
    (c) in the same enclosure
    (d) none of these

11. The additional service disconnecting means for fire pumps, emergency systems, legally required standby, or optional standby services, shall be installed remote from the one to six service disconnecting means for normal service to minimize the possibility of _____ interruption of supply.

    (a) intentional
    (b) accidental
    (c) simultaneous
    (d) prolonged

12. When the service disconnecting means is a power-operated switch or circuit breaker, it shall be able to be opened by hand in the event of a _____.

    (a) ground fault
    (b) short circuit
    (c) power surge
    (d) power supply failure

13. The service disconnecting means shall plainly indicate whether it is in the _____ position.

    (a) open or closed
    (b) tripped
    (c) up or down
    (d) correct

14. The service conductors shall be connected to the service disconnecting means by _____ or other approved means.

    (a) pressure connectors
    (b) clamps
    (c) solder
    (d) a or b

15. A meter disconnect switch located ahead of service equipment must have a short-circuit current rating equal to or greater than the available short-circuit current and be capable of interrupting the load served.

    (a) True
    (b) False

16. Electrical equipment shall not be connected to the supply side of the service disconnecting means, except for a few specific exceptions such as _____.

    (a) Type 1 surge protective devices
    (b) taps used to supply standby power systems, fire pump equipment, fire and sprinkler alarms, and load (energy) management devices
    (c) Solar photovoltaic systems
    (d) all of these

17. Each _____ service conductor shall have overload protection.

    (a) overhead
    (b) underground
    (c) ungrounded
    (d) none of these

Article 240. Overcurrent Protection

1. Overcurrent protection for conductors and equipment is designed to _____ the circuit if the current reaches a value that will cause an excessive or dangerous temperature in conductors or conductor insulation.

    (a) open
    (b) close
    (c) monitor
    (d) record

2. Conductor overload protection shall not be required where the interruption of the _____ would create a hazard, such as in a material-handling magnet circuit or fire pump circuit. However, short-circuit protection is required.

    (a) circuit
    (b) line
    (c) phase
    (d) system

3. The next higher standard rating overcurrent device above the ampacity of the ungrounded conductors being protected shall be permitted to be used, provided the _____.

    (a) conductors are not part of a branch circuit supplying more than one receptacle for cord-and-plug-connected portable loads
    (b) ampacity of the conductors doesn't correspond with the standard ampere rating of a fuse or circuit breaker
    (c) next higher standard rating selected doesn't exceed 800A
    (d) all of these

4. If the circuit's overcurrent device exceeds _____, the conductor ampacity must have a rating not less than the rating of the overcurrent device.

    (a) 800A
    (b) 1,000A
    (c) 1,200A
    (d) 2,000A

5. Overcurrent protection shall not exceed _____.

    (a) 15A for 14 AWG copper
    (b) 20A for 12 AWG copper
    (c) 30A for 10 AWG copper
    (d) all of these

6. Which of the following is not standard size fuses or inverse time circuit breakers?

    (a) 45A
    (b) 70A
    (c) 75A
    (d) 80A

7. The standard ampere ratings for fuses includes _____.

   (a) 1A
   (b) 6A
   (c) 601A
   (d) all of these

8. Supplementary overcurrent protection _____.

   (a) shall not be used in luminaires
   (b) may be used as a substitute for a branch-circuit overcurrent device
   (c) may be used to protect internal circuits of equipment
   (d) shall be readily accessible

9. Supplementary overcurrent devices used in luminaires or appliances are not required to be readily accessible.

   (a) True
   (b) False

10. A(n) _____ shall be considered equivalent to an overcurrent trip unit for the purpose of providing overcurrent protection of conductors.

    (a) current transformer
    (b) overcurrent relay
    (c) a and b
    (d) a or b

11. Conductors supplied under the tap rules are allowed to supply another conductor using the tap rules.

    (a) True
    (b) False

12. Tap conductors not over 25 ft shall be permitted, providing the _____.

    (a) ampacity of the tap conductors is not less than one-third the rating of the overcurrent device protecting the feeder conductors being tapped
    (b) tap conductors terminate in a single circuit breaker or set of fuses that limit the load to the ampacity of the tap conductors
    (c) tap conductors are suitably protected from physical damage
    (d) all of these

13. Outside feeder tap conductors can be of unlimited length without overcurrent protection at the point they receive their supply if the tap conductors _____.

    (a) are suitably protected from physical damage
    (b) terminate at a single circuit breaker or a single set of fuses that limits the load to the ampacity of the conductors
    (c) a and b
    (d) none of these

14. Overcurrent devices shall be _____.

    (a) accessible (as applied to wiring methods)
    (b) accessible (as applied to equipment)
    (c) readily accessible
    (d) inaccessible to unauthorized personnel

15. Overcurrent devices shall be readily accessible and installed so the center of the grip of the operating handle of the switch or circuit breaker, when in its highest position, is not more than _____ above the floor or working platform.

    (a) 2 ft
    (b) 4 ft 6 in.
    (c) 5 ft
    (d) 6 ft 7 in.

16. Overcurrent devices shall not be located _____.

    (a) where exposed to physical damage
    (b) near easily ignitible materials, such as in clothes closets
    (c) in bathrooms of dwelling units
    (d) all of these

17. Overcurrent devices aren't permitted to be located in the bathrooms of _____.

    (a) dwelling units
    (b) dormitories
    (c) guest rooms or guest suites of hotels or motels
    (d) all of these

18. _____ shall not be located over the steps of a stairway.

    (a) Disconnect switches
    (b) Overcurrent devices
    (c) Knife switches
    (d) Transformers

19. Enclosures for overcurrent devices shall be mounted in a _____ position unless impracticable.

    (a) vertical
    (b) horizontal
    (c) vertical or horizontal
    (d) there are no requirements

20. Fuseholders for cartridge fuses shall be so designed that it is difficult to put a fuse of any given class into a fuseholder that is designed for a _____ lower or a _____ higher than that of the class to which the fuse belongs.

    (a) voltage, wattage
    (b) wattage, voltage
    (c) voltage, current
    (d) current, voltage

21. Fuses shall be marked with their _____.

    (a) ampere and voltage rating
    (b) interrupting rating where other than 10,000A
    (c) name or trademark of the manufacturer
    (d) all of these

22. An 800A fuse rated at 1,000V _____ on a 250V system.

    (a) shall not be used
    (b) shall be used
    (c) can be used
    (d) none of these

23. Cartridge fuses and fuseholders shall be classified according to their _____ ranges.

    (a) voltage
    (b) amperage
    (c) a or b
    (d) a and b

24. Circuit breakers shall be capable of being closed and opened by manual operation. Operation by other means, such as electrical or pneumatic, shall be permitted if means for _____ operation is also provided.

    (a) automated
    (b) timed
    (c) manual
    (d) shunt trip

25. Where the circuit breaker handles are operated vertically, the up position of the handle shall be the _____ position.

    (a) on
    (b) off
    (c) tripped
    (d) any of these

26. A(n) _____ shall be of such design that any alteration of its trip point (calibration) or the time required for its operation requires dismantling of the device or breaking of a seal for other than intended adjustments.

    (a) Type S fuse
    (b) Edison-base fuse
    (c) circuit breaker
    (d) fuseholder

27. Circuit breakers shall be marked with their ampere rating in a manner that is durable and visible after installation. Such marking can be made visible by removal of a _____.

    (a) trim
    (b) cover
    (c) box
    (d) a or b

28. A circuit breaker having an interrupting current rating of other than _____ shall have its interrupting rating marked on the circuit breaker.

    (a) 5,000A
    (b) 10,000A
    (c) 22,000A
    (d) 50,000A

Article 250. Grounding and Bonding

Part I. General

1. Grounded electrical systems shall be connected to earth in a manner that will _____.

   (a) limit voltages due to lightning, line surges, or unintentional contact with higher-voltage lines
   (b) stabilize the voltage-to-ground during normal operation
   (c) facilitate overcurrent device operation in case of ground faults
   (d) a and b

2. An important consideration for limiting imposed voltage on electrical systems is to remember that bonding and grounding electrode conductors shouldn't be any longer than necessary and unnecessary bends and loops should be avoided.

   (a) True
   (b) False

3. For grounded systems, normally noncurrent-carrying conductive materials enclosing electrical conductors or equipment shall be connected to earth so as to limit the voltage-to-ground on these materials.

   (a) True
   (b) False

4. For grounded systems, normally noncurrent-carrying conductive materials enclosing electrical conductors or equipment, or forming part of such equipment, shall be connected together and to the _____ to establish an effective ground-fault current path.

   (a) ground
   (b) earth
   (c) electrical supply source
   (d) none of these

5. In grounded systems, normally noncurrent-carrying electrically conductive materials that are likely to become energized shall be _____ in a manner that establishes an effective ground-fault current path.

   (a) connected together
   (b) connected to the electrical supply source
   (c) connected to the closest grounded conductor
   (d) a and b

6. For grounded systems, electrical equipment and other electrically conductive material likely to become energized, shall be installed in a manner that creates a _____ from any point on the wiring system where a ground fault may occur to the electrical supply source.

   (a) circuit facilitating the operation of the overcurrent device
   (b) low-impedance circuit
   (c) circuit capable of safely carrying the ground-fault current likely to be imposed on it
   (d) all of these

7. For grounded systems, electrical equipment and electrically conductive material likely to become energized, shall be installed in a manner that creates a low-impedance circuit capable of safely carrying the maximum ground-fault current likely to be imposed on it from where a ground fault may occur to the _____.

   (a) ground
   (b) earth
   (c) electrical supply source
   (d) none of these

8. For grounded systems, the earth is considered an effective ground-fault current path.

   (a) True
   (b) False

9. For ungrounded systems, noncurrent-carrying conductive materials enclosing electrical conductors or equipment shall be connected to the _____ in a manner that will limit the voltage imposed by lightning or unintentional contact with higher-voltage lines.

    (a) ground
    (b) earth
    (c) electrical supply source
    (d) none of these

10. For ungrounded systems, noncurrent-carrying conductive materials enclosing electrical conductors or equipment, or forming part of such equipment, shall be connected together and to the supply system equipment in a manner that creates a low-impedance path for ground-fault current that is capable of carrying _____.

    (a) the maximum branch-circuit current
    (b) at least twice the maximum ground-fault current
    (c) the maximum fault current likely to be imposed on it
    (d) the equivalent to the main service rating

11. Electrically conductive materials that are likely to _____ in ungrounded systems shall be connected together and to the supply system grounded equipment in a manner that creates a low-impedance path for ground-fault current that is capable of carrying the maximum fault current likely to be imposed on it.

    (a) become energized
    (b) require service
    (c) be removed
    (d) be coated with paint or nonconductive materials

12. In ungrounded systems, electrical equipment, wiring, and other electrically conductive material likely to become energized shall be installed in a manner that creates a low-impedance circuit from any point on the wiring system to the electrical supply source to facilitate the operation of overcurrent devices should a(n) _____ fault from a different phase occur on the wiring system.

    (a) isolated ground
    (b) second ground
    (c) arc
    (d) high impedance

13. Equipment grounding conductors, grounding electrode conductors, and bonding jumpers shall be connected by _____.

    (a) listed pressure connectors
    (b) terminal bars
    (c) exothermic welding
    (d) any of these

14. Grounding and bonding connection devices that depend solely on _____ shall not be used.

    (a) pressure connections
    (b) solder
    (c) lugs
    (d) approved clamps

15. Ground clamps and fittings that are exposed to physical damage shall be enclosed in _____.

    (a) metal
    (b) wood
    (c) the equivalent of a or b
    (d) none of these

16. _____ on equipment to be grounded shall be removed from contact surfaces to ensure good electrical continuity.

    (a) Paint
    (b) Lacquer
    (c) Enamel
    (d) any of these

Part II. System Grounding and Bonding

17. The grounding electrode conductor shall be connected to the grounded service conductor at the _____.

    (a) load end of the service drop
    (b) load end of the service lateral
    (c) service disconnecting means
    (d) any of these

18. Where the main bonding jumper is installed from the grounded conductor terminal bar to the equipment grounding terminal bar in service equipment, the _____ conductor is permitted to be connected to the equipment grounding terminal bar.

    (a) grounding
    (b) grounded
    (c) grounding electrode
    (d) none of these

19. For a grounded system, an unspliced _____ shall be used to connect the equipment grounding conductor(s) and the service disconnecting means to the grounded conductor of the system within the enclosure for each service disconnect.

    (a) grounding electrode
    (b) main bonding jumper
    (c) busbar
    (d) insulated copper conductor

20. Where an alternating-current system operating at 1,000V or less is grounded at any point, the _____ conductor(s) shall be routed with the ungrounded conductors to each service disconnecting means and shall be connected to each disconnecting means grounded conductor(s) terminal or bus.

    (a) ungrounded
    (b) grounded
    (c) grounding
    (d) none of these

21. The grounded conductor of an alternating-current system operating at 1,000V or less shall be routed with the ungrounded conductors and connected to each disconnecting means grounded conductor terminal or bus, which is then connected to the service disconnecting means enclosure via a(n) _____ that's installed between the service neutral conductor and the service disconnecting means enclosure.

    (a) equipment bonding conductor
    (b) main bonding jumper
    (c) grounding electrode
    (d) intersystem bonding terminal

22. The grounded conductor brought to service equipment shall be routed with the phase conductors and shall not be smaller than specified in Table _____ when the service-entrance conductors are 1,100 kcmil copper and smaller.

    (a) 250.102(C)(1)
    (b) 250.122
    (c) 310.16
    (d) 430.52

23. When service-entrance conductors exceed 1,100 kcmil for copper, the required grounded conductor for the service shall be sized not less than _____ percent of the circular mil area of the largest set of ungrounded service-entrance conductor(s).

    (a) 9
    (b) 11
    (c) 12½
    (d) 15

24. Where service-entrance phase conductors are installed in parallel in two or more raceways, the size of the grounded conductor in each raceway shall be based on the total circular mil area of the parallel ungrounded service-entrance conductors in the raceway, sized in accordance with 250.24(C)(1), but not smaller than _____.

    (a) 1/0 AWG
    (b) 2/0 AWG
    (c) 3/0 AWG
    (d) 4/0 AWG

25. A grounding electrode conductor, sized in accordance with 250.66, shall be used to connect the equipment grounding conductors, the service-equipment enclosures, and, where the system is grounded, the grounded service conductor to the grounding electrode(s).

    (a) True
    (b) False

26. A main bonding jumper shall be a _____ or similar suitable conductor.

    (a) wire
    (b) bus
    (c) screw
    (d) any of these

27. Where a main bonding jumper is a screw only, the screw shall be identified by a(n) _____ that shall be visible with the screw installed.

    (a) silver or white finish
    (b) etched ground symbol
    (c) hexagonal head
    (d) green finish

28. Main bonding jumpers and system bonding jumpers shall not be smaller than specified in _____.

    (a) Table 250.102(C)(1)
    (b) Table 250.122
    (c) Table 310.15(B)(16)
    (d) Chapter 9, Table 8

29. Where the supply conductors are larger than 1,100 kcmil copper or 1,750 kcmil aluminum, the main bonding jumper shall have an area that is _____ the area of the largest phase conductor when of the same material.

    (a) at least equal to
    (b) at least 50 percent of
    (c) not less than 12½ percent of
    (d) not more than 12½ percent of

30. A grounded conductor shall not be connected to normally noncurrent-carrying metal parts of equipment on the _____ side of the system bonding jumper of a separately derived system except as otherwise permitted in Article 250.

    (a) supply
    (b) grounded
    (c) high-voltage
    (d) load

31. An unspliced _____ that is sized based on the derived phase conductors shall be used to connect the grounded conductor and the supply-side bonding jumper, or the equipment grounding conductor, or both, at a separately derived system.

    (a) system bonding jumper
    (b) equipment grounding conductor
    (c) grounded conductor
    (d) grounding electrode conductor

32. The connection of the system bonding jumper for a separately derived system shall be made _____ on the separately derived system from the source to the first system disconnecting means or overcurrent device.

    (a) in at least two locations
    (b) in every location that the grounded conductor is present
    (c) at any single point
    (d) none of these

33. Where a supply-side bonding jumper of the wire type is run with the derived phase conductors from the source of a separately derived system to the first disconnecting means, it shall be sized in accordance with 250.102(C), based on _____.

    (a) the size of the primary conductors
    (b) the size of the secondary overcurrent protection
    (c) the size of the derived ungrounded conductors
    (d) one third the size of the primary grounded conductor

34. The grounding electrode for a separately derived system shall be as near as practicable to, and preferably in the same area as, the grounding electrode conductor connection to the system.

    (a) True
    (b) False

35. For a single separately derived system, the grounding electrode conductor connects the grounded conductor of the derived system to the grounding electrode at the same point on the separately derived system where the _____ is connected.

    (a) metering equipment
    (b) transfer switch
    (c) system bonding jumper
    (d) largest circuit breaker

36. The grounding electrode conductor for a single separately derived system is used to connect the grounded conductor of the derived system to the grounding electrode.

    (a) True
    (b) False

37. Grounding electrode conductor taps from a separately derived system to a common grounding electrode conductor are permitted when a building or structure has multiple separately derived systems, provided that the taps terminate at the same point as the system bonding jumper.

    (a) True
    (b) False

38. The common grounding electrode conductor installed for multiple separately derived systems shall not be smaller than _____ copper when using a wire-type conductor.

    (a) 1/0 AWG
    (b) 2/0 AWG
    (c) 3/0 AWG
    (d) 4/0 AWG

39. Each tap conductor to a common grounding electrode conductor for multiple separately derived systems shall be sized in accordance with _____, based on the derived ungrounded conductors of the separately derived system it serves.

    (a) 250.66
    (b) 250.118
    (c) 250.122
    (d) 310.15

40. Tap connections to a common grounding electrode conductor for multiple separately derived systems shall be made at an accessible location by _____.

    (a) a connector listed as grounding and bonding equipment
    (b) listed connections to aluminum or copper busbars
    (c) the exothermic welding process
    (d) any of these

41. Tap connections to a common grounding electrode conductor for multiple separately derived systems may be made to a copper or aluminum busbar that is _____.

    (a) smaller than ¼ in. x 4 in.
    (b) not smaller than ¼ in. x 2 in.
    (c) not smaller than ½ in. x 2 in.
    (d) a and c

42. In an area served by a separately derived system, the _____ shall be connected to the grounded conductor of the separately derived system.

    (a) structural steel
    (b) metal piping
    (c) metal building skin
    (d) a and b

Part III. Grounding Electrode System and Grounding Electrode Conductor

43. Concrete-encased electrodes of _____ shall not be required to be part of the grounding electrode system where the steel reinforcing bars or rods aren't accessible for use without disturbing the concrete.

    (a) hazardous (classified) locations
    (b) health care facilities
    (c) existing buildings or structures
    (d) agricultural buildings with equipotential planes

44. In order for a metal underground water pipe to be used as a grounding electrode, it shall be in direct contact with the earth for _____.

    (a) 5 ft
    (b) 10 ft or more
    (c) less than 10 ft
    (d) 20 ft or more

45. The metal frame of a building shall be considered a grounding electrode where one of the *NEC*-prescribed methods for connection of the metal frame to earth has been met.

    (a) True
    (b) False

46. A bare 4 AWG copper conductor installed horizontally near the bottom or vertically, and within that portion of a concrete foundation or footing that is in direct contact with the earth can be used as a grounding electrode when the conductor is at least _____ ft in length.

    (a) 10
    (b) 15
    (c) 20
    (d) 25

47. An electrode encased by at least 2 in. of concrete, located horizontally near the bottom or vertically and within that portion of a concrete foundation or footing that is in direct contact with the earth, shall be permitted as a grounding electrode when it consists of _____.

    (a) at least 20 ft of ½ in. or larger steel reinforcing bars or rods
    (b) at least 20 ft of bare copper conductor of 4 AWG or larger
    (c) a or b
    (d) none of these

48. Reinforcing bars for use as a concrete-encased electrode can be bonded together by the usual steel tie wires or other effective means.

    (a) True
    (b) False

49. Where more than one concrete-encased electrode is present at a building or structure, it shall be permitted to connect to only one of them.

    (a) True
    (b) False

50. A ground ring encircling the building or structure can be used as a grounding electrode when _____.

    (a) the ring is in direct contact with the earth
    (b) the ring consists of at least 20 ft of bare copper conductor
    (c) the bare copper conductor is not smaller than 2 AWG
    (d) all of these

51. Grounding electrodes of the rod type less than _____ in. in diameter shall be listed.

    (a) ½ in.
    (b) ⅝ in.
    (c) ¾ in.
    (d) none of these

52. A buried iron or steel plate used as a grounding electrode shall expose not less than _____ of surface area to exterior soil.

    (a) 2 sq ft
    (b) 4 sq ft
    (c) 9 sq ft
    (d) 10 sq ft

53. Local metal underground systems or structures such as _____ are permitted to serve as grounding electrodes.

    (a) piping systems
    (b) underground tanks
    (c) underground metal well casings that are not bonded to a metal water pipe
    (d) all of these

54. _____ shall not be used as grounding electrodes.

    (a) Metal underground gas piping systems
    (b) Aluminum
    (c) Metal well casings
    (d) a and b

55. Where practicable, rod, pipe, and plate electrodes shall be installed _____.

    (a) directly below the electrical meter
    (b) on the north side of the building
    (c) below permanent moisture level
    (d) all of these

56. Where the resistance-to-ground of 25 ohms or less is not achieved for a single rod electrode, _____.

    (a) other means besides electrodes shall be used in order to provide grounding
    (b) the single rod electrode shall be supplemented by one additional electrode
    (c) no additional electrodes are required
    (d) none of these

57. Two or more grounding electrodes bonded together are considered a single grounding electrode system.

    (a) True
    (b) False

58. Where a metal underground water pipe is used as a grounding electrode, the continuity of the grounding path or the bonding connection to interior piping shall not rely on _____ and similar equipment.

    (a) bonding jumpers
    (b) water meters or filtering devices
    (c) grounding clamps
    (d) all of these

59. Where the supplemental electrode is a rod, that portion of the bonding jumper that is the sole connection to the supplemental grounding electrode shall not be required to be larger than _____ AWG copper.

    (a) 8
    (b) 6
    (c) 4
    (d) 1

60. When a ground ring is used as a grounding electrode, it shall be buried at a depth below the earth's surface of not less than _____.

    (a) 18 in.
    (b) 24 in.
    (c) 30 in.
    (d) 8 ft

61. Ground rod electrodes shall be installed so that at least _____ of the length is in contact with the soil.

    (a) 5 ft
    (b) 8 ft
    (c) one-half
    (d) 80 percent

62. The upper end of a ground rod electrode shall be _____ ground level unless the aboveground end and the grounding electrode conductor attachment are protected against physical damage.

    (a) above
    (b) flush with
    (c) below
    (d) b or c

63. Where rock bottom is encountered when driving a ground rod at an angle up to 45 degrees, the electrode can be buried in a trench that is at least _____ deep.

    (a) 18 in.
    (b) 30 in.
    (c) 4 ft
    (d) 8 ft

64. Auxiliary grounding electrodes can be connected to the _____.

    (a) equipment grounding conductor
    (b) grounded conductor
    (c) a and b
    (d) none of these

65. When installing auxiliary electrodes, the earth shall not be used as an effective ground-fault current path.

    (a) True
    (b) False

66. Grounding electrode conductors of the wire type shall be _____.

    (a) solid
    (b) stranded
    (c) insulated or bare
    (d) any of these

67. Where used outside, aluminum or copper-clad aluminum grounding electrode conductors shall not be terminated within _____ of the earth.

    (a) 6 in.
    (b) 12 in.
    (c) 15 in.
    (d) 18 in.

68. Bare aluminum or copper-clad aluminum grounding electrode conductors shall not be used where in direct contact with _____ or where subject to corrosive conditions.

    (a) masonry or the earth
    (b) bare copper conductors
    (c) wooden framing members
    (d) all of these

69. Grounding electrode conductors _____ and larger that are not subject to physical damage can be run exposed along the surface of the building construction if it is securely fastened to the construction.

    (a) 10 AWG
    (b) 8 AWG
    (c) 6 AWG
    (d) 4 AWG

70. Grounding electrode conductors smaller than _____ shall be in rigid metal conduit, IMC, PVC conduit, electrical metallic tubing, or cable armor.

    (a) 10 AWG
    (b) 8 AWG
    (c) 6 AWG
    (d) 4 AWG

71. Grounding electrode conductors shall be installed in one continuous length without a splice or joint, unless spliced by _____.

    (a) connecting together sections of a busbar
    (b) irreversible compression-type connectors listed as grounding and bonding equipment
    (c) the exothermic welding process
    (d) any of these

72. Ferrous metal raceways and enclosures for grounding electrode conductors shall be electrically continuous from the point of attachment to cabinets or equipment to the grounding electrode.

    (a) True
    (b) False

73. A grounding electrode conductor shall be permitted to be run to any convenient grounding electrode available in the grounding electrode system where the other electrode(s), if any, is connected by bonding jumpers in accordance with 250.53(C).

    (a) True
    (b) False

74. A service consisting of 12 AWG service-entrance conductors requires a grounding electrode conductor sized no less than _____.

    (a) 10 AWG
    (b) 8 AWG
    (c) 6 AWG
    (d) 4 AWG

75. The largest size grounding electrode conductor required is _____ copper.

    (a) 6 AWG
    (b) 1/0 AWG
    (c) 3/0 AWG
    (d) 250 kcmil

76. What size copper grounding electrode conductor is required for a service that has three sets of 600 kcmil copper conductors per phase?

    (a) 1 AWG
    (b) 1/0 AWG
    (c) 2/0 AWG
    (d) 3/0 AWG

77. In an ac system, the size of the grounding electrode conductor to a concrete-encased electrode shall not be required to be larger than a(n) _____ copper conductor.

    (a) 10 AWG
    (b) 8 AWG
    (c) 6 AWG
    (d) 4 AWG

78. Mechanical elements used to terminate a grounding electrode conductor to a grounding electrode shall be accessible.

    (a) True
    (b) False

79. An encased or buried connection to a concrete-encased, driven, or buried grounding electrode shall be accessible.

    (a) True
    (b) False

80. The connection of the grounding electrode conductor to a buried grounding electrode (driven ground rod) shall be made with a listed terminal device that is accessible.

    (a) True
    (b) False

81. Exothermic or irreversible compression connections, together with the mechanical means used to attach to fire-proofed structural metal, shall not be required to be accessible.

    (a) True
    (b) False

82. When an underground metal water piping system is used as a grounding electrode, bonding shall be provided around insulated joints and around any equipment that is likely to be disconnected for repairs or replacement.

    (a) True
    (b) False

83. Interior metal water piping located not more than _____ from the point of entrance to the building shall be permitted to be used as a conductor to interconnect electrodes that are part of the grounding electrode system.

    (a) 2 ft
    (b) 4 ft
    (c) 5 ft
    (d) 6 ft

84. The grounding conductor connection to the grounding electrode shall be made by _____.

    (a) listed lugs
    (b) exothermic welding
    (c) listed pressure connectors
    (d) any of these

Part IV. Grounding Enclosure, Raceway, and Service Cable Connections

85. Metal enclosures and raceways for other than service conductors shall be connected to the neutral conductor.

    (a) True
    (b) False

86. Short sections of metal enclosures or raceways used to provide support or protection of _____ from physical damage shall not be required to be connected to the equipment grounding conductor.

    (a) conduit
    (b) feeders under 600V
    (c) cable assemblies
    (d) none of these

Part V. Bonding

87. Bonding shall be provided where necessary to ensure _____ and the capacity to conduct safely any fault current likely to be imposed.

    (a) electrical continuity
    (b) fiduciary responsibility
    (c) listing requirements
    (d) electrical demand

88. The normally noncurrent-carrying metal parts of service equipment, such as _____, shall be bonded together.

    (a) service raceways or service cable armor
    (b) service equipment enclosures containing service conductors, including meter fittings, boxes, or the like, interposed in the service raceway or armor
    (c) service cable trays
    (d) all of these

89. Bonding jumpers for service raceways shall be used around impaired connections such as _____.

    (a) oversized concentric knockouts
    (b) oversized eccentric knockouts
    (c) reducing washers
    (d) any of these

90. Electrical continuity at service equipment, service raceways, and service conductor enclosures shall be ensured by _____.

    (a) bonding equipment to the grounded service conductor
    (b) connections utilizing threaded couplings on enclosures, if made up wrenchtight
    (c) other listed bonding devices, such as bonding-type locknuts, bushings, or bushings with bonding jumpers
    (d) any of these

91. Service raceways threaded into metal service equipment such as bosses (hubs) are considered to be effectively _____ to the service metal enclosure.

    (a) attached
    (b) bonded
    (c) grounded
    (d) none of these

92. Service metal raceways and metal-clad cables are considered effectively bonded when using threadless couplings and connectors that are _____.

    (a) nonmetallic
    (b) made up tight
    (c) sealed
    (d) classified

93. When bonding enclosures, metal raceways, frames, and fittings, any nonconductive paint, enamel, or similar coating shall be removed at _____.

    (a) contact surfaces
    (b) threads
    (c) contact points
    (d) all of these

94. Equipment bonding jumpers shall be of copper or other corrosion-resistant material.

    (a) True
    (b) False

95. Equipment bonding jumpers on the supply side of the service shall be no smaller than the sizes shown in _____.

    (a) Table 250.102(C)(1)
    (b) Table 250.122
    (c) Table 310.15(B)(16)
    (d) Table 310.15(B)(6)

96. The supply-side bonding jumper on the supply side of services shall be sized according to the _____.

    (a) overcurrent device rating
    (b) ungrounded supply conductor size
    (c) service-drop size
    (d) load to be served

97. What is the minimum size copper supply-side bonding jumper for a service raceway containing 4/0 THHN aluminum conductors?

    (a) 6 AWG aluminum
    (b) 4 AWG aluminum
    (c) 4 AWG copper
    (d) 3 AWG copper

98. Where ungrounded supply conductors are paralleled in two or more raceways or cables, the bonding jumper for each raceway or cable shall be based on the size of the _____ in each raceway or cable.

    (a) overcurrent protection for conductors
    (b) grounded conductors
    (c) ungrounded supply conductors
    (d) sum of all conductors

99. A service is supplied by three metal raceways, each containing 600 kcmil ungrounded conductors. Determine the copper supply-side bonding jumper size for each service raceway.

    (a) 1/0 AWG
    (b) 3/0 AWG
    (c) 250 kcmil
    (d) 500 kcmil

100. What is the minimum size copper equipment bonding jumper for a 40A rated circuit?

    (a) 14 AWG
    (b) 12 AWG
    (c) 10 AWG
    (d) 8 AWG

101. An equipment bonding jumper can be installed on the outside of a raceway, providing the length of the equipment bonding jumper is not more than _____ and the equipment bonding jumper is routed with the raceway.

    (a) 12 in.
    (b) 24 in.
    (c) 36 in.
    (d) 72 in.

Part VI. Equipment Grounding and Equipment Grounding Conductors

102. Listed FMC can be used as the equipment grounding conductor if the length in any ground return path does not exceed 6 ft and the circuit conductors contained in the conduit are protected by overcurrent devices rated at _____ or less.

    (a) 15A
    (b) 20A
    (c) 30A
    (d) 60A

103. Listed FMC and LFMC shall contain an equipment grounding conductor if the raceway is installed for the reason of _____.

    (a) physical protection
    (b) flexibility after installation
    (c) minimizing transmission of vibration from equipment
    (d) b or c

104. The *Code* requires the installation of an equipment grounding conductor of the wire type in _____.

    (a) Rigid metal conduit (RMC).
    (b) Intermediate metal conduit (IMC).
    (c) Electrical metallic tubing (EMT).
    (d) Listed flexible metal conduit over 6 ft in length

105. Listed liquidtight flexible metal conduit (LFMC) is acceptable as an equipment grounding conductor when it terminates in listed fittings and is protected by an overcurrent device rated 60A or less for trade sizes ⅜ through ½.

    (a) True
    (b) False

106. The armor of Type AC cable containing an aluminum bonding strip is recognized by the *NEC* as an equipment grounding conductor.

    (a) True
    (b) False

107. Type MC cable provides an effective ground-fault current path and is recognized by the *NEC* as an equipment grounding conductor when _____.

    (a) it contains an insulated or uninsulated equipment grounding conductor in compliance with 250.118(1)
    (b) the combined metallic sheath and uninsulated equipment grounding/bonding conductor of interlocked metal tape–type MC cable is listed and identified as an equipment grounding conductor
    (c) only when it is hospital grade Type MC cable
    (d) a or b

108. An equipment grounding conductor shall be identified by _____.

    (a) a continuous outer finish that is green
    (b) being bare
    (c) a continuous outer finish that is green with one or more yellow stripes
    (d) any of these

109. Conductors with the color _____ insulation shall not be used for ungrounded or grounded conductors.

    (a) green
    (b) green with one or more yellow stripes
    (c) a or b
    (d) white

110. A wire-type equipment grounding conductor is permitted to be used as a grounding electrode conductor if it meets all the requirements of Parts II, III, and IV of Article 250.

    (a) True
    (b) False

111. The equipment grounding conductor shall not be required to be larger than the circuit conductors.

    (a) True
    (b) False

112. When a single equipment grounding conductor is used for multiple circuits in the same raceway, cable, or cable tray, the single equipment grounding conductor shall be sized according to the _____.

    (a) combined rating of all the overcurrent devices
    (b) largest overcurrent device of the multiple circuits
    (c) combined rating of all the loads
    (d) any of these

113. Where conductors are run in parallel in multiple raceways or cables and include an EGC of the wire type, the equipment grounding conductor must be installed in parallel in each raceway or cable, sized in compliance with 250.122.

    (a) True
    (b) False

114. Equipment grounding conductors for feeder taps are not required to be larger than the tap conductors.

    (a) True
    (b) False

Part VII. Methods of Equipment Grounding

115. The structural metal frame of a building can be used as the required equipment grounding conductor for ac equipment.

    (a) True
    (b) False

116. Metal parts of cord-and-plug-connected equipment shall be connected to an equipment grounding conductor that terminates to a grounding-type attachment plug.

    (a) True
    (b) False

117. A grounded circuit conductor is permitted to ground non-current-carrying metal parts of equipment, raceways, and other enclosures on the supply side or within the enclosure of the ac service-disconnecting means.

    (a) True
    (b) False

118. Where circuit conductors are spliced or terminated on equipment within a box, any equipment grounding conductors associated with those circuit conductors shall be connected to the box with devices suitable for the use.

    (a) True
    (b) False

119. The arrangement of grounding connections shall be such that the disconnection or the removal of a receptacle, luminaire, or other device fed from the box does not interrupt the grounding continuity.

    (a) True
    (b) False

120. A connection between equipment grounding conductors and a metal box shall be by _____.

    (a) a grounding screw used for no other purpose
    (b) equipment listed for grounding
    (c) a listed grounding device
    (d) any of these

CHAPTER 3

WIRING METHODS AND MATERIALS

Introduction to Chapter 3—Wiring Methods and Materials

Chapter 3 covers wiring methods and materials, and provides some very specific installation requirements for conductors, cables, boxes, raceways, and fittings. This chapter includes detailed information about the installation and restrictions involved with wiring methods.

It may be because of those details that many people incorrectly apply the rules from this chapter. Be sure to pay careful attention to the details, and be sure that you make your installation comply with the rules in the *NEC*, not just completing it in the manner that you may have been taught or because "it's always been done that way." This is especially true when it comes to applying the Tables.

Violations of the rules for wiring methods found in Chapter 3 can result in problems with power quality and can lead to fire, shock, and other hazards.

The type of wiring method you'll use depends on several factors; job specifications, *Code* requirements, the environment, need, and cost are among them.

Chapter 3 begins with rules that are common to most wiring methods [Article 300]. It then covers conductors [Article 310] and enclosures [Articles 312 and 314]. The articles that follow become more specific and deal more in-depth with individual wiring methods such as specific types of cables [Articles 320 through 340] and various raceways [Articles 342 through 390]. The chapter winds up with Article 392, a support system, and the final articles [Articles 394 through 398] for open wiring.

Notice as you read through the various wiring methods that the *Code* attempts to use similar subsection numbering for similar topics from one article to the next, using the same digits after the decimal point in the section number for the same topic. This makes it easier to locate specific requirements in a particular article. For example, the rules for securing and supporting can be found in the section that ends with .30 of each article. In addition to this, you'll find a "uses permitted" and "uses not permitted" section in nearly every article.

Wiring Method Articles

- **Article 300—General Requirements for Wiring Methods and Materials.** Article 300 contains the general requirements for all wiring methods included in the *NEC*, except for signaling and communications systems, which are covered in Chapters 7 and 8.

- **Article 310—Conductors for General Wiring.** This article contains the general requirements for conductors, such as insulation markings, ampacity ratings, and conductor use. Article 310 doesn't apply to conductors that are part of flexible cords, fixture wires, or conductors that are an integral part of equipment [90.6 and 300.1(B)].

- **Article 312—Cabinets, Cutout Boxes, and Meter Socket Enclosures.** Article 312 covers the installation and construction specifications for cabinets, cutout boxes, and meter socket enclosures.

- **Article 314—Outlet, Device, Pull, and Junction Boxes, Conduit Bodies, Fittings, and Handhole Enclosures.** Installation requirements for outlet boxes, pull and junction boxes, as well as conduit bodies, and handhole enclosures are contained in this article.

Cable Articles

Articles 320 through 340 address specific types of cables. If you take the time to become familiar with the various types of cables, you'll:

- Understand what's available for doing the work.
- Recognize cable types that have special *NEC* requirements.
- Avoid buying cable that you can't install due to *Code* requirements you can't meet with that particular wiring method.

Here's a brief overview of each one:

- **Article 320—Armored Cable (Type AC).** Armored cable is an assembly of insulated conductors, 14 AWG through 1 AWG, individually wrapped with waxed paper. The conductors are contained within a flexible spiral metal (steel or aluminum) sheath that interlocks at the edges. Armored cable looks like flexible metal conduit. Many electricians call this metal cable "BX®."

- **Article 330—Metal-Clad Cable (Type MC).** Metal-clad cable encloses insulated conductors in a metal sheath of either corrugated or smooth copper or aluminum tubing, or spiral interlocked steel or aluminum. The physical characteristics of Type MC cable make it a versatile wiring method permitted in almost any location and for almost any application. The most commonly used Type MC cable is the interlocking kind, which looks similar to armored cable or flexible metal conduit.

- **Article 334—Nonmetallic-Sheathed Cable (Type NM).** Nonmetallic-sheathed cable encloses two, three, or four insulated conductors, 14 AWG through 2 AWG, within a nonmetallic outer jacket. Because this cable is nonmetallic, it contains a separate equipment grounding conductor. Nonmetallic-sheathed cable is a common wiring method used for residential and commercial branch circuits. Many electricians call this plastic-sheathed cable "Romex®."

- **Article 338—Service-Entrance Cable (Types SE and USE).** Service-entrance cable can be a single-conductor or a multiconductor assembly within an overall nonmetallic covering. This cable is used primarily for services not over 600V, but is also permitted for feeders and branch circuits.

- **Article 340—Underground Feeder and Branch-Circuit Cable (Type UF).** Underground feeder cable is a moisture-, fungus-, and corrosion-resistant cable suitable for direct burial in the earth, and it comes in sizes 14 AWG through 4/0 AWG [340.104]. Multiconductor UF cable is covered in molded plastic that surrounds the insulated conductors.

Raceway Articles

Articles 342 through 390 address specific types of raceways. Refer to Article 100 for the definition of a raceway. If you take the time to become familiar with the various types of raceways, you'll:

- Understand what's available for doing the work.
- Recognize raceway types that have special *Code* requirements.
- Avoid buying a raceway that you can't install due to *NEC* requirements you can't meet with that particular wiring method.

Here's a brief overview of each one:

- **Article 342—Intermediate Metal Conduit (Type IMC).** Intermediate metal conduit is a circular metal raceway with the same outside diameter as rigid metal conduit. The wall thickness of intermediate metal conduit is less than that of rigid metal conduit, so it has a greater interior cross-sectional area for holding conductors. Intermediate metal conduit is lighter and less expensive than rigid metal conduit, but it's permitted in all the same locations as rigid metal conduit. Intermediate metal conduit also uses a different steel alloy, which makes it stronger than rigid metal conduit, even though the walls are thinner.

- **Article 344—Rigid Metal Conduit (Type RMC).** Rigid metal conduit is similar to intermediate metal conduit, except the wall thickness is greater, so it has a smaller interior cross-sectional area. Rigid metal conduit is heavier than intermediate metal conduit and it's permitted to be installed in any location, just like intermediate metal conduit.

- **Article 348—Flexible Metal Conduit (Type FMC).** Flexible metal conduit is a raceway of circular cross section made of a helically wound, interlocked metal strip of either steel or aluminum. It's commonly called "Greenfield" or "Flex."

- **Article 350—Liquidtight Flexible Metal Conduit (Type LFMC).** Liquidtight flexible metal conduit is a raceway of circular cross section with an outer liquidtight, nonmetallic, sunlight-resistant jacket over an inner flexible metal core, with associated couplings, connectors, and fittings. It's listed for the installation of electrical conductors. Liquidtight flexible metal conduit is commonly called "Sealtite®" or simply "liquidtight." Liquidtight flexible metal conduit is of similar construction to flexible metal conduit, but it has an outer thermoplastic covering.

- **Article 352—Rigid Polyvinyl Chloride Conduit (Type PVC).** Rigid polyvinyl chloride conduit is a nonmetallic raceway of circular cross section with integral or associated couplings, connectors, and fittings. It's listed for the installation of electrical conductors.

- **Article 358—Electrical Metallic Tubing (EMT).** Electrical metallic tubing is a nonthreaded thinwall raceway of circular cross section designed for the physical protection and routing of conductors and cables. Compared to rigid metal conduit and intermediate metal conduit, electrical metallic tubing is relatively easy to bend, cut, and ream. EMT isn't threaded, so all connectors and couplings are of the threadless type. Today, it's available in a range of colors, such as red and blue.

- **Article 376—Metal Wireways.** A metal wireway is a sheet metal trough with hinged or removable covers for housing and protecting electrical conductors and cable, in which conductors are placed after the wireway has been installed as a complete system.

Cable Tray

- **Article 392—Cable Trays.** A cable tray system is a unit or assembly of units or sections with associated fittings that form a structural system used to securely fasten or support cables and raceways. A cable tray isn't a raceway; it's a support system for raceways, cables, and enclosures.

Understanding the *NEC* requirements here in Chapter 3—Wiring Methods and Materials is just as important when installing PV systems as when installing more tradition electrical system. We'll explain many of those rules in this textbook.

ARTICLE 300 GENERAL REQUIREMENTS FOR WIRING METHODS AND MATERIALS

Introduction to Article 300—General Requirements for Wiring Methods and Materials

Article 300 contains the general requirements for all wiring methods included in the *NEC*. However, the article doesn't apply to communications systems, which are covered in Chapter 8, except when Article 300 is specifically referenced in that chapter.

This article is primarily concerned with how to install, route, splice, protect, and secure conductors and raceways. How well you conform to the requirements of Article 300 will generally be evident in the finished work, because many of the requirements tend to determine the appearance of the installation. Because of this, it's often easy to spot Article 300 problems if you're looking for *Code* violations. For example, you can easily see when someone runs an equipment grounding conductor outside a raceway instead of grouping all conductors of a circuit together, as required by 300.3(B).

A good understanding of Article 300 will start you on the path to correctly installing the wiring methods included in Chapter 3. Be sure to carefully consider the accompanying illustrations, and refer to the definitions in Article 100 as needed.

2014 CHANGE ANALYSIS: Article 300 has long been titled "Wiring Methods." Wiring methods include raceways and cables, and Article 300 certainly doesn't contain all of the rules for them. The change to "General Requirements for Wiring Methods and Materials" much more accurately describes what this article is all about.

Part I. General

300.1 Scope

(A) Wiring Installations. Article 300 contains the <u>general requirements</u> for power and lighting wiring methods.

(B) Integral Parts of Equipment. The requirements contained in Article 300 don't apply to the internal parts of electrical equipment. Figure 300–1

Integral Parts of Equipment
300.1(B)

The requirements contained in Article 300 don't apply to the internal parts of electrical equipment.

Copyright 2014, www.MikeHolt.com

Figure 300–1

(C) Trade Sizes. Designators for raceway trade sizes are given in Table 300.1(C).

Author's Comment:

- Industry practice is to describe raceways using inch sizes, such as ½ in., 2 in., and so on; however, the proper reference (2005 *NEC* change) is to use "Trade Size ½," or "Trade Size 2." In this textbook we use the term "Trade Size."

300.3 Conductors

(A) Conductors. Single conductors must be installed within a Chapter 3 wiring method, such as a raceway, cable, or enclosure. Figure 300–2

Figure 300–2

Ex: Overhead conductors can be installed in accordance with 225.6.

(B) Circuit Conductors Grouped Together. All conductors of a circuit, including equipment grounding and bonding conductors, must be installed in the same raceway, cable, trench, cord, or cable tray, except as permitted by (1) through (4). Figure 300–3

(1) Paralleled Installations. Conductors installed in parallel in accordance with 310.10(H) must have all circuit conductors within the same raceway, cable tray, trench, or cable. Figure 300–4

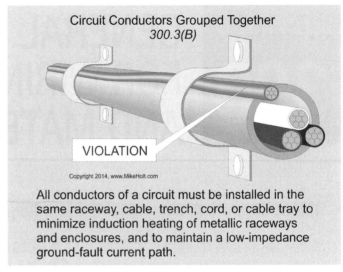

All conductors of a circuit must be installed in the same raceway, cable, trench, cord, or cable tray to minimize induction heating of metallic raceways and enclosures, and to maintain a low-impedance ground-fault current path.

Figure 300–3

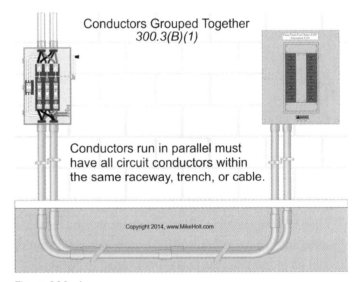

Conductors run in parallel must have all circuit conductors within the same raceway, trench, or cable.

Figure 300–4

Ex: Parallel conductors run underground can be installed in different raceways (Phase A in raceway 1, Phase B in raceway 2, and so forth), if the raceways are nonmetallic or nonmagnetic and the installation complies with 300.20(B). See 300.5(I) Ex 2.

Author's Comment:

- All conductors of a circuit must be installed in the same raceway, cable, trench, cord, or cable tray to minimize induction heating of ferrous metal raceways and enclosures, and to maintain a low-impedance ground-fault current path [250.4(A)(3)].

(2) Grounding and Bonding Conductors. For dc circuits, the equipment grounding conductor is permitted to be run separately from the circuit conductors in accordance with 250.134(B) Ex 2. Figure 300–5

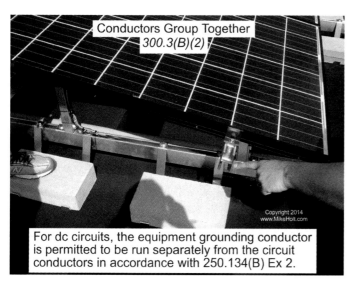

For dc circuits, the equipment grounding conductor is permitted to be run separately from the circuit conductors in accordance with 250.134(B) Ex 2.

Figure 300–5

(3) Nonferrous Wiring Methods. Circuit conductors can be installed in different raceways (Phase A in raceway 1, Phase B in raceway 2, and so on) if, in order to reduce or eliminate inductive heating, the raceway is nonmetallic or nonmagnetic and the installation complies with 300.20(B). See 300.3(B)(1) and 300.5(I) Ex 2.

(C) Conductors of Different Systems.

(1) Mixing. Power conductors of alternating-current and direct-current systems rated 1,000V or less can occupy the same raceway, cable, or enclosure if all conductors have an insulation voltage rating not less than the maximum circuit voltage.

Note 2: PV system conductors, both direct current and alternating current, are permitted to be installed in the same raceways, outlet and junction boxes, or similar fittings with each other, but they must be kept entirely independent of all other non-PV system wiring [690.4(B)]. Figure 300–6

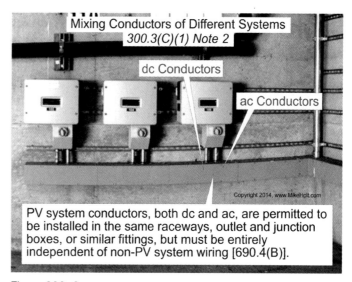

PV system conductors, both dc and ac, are permitted to be installed in the same raceways, outlet and junction boxes, or similar fittings, but must be entirely independent of non-PV system wiring [690.4(B)].

Figure 300–6

300.4 Protection Against Physical Damage

Conductors, raceways, and cables must be protected against physical damage [110.27(B)].

(A) Cables and Raceways Through Wood Members. When the following wiring methods are installed through wood members, they must comply with (1) and (2). Figure 300–7

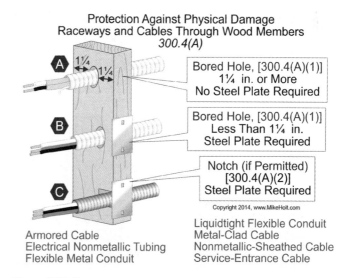

Figure 300–7

- Armored Cable, Article 320
- Electrical Nonmetallic Tubing, Article 362
- Flexible Metal Conduit, Article 348
- Liquidtight Flexible Metal Conduit, Article 350
- Liquidtight Flexible Nonmetallic Conduit, Article 356
- Metal-Clad Cable, Article 330
- Nonmetallic-Sheathed Cable, Article 334
- Service-Entrance Cable, Article 338
- Underground Feeder and Branch-Circuit Cable, Article 340

(1) Holes in Wood Members. Holes through wood framing members for the above cables or raceways must be not less than 1¼ in. from the edge of the wood member. If the edge of the hole is less than 1¼ in. from the edge, a ¹⁄₁₆ in. thick steel plate of sufficient length and width must be installed to protect the wiring method from screws and nails.

Ex 1: A steel plate isn't required to protect rigid metal conduit, intermediate metal conduit, PVC conduit, or electrical metallic tubing.

Ex 2: A listed and marked steel plate less than ¹⁄₁₆ in. thick that provides equal or better protection against nail or screw penetration is permitted. Figure 300–8

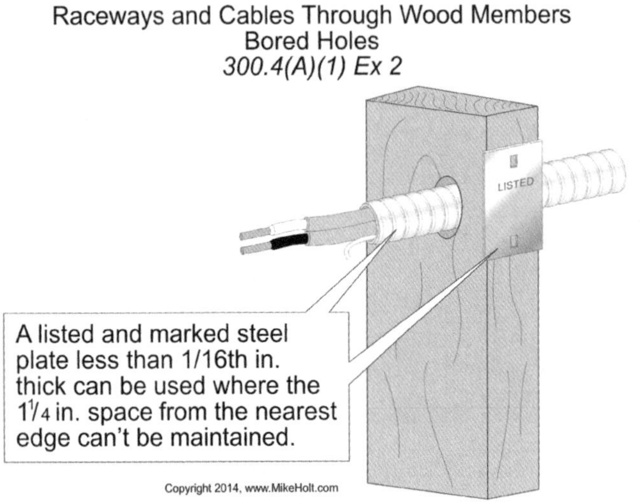

Author's Comment:

- Hardened steel plates thinner than ¹⁄₁₆ in. have been tested and found to provide better protection from screw and nail penetration than the thicker plates.

(2) Notches in Wood Members. If notching of wood framing members for cables and raceways are permitted by the building code, a ¹⁄₁₆ in. thick steel plate of sufficient length and width must be installed to protect the wiring method laid in these wood notches from screws and nails.

⚠ **CAUTION:** *When drilling or notching wood members, be sure to check with the building inspector to ensure you don't damage or weaken the structure and violate the building code.*

Ex 1: A steel plate isn't required to protect rigid metal conduit, intermediate metal conduit, PVC conduit, or electrical metallic tubing.

Ex 2: A listed and marked steel plate less than ¹⁄₁₆ in. thick that provides equal or better protection against nail or screw penetration is permitted. Figure 300–9

Raceways and Cables Through Wood Members
Bored Holes
300.4(A)(1) Ex 2

A listed and marked steel plate less than 1/16th in. thick can be used where the 1¹⁄₄ in. space from the nearest edge can't be maintained.

Copyright 2014, www.MikeHolt.com

Figure 300–8

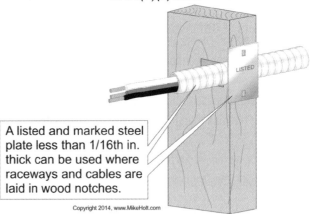

Raceways and Cables Through Wood Members
Notches in Wood
300.4(A)(2) Ex 2

A listed and marked steel plate less than 1/16th in. thick can be used where raceways and cables are laid in wood notches.

Copyright 2014, www.MikeHolt.com

Figure 300–9

(C) Behind Suspended Ceilings. Wiring methods, such as boxes, enclosures cables or raceways, installed behind panels designed to allow access must be supported in accordance with its applicable article and 300.11(A). Figure 300–10

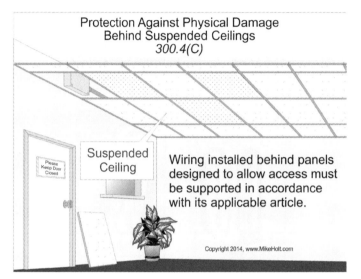

Figure 300–10

(D) Cables and Raceways Parallel to Framing Members and Furring Strips. Cables or raceways run parallel to framing members or furring strips must be protected if they're likely to be penetrated by nails or screws, by installing the wiring method so it isn't less than 1¼ in. from the nearest edge of the framing member or furring strip. If the edge of the framing member or furring strip is less than 1¼ in. away, a ¹⁄₁₆ in. thick steel plate of sufficient length and width must be installed to protect the wiring method from screws and nails.

Ex 1: Protection isn't required for rigid metal conduit, intermediate metal conduit, PVC conduit, or electrical metallic tubing.

Ex 2: For concealed work in finished buildings, or finished panels for prefabricated buildings if such supporting is impracticable, the cables can be fished between access points.

Ex 3: A listed and marked steel plate less than ¹⁄₁₆ in. thick that provides equal or better protection against nail or screw penetration is permitted.

(E) Wiring Under Roof Decking. Cables, raceways, and enclosures under metal-corrugated sheet roof decking must not be located within 1½ in. of the roof decking, measured from the lowest surface of the roof decking to the top of the cable, raceway, or box. In addition, cables, raceways, and enclosures aren't permitted in concealed locations of metal-corrugated sheet decking type roofing. Figure 300–11

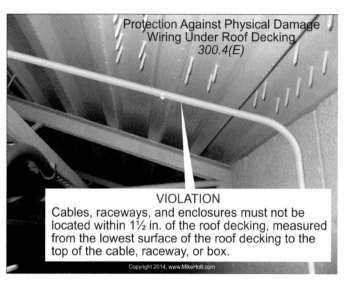

Figure 300–11

Author's Comment:

■ This requirement also applies to luminaires installed in or under roof decking [410.10(F)].

Note: Roof decking material will often be installed or replaced after the initial raceway or cabling installation which may be penetrated by the screws or other mechanical devices designed to provide "hold down" strength of the waterproof membrane or roof insulating material.

Ex: Spacing from roof decking doesn't apply to rigid metal conduit and intermediate metal conduit.

(F) Cables and Raceways Installed in Grooves. Cables and raceways installed in a groove must be protected by a ¹⁄₁₆ in. thick steel plate or sleeve, or by 1¼ in. of free space.

Author's Comment:

- An example is Type NM cable installed in a groove cut into the Styrofoam-type insulation building block structure and then covered with wallboard.

Ex 1: Protection isn't required if the cable is installed in rigid metal conduit, intermediate metal conduit, PVC conduit, or electrical metallic tubing.

Ex 2: A listed and marked steel plate less than ¹⁄₁₆ in. thick that provides equal or better protection against nail or screw penetration is permitted.

(G) Insulating Fittings. If raceways contain insulated circuit conductors 4 AWG and larger that enter an enclosure, the conductors must be protected from abrasion during and after installation by a fitting identified to provide a smooth, rounded insulating surface, such as an insulating bushing. Figure 300–12

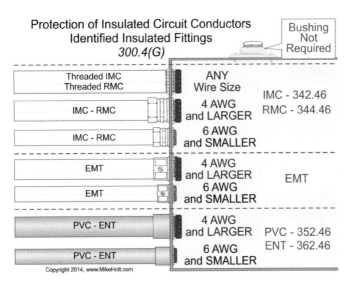

Figure 300–12

Author's Comment:

- If IMC or RMC conduit enters an enclosure without a connector, a bushing must be provided, regardless of the conductor size [342.46 and 344.46].

- An insulated fitting isn't required for a bare grounding electrode conductor. Figure 300–13

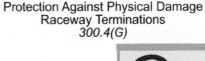

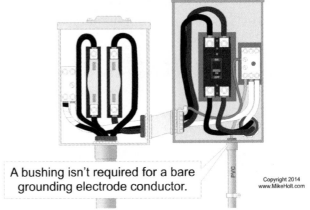

Figure 300–13

Ex: Insulating bushings aren't required if a raceway terminates in a threaded raceway entry that provides a smooth, rounded, or flared surface for the conductors, such as a hub.

(H) Structural Joints. A listed expansion/deflection fitting or other means approved by the authority having jurisdiction must be used where a raceway crosses a structural joint intended for expansion, contraction, or deflection.

300.5 Underground Installations

(A) Minimum Burial Depths. When cables or raceways are installed underground, they must have a minimum "cover" in accordance with Table 300.5. Figure 300–14

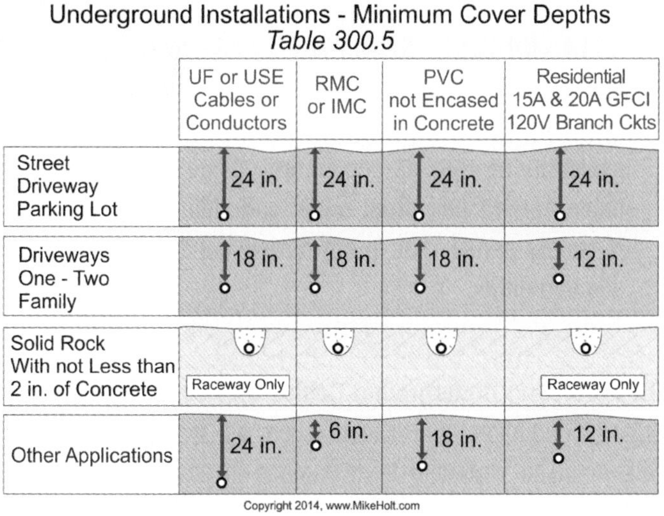

Underground Installations - Minimum Cover Depths
Table 300.5

	UF or USE Cables or Conductors	RMC or IMC	PVC not Encased in Concrete	Residential 15A & 20A GFCI 120V Branch Ckts
Street Driveway Parking Lot	24 in.	24 in.	24 in.	24 in.
Driveways One - Two Family	18 in.	18 in.	18 in.	12 in.
Solid Rock With not Less than 2 in. of Concrete	Raceway Only			Raceway Only
Other Applications	24 in.	6 in.	18 in.	12 in.

Copyright 2014, www.MikeHolt.com

Figure 300–14

Underground Installations Minimum Cover Depths
Table 300.5, Note 1

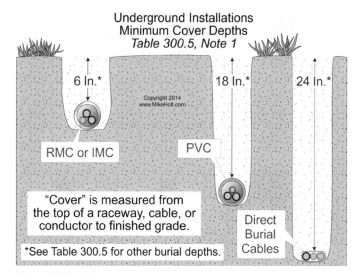

RMC or IMC

PVC

"Cover" is measured from the top of a raceway, cable, or conductor to finished grade.

Direct Burial Cables

*See Table 300.5 for other burial depths.

Figure 300–15

Table 300.5 Minimum Cover Requirements in Inches

Location	Buried Cables	Metal Raceway	Nonmetallic Raceway
Under Building	0	0	0
Dwelling Unit	24/12*	6	18
Dwelling Unit Driveway	18/12*	6	18/12*
Under Roadway	24	24	24
Other Locations	24	6	18

*Residential branch circuits rated 120V or less with GFCI protection and maximum overcurrent protection of 20A.

Note: This is a summary of the NEC's Table 300.5. See the table in the NEC for full details.

Note 1 to Table 300.5 defines "Cover" as the distance from the top of the underground cable or raceway to the top surface of finished grade. Figure 300–15

(B) Wet Locations. The interior of enclosures or raceways installed in an underground installation is considered to be a wet location. Cables and insulated conductors installed in underground enclosures or raceways <u>must comply</u> with 310.10(C). Splices within an underground enclosure must be listed as suitable for wet locations [110.14(B)]. Figure 300–16

Underground Installations Wet Locations
300.5(B)

Cables and insulated conductors installed in underground raceways and enclosures must be listed as suitable for wet locations.

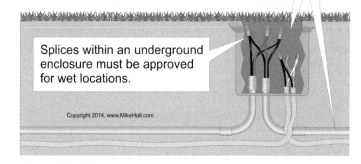

Splices within an underground enclosure must be approved for wet locations.

Copyright 2014, www.MikeHolt.com

Figure 300–16

Author's Comment:

■ The definition of a "Wet Location" as contained in Article 100, includes installations underground, in concrete slabs in direct contact with the earth, locations subject to saturation with water, and unprotected locations exposed to weather. If raceways are installed in wet locations above grade, the interior of these raceways is also considered to be a wet location [300.9].

(C) Cables and Conductors Under Buildings. Cables and conductors installed under a building must be installed in a raceway that extends past the outside walls of the building. Figure 300–17

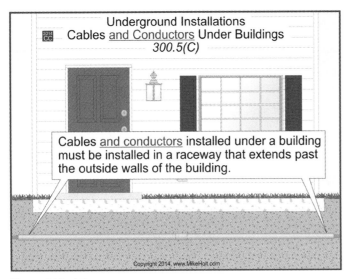

Figure 300–17

Ex 2: Type MC Cable listed for direct burial is permitted under a building without installation in a raceway [330.10(A)(5)]. Figure 300–18

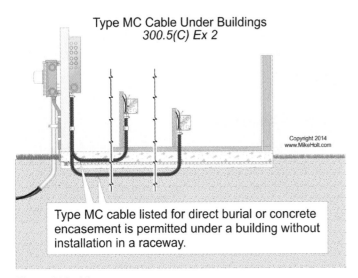

Figure 300–18

2014 CHANGE ANALYSIS: While some people use the terms "cable" and "conductor" interchangeably, the *Code* does not. A cable (almost always) is an assembly of multiple conductors. Since direct-buried cables aren't permitted under a building (generally), it makes sense that direct-buried conductors aren't allowed either.

(D) Protecting Underground Cables and Conductors. Direct-buried conductors and cables such as Types MC, UF, and USE must be protected from damage in accordance with (1) through (4).

(1) Emerging from Grade. Direct-buried cables or conductors that emerge from grade must be installed in an enclosure or raceway to protect against physical damage. Protection isn't required to extend more than 18 in. below grade, and protection above ground must extend to a height of not less than 8 ft. Figure 300–19

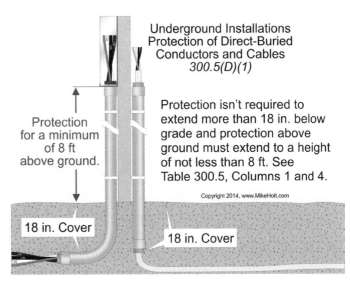

Figure 300–19

(2) Conductors Entering Buildings. Conductors that enter a building must be protected to the point of entrance.

(3) Service Conductors. Service conductors must have their location identified by a warning ribbon placed in the trench at least 12 in. above the underground conductor installation. Figure 300–20

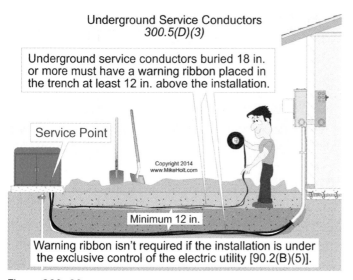

Underground Service Conductors
300.5(D)(3)

Underground service conductors buried 18 in. or more must have a warning ribbon placed in the trench at least 12 in. above the installation.

Service Point

Copyright 2014
www.MikeHolt.com

Minimum 12 in.

Warning ribbon isn't required if the installation is under the exclusive control of the electric utility [90.2(B)(5)].

Figure 300–20

(4) Enclosure or Raceway Damage. If direct-buried cables, enclosures, or raceways are subject to physical damage, the conductors must be installed in rigid metal conduit, intermediate metal conduit, <u>RTRC-XW</u>, or Schedule 80 PVC conduit.

> **2014 CHANGE ANALYSIS:** Since the introduction of Type RTRC conduit in the *NEC*, installers have been falling in love with it. It's a very, very lightweight product, it doesn't burn when pulling ropes through it, and it costs significantly less than steel. Because it's only been allowed for a short time, there are areas in the *Code* that don't address it, and changes need to be made to add it. This is a further example.

(E) Underground Splices and Taps. Direct-buried conductors or cables can be spliced or tapped underground without a splice box [300.15(G)], if the splice or tap is made in accordance with 110.14(B). Figure 300–21

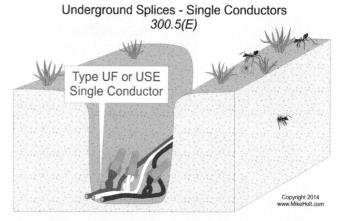

Underground Splices - Single Conductors
300.5(E)

Type UF or USE
Single Conductor

Copyright 2014
www.MikeHolt.com

Single Type UF or USE conductors can be spliced underground with a device that's listed for direct burial.

Figure 300–21

(F) Backfill. Backfill material for underground wiring must not damage the underground cable or raceway, or contribute to the corrosion of the metal raceway.

Author's Comment:

- Large rocks, chunks of concrete, steel rods, mesh, and other sharp-edged objects must not be used for backfill material, because they can damage the underground conductors, cables, or raceways.

(G) Raceway Seals. If moisture could enter a raceway and contact energized live parts, a seal must be installed at one or both ends of the raceway. Figure 300–22

Author's Comment:

- This is a common problem for equipment located downhill from the supply, or in underground equipment rooms. See 230.8 for service raceway seals and 300.7(A) for different temperature area seals.

Note: Hazardous explosive gases or vapors make it necessary to seal underground raceways that enter the building in accordance with 501.15.

Figure 300–22

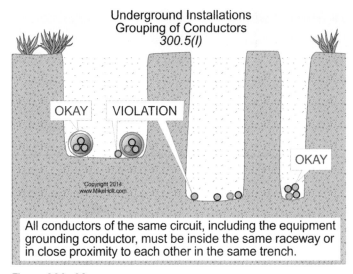

All conductors of the same circuit, including the equipment grounding conductor, must be inside the same raceway or in close proximity to each other in the same trench.

Figure 300–23

Author's Comment:

■ It isn't the intent of this Note to imply that sealing fittings of the types required in hazardous locations be installed in unclassified locations, except as required in Chapter 5. This also doesn't imply that the sealing material provides a watertight seal, but only that it prevents moisture from entering the raceways.

(H) Bushing. Raceways that terminate underground must have a bushing or fitting at the end of the raceway to protect emerging cables or conductors.

(I) Conductors Grouped Together. All conductors of the same circuit, including the equipment grounding conductor, must be inside the same raceway, or in close proximity to each other. See 300.3(B). Figure 300–23

Ex 1: Conductors can be installed in parallel in raceways, multiconductor cables, or direct-buried single-conductor cables. Each raceway or multiconductor cable must contain all conductors of the same circuit including the equipment grounding conductor. Each direct-buried single-conductor cable must be located in close proximity in the trench to the other single-conductor cables in the same parallel set of conductors, including equipment grounding conductors.

Ex 2: Parallel circuit conductors installed in accordance with 310.10(H) of the same phase or neutral can be installed in underground PVC conduits, if inductive heating at raceway terminations is reduced by the use of aluminum locknuts and cutting a slot between the individual holes through which the conductors pass as required by 300.20(B). Figure 300–24

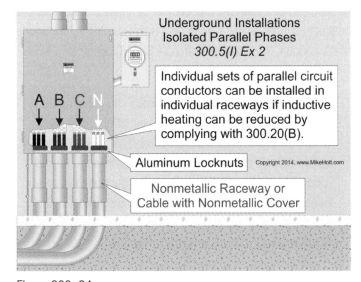

Figure 300–24

Author's Comment:

- Installing ungrounded and grounded/neutral conductors in different PVC conduits makes it easier to terminate larger parallel sets of conductors, but it will result in higher levels of electromagnetic fields (EMF).

(J) Earth Movement. Direct-buried conductors, cables, or raceways that are subject to movement by settlement or frost must be arranged to prevent damage to conductors or equipment connected to the wiring.

(K) Directional Boring. Cables or raceways installed using directional boring equipment must be approved by the authority having jurisdiction for this purpose.

Author's Comment:

- Directional boring technology uses a directional drill, which is steered continuously from point "A" to point "B." When the drill head comes out of the earth at point "B," it's replaced with a back-reamer and the duct or raceway being installed is attached to it. The size of the boring rig (hp, torque, and pull-back power) comes into play, along with the types of soil, in determining the type of raceways required. For telecommunications work, multiple poly innerducts are pulled in at one time. At major crossings, such as expressways, railroads, or rivers, outerduct may be installed to create a permanent sleeve for the innerducts.

  "Innerduct" and "outerduct" are terms usually associated with optical fiber cable installations, while "unitduct" comes with factory installed conductors. All of these come in various sizes. Galvanized rigid metal conduit, Schedule 40 and Schedule 80 PVC, HDPE conduit, and nonmetallic underground conduit with conductors (NUCC) are common wiring methods used with directional boring installations.

300.6 Protection Against Corrosion and Deterioration

Raceways, cable trays, cablebus, cable armor, boxes, cable sheathing, cabinets, elbows, couplings, fittings, supports, and support hardware must be suitable for the environment. Figure 300–25

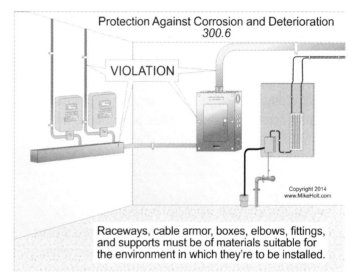

Figure 300–25

(A) Ferrous Metal Equipment. Ferrous metal raceways, enclosures, cables, cable trays, fittings, and support hardware must be protected against corrosion by a coating of listed corrosion-resistant material. Where conduit is threaded in the field, the threads must be coated with an approved electrically conductive, corrosion-resistant compound, such as cold zinc.

> **Note:** Field-cut threads are those threads that are cut anywhere other than at the factory.

Author's Comment:

- Nonferrous metal raceways, such as aluminum rigid metal conduit, don't have to meet the provisions of this section.

2014 CHANGE ANALYSIS: Well I guess that clears that up!

(1) Protected from Corrosion Solely by Enamel. If ferrous metal parts are protected from corrosion solely by enamel, they must not be used outdoors or in wet locations as described in 300.6(D).

(2) Organic Coatings on Boxes or Cabinets. Boxes or cabinets having a system of organic coatings marked "Raintight," "Rain-proof," or "Outdoor Type," can be installed outdoors.

(3) In Concrete or in Direct Contact with the Earth. Ferrous metal raceways, cable armor, boxes, cable sheathing, cabinets, elbows, couplings, nipples, fittings, supports, and support hardware can be installed in concrete or in direct contact with the earth, or in areas subject to severe corrosive influences if made of material approved for the condition, or if provided with corrosion protection approved for the condition.

Author's Comment:

■ Galvanized steel electrical metallic tubing can be installed in concrete at grade level and in direct contact with the earth, but supplementary corrosion protection is usually required (UL White Book, *Guide Information for Electrical Equipment*). Electrical metallic tubing can be installed in concrete above the ground floor slab generally without supplementary corrosion protection. Figure 300–26

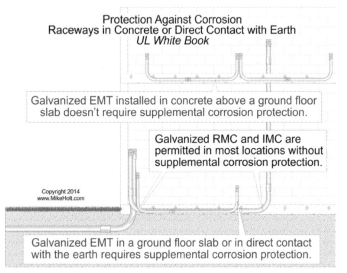

Protection Against Corrosion
Raceways in Concrete or Direct Contact with Earth
UL White Book

Galvanized EMT installed in concrete above a ground floor slab doesn't require supplemental corrosion protection.

Galvanized RMC and IMC are permitted in most locations without supplemental corrosion protection.

Copyright 2014
www.MikeHolt.com

Galvanized EMT in a ground floor slab or in direct contact with the earth requires supplemental corrosion protection.

Figure 300–26

(B) Aluminum Equipment. Aluminum raceways, cable trays, cablebus, cable armor, boxes, cable sheathing, cabinets, elbows, couplings, nipples, fittings, supports, and support hardware embedded or encased in concrete or in direct contact with the earth must be provided with supplementary corrosion protection.

(C) Nonmetallic Equipment. Nonmetallic raceways, cable trays, cablebus, boxes, cables with a nonmetallic outer jacket and internal metal armor or jacket, cable sheathing, cabinets, elbows, couplings, nipples, fittings, supports, and support hardware must be made of material identified for the condition, and must comply with (1) and (2). Figure 300–27

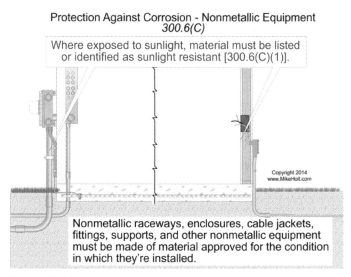

Protection Against Corrosion - Nonmetallic Equipment
300.6(C)

Where exposed to sunlight, material must be listed or identified as sunlight resistant [300.6(C)(1)].

Copyright 2014
www.MikeHolt.com

Nonmetallic raceways, enclosures, cable jackets, fittings, supports, and other nonmetallic equipment must be made of material approved for the condition in which they're installed.

Figure 300–27

(1) Exposed to Sunlight. If exposed to sunlight, the materials must be listed or identified as sunlight resistant.

(2) Chemical Exposure. If subject to exposure to chemical solvents, vapors, splashing, or immersion, materials or coatings must either be inherently resistant to chemicals based upon their listing, or be identified for the specific chemical.

(D) Indoor Wet Locations. In portions of dairy processing facilities, laundries, canneries, and other indoor wet locations, and in locations where walls are frequently washed or where there are surfaces of absorbent materials, such as damp paper or wood, the entire wiring system, where installed exposed, including all boxes, fittings, raceways, and cables, must be mounted so there's at least ¼ in. of airspace between it and the wall or supporting surface.

Author's Comment:

■ See the definitions of "Exposed" and "Location, Wet" in Article 100.

Ex: Nonmetallic raceways, boxes, and fittings are permitted without the airspace on a concrete, masonry, tile, or similar surface.

Note: Areas where acids and alkali chemicals are handled and stored may present corrosive conditions, particularly when wet or damp. Severe corrosive conditions may also be present in portions of meatpacking plants, tanneries, glue houses, and some stables; in installations immediately adjacent to a seashore or swimming pool, spa, hot tub, and fountain areas; in areas where chemical deicers are used; and in storage cellars or rooms for hides, casings, fertilizer, salt, and bulk chemicals.

300.7 Raceways Exposed to Different Temperatures

(A) Sealing. If a raceway is subjected to different temperatures, and where condensation is known to be a problem, the raceway must be filled with a material approved by the authority having jurisdiction that will prevent the circulation of warm air to a colder section of the raceway. An explosionproof seal isn't required for this purpose. Figure 300–28

(B) Expansion Fittings. Raceways must be provided with expansion fittings where necessary to compensate for thermal expansion and contraction. Figure 300–29

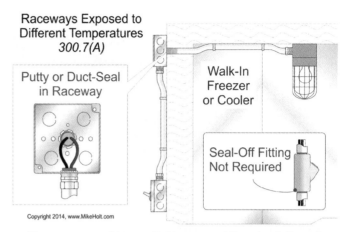

Raceways Exposed to Different Temperatures 300.7(A)

Putty or Duct-Seal in Raceway

Walk-In Freezer or Cooler

Seal-Off Fitting Not Required

Copyright 2014, www.MikeHolt.com

Raceways must be sealed to prevent the circulation of warm air to a colder section of the raceway or sleeve.

Figure 300–28

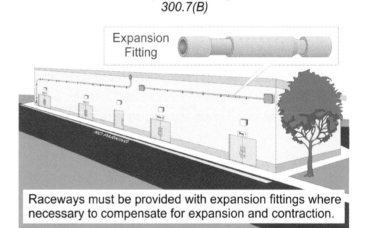

Expansion Fitting 300.7(B)

Expansion Fitting

NO PARKING

Raceways must be provided with expansion fittings where necessary to compensate for expansion and contraction.

Copyright 2014, www.MikeHolt.com

Figure 300–29

Note: Table 352.44 provides the expansion characteristics for PVC conduit. The expansion characteristics for metal raceways are determined by multiplying the values from Table 352.44 by 0.20, and the expansion characteristics for aluminum raceways are determined by multiplying the values from Table 352.44 by 0.40. Table 354.44 provides the expansion characteristics for reinforced thermosetting resin conduit (RTRC). Figure 300–30

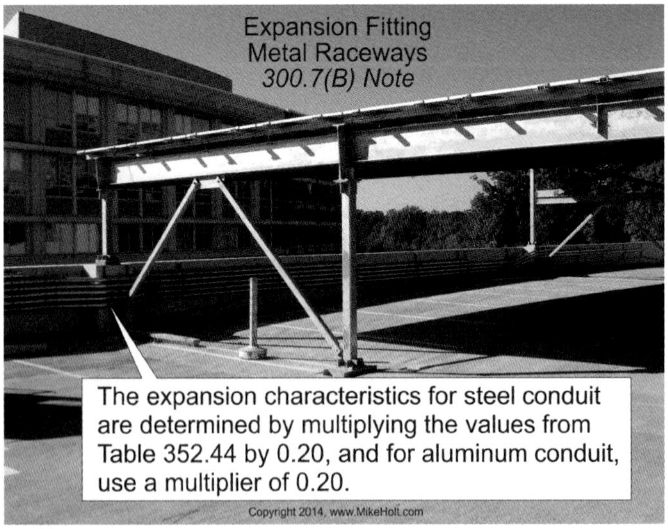

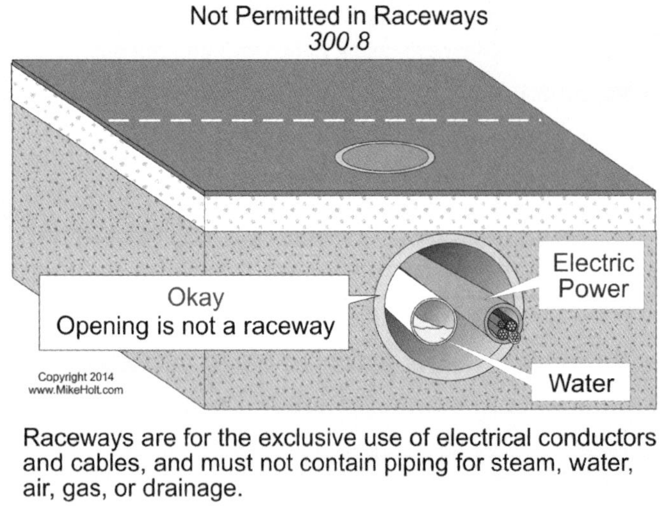

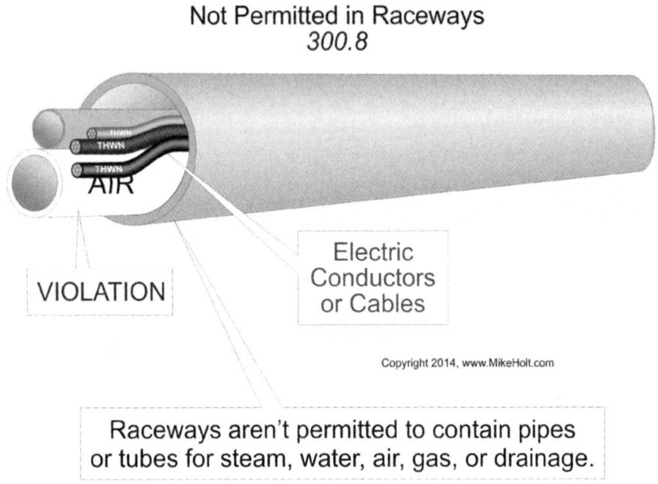

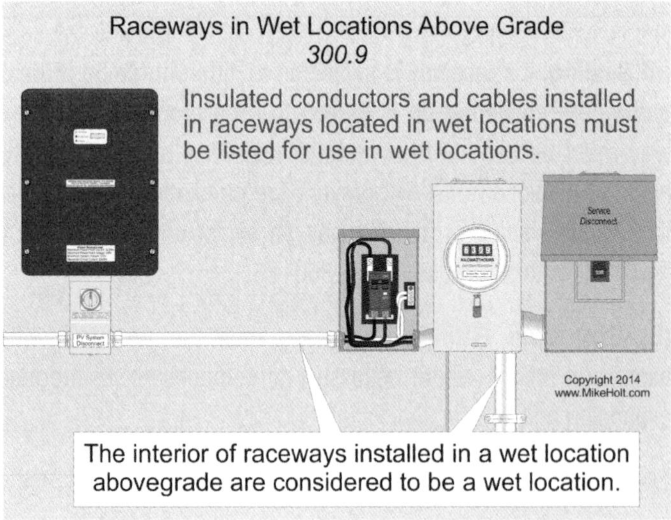

Figure 300–30

Figure 300–32

300.8 Not Permitted in Raceways

Raceways are designed for the exclusive use of electrical conductors and cables, and aren't permitted to contain nonelectrical components, such as pipes or tubes for steam, water, air, gas, drainage, and so forth. Figures 300–31 and 300–32

Figure 300–31

300.9 Raceways in Wet Locations Above Grade

Insulated conductors and cables installed in raceways in aboveground wet locations must be listed for use in wet locations in accordance with 310.10(C). Figure 300–33

Figure 300–33

300.10 Electrical Continuity

Metal raceways and enclosures for conductors must be metallically joined together to form a continuous low-impedance fault current path capable of carrying fault current to the source [110.10 and 250.4(A)(3)]. Figure 300–34

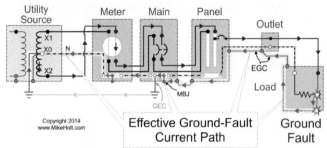

Figure 300–34

Metal raceways and enclosures for conductors must be metallically joined together to form an effective ground-fault current path to facilitate the operation of the circuit overcurrent protection device.

Raceways and cable assemblies must be mechanically secured to boxes, fittings, cabinets, and other enclosures.

Ex 1: Short lengths of metal raceways used for the support or protection of cables aren't required to be electrically continuous, nor are they required to be connected to an equipment grounding conductor [250.86 Ex 2 and 300.12 Ex].

300.12 Mechanical Continuity

Raceways and cable sheaths must be mechanically continuous between boxes, cabinets, and fittings. Figure 300–35

Ex 1: Short sections of raceways used to provide support or protection of cable from physical damage aren't required to be mechanically continuous [250.86 Ex 2 and 300.10 Ex 1].

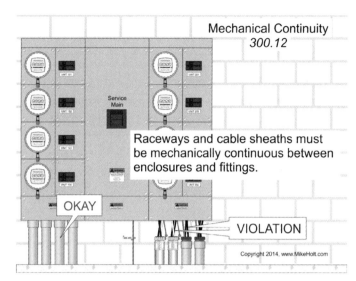

Figure 300–35

Ex 2: Raceways at the bottom of open-bottom equipment, such as switchboards, motor control centers, and transformers, aren't required to be mechanically secured to the equipment. Figure 300–36

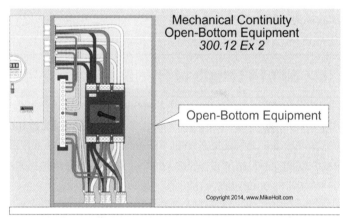

Raceways and cables installed into the bottom of open-bottom equipment aren't required to be mechanically secured to the equipment.

Figure 300–36

Author's Comment:

- When raceways are stubbed into an open-bottom switchboard, the raceway, including the end fitting, can't rise more than 3 in. above the bottom of the switchboard enclosure [408.5].

300.13 Splices and Pigtails

(A) Conductor Splices. Splices must be in enclosures in accordance with 300.15 and aren't permitted in raceways, except as permitted by 376.56, 386.56, or 388.56. Figure 300–37

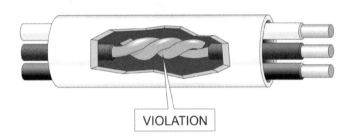

Splices in Raceway
300.13(A)

VIOLATION

Splices or taps aren't
permitted within a raceway.

Copyright 2014. www.MikeHolt.com

Figure 300–37

300.14 Length of Free Conductors

At least 6 in. of free conductor, measured from the point in the box where the conductors enter the enclosure, must be left at each outlet, junction, and switch point for splices or terminations of luminaires or devices. Figure 300–38

Boxes that have openings less than 8 in. in any dimension, must have at least 6 in. of free conductor, measured from the point where the conductors enter the box, and at least 3 in. of free conductor outside the box opening. Figure 300–39

Author's Comment:

■ The following text was the Panels' Statement when it rejected my proposal to require the free conductor length to be unspliced in the 2008 *NEC*. "The purpose of Section 300.14 is to permit access to the end of the conductor. Whether this conductor is spliced or

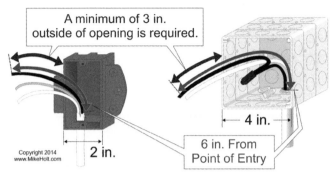

Length of Free Conductor
300.14

A minimum of 3 in.
outside of opening is required.

Copyright 2014
www.MikeHolt.com

2 in.

4 in.

6 in. From
Point of Entry

Boxes with openings less than 8 in. must have at least 6 in. of free conductor and at least 3 in. of free conductor outside the box opening.

Figure 300–38

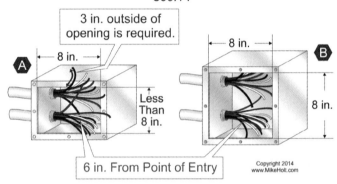

Length of Free Conductor
300.14

3 in. outside of
opening is required.

8 in.

A

8 in.

Less
Than
8 in.

B

8 in.

6 in. From Point of Entry

Copyright 2014
www.MikeHolt.com

At least 6 in. of free conductor is required at each box. Where the box opening is less than 8 in., conductors must extend at least 3 in. outside the box opening.

Figure 300–39

unspliced doesn't affect the length of this free end of the conductor. Many conductors originate inside the box and are spliced to other conductors within the box but extend out of the box for connection to a device of some kind. Making this change would not permit this very common application. Even the exception to this section states that unspliced or unterminated conductors do not have to comply with 300.14."

Ex: Six inches of free conductor isn't required for conductors that pass through a box without a splice or termination.

300.15 Boxes or Conduit Bodies

A box must be installed at each splice or termination point, except as permitted for: Figure 300–40

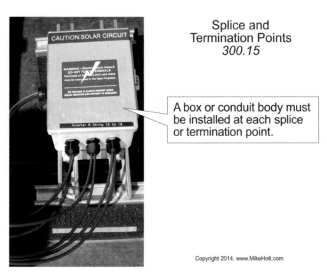

Splice and
Termination Points
300.15

A box or conduit body must be installed at each splice or termination point.

Copyright 2014, www.MikeHolt.com

Figure 300–40

- Cabinet or Cutout Boxes, 312.8
- Conduit Bodies, 314.16(C) Figure 300–41
- Luminaires, 410.64
- Surface Raceways, 386.56 and 388.56
- Wireways, 376.56

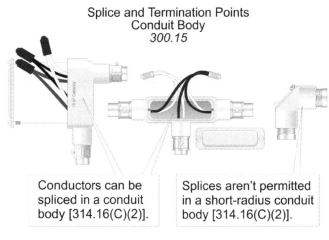

Splice and Termination Points
Conduit Body
300.15

Conductors can be spliced in a conduit body [314.16(C)(2)].

Splices aren't permitted in a short-radius conduit body [314.16(C)(2)].

Copyright 2014, www.MikeHolt.com

Figure 300–41

Fittings and Connectors. Fittings can only be used with the specific wiring methods for which they're listed and designed. For example, Type NM cable connectors must not be used with Type AC cable, and electrical metallic tubing fittings must not be used with rigid metal conduit or intermediate metal conduit, unless listed for the purpose. Figure 300–42

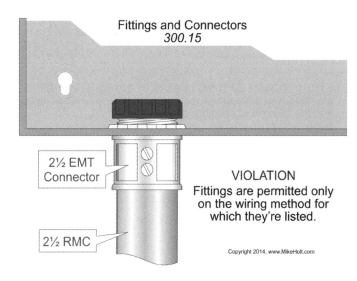

Fittings and Connectors
300.15

2½ EMT Connector

2½ RMC

VIOLATION
Fittings are permitted only on the wiring method for which they're listed.

Copyright 2014, www.MikeHolt.com

Figure 300–42

Author's Comment:

- PVC conduit couplings and connectors are permitted with electrical nonmetallic tubing if the proper glue is used in accordance with manufacturer's instructions [110.3(B)]. See 362.48.

(C) Raceways for Support or Protection. When a raceway is used for the support or protection of cables, a fitting to reduce the potential for abrasion must be placed at the location the cables enter the raceway.

(F) Fitting. A fitting is permitted in lieu of a box or conduit body where conductors aren't spliced or terminated within the fitting if it's accessible after installation. Figure 300–43

(G) Underground Splices. A box or conduit body isn't required where a splice is made underground if the conductors are spliced with a splicing device listed for direct burial. See 110.14(B) and 300.5(E).

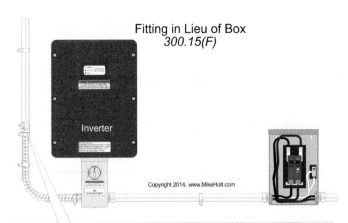

Fitting in Lieu of Box
300.15(F)

A fitting is permitted in lieu of a box or conduit body where the conductors aren't spliced or terminated within the fitting and the fitting is accessible after installation.

Figure 300–43

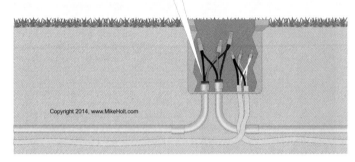

Splice and Termination Points
Handhole Enclosure
300.15(L)

A box isn't required for conductors in handhole enclosures. Splices must comply with 314.30.

Figure 300–44

Author's Comment:

■ See the definition of "Conduit Body" in Article 100.

(I) Enclosures. A box or conduit body isn't required where a splice is made in a cabinet or in cutout boxes containing switches or overcurrent devices if the splices or taps don't fill the wiring space at any cross section to more than 75 percent, and the wiring at any cross section doesn't exceed 40 percent. See 312.8 and 404.3(B).

(L) Handhole Enclosures. A box or conduit body isn't required for conductors installed in a handhole enclosure. Splices must be made in accordance with 314.30. Figure 300–44

Author's Comment:

■ Splices or terminations within a handhole must be accomplished by the use of fittings listed as suitable for wet locations [110.14(B) and 314.30(C)].

300.17 Raceway Sizing

Raceways must be large enough to permit the installation and removal of conductors without damaging the conductor's insulation.

Author's Comment:

■ When all conductors in a raceway are the same size and of the same insulation type, the number of conductors permitted can be determined by Annex C.

■ When different size conductors are installed in a raceway, conductor fill is limited to the percentages in Table 1 of Chapter 9.

Table 1, Chapter 9	
Number	**Percent Fill**
1 Conductor	53%
2 Conductors	31%
3 or more	40%

The above percentages are based on conditions where the length of the conductor and number of raceway bends are within reasonable limits [Chapter 9, Table 1, Note 1]. Figure 300–45

Raceway Fill Limitation
Chapter 9, Table 1

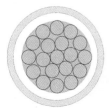 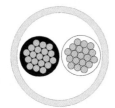 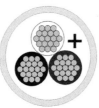

One Conductor
53% Fill

Two Conductors
31% Fill

Three or More
Conductors
40% Fill

When conductors are installed in a raceway,
conductor fill is limited to the above percentages.

Copyright 2014, www.MikeHolt.com

Figure 300–45

Question: *How many 12 THHN conductors can be installed in trade size ¾ electrical metallic tubing?* Figure 300–46

(a) 12   *(b) 13*   *(c) 14*   *(d) 16*

Answer: *(d) 16 conductors [Annex C, Table C1]*

Raceway Sizing
300.17

¾ EMT

Sixteen 12 THHN conductors
[Annex C, Table C.1]

When all conductors in a raceway are the same
size and insulation type, the number of conductors
permitted can be determined by Annex C.

Copyright 2014, www.MikeHolt.com

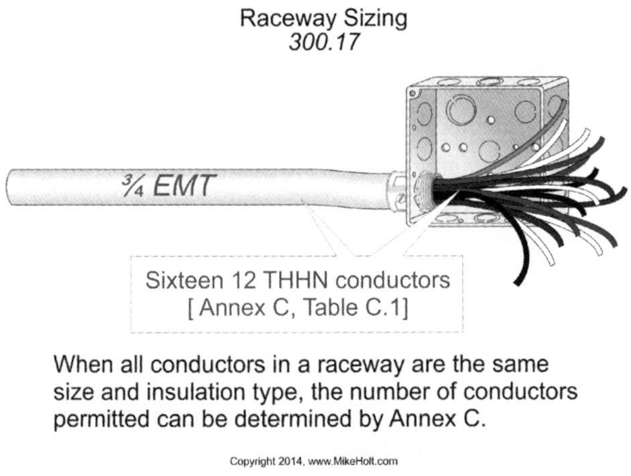

Figure 300–46

Step 1: *When sizing a raceway, first determine the total area of conductors (Chapter 9, Table 5 for insulated conductors and Chapter 9, Table 8 for bare conductors).* Figure 300–47

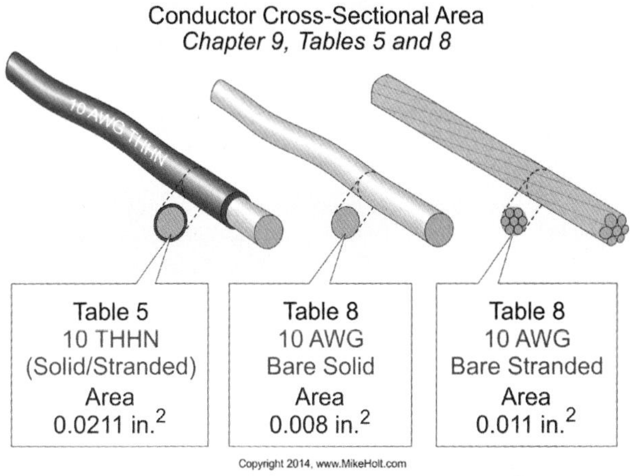

Conductor Cross-Sectional Area
Chapter 9, Tables 5 and 8

Table 5 10 THHN (Solid/Stranded) Area 0.0211 in.^{2}	Table 8 10 AWG Bare Solid Area 0.008 in.^{2}	Table 8 10 AWG Bare Stranded Area 0.011 in.^{2}

Copyright 2014, www.MikeHolt.com

Figure 300–47

Step 2: *Select the raceway from Chapter 9, Table 4, in accordance with the percent fill listed in Chapter 9, Table 1.* Figure 300–48

Raceway Cross-Sectional Area
Chapter 9 - Table 4

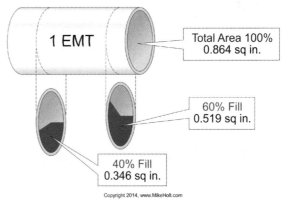

1 EMT

Total Area 100%
0.864 sq in.

60% Fill
0.519 sq in.

40% Fill
0.346 sq in.

Copyright 2014, www.MikeHolt.com

Figure 300–48

Question: *What trade size Schedule 40 PVC conduit is required for the following conductors?* Figure 300–49

    3—500 THHN
    1—250 THHN
    1—3 THHN

(a) 2   (b) 3   (c) 4   (d) 6

Raceway Sizing
300.17

Schedule 40 PVC

Step 1. Determine the conductor area, Chapter 9, Table 5.

500 kcmil = 0.7073 in.² x 3 conductors = 2.1219 in.²
250 kcmil = 0.3970 in.² x 1 conductor = 0.3970 in.²
3 AWG = 0.0973 in.² x 1 conductor = 0.0973 in.²
          Total area of the conductors = 2.6162 in.²

Step 2. Size the raceway at 40% fill, Chapter 9, Table 4.

Trade Size 3 PVC at 40 percent fill = 2.907 in.² Copyright 2014
www.MikeHolt.com

Figure 300–49

Answer: *(b) 3*

Step 1: *Determine the total area of conductors [Chapter 9, Table 5]:*

500 THHN	*0.7073 x 3 =*	*2.1219 in.²*
250 THHN	*0.3970 x 1 =*	*0.3970 in.²*
3 THHN	*0.0973 x 1 =*	*+ 0.0973 in.²*
Total Area =		*2.6162 in.²*

Step 2: *Select the raceway at 40 percent fill [Chapter 9, Table 4]:*

Trade size 3 Schedule 40 PVC = 2.907 sq in. of conductor fill at 40%.

300.18 Inserting Conductors in Raceways

(A) Complete Runs. To protect conductor insulation from abrasion during installation, raceways must be mechanically completed between the pulling points before conductors are installed. See 300.10 and 300.12. Figure 300–50

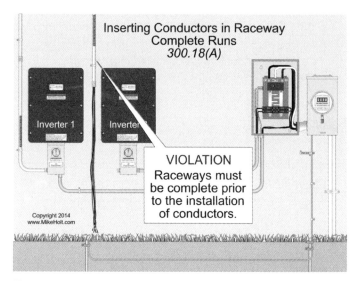

Inserting Conductors in Raceway
Complete Runs
300.18(A)

Inverter 1   Inverter

VIOLATION
Raceways must
be complete prior
to the installation
of conductors.

Copyright 2014
www.MikeHolt.com

Figure 300–50

Ex: Short sections of raceways used for the protection of cables from physical damage aren't required to be installed complete between outlet, junction, or splicing points.

(B) Welding. Metal raceways must not be supported, terminated, or connected by welding to the raceway.

300.19 Supporting Conductors in Vertical Raceways

(A) Spacing Intervals. If the vertical rise of a raceway exceeds the values of Table 300.19(A), the conductors must be supported at the top, or as close to the top as practical. Intermediate support must also be provided in increments that don't exceed the values of Table 300.19(A). Figure 300–51

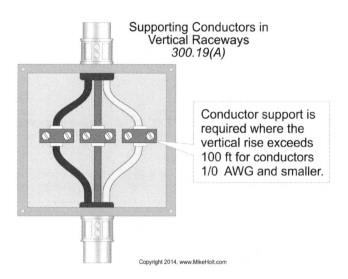

Supporting Conductors in
Vertical Raceways
300.19(A)

Conductor support is required where the vertical rise exceeds 100 ft for conductors 1/0 AWG and smaller.

Copyright 2014, www.MikeHolt.com

Figure 300–51

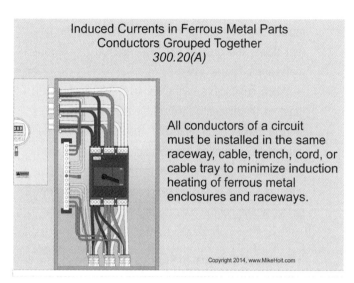

Induced Currents in Ferrous Metal Parts
Conductors Grouped Together
300.20(A)

All conductors of a circuit must be installed in the same raceway, cable, trench, cord, or cable tray to minimize induction heating of ferrous metal enclosures and raceways.

Copyright 2014, www.MikeHolt.com

Figure 300–52

Author's Comment:

- The weight of long vertical runs of conductors can cause the conductors to actually drop out of the raceway if they aren't properly secured. There have been many cases where conductors in a vertical raceway were released from the pulling "basket" or "grip" (at the top) without being secured, and the conductors fell down and out of the raceway, injuring those at the bottom of the installation.

300.20 Induced Currents in Ferrous Metal Enclosures and Raceways

(A) Conductors Grouped Together. To minimize induction heating of ferrous metal raceways and ferrous metal enclosures for alternating-current circuits, and to maintain an effective ground-fault current path, all conductors of a circuit must be installed in the same raceway, cable, trench, cord, or cable tray. See 250.102(E), 300.3(B), 300.5(I), and 392.8(D). Figure 300–52

Author's Comment:

- When alternating current (ac) flows through a conductor, a pulsating or varying magnetic field is created around the conductor. This magnetic field is constantly expanding and contracting with the amplitude of the ac current. In the United States, the frequency is 60 cycles per second (Hz). Since ac reverses polarity 120 times per second, the magnetic field that surrounds the conductor also reverses its direction 120 times per second. This expanding and collapsing magnetic field induces eddy currents in the ferrous metal parts that surround the conductors, causing the metal parts to heat up from hysteresis heating.

  Magnetic materials naturally resist the rapidly changing magnetic fields. The resulting friction produces its own additional heat—hysteresis heating—in addition to eddy current heating. A metal which offers high resistance is said to have high magnetic "permeability." Permeability can vary on a scale of 100 to 500 for magnetic materials; nonmagnetic materials have a permeability of one.

  Simply put, the molecules of steel and iron align to the polarity of the magnetic field and when the magnetic field reverses, the molecules reverse their polarity as well. This back-and-forth alignment of the molecules heats up the metal, and the more the current flows, the greater the heat rises in the ferrous metal parts. Figure 300–53

When conductors of the same circuit are grouped together, the magnetic fields of the different conductors tend to cancel each other out, resulting in a reduced magnetic field around the conductors. The lower magnetic field reduces induced currents in the ferrous metal raceways or enclosures, which reduces the hysteresis heating of the surrounding metal enclosure.

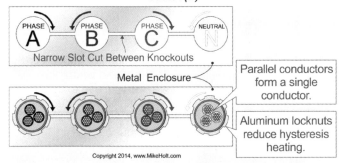

When single conductors are installed in a nonmetallic raceway, inductive heating of the metal enclosure must be minimized by cutting a slot between the individual holes through which the conductors pass.

Figure 300–54

Note: Because aluminum is a nonmagnetic metal, aluminum parts don't heat up due to hysteresis heating.

Author's Comment:

■ Aluminum conduit, locknuts, and enclosures carry eddy currents, but because aluminum is nonferrous, it doesn't heat up [300.20(B) Note].

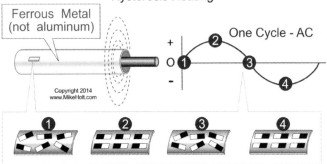

Ferrous metal (steel and iron) molecules align to the polarity of the magnetic field, and when the field reverses, the molecules reverse their polarity. This back-and-forth alignment of the molecules heats up ferrous metal parts.

Figure 300–53

⚠ WARNING: *There's been much discussion in the press on the effects of electromagnetic fields on humans. According to the Institute of Electrical and Electronics Engineers (IEEE), there's insufficient information at this time to define an unsafe electromagnetic field level.*

(B) Single Conductors. When single conductors are installed in nonmetallic raceways as permitted in 300.5(I) Ex 2, the inductive heating of the metal enclosure must be minimized by the use of aluminum and by cutting a slot between the individual holes through which the conductors pass. Figure 300–54

300.21 Spread of Fire or Products of Combustion

Electrical circuits and equipment must be installed in such a way that the spread of fire or products of combustion won't be substantially increased. Openings into or through fire-rated walls, floors, and ceilings for electrical equipment must be fire-stopped using methods approved by the authority having jurisdiction to maintain the fire-resistance rating of the fire-rated assembly. Figure 300–55

Spread of Fire or Products of Combustion
300.21

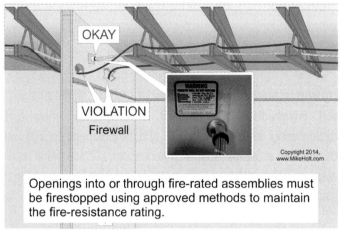

Openings into or through fire-rated assemblies must be firestopped using approved methods to maintain the fire-resistance rating.

Figure 300–55

Ducts Used for Dust, Loose Stock, or Vapor
300.22(A)

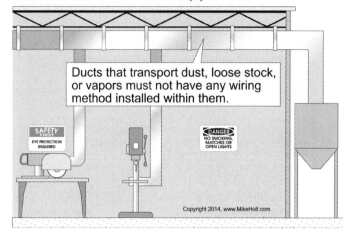

Ducts that transport dust, loose stock, or vapors must not have any wiring method installed within them.

Figure 300–56

300.22 Wiring in Ducts Not for Air Handling, Fabricated Ducts for Environmental Air, and Other Spaces for Environmental Air (Plenums)

The provisions of this section apply to the installation and uses of electrical wiring and equipment in ducts used for dust, loose stock, or vapor removal; ducts specifically fabricated for environmental air, and spaces used for environmental air (plenums).

(A) Ducts Used for Dust, Loose Stock, or Vapor. Ducts that transport dust, loose stock, or vapors must not have any wiring method installed within them. Figure 300–56

(B) Ducts Specifically Fabricated for Environmental Air. If necessary for direct action upon, or sensing of, the contained air, Type MC cable that has a smooth or corrugated impervious metal sheath without an overall nonmetallic covering, electrical metallic tubing, flexible metallic tubing, intermediate metal conduit, or rigid metal conduit without an overall nonmetallic covering can be installed in ducts specifically fabricated to transport environmental air. Flexible metal conduit in lengths not exceeding 4 ft can be used to connect physically adjustable equipment and devices within the fabricated duct.

Equipment is only permitted within the duct specifically fabricated to transport environmental air if necessary for the direct action upon, or sensing of, the contained air. Equipment, devices, and/or illumination are only permitted to be installed in the duct if necessary to facilitate maintenance and repair. Figure 300–57

Wiring in Ducts Specifically Fabricated
for Environmental Air
300.22(B)

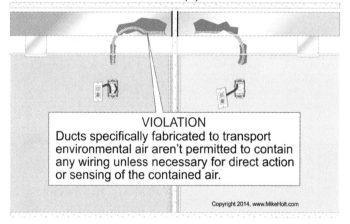

VIOLATION
Ducts specifically fabricated to transport environmental air aren't permitted to contain any wiring unless necessary for direct action or sensing of the contained air.

Figure 300–57

(C) Other Spaces Used for Environmental Air (Plenums). This section applies to spaces used for air-handling purposes, but not fabricated for environmental air-handling purposes.

This requirement doesn't apply to habitable rooms or areas of buildings, the prime purpose of which isn't air handling. Figure 300–58

Other Spaces Used as a Plenum Space
300.22(C)

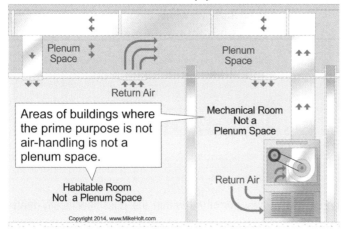

Figure 300–58

Note 1: The spaces above a suspended ceiling or below a raised floor used for environmental air are examples of the type of space to which this section applies. Figure 300–59

Other Spaces Used as a Plenum Space
300.22(C) Note 1

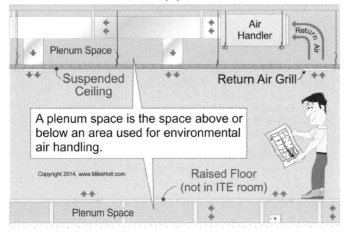

Figure 300–59

Note 2: The phrase "other space used for environmental air (plenums)" correlates with the term "plenum" in NFPA 90A, *Standard for the Installation of Air-Conditioning and Ventilating Systems*, and other mechanical codes where the ceiling is used for return air purposes, as well as some other air-handling spaces.

(1) Wiring Methods. Electrical metallic tubing, rigid metal conduit, intermediate metal conduit, armored cable, metal-clad cable without a nonmetallic cover, and flexible metal conduit can be installed in plenum spaces. If accessible, surface metal raceways or metal wireways with metal covers can be installed in a plenum space. Figure 300–60

Wiring Methods Permitted in a Plenum Space
300.22(C)(1)

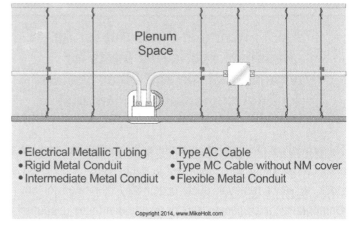

Figure 300–60

<u>Cable ties for securing and supporting must be listed as having adequate fire resistant and low smoke producing characteristics.</u>

Author's Comment:

- PVC conduit [Article 352], electrical nonmetallic tubing [Article 362], liquidtight flexible conduit, and nonmetallic cables aren't permitted to be installed in plenum spaces because they give off deadly toxic fumes when burned or superheated.

- Any wiring method suitable for the condition can be used in a space not used for environmental air-handling purposes. Figure 300–61

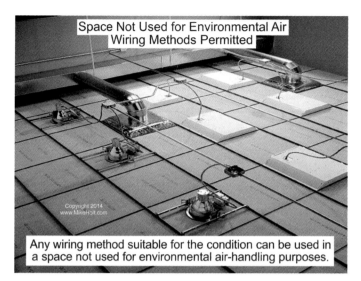

Figure 300–61

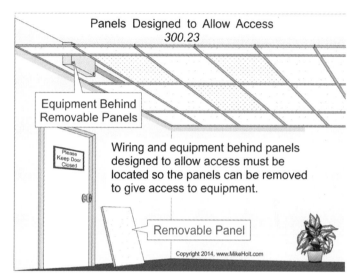

300.23 Panels Designed to Allow Access

Wiring, cables, and equipment installed behind panels must be located so the panels can be removed to give access to electrical equipment. Figure 300–62

Figure 300–62

2014 CHANGE ANALYSIS: Plenum spaces, such as those commonly found above a suspended ceiling or beneath a raised floor, use the open air space as a method of transporting the air in a building. Because this air is recycled throughout the building, the properties of any combustible material are regulated by this *Code* as well as by the mechanical code(s). If a fire were to occur in a building, the smoke produced by materials such as plastic can incapacitate the occupants very quickly. While cable ties don't add a lot of fuel to a fire, they do add to the problem, and it all adds up if it's not regulated. These cable ties must now be listed for use in plenum spaces.

ARTICLE
310

CONDUCTORS FOR GENERAL WIRING

Introduction to Article 310—Conductors for General Wiring

This article contains the general requirements for conductors, such as insulation markings, ampacity ratings, and conditions of use. It doesn't apply to conductors that are part of flexible cords, fixture wires, or to conductors that are an integral part of equipment [90.7 and 300.1(B)].

People often make mistakes in applying the ampacity tables contained in Article 310. If you study the explanations carefully, you'll avoid common errors such as applying Table 310.15(B)(17) when you should be applying Table 310.15(B)(16).

Why so many tables? Why does Table 310.15(B)(17) list the ampacity of 6 THHN as 105 amperes, while Table 310.15(B)(16) lists the same conductor as having an ampacity of only 75 amperes? To answer that, go back to Article 100 and review the definition of ampacity. Notice the phrase "conditions of use." These tables set a maximum current value at which premature failure of the conductor insulation shouldn't occur during normal use, under the conditions described in the tables.

The designations THHN, THHW, RHH, and so on, are insulation types. Every type of insulation has a limit to how much heat it can withstand. When current flows through a conductor, it creates heat. How well the insulation around a conductor can dissipate that heat depends on factors such as whether that conductor is in free air or not. Think about what happens when you put on a sweater, a jacket, and then a coat—all at the same time. You heat up. Your skin can't dissipate heat with all that clothing on nearly as well as it dissipates heat in free air. The same principal applies to conductors.

Conductor insulation also fails with age. That's why we conduct cable testing and take other measures to predict failure and replace certain conductors (for example, feeders or critical equipment conductors) while they're still within design specifications. But conductor insulation failure takes decades under normal use—and it's a maintenance issue. However, if a conductor is forced to exceed the ampacity listed in the appropriate table, and as a result its design temperature is exceeded, insulation failure happens much more rapidly—often catastrophically. Consequently, exceeding the allowable ampacity of a conductor is a serious safety issue.

Part I. General

310.1 Scope

(A) Installations. Article 310 contains the general requirements for conductors, such as insulation markings, ampacity ratings, and their use.

(B) Integral Parts of Equipment. This article doesn't apply to conductors that are an integral part of equipment [90.7 and 300.1(B)]. Figure 310–1

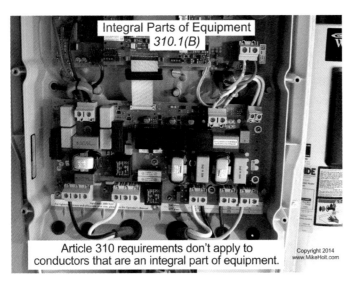

Figure 310–1

Part II. Installation

310.10 Uses Permitted

Conductors described in 310.104 can be used in any of the wiring methods recognized in Chapter 3 as permitted in this *Code [110.8]*.

(B) Dry and Damp Locations. Insulated conductors typically used in dry and damp locations include THHN, THHW, THWN, and THWN-2.

Author's Comment:

■ Refer to Table 310.104 for a complete list of conductors that may be installed in dry or damp locations.

(C) Wet Locations. Insulated conductors typically used in wet locations include:

(2) Types RHW, THHW, THWN, THWN-2, XHHW, and XHHW-2

Author's Comment:

■ Refer to Table 310.104 for a complete list of conductors that may be installed in wet locations.

(D) Locations Exposed to Direct Sunlight. Insulated conductors and cables exposed to the direct rays of the sun must be:

(1) Listed as sunlight resistant or marked as being sunlight resistant. Figure 310–2

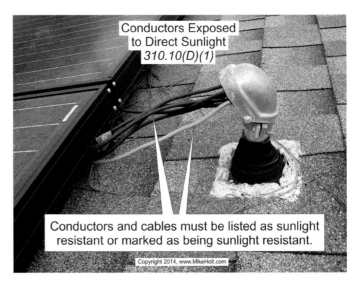

Figure 310–2

Author's Comment:

■ SE cable and the conductors contained in the cable are listed as sunlight resistant. However, according to the UL listing standard, the conductors contained in SE cable aren't required to be marked as sunlight resistant.

(2) Covered with insulating material, such as tape or sleeving materials that are listed as being sunlight resistant or marked as being sunlight resistant.

(G) Corrosive Conditions. Conductor insulation must be suitable for any substance to which it may be exposed that may have a detrimental effect on the conductor's insulation, such as oil, grease, vapor, gases, fumes, liquids, or other substances. See 110.11.

(H) Conductors in Parallel.

(1) General. Ungrounded and grounded/neutral conductors can be connected in parallel only in sizes 1/0 AWG and larger. Figure 310–3

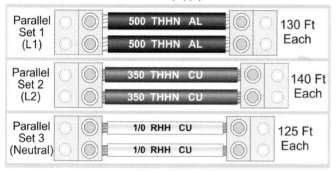

Conductors In Parallel
310.10(H)(1)

Phase and neutral conductors 1/0 and larger are permitted to be connected in parallel (electrically joined at both ends) in accordance with 310.10(H)(2) through (H)(6).

Figure 310–3

(2) Conductor and Installation Characteristics. When circuit conductors are installed in parallel, the conductors must be connected so that the current will be evenly distributed between the individual parallel conductors by requiring all circuit conductors within each parallel set to: Figure 310–4

(1) Be the same length.

(2) Consist of the same conductor material (copper/aluminum).

(3) Be the same size in circular mil area (minimum 1/0 AWG).

(4) Have the same type of insulation (like THHN).

(5) Terminate in the same method (set screw versus compression).

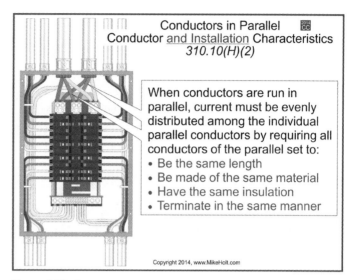

Conductors in Parallel
Conductor and Installation Characteristics
310.10(H)(2)

When conductors are run in parallel, current must be evenly distributed among the individual parallel conductors by requiring all conductors of the parallel set to:
• Be the same length
• Be made of the same material
• Have the same insulation
• Terminate in the same manner

Figure 310–4

Author's Comment:

■ Conductors aren't required to have the same physical characteristics as those of another ungrounded or grounded/neutral conductor to achieve balance.

(3) Separate Raceways or Cables. Raceways or cables containing parallel conductors must have the same electrical characteristics and the same number of conductors. Figure 310–5

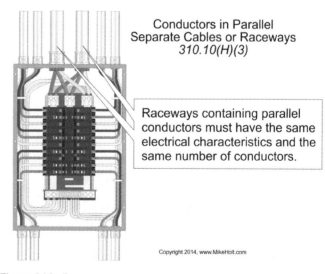

Conductors in Parallel
Separate Cables or Raceways
310.10(H)(3)

Raceways containing parallel conductors must have the same electrical characteristics and the same number of conductors.

Figure 310–5

Author's Comment:

- If one set of parallel conductors is installed in a metallic raceway and the other conductors are installed in PVC conduit, the conductors in the metallic raceway will have an increased opposition to current flow (impedance) as compared to the conductors in the nonmetallic raceway. This results in an unbalanced distribution of current between the parallel conductors.

Parallel sets of conductors aren't required to have the same physical characteristics as those of another set to achieve balance.

Author's Comment:

- For example, a 400A feeder with a neutral load of 240A can be paralleled as follows: Figure 310–6

  □ Phase A, Two—250 kcmil THHN aluminum, 100 ft
  □ Phase B, Two—3/0 THHN copper, 104 ft
  □ Phase C, Two—3/0 THHN copper, 102 ft
  □ Neutral, Two—1/0 THHN aluminum, 103 ft
  □ Equipment Grounding Conductor, Two—3 AWG copper, 101 ft*

The minimum 1/0 AWG requirement doesn't apply to equipment grounding conductors [310.10(H)(5)].

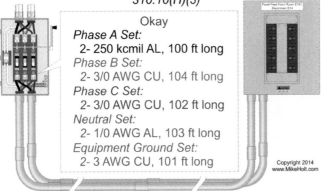

Conductors in Parallel - Separate Cables or Raceways
310.10(H)(3)

Okay
Phase A Set:
2- 250 kcmil AL, 100 ft long
Phase B Set:
2- 3/0 AWG CU, 104 ft long
Phase C Set:
2- 3/0 AWG CU, 102 ft long
Neutral Set:
2- 1/0 AWG AL, 103 ft long
Equipment Ground Set:
2- 3 AWG CU, 101 ft long

Copyright 2014
www.MikeHolt.com

For current to be evenly distributed between the individual parallel conductors, each conductor (within a parallel set) must be identical to each other.

Figure 310–6

(4) Conductor Ampacity Adjustment. Each current-carrying conductor of a paralleled set of conductors must be counted as a current-carrying conductor for the purpose of conductor ampacity adjustment, in accordance with Table 310.15(B)(3)(a). Figure 310–7

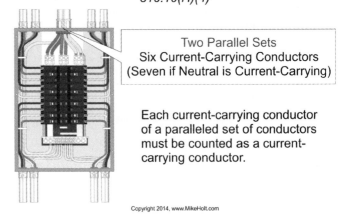

Conductors in Parallel
Conductor Ampacity Adjustment
310.10(H)(4)

Two Parallel Sets
Six Current-Carrying Conductors
(Seven if Neutral is Current-Carrying)

Each current-carrying conductor of a paralleled set of conductors must be counted as a current-carrying conductor.

Copyright 2014, www.MikeHolt.com

Figure 310–7

(5) Equipment Bonding Conductors. The equipment bonding conductors for circuits in parallel must be sized in accordance with 250.122. Figure 310–8

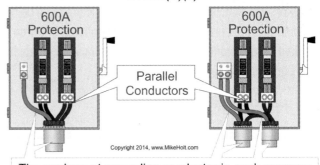

Conductors in Parallel
Equipment Grounding Conductor
310.10(H)(5)

600A Protection   600A Protection

Parallel Conductors

Copyright 2014, www.MikeHolt.com

The equipment grounding conductor in each raceway is sized to 250.122(F) based on the rating of the overcurrent device. 600A = 1 AWG [Table 250.22]

Figure 310–8

Author's Comment:

- The minimum 1/0 AWG parallel conductor size rule of 310.10(H) doesn't apply to equipment bonding conductors.

(6) Bonding Jumpers. Equipment bonding jumpers <u>or supply-side bonding jumpers</u> installed in raceways must be sized in accordance with 250.102.

310.15 Conductor Ampacity

Author's Comment:

- According to Article 100, "ampacity" means the maximum current, in amperes, a conductor can carry continuously, where the temperature of the conductor won't be raised in excess of its insulation temperature rating. Figure 310–9

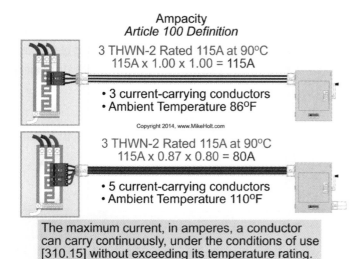

Ampacity
Article 100 Definition

3 THWN-2 Rated 115A at 90°C
115A x 1.00 x 1.00 = 115A

- 3 current-carrying conductors
- Ambient Temperature 86°F

Copyright 2014, www.MikeHolt.com

3 THWN-2 Rated 115A at 90°C
115A x 0.87 x 0.80 = 80A

- 5 current-carrying conductors
- Ambient Temperature 110°F

The maximum current, in amperes, a conductor can carry continuously, under the conditions of use [310.15] without exceeding its temperature rating.

Figure 310–9

(A) General Requirements.

(1) Tables for Engineering Supervision. The ampacity of a conductor can be determined either by using the tables in accordance with 310.15(B), or under engineering supervision as provided in 310.15(C).

Note 1: Ampacities provided by this section don't take voltage drop into consideration. See 210.19(A) Note 4, for branch circuits and 215.2(A) Note 2, for feeders.

(2) Conductor Ampacity—Lower Rating. Where more than one ampacity applies for a given circuit length, the lowest value must be used. Figure 310–10

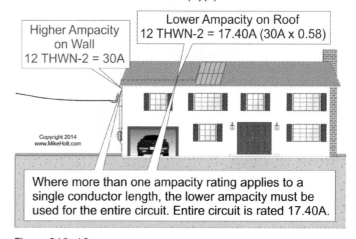

Conductor Ampacity - Lower Rating
310.15(A)(2)

Higher Ampacity on Wall
12 THWN-2 = 30A

Lower Ampacity on Roof
12 THWN-2 = 17.40A (30A x 0.58)

Copyright 2014
www.MikeHolt.com

Where more than one ampacity rating applies to a single conductor length, the lower ampacity must be used for the entire circuit. Entire circuit is rated 17.40A.

Figure 310–10

Ex: When different ampacities apply to a length of conductor, the higher ampacity is permitted for the entire circuit if the reduced ampacity length doesn't exceed 10 ft and its length doesn't exceed 10 percent of the length of the higher ampacity. Figures 310–11 and 310–12

(3) Insulation Temperature Limitation. Conductors must not be used where the operating temperature exceeds that designated for the type of insulated conductor involved.

Note 1: The insulation temperature rating of a conductor [Table 310.104(A)] is the maximum temperature a conductor can withstand over a prolonged time period without serious degradation. The main factors to consider for conductor operating temperature include:

(1) Ambient temperature may vary along the conductor length as well as from time to time [Table 310.15(B)(2)(a)].

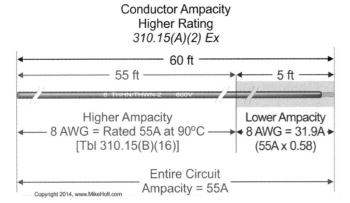

Conductor Ampacity
Higher Rating
310.15(A)(2) Ex

The higher ampacity can be used if the length of the lower ampacity isn't more than 10 ft, and it isn't longer than 10 percent of the higher ampacity length.

Figure 310–11

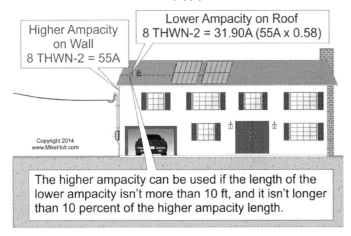

Conductor Ampacity - Higher Rating
310.15(A)(2) Ex

Figure 310–12

(2) Heat generated internally in the conductor—load current flow.

(3) The rate at which generated heat dissipates into the ambient medium.

(4) Adjacent load-carrying conductors have the effect of raising the ambient temperature and impeding heat dissipation [Table 310.15(B)(3)(a)].

Note 2: See 110.14(C)(1) for the temperature limitation of terminations.

(B) Ampacity Table. The allowable conductor ampacities listed in Table 310.15(B)(16) are based on conditions where the ambient temperature isn't over 86°F, and no more than three current-carrying conductors are bundled together. Figure 310–13

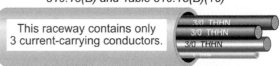

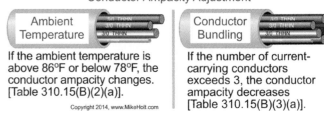

Conductor Ampacity - Correction and Adjustment
310.15(B) and Table 310.15(B)(16)

Figure 310–13

The temperature correction and adjustment factors apply to the conductor ampacity, based on the temperature rating of the conductor insulation in accordance with Table 310.15(B)(16). Figure 310–14

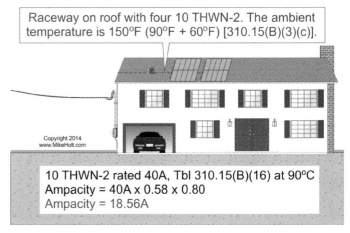

Conductor Ampacity - Temperature Correction Adjustment
310.15(B)(2)

Figure 310–14

(2) Conductor Ampacity Ambient Temperature Correction. When conductors are installed in an ambient temperature other than 78°F to 86°F, the ampacities listed in Table 310.15(B)(16) must be corrected in accordance with the multipliers listed in Table 310.15(B)(2)(a). Figure 310–15

Size	Table 310.15(B)(16) Allowable Ampacities of Insulated Conductors Based on Not More Than Three Current-Carrying Conductors and Ambient Temperature of 30°C (86°F)*						Size
	60°C (140°F)	75°C (167°F)	90°C (194°F)	60°C (140°F)	75°C (167°F)	90°C (194°F)	
AWG kcmil	TW UF	RHW THHW THW THWN XHHW USE	RHH RHW-2 THHN THHW THW-2 THWN-2 USE-2 XHHW XHHW-2	TW UF	THHN THW THWN XHHW	THHN THW-2 THWN-2 THHW XHHW XHHW-2	AWG kcmil
	Copper			Aluminum/Copper-Clad Aluminum			
14*	15	20	25				14*
12*	20	25	30	15	20	25	12*
10*	30	35	40	25	30	35	10*
8	40	50	55	35	40	45	8
6	55	65	75	40	50	55	6
4	70	85	95	55	65	75	4
3	85	100	115	65	75	85	3
2	95	115	130	75	90	100	2
1	110	130	145	85	100	115	1
1/0	125	150	170	100	120	135	1/0
2/0	145	175	195	115	135	150	2/0
3/0	165	200	225	130	155	175	3/0
4/0	195	230	260	150	180	205	4/0
250	215	255	290	170	205	230	250
300	240	285	320	195	230	260	300
350	260	310	350	210	250	280	350
400	280	335	380	225	270	305	400
500	320	380	430	260	310	350	500

*See 240.4(D)

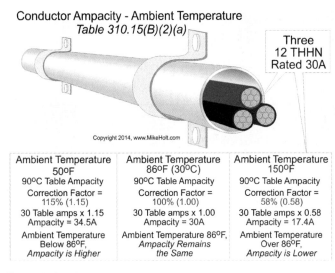

Conductor Ampacity - Ambient Temperature
Table 310.15(B)(2)(a)

Three
12 THHN
Rated 30A

Copyright 2014, www.MikeHolt.com

Ambient Temperature 50°F	Ambient Temperature 86°F (30°C)	Ambient Temperature 150°F
90°C Table Ampacity	90°C Table Ampacity	90°C Table Ampacity
Correction Factor = 115% (1.15)	Correction Factor = 100% (1.00)	Correction Factor = 58% (0.58)
30 Table amps x 1.15 Ampacity = 34.5A	30 Table amps x 1.00 Ampacity = 30A	30 Table amps x 0.58 Ampacity = 17.4A
Ambient Temperature Below 86°F, *Ampacity is Higher*	Ambient Temperature 86°F, *Ampacity Remains the Same*	Ambient Temperature Over 86°F, *Ampacity is Lower*

Figure 310–15

Table 310.15(B)(2)(a) Ambient Temperature Correction

Ambient Temperature °F	Ambient Temperature °C	Correction Factor 75°C Conductors	Correction Factor 90°C Conductors
50 or less	10 or less	1.20	1.15
51–59°F	11–15°C	1.15	1.12
60–68°F	16–20°C	1.11	1.08
69–77°F	21–25°C	1.05	1.04
78–86°F	26–30°C	1.00	1.00
87–95°F	31–35°C	0.94	0.96
96–104°F	36–40°C	0.88	0.91
105–113°F	41–45°C	0.82	0.87
114–122°F	46–50°C	0.75	0.82
123–131°F	51–55°C	0.67	0.76
132–140°F	56–60°C	0.58	0.71
141–149°F	61–65°C	0.47	0.65
150–158°F	66–70°C	0.33	0.58
159–167°F	71–75°C	0.00	0.50
168–176°F	76–80°C	0.00	0.41
177–185°F	81–85°C	0.00	0.29

(3) Conductor Ampacity Adjustment.

(a) Four or More Current-Carrying <u>Conductors</u>. Where four or more current-carrying power conductors are in a raceway longer than 24 in. [310.15(B)(3)(a)(3)], or where cables are bundled for a length longer than 24 in., the ampacity of each conductor must be reduced in accordance with Table 310.15(B)(3)(a). Figure 310–16

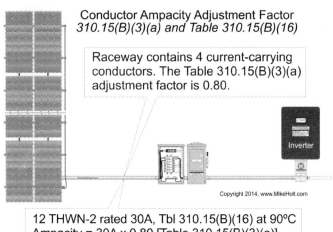

Conductor Ampacity Adjustment Factor
310.15(B)(3)(a) and Table 310.15(B)(16)

Raceway contains 4 current-carrying conductors. The Table 310.15(B)(3)(a) adjustment factor is 0.80.

Inverter

Copyright 2014, www.MikeHolt.com

12 THWN-2 rated 30A, Tbl 310.15(B)(16) at 90°C
Ampacity = 30A x 0.80 [Table 310.15(B)(3)(a)]
Ampacity = 24A

Figure 310–16

Table 310.15(B)(3)(a) Conductor Ampacity Adjustment for More Than Three Current-Carrying Conductors

Number of Conductors[1]	Adjustment
4–6	0.80 or 80%
7–9	0.70 or 70%
10–20	0.50 or 50%
21–30	0.45 or 50%
31–40	0.40 or 40%
41 and above	0.35 or 35%

[1]*Number of conductors is the total number of conductors, including spare conductors, <u>including spare conductors</u>, adjusted in accordance with 310.15(B)(5) and (B)(6). <u>It doesn't include conductors that can't be energized at the same time.</u>*

2014 CHANGE ANALYSIS: The 2011 edition of the *NEC* made an attempt to clarify the rules for ampacity adjustment as they pertain to spare conductors and other conductors that weren't clearly addressed in the rule. The attempt didn't quite work, because the title of the table, the table note, and the *Code* text seemed to argue with each other. By adding the note at the bottom of Table 310.15(B)(3)(a), it's clear that spare conductors are counted for ampacity adjustment, due to the fact that they'll probably be used eventually, and it would be a difficult sell to a customer to convince them that simply terminating these conductors to equipment suddenly makes every wire in the raceway undersized. In order to avoid that argument, the conductor is counted immediately upon installation.

Conductors that can't be energized simultaneously are also now discussed in the table. Consider a set of 3-way switches. One switch is fed by the supply conductor, while the other switch feeds the luminaire. Between these switches are two conductors, often referred to as "travelers." Regardless of the position of either switch, one of the travelers will be energized, and the other will not. If you change the position (up or down) of either switch, you'll change which of the travelers is energized, but in no case can you possibly energize both. Due to this, there's no reason to count both conductors in the ampacity adjustment, as only one of them will be adding heat.

Author's Comment:

■ Conductor ampacity reduction is required when four or more current-carrying conductors are bundled because heat generated by current flow isn't able to dissipate as quickly as when there are three or fewer current-carrying conductors. Figure 310–17

(1) Conductor ampacity adjustment of Table 310.15(B)(3)(a) doesn't apply to conductors installed in cable trays, 392.80 applies.

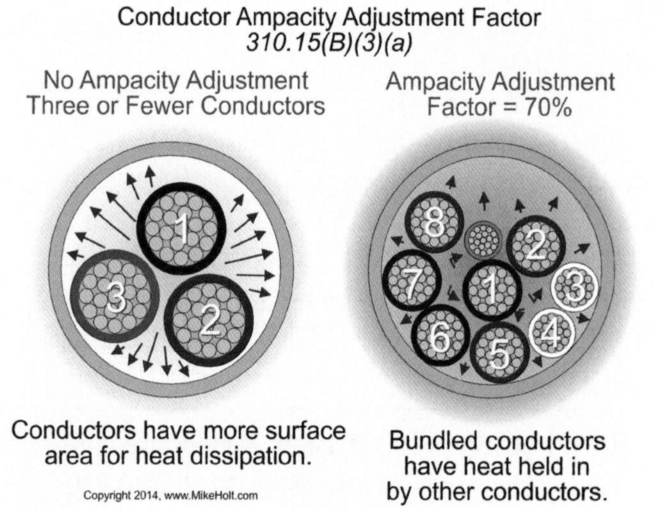

Conductor Ampacity Adjustment Factor
310.15(B)(3)(a)

No Ampacity Adjustment
Three or Fewer Conductors

Ampacity Adjustment
Factor = 70%

Conductors have more surface area for heat dissipation.

Bundled conductors have heat held in by other conductors.

Copyright 2014, www.MikeHolt.com

Figure 310–17

(2) Conductor ampacity adjustment of Table 310.15(B)(3)(a) doesn't apply to conductors in raceways having a length not exceeding 24 in.

(c) Raceways and Cables Exposed to Sunlight on Rooftops. When applying ampacity adjustment correction factors, the ambient temperature adjustment contained in Table 310.15(B)(3)(c) is added to the outdoor ambient temperature for conductors installed in raceways or cables exposed to direct sunlight on or above rooftops to determine the applicable ambient temperature for ampacity correction factors in Table 310.15(B)(2)(a) or Table 310.15(B)(2)(b). Figure 310–18

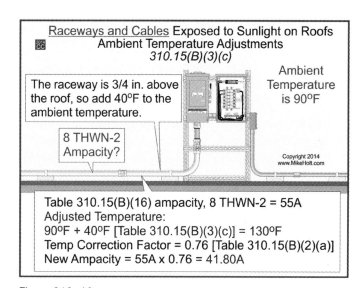

Raceways and Cables Exposed to Sunlight on Roofs
Ambient Temperature Adjustments
310.15(B)(3)(c)

The raceway is 3/4 in. above the roof, so add 40°F to the ambient temperature.

Ambient Temperature is 90°F

8 THWN-2 Ampacity?

Copyright 2014 www.MikeHolt.com

Table 310.15(B)(16) ampacity, 8 THWN-2 = 55A
Adjusted Temperature:
90°F + 40°F [Table 310.15(B)(3)(c)] = 130°F
Temp Correction Factor = 0.76 [Table 310.15(B)(2)(a)]
New Ampacity = 55A x 0.76 = 41.80A

Figure 310–18

Ex: The ampacity adjustment isn't required for conductors that are type XHHW-2.

Note: See the *ASHRAE Handbook—Fundamentals* (www.ashrae.org) as a source for <u>the ambient</u> temperatures in various locations.

Note to Table 310.15(B)(3)(c): The temperature adders in Table 310.15(B)(3)(c) are based on the <u>measured temperature rise above local climatic</u> ambient temperatures <u>due to sunlight heating</u>.

Table 310.15(B)(3)(c) Ambient Temperature Adder for <u>Raceways or Cables</u> On or Above Rooftops

Distance of <u>Raceway or Cable</u> Above Roof	C°	F°
0 to ½ in.	33	60
Above ½ in. to 3½ in.	22	40
Above 3½ in. to 12 in.	17	30
Above 12 in. to 36 in.	14	25

2014 CHANGE ANALYSIS: Of all the *NEC* rules that have been added over the last three *Code* change cycles, this is one of the most controversial. It started as an Informational Note (actually a Fine Print Note back then), and then grew into a requirement that receives dozens of proposals every three years. New to this edition of the *NEC*, the conductors in any raceway, not just circular raceways, are required to comply with this requirement. Conductors inside cable assemblies are also required to comply.

A new exception for type XHHW-2 has been added as well. Testing showed that this conductor insulation type fared much better than other 90°C conductors as it relates to the impact of high temperatures. Interestingly, this data has not only resulted in the exception being added, but has generated a lot of discussion about whether or not the whole "raceways and cables on roof-tops" is an issue worth having in the *NEC* at all. There still haven't been any documented failures to warrant the requirement, and it appears that the *Code*-Making panel is finally willing to discuss that fact.

Part III. Construction Specification

310.104 Conductor Construction and Application

Only conductors in Tables 310.104(A) though 310.104(E) can be installed, and only for the application identified in the tables.

Author's Comment:

- The following explains the lettering on conductor insulation: Figure 310–19

  - ☐ F   Fixture wires (solid or 7 strands) [Table 402.3]
  - ☐ FF   Flexible fixture wire (19 strands) [Table 402.3]
  - ☐ No H   60°C insulation rating [Table 310.104(A)]
  - ☐ H   75°C insulation rating [Table 310.104(A)]
  - ☐ HH   90°C insulation rating [Table 310.104(A)]
  - ☐ N   Nylon outer cover [Table 310.104(A)]
  - ☐ R   Thermoset insulation [Table 310.104(A)]
  - ☐ T   Thermoplastic insulation [Table 310.104(A)]
  - ☐ U   Underground [Table 310.104(A)]
  - ☐ W   Wet or damp locations [Table 310.104(A)]
  - ☐ X   Cross-linked polyethylene insulation [Table 310.104(A)]

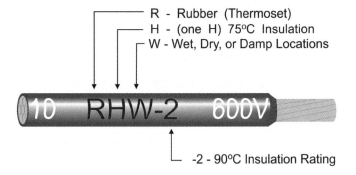

Understanding Conductor Insulation Markings
Table 310.104(A)

R - Rubber (Thermoset)
H - (one H) 75°C Insulation
W - Wet, Dry, or Damp Locations

10 RHW-2 600V

-2 - 90°C Insulation Rating

Copyright 2014, www.MikeHolt.com

Figure 310–19

310.106 Conductors

(A) Minimum Size Conductors. The smallest conductor permitted for branch circuits for residential, commercial, and industrial locations is 14 AWG copper, except as permitted elsewhere in this *Code*.

Author's Comment:

■ There's a misconception that 12 AWG copper is the smallest conductor permitted for commercial or industrial facilities. Although this isn't true based on *NEC* rules, it may be a local *Code* requirement.

(C) Stranded Conductors. Conductors 8 AWG and larger must be stranded when installed in a raceway. Figure 310–20

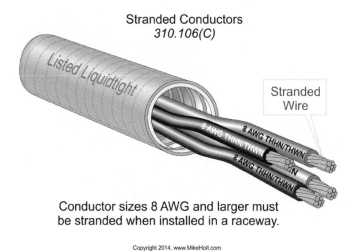

Stranded Conductors
310.106(C)

Stranded Wire

Conductor sizes 8 AWG and larger must
be stranded when installed in a raceway.

Copyright 2014, www.MikeHolt.com

Figure 310–20

Author's Comment:

■ Solid conductors are often used for the grounding electrode conductor [250.62] and for the bonding of pools, spas, and outdoor hot tubs [680.26(C)]. Technically, the practice of installing 8 AWG and larger solid conductors in a raceway for the protection of grounding and bonding conductors is a violation of this rule.

(D) Insulated. Conductors must be insulated except where specific permission allows them to be covered or bare.

310.110 Conductor Identification

(A) Grounded and Neutral Conductor. Grounded and neutral conductors must be identified in accordance with 200.6.

(B) Equipment Grounding Conductor. Equipment grounding conductors must be identified in accordance with 250.119.

(C) Ungrounded Conductors. Ungrounded conductors must be clearly distinguishable from grounded, neutral, and equipment grounding conductors.

Author's Comment:

■ If the premises wiring system has branch circuits or feeders supplied from more than one nominal voltage system, each ungrounded conductor of the branch circuit or feeder, if accessible, must be identified by system. The means of identification can be by separate color coding, marking tape, tagging, or other means approved by the authority having jurisdiction. Such identification must be permanently posted at each panelboard [210.5(C) and 215.12].

■ The *NEC* doesn't require color coding of ungrounded conductors, except for the high-leg conductor when a grounded/neutral conductor is present [110.15 and 230.56]. Although not required, electricians often use the following color system for power and lighting conductor identification:

  ☐ 120/240V, single-phase—black, red, and white
  ☐ 120/208V, three-phase—black, red, blue, and
  ☐ 120/240V, three-phase, delta-connected system— black, orange, blue, and white
  ☐ 277/480V, three-phase, wye-connected system— brown, orange, yellow, and gray; or, brown, purple, yellow, and gray

Notes

ARTICLE 312

CABINETS

Introduction to Article 312—Cabinets

This article addresses the installation and construction specifications for the items mentioned in its title. In Article 310, we observed that the conditions of use have an effect on the ampacity of a conductor. Likewise, the conditions of use have an effect on the selection and application of cabinets. For example, you can't use just any enclosure in a wet or hazardous location. The conditions of use impose special requirements for these situations.

For all such enclosures, certain requirements apply—regardless of the use. For example, you must cover any openings, protect conductors from abrasion, and allow sufficient bending room for conductors.

Notice that Article 408 covers switchboards and panelboards, with primary emphasis on the interior, or "guts," while the cabinet that's used to enclose a panelboard is covered here in Article 312. Therefore you'll find that some important considerations such as wire-bending space at the terminals of panelboards are included in this article.

Article 312 covers the installation and construction specifications for cabinets. [312.1].

Part I. Scope and Installation

312.1 Scope

Article 312 covers the installation and construction specifications for cabinets. Figure 312–1

Author's Comment:

■ A cabinet is an enclosure for either surface mounting or flush mounting and provided with a frame in which a door may be hung.

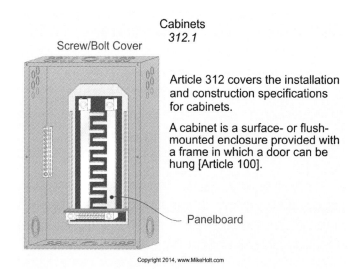

Cabinets
312.1
Screw/Bolt Cover

Article 312 covers the installation and construction specifications for cabinets.

A cabinet is a surface- or flush-mounted enclosure provided with a frame in which a door can be hung [Article 100].

— Panelboard

Copyright 2014, www.MikeHolt.com

Figure 312–1

312.2 Damp or Wet Locations

Enclosures in damp or wet locations must prevent moisture or water from entering or accumulating within the enclosure, and must be weatherproof if installed in a wet location. When the enclosure is surface mounted in a wet location, the enclosure must be mounted with not less than a ¼ in. air space between it and the mounting surface. See 300.6(D).

If raceways or cables enter above the level of uninsulated live parts of an enclosure in a wet location, a fitting listed for wet locations must be used for termination.

Author's Comment:

- A fitting listed for use in a wet location with a sealing locknut is suitable for this application.

Ex: The ¼ in. air space isn't required for nonmetallic equipment, raceways, or cables.

312.3 Installed in Walls

Cabinets installed in walls of noncombustible material must be installed so that the front edge of the enclosure is set back no more than ¼ in. from the finished surface. In walls constructed of wood or other combustible material, cabinets must be flush with the finished surface or project outward.

312.4 Repairing Gaps

Gaps around cabinets that are recessed in noncombustible surfaces (plaster, drywall, or plasterboard) having a flush-type cover, must be repaired so that there will be no gap more than ⅛ in. at the edge of the cabinet. Figure 312–2

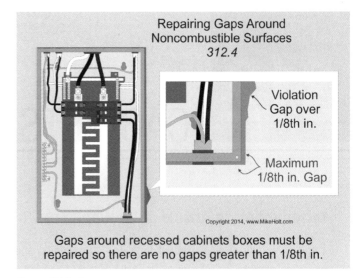

Gaps around recessed cabinets boxes must be repaired so there are no gaps greater than 1/8th in.

Figure 312–2

312.5 Enclosures

(A) Unused Openings. Openings in cabinets intended to provide entry for conductors must be <u>closed in an approved manner</u>. Figure 312–3

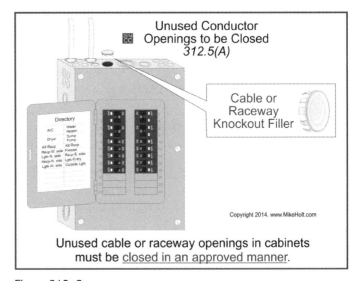

Unused cable or raceway openings in cabinets must be <u>closed in an approved manner</u>.

Figure 312–3

Author's Comment:

- Unused openings for circuit breakers must be closed by means that provide protection substantially equivalent to the wall of the enclosure [408.7]. **Figure 312–4**

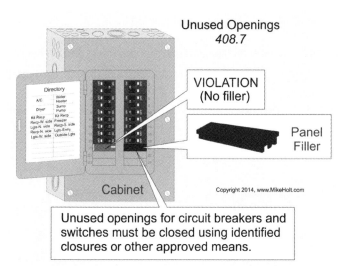

Figure 312–4

2014 CHANGE ANALYSIS: The word "adequate" is a term that should be avoided in any *Code* book, as it's far too subjective and means different things to different people. Many people talk about the fact that the *NEC* rules are often interpreted differently by various individuals. While this is true, and while it will never change, it's still worth trying to make the *Code* language less open to interpretation. Although this change doesn't completely eliminate controversy, it does decrease it. Other changes in the *NEC* that removed the word "adequate" succeeded wonderfully in removing interpretive text.

(C) Cable Termination. Cables must be secured to the cabinet with fittings designed and listed for the cable. See 300.12 and 300.15. Figure 312–5

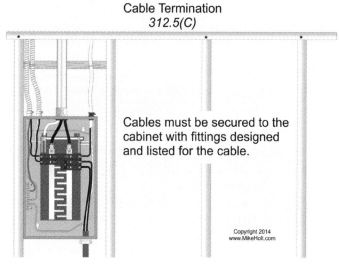

Figure 312–5

Author's Comment:

- Cable clamps or cable connectors must be used with only one cable, unless that clamp or fitting is identified for more than one cable. Some Type NM cable clamps are listed for two Type NM cables within a single fitting (UL White Book, *Guide Information for Electrical Equipment*, www.ul.com/regulators/2008_WhiteBook.pdf).

Ex: Cables with nonmetallic sheaths aren't required to be secured to the cabinet if the cables enter the top of a surface-mounted cabinet through a nonflexible raceway not less than 18 in. or more than 10 ft long, if all of the following conditions are met: Figure 312–6

(a) Each cable is fastened within 1 ft from the raceway.

(b) The raceway doesn't penetrate a structural ceiling.

(c) Fittings are provided on the raceway to protect the cables from abrasion.

(d) The raceway is sealed.

(e) Each cable sheath extends not less than ¼ in. into the panelboard.

(f) The raceway is properly secured.

(g) Conductor fill is limited to Chapter 9, Table 1 percentages.

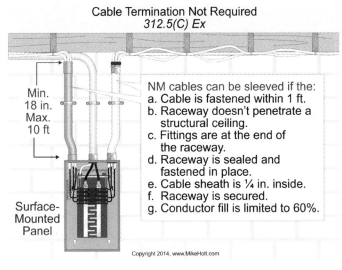

Cable Termination Not Required
312.5(C) Ex

Min. 18 in. Max. 10 ft

Surface-Mounted Panel

NM cables can be sleeved if the:
a. Cable is fastened within 1 ft.
b. Raceway doesn't penetrate a structural ceiling.
c. Fittings are at the end of the raceway.
d. Raceway is sealed and fastened in place.
e. Cable sheath is ¼ in. inside.
f. Raceway is secured.
g. Conductor fill is limited to 60%.

Copyright 2014, www.MikeHolt.com

Figure 312–6

312.6 Deflection of Conductors

Cabinets for conductors must be sized to allow conductors to be deflected in accordance with Table 312.6(A).

Table 312.6(A) Minimum Wire-Bending Space

Wire Size (AWG or kcmil)	Inches
8–6	1½
4–3	2
2	2½
1	3
1/0–2/0	3½
3/0–4/0	4
250	4½
300–350	5
400–500	6
600–700	8

312.8 Cabinets With Splices, Taps, and Feed-Through Conductors

Cabinets can be used for conductors feeding through, spliced, or tapping off to other enclosures, switches, or overcurrent devices where all of the following conditions are met:

(1) The total area of the conductors at any cross section doesn't exceed 40 percent of the cross-sectional area of the space. Figure 312–7

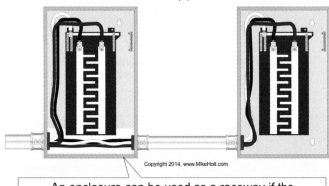

Switch and Overcurrent Device Enclosures
Splices, Taps, and Feed-Through Conductors
312.8(1)

Copyright 2014, www.MikeHolt.com

An enclosure can be used as a raceway if the conductors don't fill the wiring space to more than 40%.

Figure 312–7

(2) The total area of conductors, splices, and taps installed at any cross section doesn't exceed 75 percent of the cross-sectional area of that space.

(3) A warning label that isn't handwritten must be permanently affixed, and be of sufficient durability to withstand the environment involved [110.21(B)], on the cabinet that identifies the closest disconnecting means for feed-through conductors. Figure 312–8

2014 CHANGE ANALYSIS: With the addition of 110.21(B), several *Code* requirements such as this one have been revised. 110.21(B) requires that field-applied labels be permanently affixed, be suitable for the environment, and not be handwritten.

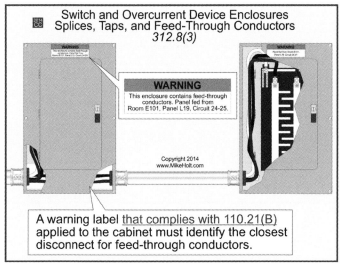

Figure 312–8

Notes

Mike Holt's Illustrated Guide to Understanding NEC Requirements for Solar Photovoltaic Systems

ARTICLE 314

OUTLET, DEVICE, PULL AND JUNCTION BOXES; CONDUIT BODIES; AND HANDHOLE ENCLOSURES

Introduction to Article 314—Outlet, Device, Pull and Junction Boxes; Conduit Bodies; and Handhole Enclosures

Article 314 contains installation requirements for outlet boxes, pull and junction boxes, conduit bodies, and handhole enclosures. As with the cabinets, cutout boxes, and meter socket enclosures covered in Article 312, the conditions of use have a bearing on the type of material and equipment selected for a particular installation. If a raceway is installed in a wet location, for example, the correct fittings and the proper installation methods must be used.

The information here will help you size an outlet box using the proper cubic-inch capacity as well as calculating the minimum dimensions for larger pull boxes. There are limits on the amount of weight that can be supported by an outlet box and rules on how to support a device or outlet box to various surfaces. Article 314 will help you understand these types of rules so that your installation will be compliant with the *NEC*. As always, the clear illustrations in this article will help you visualize the finished installation.

Part I. Scope and General

314.1 Scope

Article 314 contains the installation requirements for outlet boxes, conduit bodies, pull and junction boxes, and handhole enclosures. Figure 314–1

314.3 Nonmetallic Boxes

Nonmetallic boxes can only be used with nonmetallic cables and raceways.

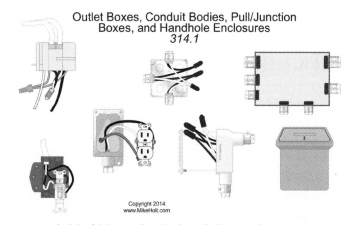

Outlet Boxes, Conduit Bodies, Pull/Junction Boxes, and Handhole Enclosures
314.1

Copyright 2014
www.MikeHolt.com

Article 314 contains the installation requirements for outlet boxes, conduit bodies, pull and junction boxes, and handhole enclosures.

Figure 314–1

Ex 1: Metal raceways and metal cables can be used with non-metallic boxes if all raceways are bonded together in the non-metallic box. Figure 314–2

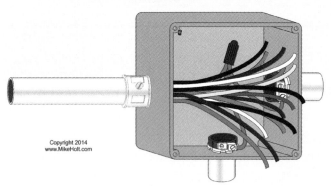

Nonmetallic Boxes - Metal Raceways
314.3 Ex 1

Copyright 2014
www.MikeHolt.com

Metal raceways can terminate to a nonmetallic box where internal bonding means are provided between all entries.

Figure 314–2

314.4 Metal Boxes

Metal boxes containing circuits that operate at 50V or more must be connected to an equipment grounding conductor of a type listed in 250.118 [250.112(I) and 250.148].

Part II. Installation

314.15 Damp or Wet Locations

Boxes, conduit bodies, and fittings in damp or wet locations must prevent moisture or water from entering or accumulating within the enclosure. Boxes, conduit bodies, and fittings installed in wet locations must be listed for use in wet locations.

Drainage openings can be installed in the field if they aren't larger than ¼ in. For listed drainage fittings, the holes can be larger, but must be in accordance with the manufacturer's instructions. Figure 314–3

Boxes and Conduit Bodies
in Damp or Wet Locations
314.15

Copyright 2014
www.MikeHolt.com

Drainage openings can be field installed if not larger than 1/4 in. Holes can be larger for listed drainage fittings per manufacturer's instructions.

Figure 314–3

Author's Comment:

- If handhole enclosures without bottoms are installed, all enclosed conductors and any splices or terminations must be listed as suitable for wet locations [314.30(C)].

2014 CHANGE ANALYSIS: People have been drilling holes in the bottom of enclosures for years in order to facilitate drainage when the design of the box isn't good enough. Although this has been accepted by most inspectors, it hasn't been addressed in the *Code*. With the inclusion of this new text, inspectors (and installers) now have guidance about the size of holes that can be added. If holes larger than ¼ in. are needed (although I'm not sure why they would be), there must be provisions in the instructions of the enclosure that allow for it.

314.17 Conductors That Enter Boxes or Conduit Bodies

(A) Openings to Be Closed. Openings through which cables or raceways enter must be <u>closed in an approved manner</u>.

Author's Comment:

- Unused cable or raceway openings in electrical equipment must be effectively closed by fittings that provide protection substantially equivalent to the wall of the equipment [110.12(A)]. Figure 314–4

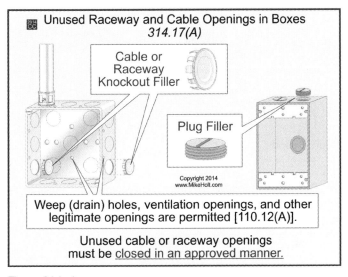

Figure 314–4

(B) Metal Boxes and Conduit Bodies. Raceways and cables must be mechanically fastened to metal boxes or conduit bodies by fittings designed for the wiring method. See 300.12 and 300.15. Figure 314–5

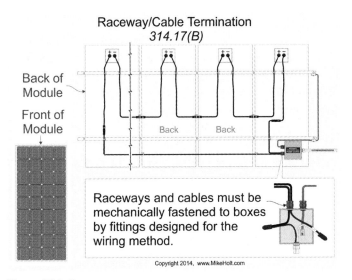

Figure 314–5

2014 CHANGE ANALYSIS: The word "adequate" is a term that should be avoided in any *Code* book, as it's far too subjective and means different things to different people. Many people talk about the fact that the *NEC* rules are often interpreted differently by various individuals. While this is true, and while it will never change, it's still worth trying to make the *Code* language less open to interpretation. Although this change doesn't completely eliminate controversy, it does decrease it. Other changes in the *NEC* that removed the word "adequate" succeeded wonderfully in removing interpretive text.

314.23 Support of Boxes and Conduit Bodies

Boxes must be securely supported by one of the following methods:

(A) Surface. Boxes can be fastened to any surface that provides adequate support.

(B) Structural Mounting. Boxes can be supported from any structural member, or they can be supported from grade by a metal, plastic, or wood brace.

(1) Nails and Screws. Nails or screws can be used to fasten boxes, provided the exposed threads of screws are protected to prevent abrasion of conductor insulation.

(2) Braces. Metal braces no less than 0.02 in. thick and wood braces not less than a nominal 1 in. x 2 in. can support a box.

(E) Raceway—Boxes and Conduit Bodies Without Devices or Luminaires. Two intermediate metal or rigid metal conduits, threaded wrenchtight into the enclosure, can be used to support an outlet box that doesn't contain a device or luminaire, if each raceway is supported within 36 in. of the box or within 18 in. of the box if all conduit entries are on the same side.

Ex: Conduit bodies are permitted to be supported by any of the following wiring methods:

(1) *Intermediate metal conduit, Type IMC*

(2) *Rigid metal conduit, Type RMC*

(3) *Rigid polyvinyl chloride conduit, Type PVC*

(4) *Reinforced thermosetting resin conduit, Type RTRC*

(5) *Electrical metallic tubing, Type EMT*

2014 CHANGE ANALYSIS: The phrase "of a building" was removed from 314.23(B). I can just hear the members of the *Code*-Making Panel voting on this rule: The word "structure" is defined in Article 100 as "that which is built or constructed." All buildings are structures. Not all structures are buildings. Does this rule apply only to the structural members of a building, and not the structural members of a structure? Or is it supposed to mean that non-structural members of other structures can't be used even though they're members that are structurally sound? Forget it—let's just delete "of a building" and talk about something else!

314.28 Boxes and Conduit Bodies for Conductors 4 AWG and Larger

Boxes and conduit bodies containing conductors 4 AWG and larger that are required to be insulated must be sized so the conductor insulation won't be damaged. Figure 314–6

Author's Comment:

■ The requirements for sizing boxes and conduit bodies containing conductors 6 AWG and smaller are contained in 314.16.

■ If conductors 4 AWG and larger enter a box or other enclosure, a fitting that provides a smooth, rounded, insulating surface, such as a bushing or adapter, is required to protect the conductors from abrasion during and after installation [300.4(G)]. Figure 314–7

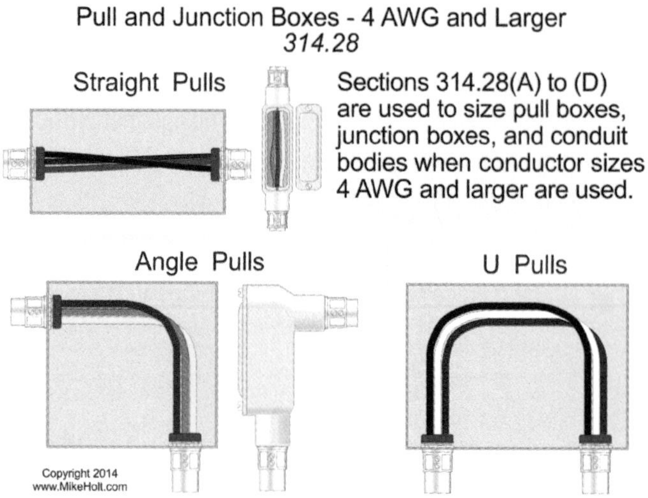

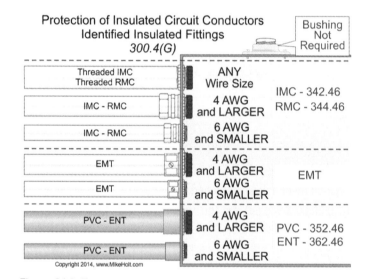

Pull and Junction Boxes - 4 AWG and Larger
314.28

Straight Pulls

Sections 314.28(A) to (D) are used to size pull boxes, junction boxes, and conduit bodies when conductor sizes 4 AWG and larger are used.

Angle Pulls   U Pulls

Copyright 2014
www.MikeHolt.com

Figure 314–6

Protection of Insulated Circuit Conductors
Identified Insulated Fittings
300.4(G)

Bushing Not Required

Threaded IMC / Threaded RMC	ANY Wire Size	IMC - 342.46
IMC - RMC	4 AWG and LARGER	RMC - 344.46
IMC - RMC	6 AWG and SMALLER	
EMT	4 AWG and LARGER	EMT
EMT	6 AWG and SMALLER	
PVC - ENT	4 AWG and LARGER	PVC - 352.46
PVC - ENT	6 AWG and SMALLER	ENT - 362.46

Copyright 2014, www.MikeHolt.com

Figure 314–7

(A) Minimum Size. For raceways containing conductors 4 AWG and larger, the minimum dimensions of boxes and conduit bodies must comply with the following:

(1) Straight Pulls. The minimum distance from where the conductors enter the box or conduit body to the opposite wall must not be less than eight times the trade size of the largest raceway. Figure 314–8

(2) Angle Pulls, U Pulls, or Splices.

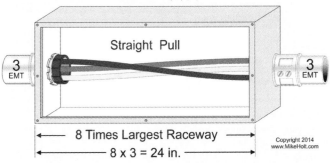

Pull Box or Conduit Body Sizing - Straight Pull
Insulated 4 AWG or Larger
314.28(A)(1)

The distance from the conductors' entry to the opposite wall must not be less than 8 times the trade size of the largest raceway.

Figure 314–8

Angle Pulls. The distance from the raceway entry of the box or conduit body to the opposite wall must not be less than six times the trade size of the largest raceway, plus the sum of the trade sizes of the remaining raceways on the same wall and row. Figure 314–9

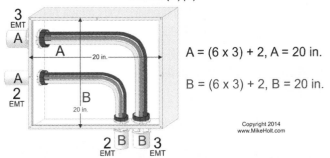

Pull Box or Conduit Body Sizing - Angle Pull
Insulated 4 AWG or Larger
314.28(A)(2)

A = (6 x 3) + 2, A = 20 in.

B = (6 x 3) + 2, B = 20 in.

The distance (measured from the conductor wall entry to the opposite wall) must not be less than 6 times the trade size of the largest raceway, plus the sum of the diameters of the remaining raceways on the same wall and row.

Figure 314–9

U Pulls. When a conductor enters and leaves from the same wall of the box, the distance from where the raceways enter to the opposite wall must not be less than six times the trade size of the largest raceway, plus the sum of the trade sizes of the remaining raceways on the same wall and row. Figure 314–10

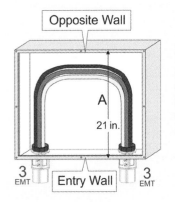

Pull Box Sizing - U Pull
Insulated 4 AWG or Larger
314.28(A)(2)

A: U Pull Sizing: The distance must not be less than 6 times the largest raceway, plus the sum of the other raceways on the same wall and row.
A = (6 x 3) + 3 = 21 in.

Figure 314–10

Splices. When conductors are spliced, the distance from where the raceways enter to the opposite wall must not be less than six times the trade size of the largest raceway, plus the sum of the trade sizes of the remaining raceways on the same wall and row. Figure 314–11

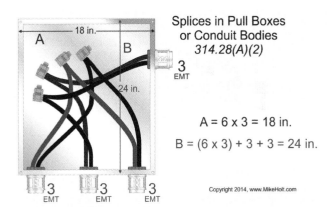

Splices in Pull Boxes or Conduit Bodies
314.28(A)(2)

A = 6 x 3 = 18 in.

B = (6 x 3) + 3 + 3 = 24 in.

When conductors are spliced, the distance from where the raceways enter to the opposite wall must not be less than six times the trade size of the largest raceway plus the sum of all other raceways on the same wall and row.

Figure 314–11

Rows. If there are multiple rows of raceway entries, each row is calculated individually and the row with the largest distance must be used. Figure 314–12

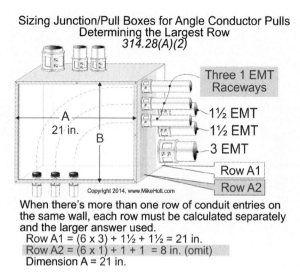

Sizing Junction/Pull Boxes for Angle Conductor Pulls
Determining the Largest Row
314.28(A)(2)

When there's more than one row of conduit entries on the same wall, each row must be calculated separately and the larger answer used.
Row A1 = (6 x 3) + 1½ + 1½ = 21 in.
Row A2 = (6 x 1) + 1 + 1 = 8 in. (omit)
Dimension A = 21 in.

Figure 314–12

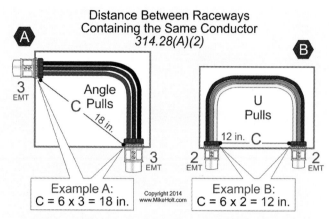

Distance Between Raceways
Containing the Same Conductor
314.28(A)(2)

Example A:
C = 6 x 3 = 18 in.

Example B:
C = 6 x 2 = 12 in.

The distance between raceways containing the same conductor must not be less than 6 times the trade size of the larger raceway entry.

Figure 314–14

Ex: When conductors enter an enclosure with a removable cover, the distance from where the conductors enter to the removable cover must not be less than the bending distance as listed in Table 312.6(A) for one conductor per terminal. Figure 314–13

(3) Smaller Dimensions. Listed boxes or listed conduit bodies smaller than those required in 314.28(A)(1) and 314.28(A)(2) are permitted, if the enclosure is permanently marked with the maximum number and maximum size of conductors.

(B) Conductors in Pull or Junction Boxes. Pull boxes or junction boxes with any dimension over 6 ft must have all conductors cabled or racked in an approved manner.

(C) Covers. Pull boxes, junction boxes, and conduit bodies must have a cover suitable for the conditions. Metal covers must be connected to an equipment grounding conductor of a type recognized in 250.118, in accordance with 250.110 [250.4(A)(3)]. Figure 314–15

(E) Power Distribution Block. Power distribution blocks installed in junction boxes over 100 cu in. must comply with the following: Figure 314–16

(1) Installation. Be listed as a power distribution block.

(2) Size. Be installed in a box not smaller than required by the installation instructions of the power distribution block.

(3) Wire-Bending Space. The junction box is sized so that the wire-bending space requirements of 312.6 can be met.

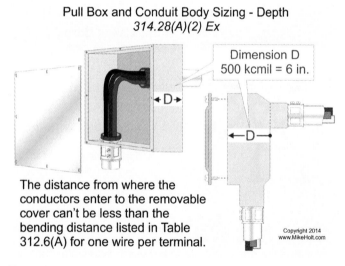

Pull Box and Conduit Body Sizing - Depth
314.28(A)(2) Ex

Dimension D
500 kcmil = 6 in.

The distance from where the conductors enter to the removable cover can't be less than the bending distance listed in Table 312.6(A) for one wire per terminal.

Figure 314–13

Distance Between Raceways. The distance between raceways enclosing the same conductor must not be less than six times the trade size of the largest raceway, measured from the raceways' nearest edge-to-nearest edge. Figure 314–14

Pull Box, Junction Box, and Conduit Body Covers
314.28(C)

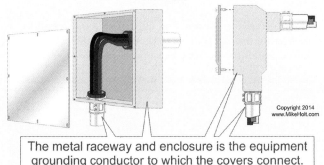

The metal raceway and enclosure is the equipment grounding conductor to which the covers connect.

Metal covers for pull boxes, junction boxes, and conduit bodies must be connected to an equipment grounding conductor in accordance with 250.110.

Figure 314–15

Power Distribution Blocks in Pull/Junction Boxes
314.28(E)

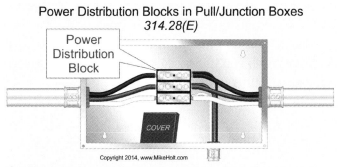

Power distribution blocks in pull and junction boxes must:
(1) Be listed as a power distribution block.
(2) Be installed in a box with dimensions not smaller than specified in the installation instructions of the block.
(3) Comply with 312.6 for wire-bending space at terminals
(4) Have no uninsulated exposed live parts, whether the junction/pull box cover is on or off.

Figure 314–16

(4) Live Parts. Exposed live parts on the power distribution block aren't present when the junction box cover is removed.

(5) Through Conductors. Where the junction box has conductors that don't terminate on the power distribution block(s), the through conductors must be arranged so the power distribution block terminals are unobstructed following installation.

314.29 Wiring to be Accessible

Boxes, conduit bodies, and handhole enclosures must be installed so that the wiring is accessible without removing any part of the building <u>structure or</u> sidewalks, paving, or earth. Figure 314–17

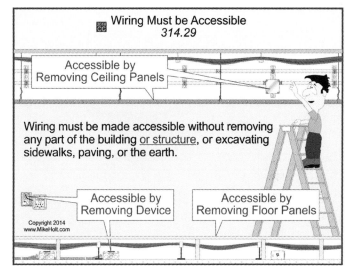

Figure 314–17

Ex: Listed boxes and handhole enclosures can be buried if covered by gravel, light aggregate, or noncohesive granulated soil and if their location is effectively identified and accessible for excavation.

2014 CHANGE ANALYSIS: All buildings are structures. Not all structures are buildings. Here we go again.

314.30 Handhole Enclosures

Handhole enclosures must be identified for underground use, and be designed and installed to withstand all loads likely to be imposed on them. Figure 314–18

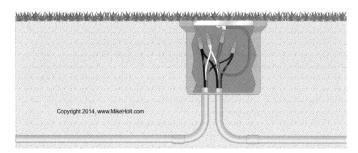

Handhole Enclosure
314.30

Handhole enclosures must be identified for underground use, and be designed and installed to withstand all loads likely to be imposed.

Figure 314–18

(A) Size. Handhole enclosures must be sized in accordance with 314.28(A). For handhole enclosures without bottoms, the measurement to the removable cover is taken from the end of the raceway or cable assembly. When the measurement is taken from the end of the raceway or cable assembly, the values in Table 312.6(A) for one wire per terminal can be used [314.28(A)(2) Ex].

(B) Mechanical Raceway and Cable Connection. Underground raceways and cables entering a handhole enclosure aren't required to be mechanically connected to the handhole enclosure. Figure 314–19

(C) Enclosure Wiring. Splices or terminations within a handhole must be listed as suitable for wet locations [110.14(B)].

(D) Covers. Handhole enclosure covers must have an identifying mark or logo that prominently identifies the function of the enclosure, such as "electric." Handhole enclosure covers must require the use of tools to open, or they must weigh over 100 lb.

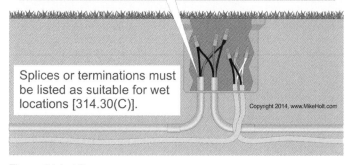

Handhole Enclosure
Mechanical Raceway and Cable Connection
314.30(B)

Underground raceways and cables entering a handhole enclosure aren't required to be mechanically connected to the handhole enclosure.

Splices or terminations must be listed as suitable for wet locations [314.30(C)].

Figure 314–19

Metal covers and exposed conductive surfaces of handhole enclosures containing branch circuit or feeder conductors must be connected to an equipment grounding conductor sized in accordance with 250.122, based on the rating of the overcurrent device [250.102(D)]. Figure 314–20

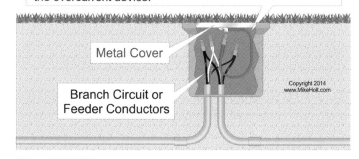

Handhole Enclosure
Bonding Exposed Conductive Surfaces
314.30(D)

Metal covers and exposed conductive surfaces of handhole enclosures containing branch circuit or feeder conductors must be connected to an equipment grounding conductor sized in accordance with 250.122, based on the rating of the overcurrent device.

Metal Cover

Branch Circuit or Feeder Conductors

Figure 314–20

Metal covers and exposed conductive surfaces of handhole enclosures containing service conductors must be connected to a supply-side bonding jumper sized in accordance with Table 250.102(C)(1), based on the size of service conductors [250.92 and 250.102(C)].

ARTICLE 320

ARMORED CABLE (TYPE AC)

Introduction to Article 320—Armored Cable (Type AC)

Armored cable is an assembly of insulated conductors, 14 AWG through 1 AWG, individually wrapped within waxed paper and enclosed within a flexible spiral metal sheath. The outside appearance of armored cable looks like flexible metal conduit as well as metal-clad cable to the casual observer. This cable has been referred to as "BX®" cable over the years and used in residential wiring in some areas of the country.

Part I. General

320.1 Scope

This article covers the use, installation, and construction specifications of armored cable, Type AC.

320.2 Definition

Armored Cable (Type AC). A fabricated assembly of conductors in a flexible interlocked metal armor with an internal bonding strip in intimate contact with the armor for its entire length. See 320.100. Figure 320–1

Armored Cable - Type AC
320.2 Definition

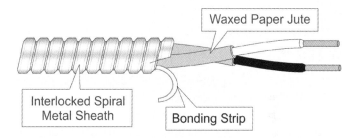

A fabricated assembly of conductors in a flexible interlocked metal armor with an internal bonding strip in intimate contact with the armor for its entire length.

Copyright 2014, www.MikeHolt.com

Figure 320–1

Author's Comment:

- The conductors are contained within a flexible metal sheath that interlocks at the edges, with an internal aluminum bonding strip, giving the cable an outside appearance similar to that of flexible metal conduit. Many electricians call this metal cable "BX®." The advantages of any flexible cables, as compared to race-way wiring methods, are that there's no limit to the number of bends between terminations and the cable can be quickly installed.

Part II. Installation

320.10 Uses Permitted

Type AC cable is permitted as follows:

(1) For feeders and branch circuits in both exposed and con-cealed installations.

(2) In cable trays.

(3) In dry locations.

(4) Embedded in plaster or brick, except in damp or wet locations.

(5) In air voids where not exposed to excessive moisture or dampness.

Author's Comment:

- Type AC cable is also permitted to be installed in a plenum space [300.22(C)(1)].

320.12 Uses Not Permitted

Type AC cable must not be installed in any of the following loca-tions:

(1) If subject to physical damage.

(2) In damp or wet locations.

(3) In air voids of masonry block or tile walls where such walls are exposed or subject to excessive moisture or dampness.

(4) Where exposed to corrosive conditions.

320.15 Exposed Work

Exposed Type AC cable must closely follow the surface of the building finish or running boards. Type AC cable installed on the bottom of floor or ceiling joists must be secured at every joist, and must not be subject to physical damage. Figure 320–2

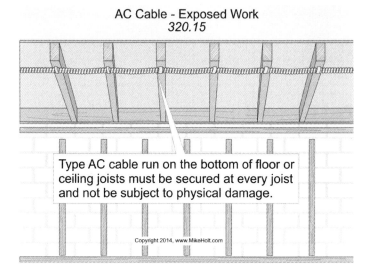

AC Cable - Exposed Work
320.15

Type AC cable run on the bottom of floor or ceiling joists must be secured at every joist and not be subject to physical damage.

Copyright 2014, www.MikeHolt.com

Figure 320–2

320.17 Through or Parallel to Framing Members

Type AC cable installed through, or parallel to, framing members or furring strips must be protected against physical damage from penetration by screws or nails by maintaining 1¼ in. of separation, or by installing a suitable metal plate in accordance with 300.4(A), (C), and (D).

320.23 In Accessible Attics or Roof Spaces

(A) Cables Run Across the Top of Floor Joists. Where run across the top of floor joists, or across the face of rafters or studding within 7 ft of the floor or the floor joists, the cable must be protected <u>by guard</u> strips that are at least as high as the cable. If this space isn't accessible by permanent stairs or ladders, protection is required only within 6 ft of the nearest edge of the scuttle hole or attic entrance. Figure 320–3

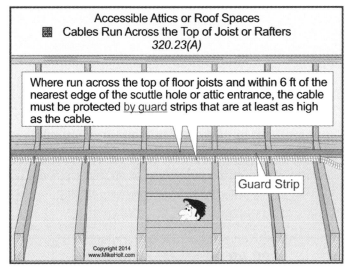

Figure 320–3

2014 CHANGE ANALYSIS: The word "substantial" has been removed from this requirement. Finding two people who agree entirely on what a "substantial guard strip" is would be difficult. Among the many words that shouldn't be found in the *Code* book is "substantial." Sometimes subjective terms have to be used, and the *NEC* is never going to be perfect, but terms like "substantial" should probably be removed whenever possible, as it was here.

(B) Cable Installed Parallel to Framing Members. Where Type AC cable is installed on the side of rafters, studs, ceiling joists, or floor joists, no protection is required if the cable is installed and supported so the nearest outside surface of the cable or raceway is at least 1¼ in. from the nearest edge of the framing member [300.4(D)].

320.24 Bends

Type AC cable must not be bent in a manner that will damage the cable. This is accomplished by limiting bending of the inner edge of the cable to a radius of not less than five times the diameter of the cable. Figure 320–4

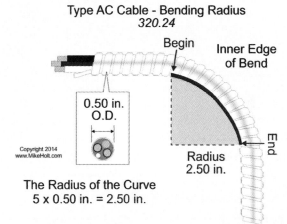

Figure 320–4

320.30 Securing and Supporting

(A) General. Type AC cable must be supported and secured by staples, cable ties, straps, hangers, or similar fittings, designed and installed so as not to damage the cable.

(B) Securing. Type AC cable must be secured within 12 in. of every outlet box, junction box, cabinet, or fitting, and at intervals not exceeding 4½ ft.

Author's Comment:

■ Type AC cable is considered secured when installed horizontally through openings in wooden or metal framing members [320.30(C)].

(C) Supporting. Type AC cable must be supported at intervals not exceeding 4½ ft. Cables installed horizontally through wooden or metal framing members are considered supported if support intervals don't exceed 4½ ft. Figure 320–5

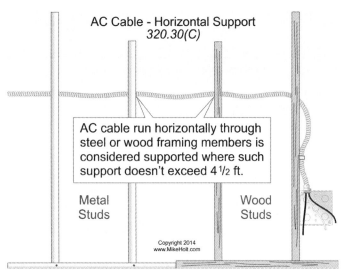

Figure 320–5

320.40 Boxes and Fittings

Type AC cable must terminate in boxes or fittings specifically listed for Type AC cable that protect the conductors from abrasion [300.15].

Author's Comment:

■ An insulating anti-short bushing, sometimes called a "redhead," must be installed at all Type AC cable terminations. The termination fitting must permit the visual inspection of the anti-short bushing once the cable has been installed. Figure 320–6

■ The internal aluminum bonding strip within the cable serves no electrical purpose once outside the cable, and can be cut off, but many electricians use it to secure the anti-short bushing to the cable. See 320.108.

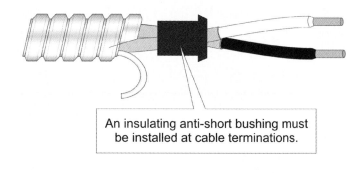

An insulating anti-short bushing must be installed at cable terminations.

Figure 320–6

■ Conductors 4 AWG and larger that enter an enclosure must be protected from abrasion during and after installation by a fitting that provides a smooth, rounded, insulating surface, such as an insulating bushing unless the design of the box, fitting, or enclosure provides equivalent protection in accordance with 300.4(G).

320.80 Conductor Ampacity

(A) Thermal Insulation. Conductor ampacity is calculated on the 90°C insulation rating of the conductors, however the conductors must be sized to the termination temperature rating in accordance with 110.14(C)(1). Figure 320–7

Question: *What's the ampacity of four 12 THHN current-carrying conductors installed in Type AC cable?*

(a) 18A   (b) 24A   (c) 27A   (d) 30A

Answer: *(b) 24A*

Table 310.15(B)(16) ampacity if 12 THHN is 30A
Conductor Adjusted Ampacity = 30A x 0.80
  [Table 310.15(B)(3)(a)]
Conductor Adjusted Ampacity = 24A

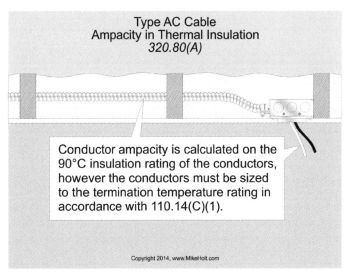

Figure 320–7

Part III. Construction Specifications

320.100 Construction

Type AC cable must have an armor of flexible metal tape with an internal aluminum bonding strip in intimate contact with the armor for its entire length.

Author's Comment:

- The best method of cutting Type AC cable is to use a tool specially designed for the purpose, such as a rotary armor cutter.

- When cutting Type AC cable with a hacksaw, be sure to cut only one spiral of the cable and be careful not to nick the conductors; this is done by cutting the cable at an angle. Breaking the cable spiral (bending the cable very sharply), then cutting the cable with a pair of dikes isn't a good practice.

320.108 Equipment Grounding Conductor

Type AC cable must provide an adequate path for fault current as required by 250.4(A)(5) or 250.4(B)(4) to act as an equipment grounding conductor. Figure 320–8

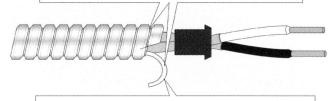

Figure 320–8

Author's Comment:

- The internal aluminum bonding strip isn't an equipment grounding conductor, but it allows the interlocked armor to serve as an equipment grounding conductor because it reduces the impedance of the armored spirals to ensure that a ground fault will be cleared. It's the combination of the aluminum bonding strip and the cable armor that creates the equipment grounding conductor. Once the bonding strip exits the cable, it can be cut off because it no longer serves any purpose. The effective ground-fault current path must be maintained by the use of fittings specifically listed for Type AC cable [320.40]. See 300.12, 300.15, and 300.10.

Notes

Mike Holt's Illustrated Guide to Understanding NEC Requirements for Solar Photovoltaic Systems

ARTICLE 330

METAL-CLAD CABLE (TYPE MC)

Introduction to Article 330—Metal-Clad Cable (Type MC)

Metal-clad cable encloses insulated conductors in a metal sheath of either corrugated or smooth copper or aluminum tubing, or spiral interlocked steel or aluminum. The physical characteristics of Type MC cable make it a versatile wiring method that you can use in almost any location, and for almost any application. The most commonly used Type MC cable is the interlocking kind, which looks similar to armored cable or flexible metal conduit. Traditional interlocked Type MC cable isn't permitted to serve as an equipment grounding conductor, therefore it must contain an equipment grounding conductor in accordance with 250.118(1). There's a fairly new product available called interlocked Type MC^AP cable that contains a bare aluminum grounding/bonding conductor running just below the metal armor, which allows the sheath to serve as an equipment grounding conductor [250.118(10)(b)].

Part I. General

330.1 Scope

Article 330 covers the use, installation, and construction specifications of metal-clad cable.

330.2 Definition

Metal-Clad Cable (Type MC). A factory assembly of insulated circuit conductors, with or without optical fiber members, enclosed in an armor of interlocking metal tape or a smooth or corrugated metallic sheath. Figure 330–1

Author's Comment:

■ Because the outer sheath of interlocked Type MC cable isn't listed as an equipment grounding conductor, it contains an equipment grounding conductor [330.108].

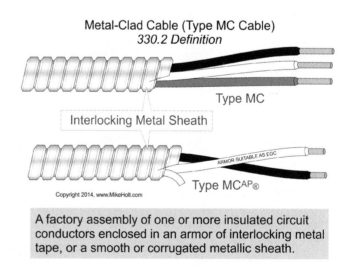

Metal-Clad Cable (Type MC Cable)
330.2 Definition

Interlocking Metal Sheath

Type MC

ARMOR SUITABLE AS EGC

Type MC^AP®

Copyright 2014, www.MikeHolt.com

A factory assembly of one or more insulated circuit conductors enclosed in an armor of interlocking metal tape, or a smooth or corrugated metallic sheath.

Figure 330–1

Part II. Installation

330.10 Uses Permitted

(A) General Uses.

(1) In branch circuits, feeders, and services

(2) In power, lighting, control, and signal circuits

(3) Indoors or outdoors

(4) Exposed or concealed

(5) Directly buried (if identified for the purpose)

(6) In a cable tray

(7) In a raceway

(8) As aerial cable on a messenger

(9) In hazardous locations as permitted in 501.10(B), 502.10(B), and 503.10

(10) Embedded in plaster or brick except in damp or wet locations

(11) In wet locations, where <u>a corrosion-resistant jacket is provided over the metal sheath and</u> any of the following are met:

   a. The metallic covering is impervious to moisture.

   b. A <u>jacket</u> is provided under the metal covering that's <u>moisture resistant</u>.

   c. The insulated conductors under the metallic covering are listed for use in wet <u>locations</u>. Figure 330–2

(12) If single-conductor cables are used, all circuit conductors must be grouped together to minimize induced voltage on the sheath [300.3(B)].

(B) Specific Uses.

(1) Cable Tray. Type MC cable installed in a cable tray must comply with 392.10, 392.12, 392.18, 392.20, 392.22, 392.30, 392.46, 392.56, 392.60(C), and 392.80

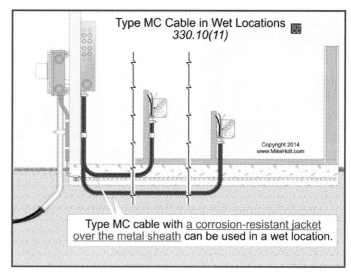

Type MC cable with <u>a corrosion-resistant jacket over the metal sheath</u> can be used in a wet location.

Figure 330–2

(2) Direct Buried. Direct-buried cables must be protected in accordance with 300.5.

(3) Installed as Service-Entrance Cable. Type MC cable is permitted for service entrances, when installed in accordance with 230.43.

(4) Installed Outside of Buildings. Type MC cable installed outside of buildings must comply with 225.10, 396.10, and 396.12.

2014 CHANGE ANALYSIS: In the 2011 edition of the *Code* the metallic sheath of the cable only needed to be corrosion resistant if option "c" was being used (wet location conductors inside a corrosion-resistant metal sheath). Anytime MC cable is used in a wet location, it makes sense that the sheath should be corrosion resistant, so the language was moved from item "c" to the opening statement of the subsection, thereby requiring corrosion resistance for any MC cable used in a wet location.

Item (b) was revised to change "moisture impervious" to "moisture resistant." An impervious material is one that absolutely doesn't allow penetration of water, ever. Considering how MC cable is manufactured, this is probably an impossibility, and isn't necessary anyway.

330.12 Uses Not Permitted

Type MC cable must not be used where:

(1) Subject to physical damage.

(2) Exposed to the destructive corrosive conditions in (a) or (b), unless the metallic sheath or armor is resistant or protected by material resistant to the conditions:

(a) Direct burial in the earth or embedded in concrete unless identified for the application.

(b) Exposed to cinder fills, strong chlorides, caustic alkalis, or vapors of chlorine, or of hydrochloric acids.

330.17 Through or Parallel to Framing Members

Type MC cable installed through or parallel to framing members or furring strips must be protected against physical damage from penetration of screws or nails by maintaining a 1¼ in. separation, or by installing a suitable metal plate in accordance with 300.4(A), (C), and (D). Figure 330–3

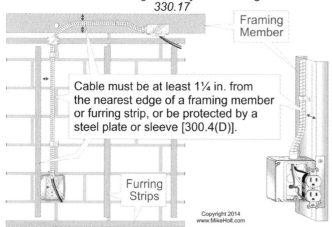

MC Cable Parallel to Framing Members and Furring Strips
Protection Against Physical Damage
330.17

Framing Member

Cable must be at least 1¼ in. from the nearest edge of a framing member or furring strip, or be protected by a steel plate or sleeve [300.4(D)].

Furring Strips

Copyright 2014
www.MikeHolt.com

Figure 330–3

330.23 In Accessible Attics or Roof Spaces

Type MC cable installed in accessible attics or roof spaces must comply with 320.23.

Author's Comment:

■ On the Surface of Floor Joists, Rafters, or Studs. In attics and roof spaces that are accessible, substantial guards must protect cables installed across the top of floor joists, or across the face of rafters or studding within 7 ft of the floor or floor joists. If this space isn't accessible by permanent stairs or ladders, protection is required only within 6 ft of the nearest edge of the scuttle hole or attic entrance [320.23(A)].

■ Along the Side of Framing Members [320.23(B)]. When Type MC cable is installed on the side of rafters, studs, or floor joists, no protection is required if the cable is installed and supported so the nearest outside surface of the cable or raceway is at least 1¼ in. from the nearest edge of the framing member where nails or screws are likely to penetrate [300.4(D)].

330.24 Bends

Bends must be made so that the cable won't be damaged, and the radius of the curve of any bend at the inner edge of the cable must not be less than what's dictated in each of the following instances:

(A) Smooth-Sheath Cables.

(1) Smooth-sheath Type MC cables must not be bent so the bending radius of the inner edge of the cable is less than 10 times the external diameter of the metallic sheath for cable up to ¾ in. in external diameter.

(B) Interlocked or Corrugated Sheath. Interlocked- or corrugated-sheath Type MC cable must not be bent so the bending radius of the inner edge of the cable is less than seven times the external diameter of the cable. Figure 330–4

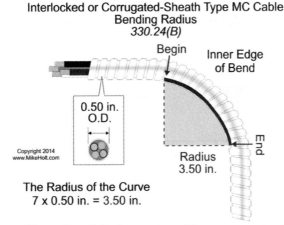

Interlocked or Corrugated-Sheath Type MC Cable
Bending Radius
330.24(B)

0.50 in. O.D.

Begin

Inner Edge of Bend

End

Radius 3.50 in.

The Radius of the Curve
7 x 0.50 in. = 3.50 in.

The radius of the inner edge of the curve must not
be less than 7 times the diameter of the cable.

Figure 330–4

330.30 Securing and Supporting

(A) General. Type MC cable must be supported and secured by staples, cable ties, straps, hangers, or similar fittings designed and installed so as not to damage the cable.

(B) Securing. Type MC cable with four or less conductors sized no larger than 10 AWG must be secured within 12 in. of every outlet box, junction box, cabinet, or fitting and at intervals not exceeding 6 ft. Figure 330–5

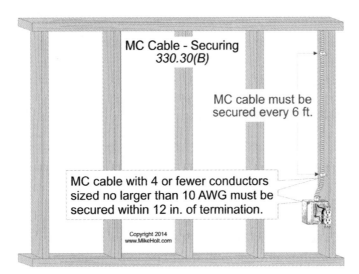

MC Cable - Securing
330.30(B)

MC cable must be secured every 6 ft.

MC cable with 4 or fewer conductors sized no larger than 10 AWG must be secured within 12 in. of termination.

Figure 330–5

Listed cables with ungrounded conductors 250 kcmil and larger can be secured at 10-foot intervals when installed vertically.

2014 CHANGE ANALYSIS: MC cables with large conductors (250 kcmil and larger) have been used in high-rise buildings, and they have an excellent track record. Due to this, the vertical securing requirements have been lessened.

(C) Supporting. Type MC cable must be supported at intervals not exceeding 6 ft. Cables installed horizontally through wooden or metal framing members are considered secured and supported if such support doesn't exceed 6-foot intervals. Figure 330–6

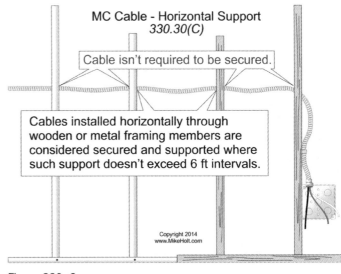

MC Cable - Horizontal Support
330.30(C)

Cable isn't required to be secured.

Cables installed horizontally through wooden or metal framing members are considered secured and supported where such support doesn't exceed 6 ft intervals.

Figure 330–6

330.40 Fittings

Fittings used to secure Type MC cable to boxes or other enclosures must be listed and identified for such use [300.15].

Author's Comment:

- The *NEC* doesn't require anti-short bushings (red heads) at the termination of Type MC cable, but if they're supplied it's considered by many to be a good practice to use them.

■ Conductors 4 AWG and larger that enter an enclosure must be protected from abrasion during and after installation by a fitting that provides a smooth, rounded, insulating surface, such as an insulating bushing unless the design of the box, fitting, or enclosure provides equivalent protection in accordance with 300.4(G).

330.80 Conductor Ampacities

Conductor ampacity is calculated on the 90°C insulation rating of the conductors; however, the conductors must be sized to the termination temperature rating in accordance with 110.14(C)(1).

Part III. Construction Specifications

330.108 Equipment Grounding Conductor

If Type MC cable is to serve as an equipment grounding conductor, it must comply with 250.118(10) and 250.122.

Author's Comment:

■ The outer sheath of:

□ Traditional interlocked Type MC cable isn't permitted to serve as an equipment grounding conductor, therefore this cable must contain an insulated equipment grounding conductor in accordance with 250.118(1). Figure 330–7

□ Interlocked Type MC^{AP} cable containing an aluminum grounding/bonding conductor running just below the metal armor is listed to serve as an equipment grounding conductor [250.118(10)(b)]. Figure 330–8

□ Smooth or corrugated-tube Type MC cable is listed to serve as an equipment grounding conductor [250.118(10)(c)].

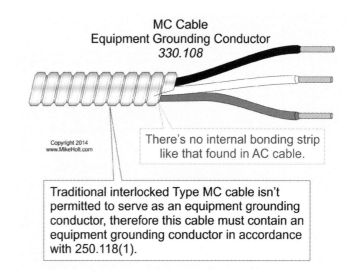

MC Cable
Equipment Grounding Conductor
330.108

Copyright 2014
www.MikeHolt.com

There's no internal bonding strip like that found in AC cable.

Traditional interlocked Type MC cable isn't permitted to serve as an equipment grounding conductor, therefore this cable must contain an equipment grounding conductor in accordance with 250.118(1).

Figure 330–7

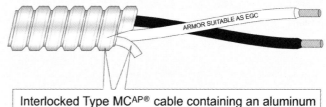

MC Cable
Equipment Grounding Conductor
330.108

ARMOR SUITABLE AS EGC

Interlocked Type MC$^{AP®}$ cable containing an aluminum grounding/bonding conductor running just below the metal armor is listed to serve as an equipment grounding conductor [250.118(10)(b)].

Copyright 2014, www.MikeHolt.com

Figure 330–8

Mike Holt's Illustrated Guide to Understanding NEC Requirements for Solar Photovoltaic Systems

ARTICLE 338

SERVICE-ENTRANCE CABLE (TYPES SE AND USE)

Introduction to Article 338—Service-Entrance Cable (Types SE and USE)

Service-entrance cable is a single conductor or multiconductor assembly with or without an overall moisture-resistant covering. This cable is used primarily for services, but can also be used for feeders and branch circuits when the limitations of this article are observed.

Part I. General

338.1 Scope

Article 338 covers the use, installation, and construction specifications of service-entrance cable, Types SE and USE.

338.2 Definitions

Service-Entrance Cable. Service-entrance cable is a single or multiconductor assembly, with or without an overall covering, used primarily for services.

Type SE. SE and SER cables have a flame-retardant, moisture-resistant covering and are permitted only in aboveground installations. These cables are permitted for branch circuits or feeders when installed in accordance with 338.10(B).

Author's Comment:

- SER cable is SE cable with an insulated grounded/neutral conductor, resulting in three insulated conductors with an uninsulated equipment grounding conductor. SER cable is round, while 2-wire SE cable is flat.

Type USE. USE cable is identified as a wiring method permitted for underground use; its covering is moisture resistant, but not required to be flame retardant. Figure 338–1

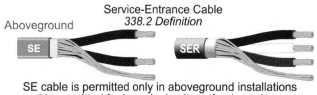

Service-Entrance Cable
338.2 Definition

Aboveground

SE cable is permitted only in aboveground installations and is permitted for branch circuits or feeders when installed according to 338.10(B).

Underground Only

USE cable is identified for underground use. Its covering is moisture resistant but not required to be flame retardant, and it isn't suitable for use within a premises.

A single or multiconductor assembly with or without an overall covering used primarily for services not over 600V.

Figure 338–1

Author's Comment:

- USE cable isn't permitted to be installed indoors [338.10(B)], except single-conductor USE dual rated as RHH/RHW.

Part II. Installation

338.10 Uses Permitted

(A) Service-Entrance Conductors. Service-entrance cable used as service-entrance conductors must be installed in accordance with Article 230.

(B) Branch Circuits or Feeders.

(1) Insulated Conductor. Type SE service-entrance cable is permitted for branch circuits and feeders where the circuit conductors are insulated by thermoset or thermoplastic.

(2) Uninsulated Conductor. SE cable is permitted for branch circuits and feeders if the insulated conductors are used for circuit wiring, and the uninsulated conductor is only used for equipment grounding purposes.

Ex: In existing installations, uninsulated conductors may be used for the grounded/neutral conductor if the uninsulated grounded/neutral conductor of the cable originates in service equipment.

(3) Temperature Limitations. SE cable must not be subjected to conductor temperatures exceeding its insulation rating.

(4) Installation Methods for Branch Circuits and Feeders. SE cable used for branch circuits or feeders must comply with (a) and (b).

(a) Interior Installations. SE cable used for interior branch circuit or feeder wiring must be installed in accordance with the same requirements as Type NM Cable—Article 334, excluding 334.80.

The maximum conductor temperature rating can be used [310.15(B)(2)] for ampacity adjustment and correction purposes.

 CAUTION: *Underground service-entrance cable (USE) isn't permitted for interior wiring because it doesn't have flame-retardant insulation. It's only permitted in interior wiring when dual-listed as wire type, such as RHW, in accordance with Table 310.104.*

(b) Exterior Installations. The cable must be supported in accordance with 334.30 and where run underground the cable must comply with Part II of Article 340.

Ex: Single-conductor and multi-rated USE conductors aren't restricted to the 60°C rating required by 340.80.

2014 CHANGE ANALYSIS: Previous editions of the *NEC* required that all USE cables installed as underground feeders and branch circuits be subject to the 60°C ampacity requirement of 340.80. This rule was added several *Code* cycles ago, but with no real technical substantiation, and therefore never should've been in the *NEC* at all. For this reason, we now have an exception for single-conductor and multi-rated USE conductors.

338.12 Uses Not Permitted

(A) Service-Entrance Cable. SE cable isn't permitted under the following conditions or locations:

(1) If subject to physical damage unless protected in accordance with 230.50(A).

(2) Underground with or without a raceway.

(B) Underground Service-Entrance Cable. USE cable isn't permitted:

(1) For interior wiring.

(2) Above ground, except where protected against physical damage in accordance with 300.5(D). Figure 338–2

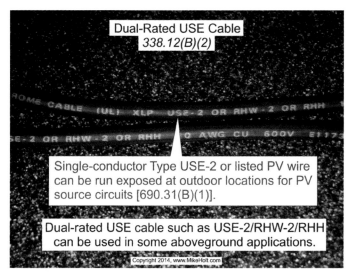

Figure 338–2

338.24 Bends

Bends in cable must be made so the protective coverings of the cable aren't damaged, and the radius of the curve of the inner edge is at least five times the diameter of the cable. Figure 338–3

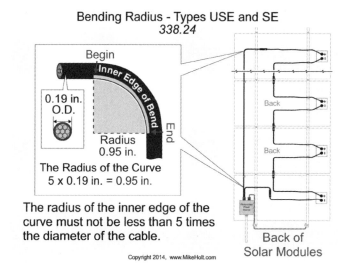

Figure 338–3

Notes

Mike Holt's Illustrated Guide to Understanding NEC Requirements for Solar Photovoltaic Systems

UNDERGROUND FEEDER AND BRANCH-CIRCUIT CABLE (TYPE UF)

Introduction to Article 340—Underground Feeder and Branch-Circuit Cable (Type UF)

UF cable is a moisture-, fungus-, and corrosion-resistant cable suitable for direct burial in the earth.

Part I. General

340.1 Scope

Article 340 covers the use, installation, and construction specifications of underground feeder and branch-circuit cable, Type UF.

340.2 Definition

Underground Feeder and Branch-Circuit Cable (Type UF). A factory assembly of insulated conductors with an integral or an overall covering of nonmetallic material suitable for direct burial in the earth. Notice that Type UF isn't allowed as a service cable. Figure 340–1

Author's Comment:

- UF cable is a moisture-, fungus-, and corrosion-resistant cable suitable for direct burial in the earth. It comes in sizes 14 AWG through 4/0 AWG [340.104]. The covering of multiconductor Type UF cable is molded plastic that encases the insulated conductors.

Underground Feeder and Branch-Circuit Cable
Type UF Cable
340.2 Definition

14/2 w/G   UF   600V

A factory assembly of insulated conductors with an integral or an overall covering of nonmetallic material suitable for direct burial in the earth.

Copyright 2014, www.MikeHolt.com

Figure 340–1

- Because the covering of Type UF cable encapsulates the insulated conductors, it's difficult to strip off the outer jacket to gain access to the conductors, but this covering provides excellent corrosion protection. Be careful not to damage the conductor insulation or cut yourself when you remove the outer cover.

340.6 Listing Requirements

Type UF cable must be listed.

Part II. Installation

340.10 Uses Permitted

(1) Underground, in accordance with 300.5.

(2) As a single conductor in the same trench or raceway with circuit conductors.

(3) As interior or exterior wiring in wet, dry, or corrosive locations.

(4) As Type NM cable, when installed in accordance with Article 334.

(5) For solar PV systems, in accordance with 690.31.

(6) As single-conductor cables for nonheating leads for heating cables, as provided in 424.43.

(7) Supported by cable trays.

340.12 Uses Not Permitted

(1) As services [230.43].

(2) In commercial garages [511.3].

(3) In theaters [520.5].

(4) In motion picture studios [530.11].

(5) In storage battery rooms [Article 480].

(6) In hoistways [Article 620].

(7) In hazardous locations, except as specifically permitted by other articles in the *Code*.

(8) Embedded in concrete.

(9) Exposed to direct sunlight unless identified.

(10) If subject to physical damage.

(11) As overhead messenger-supported wiring.

Author's Comment:

- UF cable isn't permitted in ducts or plenum spaces [300.22], or in patient care spaces [517.13].

340.24 Bends

Bends in cables must be made so that the protective covering of the cable isn't damaged, and the radius of the curve of the inner edge must not be less than five times the diameter of the cable.

340.80 Ampacity

The ampacity of conductors contained in UF cable is based on the 60°C insulation rating listed in Table 310.15(B)(16).

340.112 Insulation

The conductors of UF cable must be one of the moisture-resistant types listed in Table 310.104(A) suitable for branch-circuit wiring. If installed as a substitute wiring method for Type NM cable, the conductor insulation must be rated 90°C (194°F).

ARTICLE 342 INTERMEDIATE METAL CONDUIT (TYPE IMC)

Introduction to Article 342—Intermediate Metal Conduit (Type IMC)

Intermediate metal conduit (IMC) is a circular metal raceway with an outside diameter equal to that of rigid metal conduit. The wall thickness of intermediate metal conduit is less than that of rigid metal conduit (RMC), so it has a greater interior cross-sectional area for containing conductors. Intermediate metal conduit is lighter and less expensive than rigid metal conduit, but it can be used in all of the same locations as rigid metal conduit. Intermediate metal conduit also uses a different steel alloy that makes it stronger than rigid metal conduit, even though the walls are thinner. Intermediate metal conduit is manufactured in both galvanized steel and aluminum; the steel type is much more common.

Part I. General

342.1 Scope

Article 342 covers the use, installation, and construction specifications of intermediate metal conduit and associated fittings.

342.2 Definition

Intermediate Metal Conduit (Type IMC). A listed steel raceway of circular cross section that can be threaded with integral or associated couplings. It's listed for the installation of electrical conductors, and is used with listed fittings to provide electrical continuity. Figure 342–1

Author's Comment:

■ The type of steel from which intermediate metal conduit is manufactured, the process by which it's made, and the corrosion protection applied are all equal, or superior, to that of rigid metal conduit.

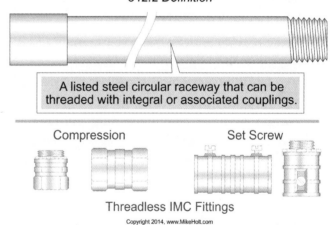

Intermediate Metal Conduit (Type IMC)
342.2 Definition

A listed steel circular raceway that can be threaded with integral or associated couplings.

Compression   Set Screw

Threadless IMC Fittings
Copyright 2014, www.MikeHolt.com

Figure 342–1

342.6 Listing Requirements

Intermediate metal conduit and its associated fittings, such as elbows and couplings, must be listed.

Part II. Installation

342.10 Uses Permitted

(A) All Atmospheric Conditions and Occupancies. Intermediate metal conduit is permitted in all atmospheric conditions and occupancies.

(B) Corrosion Environments. Intermediate metal conduit, elbows, couplings, and fittings can be installed in concrete, in direct contact with the earth, or in areas subject to severe corrosive influences if provided with corrosion protection and judged suitable for the condition in accordance with 300.6.

(C) Cinder Fill. IMC can be installed in or under cinder fill subject to permanent moisture when protected on all sides by 2 in. of noncinder concrete; where the conduit isn't less than 18 in. under the fill; or where protected by corrosion protection judged suitable for the condition.

(D) Wet Locations. Support fittings, such as screws, straps, and so forth, installed in a wet location must be made of corrosion-resistant material, or be protected by corrosion-resistant coatings in accordance with 300.6.

⚠ **CAUTION:** *Supplementary coatings for corrosion protection haven't been investigated by a product testing and listing agency, and these coatings are known to cause cancer in laboratory animals. There's a documented case where an electrician was taken to the hospital for lead poisoning after using a supplemental coating product (asphalted paint) in a poorly ventilated area. As with all products, be sure to read and follow all product instructions, including material data safety sheets, particularly when petroleum-based chemicals (volatile organic compounds) may be in the material.*

342.14 Dissimilar Metals

If practical, contact with dissimilar metals should be avoided to prevent the deterioration of the metal because of galvanic action. Aluminum fittings and enclosures, however, can be used with steel intermediate metal conduit.

342.20 Trade Size

(A) Minimum. Intermediate metal conduit smaller than trade size ½ must not be used.

(B) Maximum. Intermediate metal conduit larger than trade size 4 must not be used.

342.22 Number of Conductors

The number of conductors in IMC isn't permitted to exceed the percentage fill specified in Table 1, Chapter 9. Raceways must be large enough to permit the installation and removal of conductors without damaging the conductor insulation. When all conductors in a raceway are the same size and insulation, the number of conductors permitted can be found in Annex C for the raceway type.

> **Question:** *How many 10 THHN conductors can be installed in trade size 1 IMC?*
>
> *(a) 12 (b) 14 (c) 16 (d) 18*
>
> **Answer:** *(d) 18 conductors [Annex C, Table C4]*

Author's Comment:

- See 300.17 for additional examples on how to size raceways when conductors aren't all the same size.

Cables can be installed in intermediate metal conduit, as long as the number of cables doesn't exceed the allowable percentage fill specified in Table 1, Chapter 9.

342.24 Bends

Raceway bends must not be made in any manner that will damage the raceway, or significantly change its internal diameter (no kinks). The radius of the curve of the inner edge of any field bend must not be less than shown in Table 2, Chapter 9.

Author's Comment:

- This is usually not a problem, because benders are made to comply with this table. However, when using a hickey bender (short-radius bender), be careful not to over-bend the raceway.

342.26 Number of Bends (360°)

To reduce the stress and friction on conductor insulation, the maximum number of bends (including offsets) between pull points must not exceed 360°. Figure 342–2

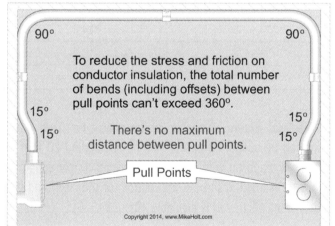

IMC - Number of Bends
342.26

90°   90°

To reduce the stress and friction on conductor insulation, the total number of bends (including offsets) between pull points can't exceed 360°.

15°   15°

15°   There's no maximum distance between pull points.   15°

Pull Points

Copyright 2014, www.MikeHolt.com

Figure 342–2

Author's Comment:

- There's no maximum distance between pull boxes because this is a design issue, not a safety issue.

342.28 Reaming

When the raceway is cut in the field, reaming is required to remove the burrs and rough edges.

Author's Comment:

- It's a commonly accepted practice to ream small raceways with a screwdriver or the backside of pliers. However, when the raceway is cut with a three-wheel pipe cutter, a reaming tool is required to remove the sharp edge of the indented raceway. When conduits are threaded in the field, the threads must be coated with an electrically conductive, corrosion-resistant compound approved by the authority having jurisdiction, in accordance with 300.6(A).

342.30 Securing and Supporting

Intermediate metal conduit must be installed as a complete system in accordance with 300.18 [300.10 and 300.12], and it must be securely fastened in place and supported in accordance with (A) and (B).

(A) Securely Fastened. IMC must be secured in accordance with one of the following:

(1) Fastened within 3 ft of each outlet box, junction box, device box, cabinet, conduit body, or other conduit termination. Figure 342–3

Author's Comment:

- Fastening is required within 3 ft of terminations, not within 3 ft of each coupling.

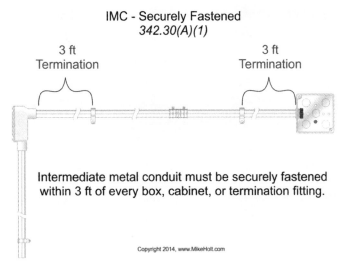

IMC - Securely Fastened
342.30(A)(1)

3 ft
Termination

3 ft
Termination

Intermediate metal conduit must be securely fastened
within 3 ft of every box, cabinet, or termination fitting.

Copyright 2014, www.MikeHolt.com

Figure 342–3

(2) When structural members don't permit the raceway to be
secured within 3 ft of a box or termination fitting, the raceway must be secured within 5 ft of the termination. Figure
342–4

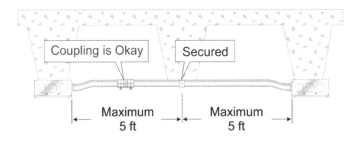

IMC - Securely Fastened to Structural Members
342.30(A)(2)

Coupling is Okay

Secured

Maximum
5 ft

Maximum
5 ft

Where structural members don't permit fastening within
3 ft of termination, it must be secured within 5 ft.

Copyright 2014, www.MikeHolt.com

Figure 342–4

(3) Conduits aren't required to be securely fastened within 3 ft
of the service head for an above-the-roof termination of a
mast.

(B) Supports.

(1) General. Intermediate metal conduit must generally be supported at intervals not exceeding 10 ft.

(2) Straight Horizontal Runs. Straight horizontal runs made
with threaded couplings can be supported in accordance with
the distances listed in Table 344.30(B)(2). Figure 342–5

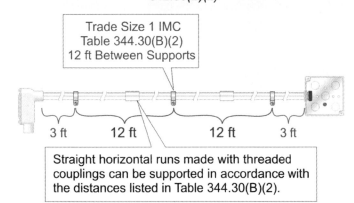

IMC - Support of Straight Runs
342.30(B)(2)

Trade Size 1 IMC
Table 344.30(B)(2)
12 ft Between Supports

3 ft   12 ft   12 ft   3 ft

Straight horizontal runs made with threaded
couplings can be supported in accordance with
the distances listed in Table 344.30(B)(2).

Copyright 2014, www.MikeHolt.com

Figure 342–5

Table 344.30(B)(2)	
Trade Size	**Support Spacing**
½—¾	10 ft
1	12 ft
1¼—1½	14 ft
2—2½	16 ft
3 and larger	20 ft

(3) Vertical Risers. Exposed vertical risers for fixed equipment can be supported at intervals not exceeding 20 ft, if the
conduit is made up with threaded couplings, firmly supported,
securely fastened at the top and bottom of the riser, and if no
other means of support is available. Figure 342–6

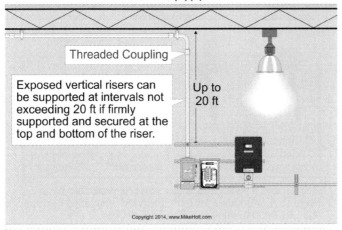

Figure 342–6

(4) Horizontal Runs. Conduits installed horizontally in bored or punched holes in wood or metal framing members, or notches in wooden members are considered supported, but the raceway must be secured within 3 ft of termination.

Author's Comment:

■ IMC must be provided with expansion fittings if necessary to compensate for thermal expansion and contraction [300.7(B)]. The expansion characteristics for metal raceways are determined by multiplying the values from Table 352.44 by 0.20, and the expansion characteristics for aluminum raceways is determined by multiplying the values from Table 352.44 by 0.40 [300.7 Note].

342.42 Couplings and Connectors

(A) Installation. Threadless couplings and connectors must be made up tight to maintain an effective ground-fault current path to safely conduct fault current in accordance with 250.4(A)(5), 250.96(A), and 300.10.

Author's Comment:

■ Loose locknuts have been found to burn clear before a fault was cleared because loose termination fittings increase the impedance of the fault current path.

If buried in masonry or concrete, threadless fittings must be the concrete-tight type. If installed in wet locations, they must be listed for use in wet locations in accordance with 314.15(A).

Threadless couplings and connectors must not be used on threaded conduit ends unless listed for the purpose.

(B) Running Threads. Running threads aren't permitted for the connection of couplings, but they're permitted at other locations. Figure 342–7

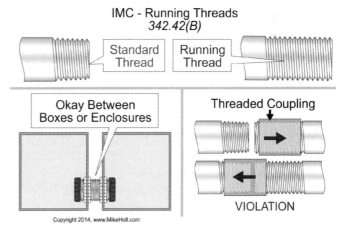

Running threads aren't permitted for the connection of couplings, but they're permitted at other locations.

Figure 342–7

342.46 Bushings

To protect conductors from abrasion, a metal or plastic bushing must be installed on conduit termination threads, regardless of conductor size, unless the box, fitting, or enclosure is designed to provide this protection.

Note: Conductors 4 AWG and larger that enter an enclosure must be protected from abrasion, during and after installation, by a fitting that provides a smooth, rounded, insulating surface, such as an insulating bushing, unless the design of the box, fitting, or enclosure provides equivalent protection, in accordance with 300.4(G). Figure 342–8

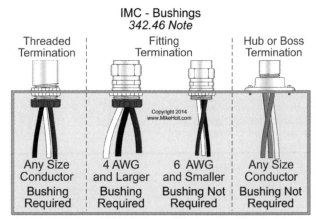

Conductors 4 AWG and larger must be protected by a fitting that provides a smooth, rounded, insulating surface, such as an insulating bushing [300.4(G)].

Figure 342–8

RIGID METAL CONDUIT (TYPE RMC)

Introduction to Article 344—Rigid Metal Conduit (Type RMC)

Rigid metal conduit, commonly called "rigid," has long been the standard raceway for providing protection from physical impact and from difficult environments. The outside diameter of rigid metal conduit is the same as intermediate metal conduit. However, the wall thickness of rigid metal conduit is greater than intermediate metal conduit; therefore the interior cross-sectional area is smaller. Rigid metal conduit is heavier and more expensive than intermediate metal conduit, and it can be used in any location. Rigid metal conduit is manufactured in both galvanized steel and aluminum; the steel type is much more common.

Part I. General

344.1 Scope

Article 344 covers the use, installation, and construction specifications of rigid metal conduit and associated fittings.

344.2 Definition

Rigid Metal Conduit (Type RMC). A listed metal raceway of circular cross section with integral or associated couplings for the installation of electrical conductors, and used with listed fittings to provide electrical continuity. Figure 344–1

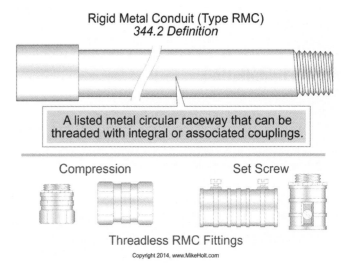

Figure 344–1

Author's Comment:

- When the mechanical and physical characteristics of rigid metal conduit are desired and a corrosive environment is anticipated, a PVC-coated raceway system is commonly used. This type of raceway is frequently used in the petrochemical industry. The common trade name of this coated raceway is "Plasti-bond®," and it's commonly referred to as "Rob Roy conduit." The benefits of the improved corrosion protection can be achieved only when the system is properly installed. Joints must be sealed in accordance with the manufacturer's instructions, and the coating must not be damaged with tools such as benders, pliers, and pipe wrenches. Couplings are available with an extended skirt that can be properly sealed after installation.

344.6 Listing Requirements

Rigid metal conduit, elbows, couplings, and associated fittings must be listed.

Part II. Installation

344.10 Uses Permitted

(A) Atmospheric Conditions and Occupancies.

(1) Galvanized Steel and Stainless Steel. Galvanized steel and stainless steel rigid metal conduit is permitted in all atmospheric conditions and occupancies.

(2) Red Brass. Red brass rigid metal conduit is permitted for direct burial and swimming pool applications.

(3) Aluminum. Rigid aluminum conduit is permitted if judged suitable for the environment.

(B) Corrosion Environments.

(1) Galvanized Steel, Stainless Steel, and Red Brass. Rigid metal conduit fittings, elbows, and couplings can be installed in

concrete, in direct contact with the earth, or in areas subject to severe corrosive influences judged suitable for the condition.

(2) Aluminum. Rigid aluminum conduit must be provided with supplementary corrosion protection approved by the authority having jurisdiction if encased in concrete or in direct contact with the earth.

(C) Cinder Fill. Galvanized steel, stainless steel, and red brass RMC is permitted in or under cinder fill subject to permanent moisture, when protected on all sides by a layer of noncinder concrete not less than 2 in. thick; where the conduit isn't less than 18 in. under the fill; or where protected by corrosion protection judged suitable for the condition.

(D) Wet Locations. Support fittings, such as screws, straps, and so forth, installed in a wet location must be made of corrosion-resistant material or protected by corrosion-resistant coatings in accordance with 300.6.

⚠ **CAUTION:** *Supplementary coatings (asphalted paint) for corrosion protection haven't been investigated by a product testing and listing agency, and these coatings are known to cause cancer in laboratory animals.*

344.14 Dissimilar Metals

If practical, contact with dissimilar metals should be avoided to prevent the deterioration of the metal because of galvanic action. Aluminum fittings and enclosures, however, can be used with rigid metal conduit.

344.20 Trade Size

(A) Minimum. Rigid metal conduit smaller than trade size ½ must not be used.

(B) Maximum. Rigid metal conduit larger than trade size 6 must not be used.

344.22 Number of Conductors

Raceways must be large enough to permit the installation and removal of conductors without damaging the conductors' insulation. When all conductors in a raceway are the same size and insulation, the number of conductors permitted can be found in Annex C for the raceway type.

> **Question:** How many 8 THHN conductors can be installed in trade size 1½ RMC?
>
> (a) 16   (b) 18   (c) 20   (d) 22
>
> **Answer:** 22 conductors [Annex C, Table C8]

Author's Comment:

■ See 300.17 for additional examples on how to size raceways when conductors aren't all the same size.

Cables can be installed in rigid metal conduit, as long as the number of cables doesn't exceed the allowable percentage fill specified in Table 1, Chapter 9.

344.24 Bends

Raceway bends must not be made in any manner that would damage the raceway, or significantly change its internal diameter (no kinks). The radius of the curve of the inner edge of any field bend must not be less than shown in Table 2, Chapter 9.

Author's Comment:

■ This is usually not a problem because benders are made to comply with this table. However, when using a hickey bender (short-radius bender), be careful not to over-bend the raceway.

344.26 Number of Bends (360°)

To reduce the stress and friction on conductor insulation, the maximum number of bends (including offsets) between pull points must not exceed 360°. Figure 344–2

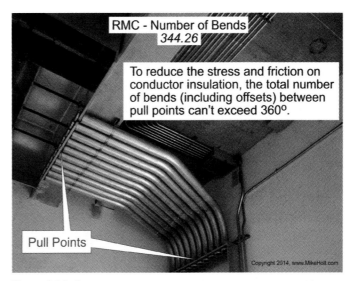

Figure 344–2

Author's Comment:

■ There's no maximum distance between pull boxes because this is a design issue, not a safety issue.

344.28 Reaming

When the raceway is cut in the field, reaming is required to remove the burrs and rough edges.

Author's Comment:

■ It's a commonly accepted practice to ream small raceways with a screwdriver or the backside of pliers. However, when the raceway is cut with a three-wheel pipe cutter, a reaming tool is required to remove the sharp edge of the indented raceway. When conduit is threaded in the field, the threads must be coated with an electrically conductive, corrosion-resistant compound approved by the authority having jurisdiction, in accordance with 300.6(A).

344.30 Securing and Supporting

Rigid metal conduit must be installed as a complete system in accordance with 300.18 [300.10 and 300.12], and it must be securely fastened in place and supported in accordance with (A) and (B).

(A) Securely Fastened. RMC must be secured in accordance with one of the following:

(1) Fastened within 3 ft of each outlet box, junction box, device box, cabinet, conduit body, or other conduit termination. Figure 344–3

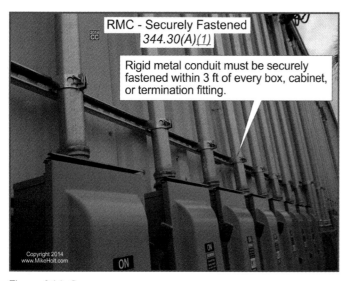

Figure 344–3

Author's Comment:

- Fastening is required within 3 ft of terminations, not within 3 ft of each coupling.

(2) When structural members don't permit the raceway to be secured within 3 ft of a box or termination fitting, the raceway must be secured within 5 ft of the termination. Figure 344–4

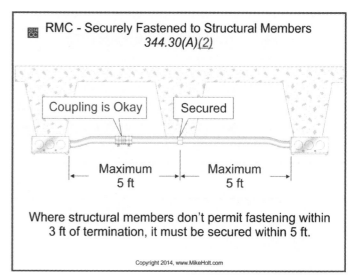

Figure 344–4

2014 CHANGE ANALYSIS: Although this change certainly isn't going to change the world, it improves the *NEC*. Over the last few *Code* cycles, a real effort has been made to change long paragraphs into itemized lists. While it may seem odd, considering that the requirements don't change, converting these paragraphs into lists really does go a long way toward enhancing the usability of the *NEC*.

Perhaps the best example of how lists work better than paragraphs is comparing the 2011 edition of 312.8 to the 2008 edition. The issue of splicing in a cabinet that contains a panelboard was confusing for many *Code* users for many years. Without changing any rules, the issue became crystal clear in 2011. How was this achieved? By putting exactly the same rules into an itemized list.

(B) Supports.

(1) General. Rigid metal conduit must be supported at intervals not exceeding 10 ft.

(2) Straight Horizontal Runs. Straight horizontal runs made with threaded couplings can be supported in accordance with the distances listed in Table 344.30(B)(2). Figure 344–5

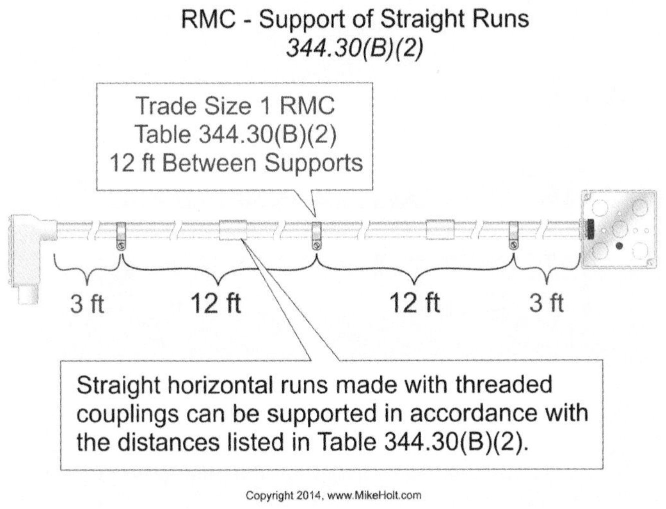

RMC - Support of Straight Runs
344.30(B)(2)

Trade Size 1 RMC
Table 344.30(B)(2)
12 ft Between Supports

3 ft   12 ft   12 ft   3 ft

Straight horizontal runs made with threaded couplings can be supported in accordance with the distances listed in Table 344.30(B)(2).

Copyright 2014, www.MikeHolt.com

Figure 344–5

Table 344.30(B)(2)	
Trade Size	Support Spacing
½–¾	10 ft
1	12 ft*
1¼–1½	14 ft
2–2½	16 ft
3 and larger	20 ft

(3) Vertical Risers. Exposed vertical risers for fixed equipment can be supported at intervals not exceeding 20 ft, if the conduit is made up with threaded couplings, firmly supported, securely fastened at the top and bottom of the riser, and if no other means of support is available. Figure 344–6

(4) Horizontal Runs. Conduits installed horizontally in bored or punched holes in wood or metal framing members, or notches in wooden members, are considered supported, but the raceway must be secured within 3 ft of termination.

Author's Comment:

■ Rigid metal conduit must be provided with expansion fittings if necessary to compensate for thermal expansion and contraction [300.7(B)]. The expansion characteristics for metal raceways are determined by multiplying

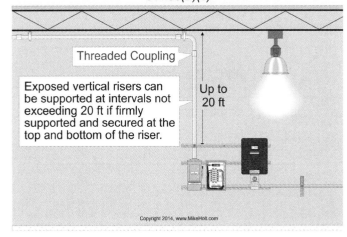

RMC - Support of Vertical Risers
344.30(B)(3)

Threaded Coupling

Exposed vertical risers can be supported at intervals not exceeding 20 ft if firmly supported and secured at the top and bottom of the riser.

Up to 20 ft

Copyright 2014, www.MikeHolt.com

Figure 344–6

the values from Table 352.44 by 0.20, and the expansion characteristics for aluminum raceways is determined by multiplying the values from Table 352.44 by 0.40 [300.7 Note].

344.42 Couplings and Connectors

(A) Installation. Threadless couplings and connectors must be made up tight to maintain an effective ground-fault current path to safely conduct fault current in accordance with 250.4(A)(5), 250.96(A), and 300.10.

Author's Comment:

■ Loose locknuts have been found to burn clear before a fault was cleared because loose connections increase the impedance of the fault current path.

If buried in masonry or concrete, threadless fittings must be the concrete-tight type. If installed in wet locations, they must be listed for use in wet locations, in accordance with 314.15(A).

Threadless couplings and connectors must not be used on threaded conduit ends, unless listed for the purpose.

(B) Running Threads. Running threads aren't permitted for the connection of couplings, but they're permitted at other locations. Figure 344–7

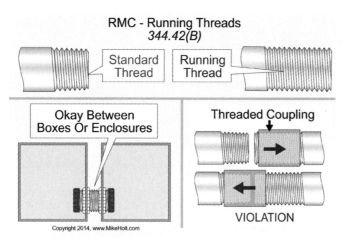

RMC - Running Threads
344.42(B)

Standard Thread | Running Thread

Okay Between Boxes Or Enclosures

Threaded Coupling

VIOLATION

Copyright 2014, www.MikeHolt.com

Running threads aren't permitted for the connection of couplings, but they're permitted at other locations.

Figure 344–7

344.46 Bushings

To protect conductors from abrasion, a metal or plastic bushing must be installed on conduit threads at terminations, regardless of conductor size, unless the box, fitting, or enclosure is designed to provide this protection.

Note: Conductors 4 AWG and larger that enter an enclosure must be protected from abrasion, during and after installation, by a fitting that provides a smooth, rounded, insulating surface, such as an insulating bushing, unless the design of the box, fitting, or enclosure provides equivalent protection, in accordance with 300.4(G). Figure 344–8

Part III. Construction Specifications

344.100 Construction

RMC must be constructed of one of the following:

(1) Steel (with or without protective coatings)

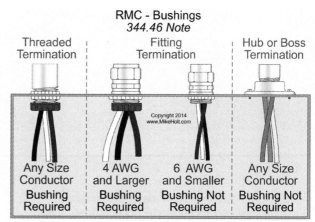

RMC - Bushings
344.46 Note

Threaded Termination | Fitting Termination | Hub or Boss Termination

Copyright 2014 www.MikeHolt.com

Any Size Conductor Bushing Required | 4 AWG and Larger Bushing Required | 6 AWG and Smaller Bushing Not Required | Any Size Conductor Bushing Not Required

Conductors 4 AWG and larger must be protected by a fitting that provides a smooth, rounded, insulating surface, such as an insulating bushing [300.4(G)].

Figure 344–8

(2) Aluminum

(3) Red brass

(4) Stainless steel

2014 CHANGE ANALYSIS: In order to provide consistency with other Chapter three wiring method articles, this new section has been created. No new information has been provided, since the added language is really just relocated from the definition that was in 344.2.

344.130 Standard Lengths

The standard length of RMC must be 10 ft including an attached coupling, and each end must be threaded. Longer or shorter lengths with or without a coupling and threaded or unthreaded are permitted.

ARTICLE 348

FLEXIBLE METAL CONDUIT (TYPE FMC)

Introduction to Article 348—Flexible Metal Conduit (Type FMC)

Flexible metal conduit (FMC), commonly called "Greenfield" or "flex," is a raceway of an interlocked metal strip of either steel or aluminum. It's primarily used for the final 6 ft or less of raceways between a more rigid raceway system and equipment that moves, shakes, or vibrates. Examples of such equipment include pump motors and industrial machinery.

Part I. General

348.1 Scope

Article 348 covers the use, installation, and construction specifications for flexible metal conduit and associated fittings.

348.2 Definition

Flexible Metal Conduit (Type FMC). A raceway of circular cross section made of a helically wound, formed, interlocked metal strip. Figure 348–1

348.6 Listing Requirements

Flexible metal conduit and associated fittings must be listed.

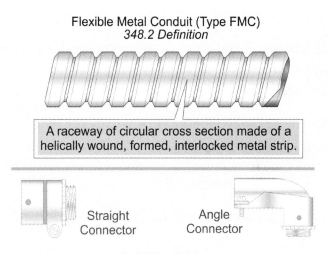

Flexible Metal Conduit (Type FMC)
348.2 Definition

A raceway of circular cross section made of a helically wound, formed, interlocked metal strip.

Straight Connector

Angle Connector

Copyright 2014, www.MikeHolt.com

Figure 348–1

Part II. Installation

348.10 Uses Permitted

Flexible metal conduit is permitted exposed or concealed.

348.12 Uses Not Permitted

(1) In wet locations.

(2) In hoistways, other than as permitted in 620.21(A)(1).

(3) In storage battery rooms.

(4) In any hazardous location, except as permitted by 501.10(B).

(5) Exposed to material having a deteriorating effect on the installed conductors.

(6) Underground or embedded in poured concrete.

(7) If subject to physical damage.

348.20 Trade Size

(A) Minimum. Flexible metal conduit smaller than trade size ½ must not be used, except trade size ⅜ can be used for the following applications:

(1) For enclosing the leads of motors.

(2) Not exceeding 6 ft in length:

   a. For utilization equipment,

   b. As part of a listed assembly, or

   c. For luminaire tap connections in accordance with 410.117(C).

(3) In manufactured wiring systems, 604.6(A).

(4) In hoistways, 620.21(A)(1).

(5) As part of a listed luminaire assembly in accordance with 410.137(C).

(B) Maximum. Flexible metal conduit larger than trade size 4 must not be used.

348.22 Number of Conductors

Trade Size ½ and Larger. Flexible metal conduit must be large enough to permit the installation and removal of conductors without damaging the conductors' insulation. When all conductors in a raceway are the same size and insulation, the number of conductors permitted can be found in Annex C for the raceway type.

> **Question:** How many 6 THHN conductors can be installed in trade size 1 flexible metal conduit?
>
> (a) 2   (b) 4   (c) 6   (d) 8
>
> **Answer:** (c) 6 conductors [Annex C, Table C3]

Author's Comment:

■ See 300.17 for additional examples on how to size raceways when conductors aren't all the same size.

Trade Size ⅜. The number and size of conductors in trade size ⅜ flexible metal conduit must comply with Table 348.22.

> **Question:** How many 12 THHN conductors can be installed in trade size ⅜ flexible metal conduit that uses outside fittings?
>
> (a) 1   (b) 3   (c) 5   (d) 7
>
> **Answer:** (b) 3 conductors [Table 348.22]

One insulated, covered, or bare equipment grounding conductor of the same size is permitted with the circuit conductors. See the "*" note at the bottom of Table 348.22.

Cables can be installed in flexible metal conduit as long as the number of cables doesn't exceed the allowable percentage fill specified in Table 1, Chapter 9.

348.24 Bends

Bends must be made so that the conduit won't be damaged, and its internal diameter won't be effectively reduced. The radius of the curve of the inner edge of any field bend must not be less than shown in Table 2, Chapter 9 using the column "Other Bends."

348.26 Number of Bends (360°)

To reduce the stress and friction on conductor insulation, the maximum number of bends (including offsets) between pull points must not exceed 360°.

Author's Comment:

■ There's no maximum distance between pull boxes because this is a design issue, not a safety issue.

348.28 Trimming

The cut ends of flexible metal conduit must be trimmed to remove the rough edges, but this isn't necessary if fittings are threaded into the convolutions.

348.30 Securing and Supporting

(A) Securely Fastened. Flexible metal conduit must be securely fastened by a means approved by the authority having jurisdiction within 1 ft of termination, and it must be secured and supported at intervals not exceeding 4½ ft. Figure 348–2

Ex 1: Flexible metal conduit isn't required to be securely fastened or supported where fished between access points through concealed spaces and supporting is impracticable.

Ex 2: If flexibility is necessary after installation, unsecured lengths from the last point the raceway is securely fastened must not exceed:

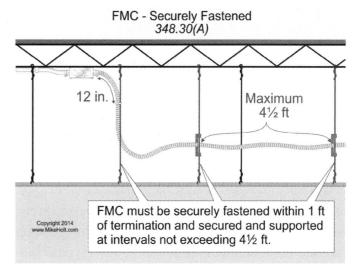

FMC - Securely Fastened
348.30(A)

12 in.

Maximum 4½ ft

Copyright 2014
www.MikeHolt.com

FMC must be securely fastened within 1 ft of termination and secured and supported at intervals not exceeding 4½ ft.

Figure 348–2

(1) 3 ft for trade sizes ½ through 1¼

(2) 4 ft for trade sizes 1½ through 2

(3) 5 ft for trade sizes 2½ and larger

(B) Horizontal Runs. Flexible metal conduit installed horizontally in bored or punched holes in wood or metal framing members, or notches in wooden members, is considered supported, but the raceway must be secured within 1 ft of terminations. Figure 348–3

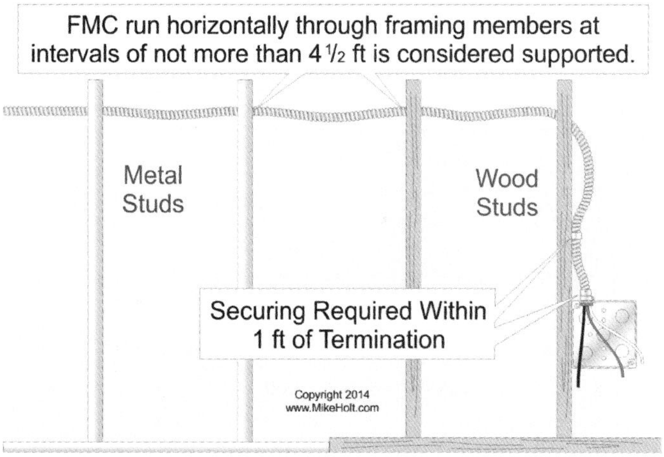

FMC - Horizontal Support
348.30(B)

FMC run horizontally through framing members at intervals of not more than 4½ ft is considered supported.

Metal Studs

Wood Studs

Securing Required Within 1 ft of Termination

Copyright 2014
www.MikeHolt.com

Figure 348–3

348.42 Fittings

Angle connectors must not be concealed.

348.60 Grounding and Bonding

If flexibility is necessary to minimize the transmission of vibration from equipment or to provide flexibility for equipment that requires movement after installation, an equipment grounding conductor of the wire type must be installed with the circuit conductors in accordance with 250.118(5), and sized in accordance with 250.122 based on the rating of the overcurrent device.

If flexibility isn't necessary after installation, and vibration isn't a concern, the metal armor of flexible metal conduit can serve as an equipment grounding conductor if the circuit conductors contained in the raceway are protected by an overcurrent device rated 20A or less, and the combined length of the flexible metal raceway in the same ground-fault return path doesn't exceed 6 ft [250.118(5)]. Figure 348–4

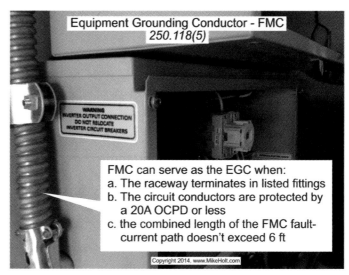

Figure 348–4

ARTICLE 350
LIQUIDTIGHT FLEXIBLE METAL CONDUIT (TYPE LFMC)

Introduction to Article 350—Liquidtight Flexible Metal Conduit (Type LFMC)

Liquidtight flexible metal conduit (LFMC), with its associated connectors and fittings, is a flexible raceway commonly used for connections to equipment that vibrates or is required to move occasionally. Liquidtight flexible metal conduit is commonly called "Sealtight®" or "liquidtight." Liquidtight flexible metal conduit is of similar construction to flexible metal conduit, but it also has an outer liquidtight thermoplastic covering. It has the same primary purpose as flexible metal conduit, but it also provides protection from moisture and some corrosive effects.

Part I. General

350.1 Scope

Article 350 covers the use, installation, and construction specifications of liquidtight flexible metal conduit and associated fittings.

350.2 Definition

Liquidtight Flexible Metal Conduit (Type LFMC). A raceway of circular cross section, having an outer liquidtight, nonmetallic, sunlight-resistant jacket over an inner flexible metal core, with associated connectors and fittings for the installation of electric conductors. Figure 350–1

350.6 Listing Requirements

Liquidtight flexible metal conduit and its associated fittings must be listed.

Liquidtight Flexible Metal Conduit (Type LFMC)
350.2 Definition

A circular raceway having an outer liquidtight, nonmetallic, sunlight-resistant jacket over an inner flexible metal core.

Copyright 2014, www.MikeHolt.com

Figure 350–1

Part II. Installation

350.10 Uses Permitted

(A) Permitted Use. Listed liquidtight flexible metal conduit is permitted, either exposed or concealed, at any of the following locations:

(1) If flexibility or protection from liquids, vapors, or solids is required.

(2) In hazardous locations, as permitted in 501.10(B), 502.10(A)(2), 502.10(B)(2), or 503.10(A)(3).

(3) For direct burial, if listed and marked for this purpose.

350.12 Uses Not Permitted

(1) If subject to physical damage.

(2) If the combination of the ambient and conductor operating temperatures exceeds the rating of the raceway.

350.20 Trade Size

(A) Minimum. Liquidtight flexible metal conduit smaller than trade size ½ must not be used.

Ex: Liquidtight flexible metal conduit can be smaller than trade size ½ if installed in accordance with 348.20(A).

Author's Comment:

- According to 348.20(A), LFMC smaller than trade size ½ is permitted for the following:

  (1) For enclosing the leads of motors.
  (2) Not exceeding 6 ft in length:
      a. For utilization equipment,
      b. As part of a listed assembly, or
      c. For tap connections to luminaires as permitted by 410.117(C).
  (3) In manufactured wiring systems, 604.6(A).
  (4) In hoistways, 620.21(A)(1).
  (5) As part of a listed assembly to connect wired luminaire sections, 410.137(C).

(B) Maximum. Liquidtight flexible metal conduit larger than trade size 4 must not be used.

350.22 Number of Conductors

(A) Raceway Trade Size ½ and Larger. Raceways must be large enough to permit the installation and removal of conductors without damaging the insulation. When all conductors in a raceway are the same size and insulation, the number of conductors permitted can be found in Annex C for the raceway type.

> **Question:** How many 6 THHN conductors can be installed in trade size 1 LFMC? Figure 350–2
>
> (a) 3   (b) 5   (c) 7   (d) 9
>
> **Answer:** (c) 7 conductors [Annex C, Table C.7]

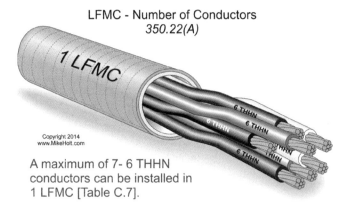

LFMC - Number of Conductors
350.22(A)

Copyright 2014
www.MikeHolt.com

A maximum of 7- 6 THHN conductors can be installed in 1 LFMC [Table C.7].

When all conductors in a raceway are the same size and insulation, the number of conductors permitted can be found in Annex C.

Figure 350–2

Author's Comment:

- See 300.17 for additional examples on how to size raceways when conductors aren't all the same size.

Cables can be installed in liquidtight flexible metal conduit as long as the number of cables doesn't exceed the allowable percentage fill specified in Table 1, Chapter 9.

(B) Raceway Trade Size ⅜. The number and size of conductors in a trade size ⅜ liquidtight flexible metal conduit must comply with Table 348.22.

> **Question:** *How many 12 THHN conductors can be installed in trade size ⅜ LFMC that uses outside fittings?*
>
> *(a) 1   (b) 3   (c) 5   (d) 7*
>
> **Answer:** *(b) 3 conductors [Table 348.22]*

One insulated, covered, or bare equipment grounding conductor of the same size is permitted with the circuit conductors. See the "*" note at the bottom of Table 348.22.

350.24 Bends

Bends must be made so that the conduit won't be damaged and the internal diameter of the conduit won't be effectively reduced. The radius of the curve of the inner edge of any field bend must not be less than shown in Table 2, Chapter 9 using the column "Other Bends."

350.26 Number of Bends (360°)

To reduce the stress and friction on conductor insulation, the maximum number of bends (including offsets) between pull points must not exceed 360°.

Author's Comment:

- There's no maximum distance between pull boxes because this is a design issue, not a safety issue.

350.30 Securing and Supporting

Liquidtight flexible metal conduit must be securely fastened in place and supported in accordance with (A) and (B).

(A) Securely Fastened. Liquidtight flexible metal conduit must be securely fastened by a means approved by the authority having jurisdiction within 1 ft of termination, and must be secured and supported at intervals not exceeding 4½ ft. Figure 350–3

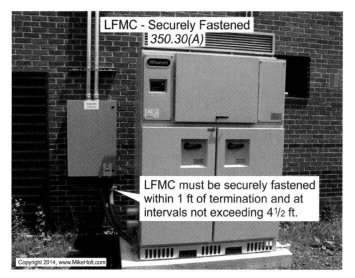

Figure 350–3

Ex 1: Liquidtight flexible metal conduit isn't required to be securely fastened or supported where fished between access points through concealed spaces and supporting is impracticable.

Ex 2: If flexibility is necessary after installation, unsecured lengths from the last point where the raceway is securely fastened must not exceed: Figure 350–4

(1) 3 ft for trade sizes ½ through 1¼

(2) 4 ft for trade sizes 1½ through 2

(3) 5 ft for trade sizes 2½ and larger

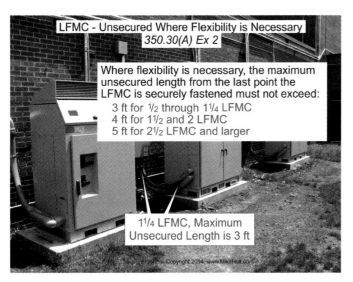

LFMC - Unsecured Where Flexibility is Necessary
350.30(A) Ex 2

Where flexibility is necessary, the maximum unsecured length from the last point the LFMC is securely fastened must not exceed:
3 ft for ½ through 1¼ LFMC
4 ft for 1½ and 2 LFMC
5 ft for 2½ LFMC and larger

1¼ LFMC, Maximum Unsecured Length is 3 ft

Figure 350–4

(B) Horizontal Runs. Liquidtight flexible metal conduit installed horizontally in bored or punched holes in wood or metal framing members, or notches in wooden members, is considered supported, but the raceway must be secured within 1 ft of termination.

350.42 Fittings

Fittings used with LFMC must be listed. Angle connectors must not be concealed. Straight fittings can be buried where marked as suitable for direct burial.

2014 CHANGE ANALYSIS: For whatever reason, the requirement of 350.6 has been copied and pasted into this section. Unlisted fittings weren't allowed before, due to 350.6, and they still aren't. New to this edition of the *NEC*, however, is an allowance for straight fittings to be buried if used in accordance with their listing. This isn't technically a change, since nothing in the previous *Code* prohibited the practice, but it certainly is more obvious now.

350.60 Grounding and Bonding

If flexibility is necessary to minimize the transmission of vibration from equipment or to provide flexibility for equipment that requires movement after installation, an equipment grounding conductor of the wire type must be installed with the circuit conductors in accordance with 250.118(6), and sized in accordance with 250.122 based on the rating of the overcurrent device.

If flexibility isn't necessary after installation, and vibration isn't a concern, the metal armor of flexible metal conduit can serve as an equipment grounding conductor if the circuit conductors contained in the raceway are protected by an overcurrent device rated 20A or less, and the combined length of the flexible metal raceway in the same ground-fault return path doesn't exceed 6 ft [250.118(6)].

If an equipment bonding jumper is installed outside of a raceway, the length of the equipment bonding jumper must not exceed 6 ft, and it must be routed with the raceway or enclosure in accordance with 250.102(E)(2).

ARTICLE 352

RIGID POLYVINYL CHLORIDE CONDUIT (TYPE PVC)

Introduction to Article 352—Rigid Polyvinyl Chloride Conduit (Type PVC)

Rigid polyvinyl chloride conduit (PVC) is a rigid nonmetallic conduit that provides many of the advantages of rigid metal conduit, while allowing installation in areas that are wet or corrosive. It's an inexpensive raceway, and easily installed. It's lightweight, easily cut and glued together, and relatively strong. However, conduits manufactured from polyvinyl chloride (PVC) are brittle when cold, and they sag when hot. This type of conduit is commonly used as an underground raceway because of its low cost, ease of installation, and resistance to corrosion and decay.

Part I. General

352.1 Scope

Article 352 covers the use, installation, and construction specifications of PVC conduit and associated fittings.

352.2 Definition

Rigid Polyvinyl Chloride Conduit (PVC). A rigid nonmetallic raceway of circular cross section with integral or associated couplings, connectors, and fittings listed for the installation of electrical conductors and cables. Figure 352–1

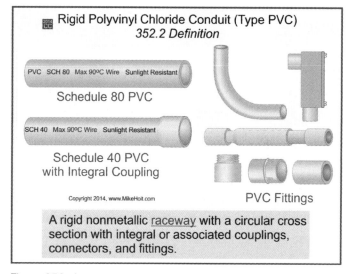

Rigid Polyvinyl Chloride Conduit (Type PVC)
352.2 Definition

PVC SCH 80 Max 90°C Wire Sunlight Resistant

Schedule 80 PVC

SCH 40 Max 90°C Wire Sunlight Resistant

Schedule 40 PVC
with Integral Coupling

Copyright 2014, www.MikeHolt.com

PVC Fittings

A rigid nonmetallic raceway with a circular cross section with integral or associated couplings, connectors, and fittings.

Figure 352–1

2014 CHANGE ANALYSIS: According to the *NEC* Style Manual, a definition shouldn't contain the term being defined. In order to satisfy this requirement, the word "conduit" (which is included in the term being defined) was changed to "raceway." Many other definitions throughout the *Code* were changed in the same manner, but they won't be discussed any further.

Part II. Installation

352.10 Uses Permitted

Note: In extreme cold, PVC conduit can become brittle, and is more susceptible to physical damage.

(A) Concealed. PVC conduit can be concealed within walls, floors, or ceilings, directly buried, or embedded in concrete in buildings of any height. Figure 352–2

Figure 352–2

(B) Corrosive Influences. PVC conduit is permitted in areas subject to severe corrosion for which the material is specifically approved by the authority having jurisdiction.

Author's Comment:

- If subject to exposure to chemical solvents, vapors, splashing, or immersion, materials or coatings must either be inherently resistant to chemicals based upon their listing, or be identified for the specific chemical reagent [300.6(C)(2)].

(D) Wet Locations. PVC conduit is permitted in wet locations such as dairies, laundries, canneries, car washes, and other areas frequently washed or in outdoor locations. Support fittings such as straps, screws, and bolts must be made of corrosion-resistant materials, or must be protected with a corrosion-resistant coating, in accordance with 300.6(A).

(E) Dry and Damp Locations. PVC conduit is permitted in dry and damp locations, except where limited in 352.12.

(F) Exposed. Schedule 40 PVC conduit is permitted for exposed locations where not subject to physical damage. Figure 352–3

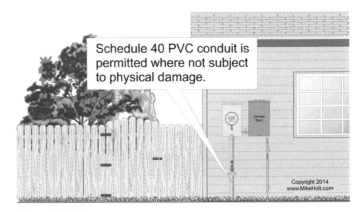

Figure 352–3

If PVC conduit is exposed to physical damage, the raceway must be identified for the application.

Note: PVC Schedule 80 conduit is identified for use in areas subject to physical damage. Figure 352–4

(G) Underground. PVC conduit installed underground must comply with the burial requirements of 300.5.

(H) Support of Conduit Bodies. PVC conduit is permitted to support nonmetallic conduit bodies that aren't larger than the largest trade size of an entering raceway. These conduit bodies can't support luminaires or other equipment, and aren't permitted to contain devices, other than splicing devices permitted by 110.14(B) and 314.16(C)(2).

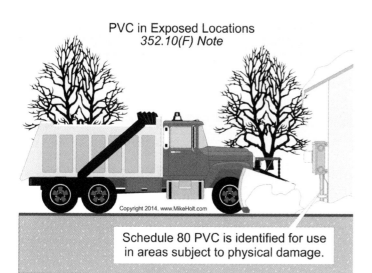

PVC in Exposed Locations
352.10(F) Note

Schedule 80 PVC is identified for use in areas subject to physical damage.

Figure 352–4

(I) Insulation Temperature Limitations. Conductors rated at a temperature higher than the listed temperature rating of PVC conduit must not be operated at a temperature above the raceway's listed temperature rating. Figure 352–5

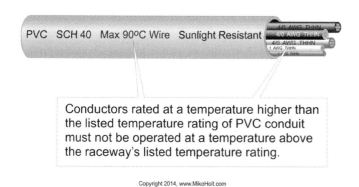

PVC - Insulation Temperature Limitations
352.10(I)

PVC SCH 40 Max 90°C Wire Sunlight Resistant

Conductors rated at a temperature higher than the listed temperature rating of PVC conduit must not be operated at a temperature above the raceway's listed temperature rating.

Figure 352–5

352.12 Uses Not Permitted

(A) Hazardous Locations. PVC conduit isn't permitted to be used in hazardous locations except as permitted by 501.10(A)(1)(a) Ex, 501.10(B)(6), 503.10(A), 504.20, 514.8 Ex 2, and 515.8.

(B) Support of Luminaires. PVC conduit must not be used for the support of luminaires or other equipment not described in 352.10(H).

Author's Comment:

- PVC conduit is permitted to support conduit bodies in accordance with 314.23(E) Ex.

(C) Physical Damage. Schedule 40 PVC conduit must not be installed if subject to physical damage, unless identified for the application.

Author's Comment:

- PVC Schedule 80 conduit is identified for use in areas subject to physical damage [352.10(F) Note].

(D) Ambient Temperature. PVC conduit must not be installed if the ambient temperature exceeds 50°C (122°F).

352.20 Trade Size

(A) Minimum. PVC conduit smaller than trade size ½ must not be used.

(B) Maximum. PVC conduit larger than trade size 6 must not be used.

352.22 Number of Conductors

Raceways must be large enough to permit the installation and removal of conductors without damaging the conductors' insulation, and the number of conductors must not exceed that permitted by the percentage fill specified in Table 1, Chapter 9.

When all conductors in a raceway are the same size and insulation, the number of conductors permitted can be found in Annex C for the raceway type.

Question: How many 4/0 THHN conductors can be installed in trade size 2 Schedule 40 PVC?

(a) 2　　　　(b) 4　　　　(c) 6　　　　(d) 8

Answer: (b) 4 conductors [Annex C, Table C10]

Author's Comment:

- Schedule 80 PVC conduit has the same outside diameter as Schedule 40 PVC conduit, but the wall thickness of Schedule 80 PVC conduit is greater, which results in a reduced interior area for conductor fill.

Question: How many 4/0 THHN conductors can be installed in trade size 2 Schedule 80 PVC conduit?

(a) 3　　　　(b) 5　　　　(c) 7　　　　(d) 9

Answer: (a) 3 conductors [Annex C, Table C9]

Author's Comment:

- See 300.17 for additional examples on how to size raceways when conductors aren't all the same size.

Cables can be installed in PVC conduit, as long as the number of cables doesn't exceed the allowable percentage fill specified in Table 1, Chapter 9.

352.24 Bends

Raceway bends must not be made in any manner that will damage the raceway, or significantly change its internal diameter (no kinks). The radius of the curve of the inner edge of any field bend must not be less than shown in Table 2, Chapter 9.

Author's Comment:

- Be sure to use equipment designed for heating the non-metallic raceway so it's pliable for bending (for example, a "hot box"). Don't use open-flame torches.

352.26 Number of Bends (360°)

To reduce the stress and friction on conductor insulation, the maximum number of bends (including offsets) between pull points must not exceed 360°. Figure 352–6

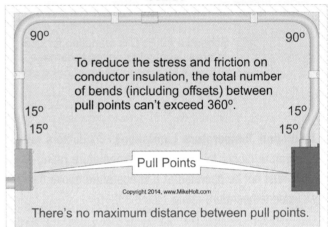

Figure 352–6

352.28 Trimming

The cut ends of PVC conduit must be trimmed (inside and out) to remove the burrs and rough edges.

Author's Comment:

- Trimming PVC conduit is very easy; most of the burrs will rub off with fingers, and a knife will smooth the rough edges.

352.30 Securing and Supporting

PVC conduit must be securely fastened and supported in accordance with (A) and (B) and the raceway must be fastened in a manner that permits movement from thermal expansion or contraction. Figure 352–7

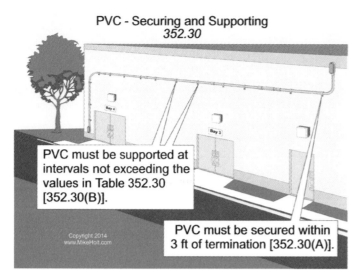

PVC - Securing and Supporting
352.30

PVC must be supported at intervals not exceeding the values in Table 352.30 [352.30(B)].

PVC must be secured within 3 ft of termination [352.30(A)].

Figure 352–7

(A) Secured. PVC conduit must be secured within 3 ft of every box, cabinet, or termination fitting, such as a conduit body.

(B) Supports. PVC conduit must be supported at intervals not exceeding the values in Table 352.30.

Table 352.30	
Trade Size	Support Spacing
½–1	3 ft
1¼–2	5 ft
2½–3	6 ft
3½–5	7 ft
6	8 ft

PVC conduit installed horizontally in bored or punched holes in wood or metal framing members, or notches in wooden members, is considered supported, but the raceway must be secured within 3 ft of termination.

352.44 Expansion Fittings

If PVC conduit is installed in a straight run between securely mounted items, such as boxes, cabinets, elbows, or other conduit terminations, expansion fittings must be provided to compensate for thermal expansion and contraction of the raceway

in accordance with Table 352.44, if the length change is determined to be ¼ in. or greater. Figure 352–8

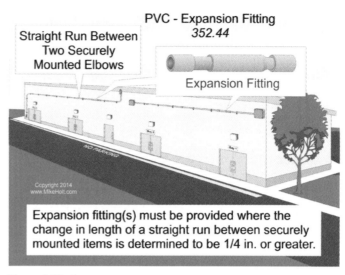

PVC - Expansion Fitting
352.44

Straight Run Between Two Securely Mounted Elbows

Expansion Fitting

Expansion fitting(s) must be provided where the change in length of a straight run between securely mounted items is determined to be 1/4 in. or greater.

Figure 352–8

Author's Comment:

- Table 352.44 in the *NEC* was created based on the following formula: Figure 352–9

Expansion/Contraction Inches =
Raceway Length/100 x [(Temp Change/100) x 4.00]

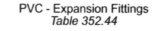
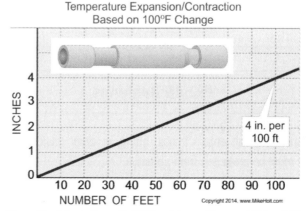

PVC - Expansion Fittings
Table 352.44
Temperature Expansion/Contraction
Based on 100°F Change

4 in. per 100 ft

Expn-Cont In. = (Length/100) x (Temp Change/100 x 4.0)

Figure 352–9

PVC Expansion/Contraction

Conditions: *PVC conduit 100 ft long is installed on a roof when the ambient temperature is 80°F. After installation, the temperature can be as low as 10°F and as high as 150°F.*

Question 1: *If the temperature rises from 80°F to 150°F, the PVC conduit will expand _____ in.* **Figure 352–10**

(a) 0.50   (b) 0.70   (c) 1.40   (d) 2.80

Answer: *(d) 2.80 in.*

> *Expansion/Contraction Inches = Raceway Length/100 x ((Temp °F Change/100) x 4.00)*

Expansion/Contraction Inches = (100/100) x ((70°F/100) x 4.00)

Expansion/Contraction Inches = 2.80 in.

Question 2: *If the temperature decreases from 80°F to 10°F, the PVC conduit will contract _____ in.* **Figure 352–11**

(a) -0.50   (b) -0.70   (c) -1.40   (d) -2.80

Answer: *(d) -2.80 in.*

> *Expansion/Contraction Inches = Raceway Length/100 x ((Temp °F Change/100) x 4.00)*

Expansion/Contraction Inches = (100/100) x ((-70°F/100) x 4.00)

Expansion/Contraction Inches = -2.80 in.

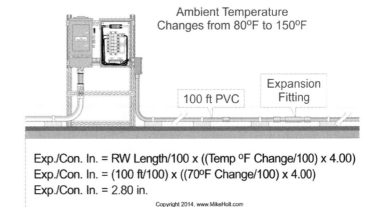

PVC - Expansion Fittings
Table 352.44

Ambient Temperature Changes from 80°F to 150°F

100 ft PVC   Expansion Fitting

Exp./Con. In. = RW Length/100 x ((Temp °F Change/100) x 4.00)
Exp./Con. In. = (100 ft/100) x ((70°F Change/100) x 4.00)
Exp./Con. In. = 2.80 in.

Copyright 2014, www.MikeHolt.com

Figure 352–10

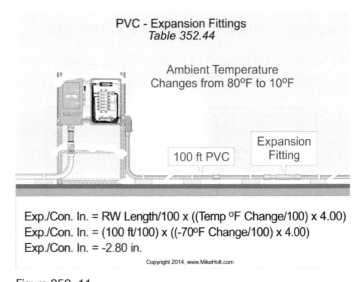

PVC - Expansion Fittings
Table 352.44

Ambient Temperature Changes from 80°F to 10°F

100 ft PVC   Expansion Fitting

Exp./Con. In. = RW Length/100 x ((Temp °F Change/100) x 4.00)
Exp./Con. In. = (100 ft/100) x ((-70°F Change/100) x 4.00)
Exp./Con. In. = -2.80 in.

Copyright 2014, www.MikeHolt.com

Figure 352–11

352.46 Bushings

Where a conduit enters a box, fitting, or other enclosure, the wire must be protected from abrasion.

Note: Conductors 4 AWG and larger that enter an enclosure must be protected from abrasion, during and after installation, by a fitting that provides a smooth, rounded insulating surface, such as an insulating bushing, unless the design of the box, fitting, or enclosure provides equivalent protection, in accordance with 300.4(G). **Figure 352–12**

Author's Comment:

- When PVC conduit is stubbed into an open-bottom switchboard, the raceway, including the end fitting (bell-end), must not rise more than 3 in. above the bottom of the switchboard enclosure [300.16(B) and 408.5].

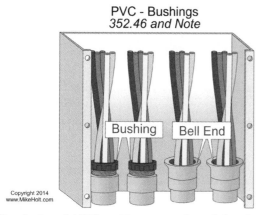

PVC - Bushings
352.46 and Note

Copyright 2014
www.MikeHolt.com

Conductors 4 AWG and larger require a fitting that provides a smooth, rounded, insulating surface to protect the wire during and after installation. See 300.4(G).

Figure 352–12

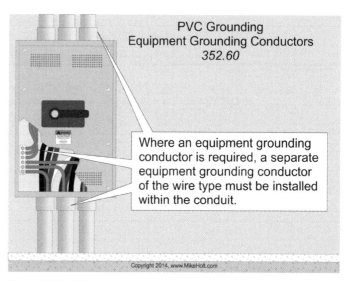

PVC Grounding
Equipment Grounding Conductors
352.60

Where an equipment grounding conductor is required, a separate equipment grounding conductor of the wire type must be installed within the conduit.

Copyright 2014, www.MikeHolt.com

Figure 352–13

352.48 Joints

Joints, such as couplings and connectors, must be made in a manner approved by the authority having jurisdiction.

Author's Comment:

■ Follow the manufacturer's instructions for the raceway, fittings, and glue. Some glue requires the raceway surface to be cleaned with a solvent before being applied. After applying glue to both surfaces, a quarter turn of the fitting is required.

352.60 Equipment Grounding Conductor

If equipment grounding is required, a separate equipment grounding conductor of the wire type must be installed within the conduit [300.2(B)]. Figure 352–13

Ex 2: An equipment grounding conductor isn't required in PVC conduit if the grounded/neutral conductor is used to ground service equipment, as permitted in 250.142(A) [250.24(C)]. Figure 352–14

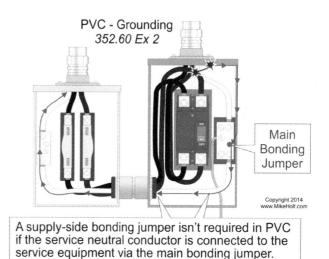

PVC - Grounding
352.60 Ex 2

Main Bonding Jumper

Copyright 2014
www.MikeHolt.com

A supply-side bonding jumper isn't required in PVC if the service neutral conductor is connected to the service equipment via the main bonding jumper.

Figure 352–14

Mike Holt's Illustrated Guide to Understanding NEC Requirements for Solar Photovoltaic Systems

ARTICLE 358
ELECTRICAL METALLIC TUBING (TYPE EMT)

Introduction to Article 358—Electrical Metallic Tubing (Type EMT)

Electrical metallic tubing (EMT) is a lightweight raceway that's relatively easy to bend, cut, and ream. Because it isn't threaded, all connectors and couplings are of the threadless type and provide quick, easy, and inexpensive installation when compared to other metallic conduit systems, which makes it very popular. Electrical metallic tubing is manufactured in both galvanized steel and aluminum; the steel type is used the most.

Part I. General

358.1 Scope

Article 358 covers the use, installation, and construction specifications of electrical metallic tubing.

358.2 Definition

Electrical Metallic Tubing (Type EMT). A metallic tubing of circular cross section used for the installation and physical protection of electrical conductors when joined together with fittings. Figure 358–1

358.6 Listing Requirement

Electrical metallic tubing, elbows, and associated fittings must be listed.

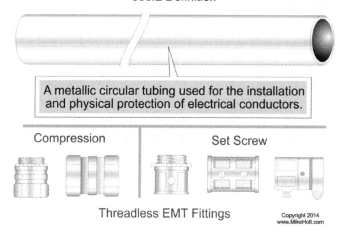

Electrical Metallic Tubing (Type EMT)
358.2 Definition

A metallic circular tubing used for the installation and physical protection of electrical conductors.

Compression   Set Screw

Threadless EMT Fittings

Copyright 2014
www.MikeHolt.com

Figure 358–1

Part II. Installation

358.10 Uses Permitted

(A) Exposed and Concealed. Electrical metallic tubing is permitted exposed or concealed.

(B) Corrosion Protection. Electrical metallic tubing, elbows, couplings, and fittings can be installed in concrete, in direct contact with the earth, or in areas subject to severe corrosive influences if protected by corrosion protection and approved as suitable for the condition. Figure 358–2

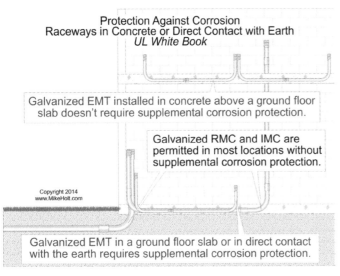

Figure 358–2

⚠ **CAUTION:** *Supplementary coatings for corrosion protection (asphalted paint) haven't been investigated by a product testing and listing agency and these coatings are known to cause cancer in laboratory animals.*

(C) Wet Locations. Support fittings, such as screws, straps, and so on, installed in a wet location must be made of corrosion-resistant material, or a corrosion-resistant coating must protect them in accordance with 300.6.

Author's Comment:

- Fittings used in wet locations must be listed for the application (wet location) [314.15]. For more information, visit www.etpfittings.com.

358.12 Uses Not Permitted

EMT must not be used under the following conditions:

(1) Where, during installation or afterward, it will be subject to severe physical damage.

(2) If protected from corrosion solely by enamel.

(3) In cinder concrete or cinder fill where subject to permanent moisture, unless encased in not less than 2 in. of concrete.

(4) In any hazardous location, except as permitted by 502.10, 503.10, and 504.20.

(5) For the support of luminaires or other equipment (like boxes), except conduit bodies no larger than the largest trade size of the tubing that can be supported by the raceway.

(6) If practical, contact with dissimilar metals must be avoided to prevent the deterioration of the metal because of galvanic action.

Ex: Aluminum fittings are permitted on steel electrical metallic tubing, and steel fittings are permitted on aluminum EMT.

358.20 Trade Size

(A) Minimum. Electrical metallic tubing smaller than trade size ½ isn't permitted.

(B) Maximum. Electrical metallic tubing larger than trade size 4 isn't permitted.

358.22 Number of Conductors

Raceways must be large enough to permit the installation and removal of conductors without damaging the conductor insulation. When all conductors in a raceway are the same size and insulation, the number of conductors permitted can be found in Annex C for the raceway type.

Question: *How many 12 THHN conductors can be installed in trade size 1 EMT?* Figure 358–3

(a) 26　　　*(b) 28*　　　*(c) 30*　　　*(d) 32*

Answer: *(a) 26 conductors [Annex C, Table C.1]*

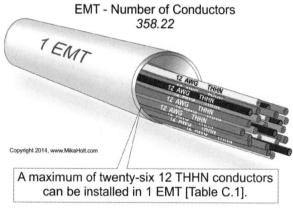

EMT - Number of Conductors
358.22

A maximum of twenty-six 12 THHN conductors can be installed in 1 EMT [Table C.1].

When all conductors in a raceway are the same size and insulation, the number of conductors permitted can be found in Annex C.

Figure 358–3

Author's Comment:

- See 300.17 for additional examples on how to size raceways when conductors aren't all the same size.

Cables can be installed in electrical metallic tubing, as long as the number of cables doesn't exceed the allowable percentage fill specified in Table 1, Chapter 9.

358.24 Bends

Raceway bends must not be made in any manner that will damage the raceway, or significantly change its internal diameter (no kinks). The radius of the curve of the inner edge of any field bend must not be less than shown in Chapter 9, Table 2 for one-shot and full shoe benders.

Author's Comment:

- This typically isn't a problem, because most benders are made to comply with this table.

358.26 Number of Bends (360°)

To reduce the stress and friction on conductor insulation, the maximum number of bends (including offsets) between pull points can't exceed 360°. Figure 358–4

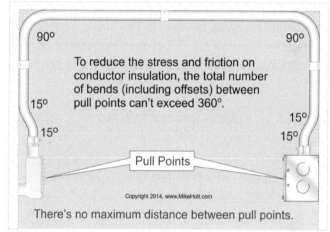

EMT - Number of Bends
358.26

To reduce the stress and friction on conductor insulation, the total number of bends (including offsets) between pull points can't exceed 360°.

Pull Points

There's no maximum distance between pull points.

Figure 358–4

Author's Comment:

- There's no maximum distance between pull boxes because this is a design issue, not a safety issue.

358.28 Reaming and Threading

(A) Reaming. Reaming to remove the burrs and rough edges is required when the raceway is cut.

Author's Comment:

- It's considered an accepted practice to ream small raceways with a screwdriver or the backside of pliers.

(B) Threading. Electrical metallic tubing must not be threaded.

358.30 Securing and Supporting

Electrical metallic tubing must be installed as a complete system in accordance with 300.18 [300.10 and 300.12], and it must be securely fastened in place and supported in accordance with (A) and (B).

(A) Securely Fastened. Electrical metallic tubing must generally be securely fastened within 3 ft of every box, cabinet, or termination fitting, and at intervals not exceeding 10 ft. Figure 358–5

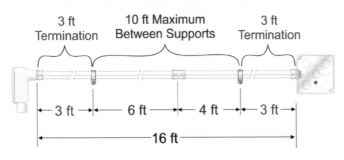

EMT - Securely Fastened
358.30(A)

EMT must be securely fastened within 3 ft of termination fittings and at intervals not exceeding 10 ft.

Copyright 2014, www.MikeHolt.com

Figure 358–5

Author's Comment:

- Fastening is required within 3 ft of termination, not within 3 ft of a coupling.

Ex 1: When structural members don't permit the raceway to be secured within 3 ft of a box or termination fitting, an unbroken raceway can be secured within 5 ft of a box or termination fitting. Figure 358–6

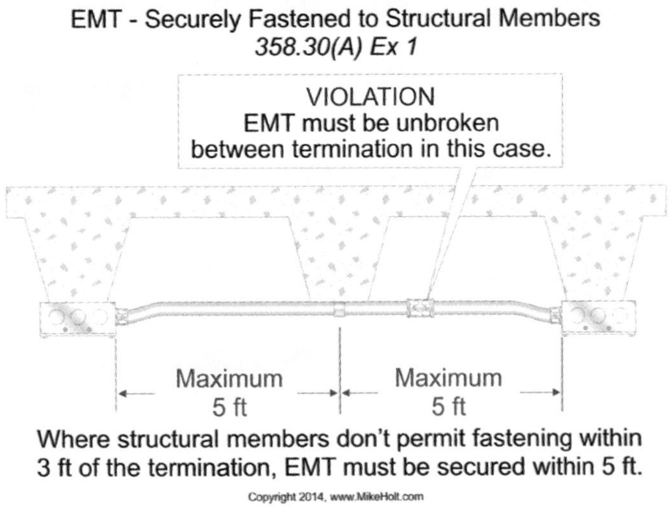

EMT - Securely Fastened to Structural Members
358.30(A) Ex 1

Where structural members don't permit fastening within 3 ft of the termination, EMT must be secured within 5 ft.

Copyright 2014, www.MikeHolt.com

Figure 358–6

(B) Horizontal Runs. Electrical metallic tubing installed horizontally in bored or punched holes in wood or metal framing members, or notches in wooden members, is considered supported, but the raceway must be secured within 3 ft of termination.

358.42 Couplings and Connectors

Couplings and connectors must be made up tight to maintain an effective ground-fault current path to safely conduct fault current in accordance with 250.4(A)(5), 250.96(A), and 300.10.

If buried in masonry or concrete, threadless electrical metallic tubing fittings must be of the concrete-tight type. If installed in wet locations, fittings must be listed for use in wet locations in accordance with 314.15(A).

Author's Comment:

■ Conductors 4 AWG and larger that enter an enclosure must be protected from abrasion, during and after installation, by a fitting that provides a smooth, rounded, insulating surface, such as an insulating bushing, unless the design of the box, fitting, or enclosure provides equivalent protection, in accordance with 300.4(G). Figure 358–7

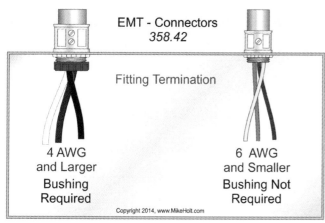

Conductors 4 AWG and larger must be protected by a fitting that provides a smooth, rounded, insulating surface, such as an insulating bushing [300.4(G)].

Figure 358–7

358.60 Grounding

EMT is permitted to serve as an equipment grounding conductor [250.118(4)]. Figure 358–8

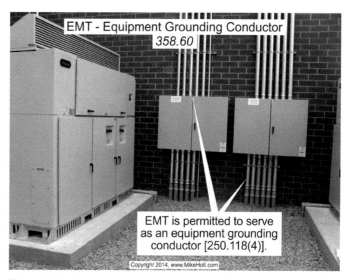

Figure 358–8

Notes

ARTICLE 376

METAL WIREWAYS

Introduction to Article 376—Metal Wireways

Metal wireways are commonly used where access to the conductors within a raceway is required to make terminations, splices, or taps to several devices at a single location. High cost precludes their use for other than short distances, except in some commercial or industrial occupancies where the wiring is frequently revised.

Author's Comment:

■ Both metal wireways and nonmetallic wireways are often incorrectly called "troughs," "auxiliary gutters," "auxiliary wireways," or "gutters" in the field.

Part I. General

376.1 Scope

Article 376 covers the use, installation, and construction specifications of metal wireways and associated fittings.

376.2 Definition

Metal Wireway. A sheet metal trough with hinged or removable covers for housing and protecting electric conductors and cable, and in which conductors are placed after the <u>raceway</u> has been installed. Figure 376–1

A sheet metal trough with hinged or removable covers for housing and protecting electric wires and cable, and in which conductors are placed after the <u>raceway</u> has been installed.

Figure 376–1

Part II. Installation

376.10 Uses Permitted

(1) Exposed.

(2) In any hazardous locations, as permitted by other articles in the *Code.*

(3) Wet locations where listed for the purpose.

(4) Unbroken through walls, partitions, and floors.

Author's Comment:

■ See 501.10(B), 502.10(B), and 504.20 for metal wireways used in hazardous locations.

376.12 Uses Not Permitted

(1) Where subject to severe physical damage.

(2) Where subject to corrosive environments.

376.21 Conductors—Maximum Size

The maximum size conductor permitted in a wireway must not be larger than that for which the wireway is designed.

376.22 Number of Conductors and Ampacity

The number of conductors and their ampacity must comply with 376.22(A) and (B).

(A) Number of Conductors. The maximum number of conductors permitted in a wireway is limited to 20 percent of the cross-sectional area of the wireway. Figure 376–2

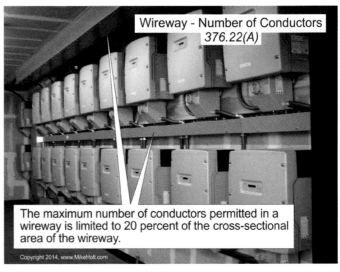

The maximum number of conductors permitted in a wireway is limited to 20 percent of the cross-sectional area of the wireway.

Copyright 2014, www.MikeHolt.com

Figure 376–2

Author's Comment:

■ Splices and taps must not fill more than 75 percent of the wiring space at any cross section [376.56].

(B) Conductor Ampacity Adjustment Factors. When more than 30 current-carrying conductors are installed in <u>any cross-sectional area of the wireway</u>, the conductor ampacity, as listed in Table 310.15(B)(16), must be adjusted in accordance with Table 310.15(B)(3)(a). Figure 376–3

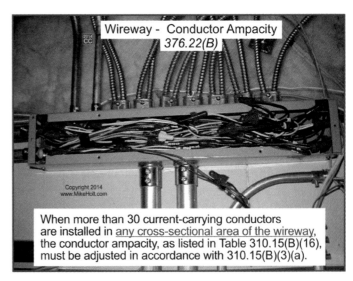

When more than 30 current-carrying conductors are installed in <u>any cross-sectional area of the wireway</u>, the conductor ampacity, as listed in Table 310.15(B)(16), must be adjusted in accordance with 310.15(B)(3)(a).

Copyright 2014 www.MikeHolt.com

Figure 376–3

2014 CHANGE ANALYSIS: The issue of limiting the number (ampacities) of conductors in a wireway certainly makes sense. The more current-carrying conductors there are in proximity with each other, the more heat there will be. The key word here, however, is "proximity." A wireway that's 100 ft long, for example, might contain 31 current-carrying conductors. If these conductors are 10 feet away from any other conductors in the wireway, there certainly won't be any additional heating involved. It's where these conductors are in the same cross section that heat becomes a real problem. This change clarifies and solidifies this concept, and it should be a welcome change to those who desire *Code* rules that make sense.

376.23 Wireway Sizing

(A) Sizing for Conductor Bending Radius. If conductors are bent within a metal wireway, the wireway must be sized to meet the bending radius requirements contained in Table 312.6(A), based on one wire per terminal. Figure 376–4

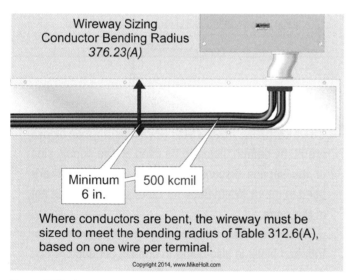

Figure 376–4

376.30 Supports

Wireways must be supported in accordance with (A) and (B).

(A) Horizontal Support. If installed horizontally, metal wireways must be supported at each end and at intervals not exceeding 5 ft.

(B) Vertical Support. If installed vertically, metal wireways must be securely supported at intervals not exceeding 15 ft, with no more than one joint between supports.

376.56 Splices, Taps, and Power Distribution Blocks

(A) Splices and Taps. Splices and taps in metal wireways must be accessible, and they must not fill the wireway to more than 75 percent of its cross-sectional area. Figure 376–5

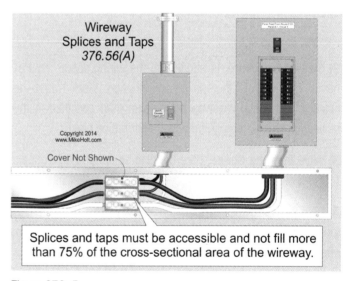

Figure 376–5

Author's Comment:

- The maximum number of conductors permitted in a metal wireway is limited to 20 percent of its cross-sectional area at any point [376.22(A)].

(B) Power Distribution Blocks.

(1) Installation. Power distribution blocks installed in wireways must be listed, <u>and if they're installed on the supply side of the service disconnect they must be listed specifically for that application.</u> Figure 376–6

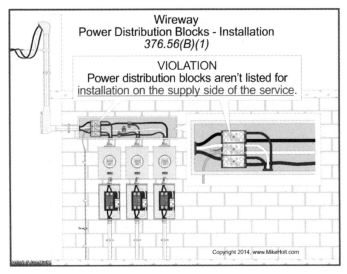

Figure 376–6

(2) Size of Enclosure. In addition to the wiring space requirements [376.56(A)], the power distribution block must be installed in a metal wireway not smaller than specified in the installation instructions of the power distribution block.

(3) Wire Bending Space. Wire bending space at the terminals of power distribution blocks must comply with 312.6(B).

(4) Live Parts. Power distribution blocks must not have uninsulated exposed live parts in the metal wireway after installation, whether or not the wireway cover is installed. Figure 376–7

(5) Conductors. <u>Conductors must be installed so that the terminals of the power distribution block aren't obstructed.</u> Figure 376–8

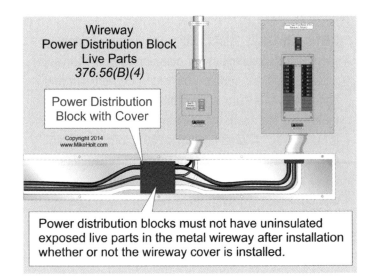

Figure 376–7

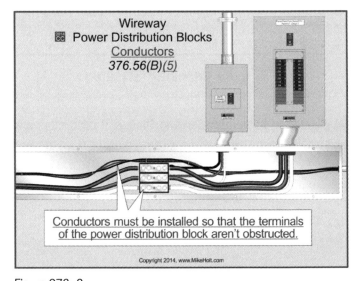

Figure 376–8

2014 CHANGE ANALYSIS: Power distribution blocks aren't, by default, listed to be used on the supply side of the service disconnect. This is information that's been in the UL White Book for quite some time, but not in the *Code*.

More often than not, a wireway with a power distribution block is also going to contain conductors that don't terminate on the block. When this is the case, the conductors must allow for the terminals of the block to be accessed. This is a difficult concept to argue against.

ARTICLE 392

CABLE TRAYS

Introduction to Article 392—Cable Trays

A cable tray system is a unit or an assembly of units or sections with associated fittings that forms a structural system used to securely fasten or support cables and raceways. A cable tray isn't a raceway.

Cable tray systems include ladder, ventilated trough, ventilated channel, solid bottom, and other similar structures. They're manufactured in many forms, from a simple hanger or wire mesh to a substantial, rigid, steel support system. Cable trays are designed and manufactured to support specific wiring methods, as identified in 392.10(A).

Part I. General

392.1 Scope

Article 392 covers cable tray systems, including ventilated trough, ventilated channel, solid bottom, and other similar structures.

392.2 Definition

Cable Tray System. A unit or assembly of units or sections with associated fittings forming a rigid structural system used to securely fasten or support cables and raceways. Figure 392–1

Author's Comment:

- Cable tray isn't a type of raceway. It's a support system for cables and raceways.

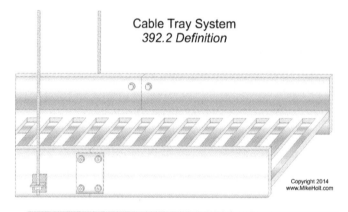

Cable Tray System
392.2 Definition

Copyright 2014
www.MikeHolt.com

A unit or assembly of units or sections with associated fittings forming a rigid structural system used to securely fasten or support cables and raceways.

Figure 392–1

Part II. Installation

392.10 Uses Permitted

Cable trays can be used as a support system for service, feeder, or branch-circuit conductors, as well as communications circuits, control circuits, and signaling circuits.

Author's Comment:

- Cable trays used to support service-entrance conductors must contain only service-entrance conductors unless a solid fixed barrier separates the service-entrance conductors from other conductors [230.44].

- Cable tray installations aren't limited to industrial establishments.

- If exposed to the direct rays of the sun, insulated conductors and jacketed cables must be identified as being sunlight resistant. The manufacturer must identify cable trays and associated fittings for their intended use.

(A) Wiring Methods. Any wiring methods listed in Table 392.10(A) can be installed in a cable tray.

Table 392.10(A) Wiring Methods	
Wiring Method	**Article/Section**
Armored Cable	320
CATV cables	820
CATV raceways	820
Class 2 & 3 cables	725
Communications cables	800
Communications raceways	725, 770, and 800
Electrical metallic tubing	358
Electrical nonmetallic tubing	362
Fire alarm cables	760
Flexible metal conduit	348
Instrumentation tray cable	727

Table 392.10(A) Wiring Methods (continued)	
Wiring Method	**Article/Section**
Intermediate metal conduit	342
Liquidtight flexible metal conduit	350
Liquidtight flexible nonmetallic conduit	356
Metal-clad cable	330
Nonmetallic-sheathed cable	334
Nonpower-limited fire alarm cable	760
Polyvinyl chloride PVC conduit	352
Power and control tray cable	336
Power-limited fire alarm cable	760
Power-limited tray cable	Table 725.154 and 725.179(E) and 725.71(F)
Rigid metal conduit	344
Service-entrance cable	338
Signaling raceway	725
Underground feeder and branch-circuit cable	340

(B) In Industrial Establishments. Where conditions of maintenance and supervision ensure that only qualified persons service the installed cable tray system, single-conductor cables can be installed in accordance with the following:

(1) Single-conductor cables are permitted in accordance with (B)(1)(a) through (B)(1)(c).

(a) 1/0 AWG and larger listed and marked for use in cable trays.

(c) Equipment grounding conductors must be 4 AWG and larger.

(C) Hazardous Locations. Cable trays in hazardous locations must contain only the cable types and raceways permitted by the *Code* for the application

Author's Comment:

- For permitted cable types, see 501.10, 502.10, 503.10, 504.20, and 505.15.

(D) Nonmetallic Cable Trays. In addition to the uses permitted elsewhere in Article 392, nonmetallic cable trays can be installed in corrosive areas, and in areas requiring voltage isolation.

392.12 Uses Not Permitted

Cable tray systems aren't permitted in hoistways, or where subject to severe physical damage.

392.18 Cable Tray Installations

(A) Complete System. Cable trays must be installed as a complete system, except mechanically discontinuous segments between cable tray runs, or between cable tray runs and equipment are permitted. The system must provide for the support of the cables and raceways in accordance with their corresponding articles.

(B) Completed Before Installation. Each run of cable tray must be completed before the installation of cables or conductors.

(D) Through Partitions and Walls. Cable trays can extend through partitions and walls, or vertically through platforms and floors if the installation is made in accordance with the firestopping requirements of 300.21.

(E) Exposed and Accessible. Cable trays must be exposed and accessible, except as permitted by 392.18(D).

(F) Adequate Access. Sufficient space must be provided and maintained about cable trays to permit adequate access for installing and maintaining the cables.

(G) Raceways, Cables, and Boxes Supported from Cable Trays. In industrial facilities where conditions of maintenance and supervision ensure only qualified persons will service the installation, and if the cable tray system is designed and installed to support the load, cable tray systems can support raceways, cables, boxes, and conduit bodies. Figure 392–2

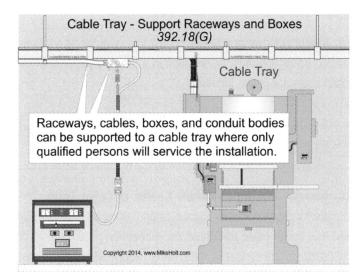

Figure 392–2

For raceways terminating at the tray, a listed cable tray clamp or adapter must be used to securely fasten the raceway to the cable tray system. The raceway must be supported in accordance with the appropriate raceway article.

Raceways or cables running parallel to the cable tray system can be attached to the bottom or side of a cable tray system. The raceway or cable must be fastened and supported in accordance with the appropriate raceway or cable's *Code* article.

Boxes and conduit bodies attached to the bottom or side of a cable tray system must be fastened and supported in accordance with 314.23.

392.20 Cable and Conductor Installation

(C) Connected in Parallel. To prevent unbalanced current in the parallel conductors due to inductive reactance, all circuit conductors of a parallel set [310.10(H)] must be bundled together and secured to prevent excessive movement due to fault current magnetic forces.

(D) Single Conductors. Single conductors of a circuit not connected in parallel must be installed in a single layer, unless the conductors are bound together.

392.22 Number of Conductors or Cables

(A) Number of Multiconductor Cables in Cable Trays. The number of multiconductor cables, rated 2,000V or less, permitted in a single cable tray must not exceed the requirements of this section. The conductor sizes herein apply to both aluminum and copper conductors.

(1) Any Mixture of Cables. If ladder or ventilated trough cable trays contain multiconductor power or lighting cables, the maximum number of cables must conform to the following:

(a) If all of the cables are 4/0 AWG and larger, the sum of the diameters of all cables must not exceed the cable tray width, and the cables must be installed in a single layer.

392.30 Securing and Supporting

(A) Cable Trays. Cable trays must be supported at intervals in accordance with the manufacturer's installation instructions.

(B) Cables and Conductors. Cables and conductors must be secured to and supported by the cable tray system in accordance with the following:

(1) In other than horizontal runs, the cables must be fastened securely to transverse members of the cable runs.

(2) Supports for cable trays must be provided to prevent stress on cables where they enter raceways or other enclosures from cable tray systems.

(3) The system must provide for the support of cables and raceway wiring methods in accordance with their corresponding articles. Where cable trays support individual conductors and where the conductors pass from one cable tray to another, or from a cable tray to raceway(s) or from a cable tray to equipment where the conductors are terminated, the distance between the cable trays or between the cable tray and the raceway(s) or the equipment must not exceed 6 ft. The conductors must be secured to the cable tray(s) at the transition, and must be protected, by guarding or by location, from physical damage.

392.46 Bushed Raceway

A box isn't required where cables or conductors exit a bushed raceway used for the support or protection of the conductors.

392.56 Cable Splices

Splices are permitted in a cable tray if the splice is accessible and insulated by a method approved by the authority having jurisdiction. Splices can project above the side rails of the cable tray if not subject to physical damage. Figure 392–3

392.60 Equipment Grounding Conductor

(A) Metal Cable Trays. Metal cable trays can be used as equipment grounding conductors where continuous maintenance and supervision ensure that only qualified persons service the cable tray system. Figure 392–4

The metal cable trays containing single conductors must be bonded together to ensure that they have the capacity to conduct safely any fault current likely to be imposed in accordance with 250.96(A).

Splices in Cable Tray
392.56

Cable Tray

Splices are permitted in a cable tray if the splice is accessible and insulated by a method approved by the AHJ. Splices can project above the side rails of the cable tray where not subject to physical damage.

Copyright 2014, www.MikeHolt.com

Figure 392–3

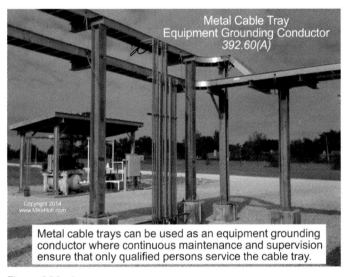

Metal Cable Tray
Equipment Grounding Conductor
392.60(A)

Copyright 2014
www.MikeHolt.com

Metal cable trays can be used as an equipment grounding conductor where continuous maintenance and supervision ensure that only qualified persons service the cable tray.

Figure 392–4

(B) Serve as Equipment Grounding Conductor. Metal cable trays can serve as equipment grounding conductors where the following requirements have been met [392.10(C)]:

(1) Metal cable trays and fittings can serve as an equipment grounding conductor if identified for this purpose. Figure 392–5

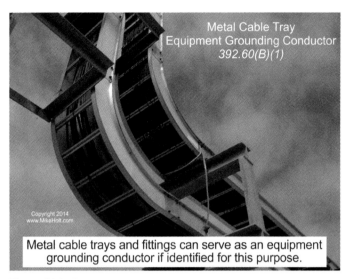

Metal Cable Tray
Equipment Grounding Conductor
392.60(B)(1)

Copyright 2014
www.MikeHolt.com

Metal cable trays and fittings can serve as an equipment grounding conductor if identified for this purpose.

Figure 392–5

(4) Cable tray sections, fittings, and connected raceways are effectively bonded to each other to ensure electrical continuity and the capacity to conduct safely any fault current likely to be imposed on them [250.96(A)]. This is accomplished by using bolted mechanical connectors or bonding jumpers sized in accordance with 250.102.

392.80 Ampacity of Conductors

(A) Ampacity in Cable Trays.

(1) The allowable ampacity of multiconductor cables installed in accordance with 392.22(A) must be as given in Table 310.15(B)(16) and Table 310.15(B)(18).

(a) The conductor ampacity adjustment factors of 310.15(B)(3)(a) apply to a given cable if it contains more than three current-carrying conductors. The conductor adjustment factors only apply to the number of current-carrying conductors in the cable and not to the number of conductors in the cable tray.

CHAPTER 3 PRACTICE QUESTIONS

Please use the 2014 *Code* book to answer the following questions.

Article 300. General Requirements for Wiring Methods and Materials

1. All conductors of the same circuit, including the grounded and equipment grounding conductors, shall be contained within the same _____, unless otherwise permitted elsewhere in the *Code*.

   (a) raceway
   (b) cable
   (c) trench
   (d) all of these

2. Conductors of ac and dc circuits, rated 1,000V or less, shall be permitted to occupy the same _____ provided that all conductors have an insulation rating equal to the maximum voltage applied to any conductor.

   (a) enclosure
   (b) cable
   (c) raceway
   (d) any of these

3. What is the minimum cover requirement for direct burial Type UF cable installed outdoors that supplies a 120V, 30A circuit?

   (a) 6 in.
   (b) 12 in.
   (c) 18 in.
   (d) 24 in.

4. Rigid metal conduit that is directly buried outdoors shall have at least _____ in. of cover.

   (a) 6
   (b) 12
   (c) 18
   (d) 24

5. When installing PVC conduit underground without concrete cover, there shall be a minimum of _____ in. of cover.

   (a) 6
   (b) 12
   (c) 18
   (d) 22

6. What is the minimum cover requirement for Type UF cable supplying power to a 120V, 15A GFCI-protected circuit outdoors under a driveway of a one-family dwelling?

   (a) 6 in.
   (b) 12 in.
   (c) 16 in.
   (d) 24 in.

7. Type UF cable used with a 24V landscape lighting system can have a minimum cover of _____ in.

   (a) 6
   (b) 12
   (c) 18
   (d) 24

8. _____ is defined as the area between the top of direct-burial cable and the top surface of the finished grade.

   (a) Notch
   (b) Cover
   (c) Gap
   (d) none of these

9. The interior of underground raceways shall be considered a _____ location.

   (a) wet
   (b) dry
   (c) damp
   (d) corrosive

10. Type MC Cable listed for _____ is permitted to be installed underground under a building without installation in a raceway.

    (a) direct burial
    (b) damp and wet locations
    (c) rough service
    (d) b and c

11. Where direct-buried conductors and cables emerge from grade, they shall be protected by enclosures or raceways to a point at least _____ ft above finished grade.

    (a) 3
    (b) 6
    (c) 8
    (d) 10

12. Direct-buried service conductors that are not encased in concrete and that are buried 18 in. or more below grade shall have their location identified by a warning ribbon placed in the trench at least _____ in. above the underground installation.

    (a) 6
    (b) 10
    (c) 12
    (d) 18

13. Direct-buried conductors or cables can be spliced or tapped without the use of splice boxes when the splice or tap is made in accordance with 110.14(B).

    (a) True
    (b) False

14. Backfill used for underground wiring shall not _____.

    (a) damage the wiring method
    (b) prevent compaction of the fill
    (c) contribute to the corrosion of the raceway
    (d) all of these

15. Conduits or raceways through which moisture may contact live parts shall be _____ at either or both ends.

    (a) sealed
    (b) plugged
    (c) bushed
    (d) a or b

16. When installing direct-buried cables, a _____ shall be used at the end of a conduit that terminates underground.

    (a) splice kit
    (b) terminal fitting
    (c) bushing
    (d) b or c

17. All conductors of the same circuit shall be _____, unless otherwise specifically permitted in the *Code*.

    (a) in the same raceway or cable
    (b) in close proximity in the same trench
    (c) the same size
    (d) a or b

18. Each direct-buried single conductor cable must be located _____ in the trench to the other single conductor cables in the same parallel set of conductors, including equipment grounding conductors.

    (a) perpendicular
    (b) bundled together
    (c) in close proximity
    (d) spaced apart

19. Direct-buried conductors, cables, or raceways, which are subject to movement by settlement or frost, shall be arranged to prevent damage to the _____ or to equipment connected to the raceways.

    (a) siding of the building mounted on
    (b) landscaping around the cable or raceway
    (c) enclosed conductors
    (d) expansion fitting

20. Cables or raceways installed using directional boring equipment shall be _____ for this purpose.

    (a) marked
    (b) listed
    (c) labeled
    (d) approved

21. Raceways, cable trays, cablebus, auxiliary gutters, cable armor, boxes, cable sheathing, cabinets, elbows, couplings, fittings, supports, and support hardware shall be of materials suitable for _____.

    (a) corrosive locations
    (b) wet locations
    (c) the environment in which they are to be installed
    (d) none of these

22. Where corrosion protection is necessary for ferrous metal equipment and the conduit is threaded in the field, the threads shall be coated with a(n) _____ electrically conductive, corrosion-resistant compound.

    (a) marked
    (b) listed
    (c) labeled
    (d) approved

23. Which of the following metal parts shall be protected from corrosion?

    (a) Ferrous metal raceways.
    (b) Ferrous metal elbows.
    (c) Ferrous boxes.
    (d) all of these

24. Ferrous metal raceways, boxes, fittings, supports, and support hardware can be installed in concrete or in direct contact with the earth or other areas subject to severe corrosive influences, where _____ approved for the conditions.

    (a) the soil is
    (b) made of material
    (c) the qualified installer is
    (d) none of these

25. Aluminum raceways, cable trays, cablebus, auxiliary gutters, cable armor, boxes, cable sheathing, cabinets, elbows, couplings, nipples, fittings, supports, and support hardware _____ shall be provided with supplementary corrosion protection.

    (a) embedded or encased in concrete
    (b) in direct contact with the earth
    (c) likely to become energized
    (d) a or b

26. Where exposed to sunlight, nonmetallic raceways, cable trays, boxes, cables with a nonmetallic outer jacket, fittings, and support hardware shall be _____.

    (a) listed as sunlight resistant
    (b) identified as sunlight resistant
    (c) a and b
    (d) a or b

27. Where nonmetallic wiring methods are subject to exposure to chemical solvents or vapors, they shall be inherently resistant to chemicals based upon their being _____.

    (a) listed for the chemical
    (b) identified for the chemical
    (c) a and b
    (d) a or b

28. An exposed wiring system for indoor wet locations where walls are frequently washed shall be mounted so that there is at least a _____ between the mounting surface and the electrical equipment.

    (a) ¼ in. airspace
    (b) separation by insulated bushings
    (c) separation by noncombustible tubing
    (d) none of these

29. In general, areas where acids and alkali chemicals are handled and stored may present corrosive conditions, particularly when wet or damp.

    (a) True
    (b) False

30. Where portions of a cable raceway or sleeve are subjected to different temperatures and condensation is known to be a problem, the _____ shall be filled with an approved material to prevent the circulation of warm air to a colder section of the raceway or sleeve.

    (a) raceway
    (b) sleeve
    (c) a or b
    (d) none of these

31. Raceways shall be provided with expansion fittings where necessary to compensate for thermal expansion and contraction.

    (a) True
    (b) False

32. Raceways or cable trays containing electric conductors shall not contain any pipe or tube for steam, water, air, gas, drainage, or any service other than _____.

    (a) as permitted by the authority having jurisdiction
    (b) electrical
    (c) pneumatic
    (d) as designed by the engineer

33. Where raceways are installed in wet locations above grade, the interior of these raceways shall be considered a _____ location.

    (a) wet
    (b) dry
    (c) damp
    (d) corrosive

34. Metal raceways, cable armor, and other metal enclosures shall be _____ joined together into a continuous electric conductor so as to provide effective electrical continuity.

    (a) electrically
    (b) permanently
    (c) metallically
    (d) none of these

35. Metal or nonmetallic raceways, cable armors, and cable sheaths _____ between cabinets, boxes, fittings, or other enclosures or outlets.

    (a) can be attached with electrical tape
    (b) are allowed gaps for expansion
    (c) shall be continuous
    (d) none of these

36. Raceways and cables installed into the _____ of open bottom equipment shall not be required to be mechanically secured to the equipment.

    (a) bottom
    (b) sides
    (c) top
    (d) any of these

37. Conductors in raceways shall be _____ between outlets, boxes, devices, and so forth.

    (a) continuous
    (b) installed
    (c) copper
    (d) in conduit

38. When the opening to an outlet, junction, or switch point is less than 8 in. in any dimension, each conductor shall be long enough to extend at least _____ in. outside the opening of the enclosure.

    (a) 0
    (b) 3
    (c) 6
    (d) 12

39. Fittings and connectors shall be used only with the specific wiring methods for which they are designed and listed.

    (a) True
    (b) False

40. A box or conduit body shall not be required where cables enter or exit from conduit or tubing that is used to provide cable support or protection against physical damage.

    (a) True
    (b) False

41. A box or conduit body shall not be required for splices and taps in direct-buried conductors and cables as long as the splice is made with a splicing device that is identified for the purpose.

    (a) True
    (b) False

42. A box or conduit body shall not be required for conductors in handhole enclosures, except where connected to electrical equipment.

    (a) True
    (b) False

43. The number and size of conductors permitted in a raceway is limited to _____.

    (a) permit heat to dissipate
    (b) prevent damage to insulation during installation
    (c) prevent damage to insulation during removal of conductors
    (d) all of these

44. Raceways shall be _____ between outlet, junction, or splicing points prior to the installation of conductors.

    (a) installed complete
    (b) tested for ground faults
    (c) a minimum of 80 percent complete
    (d) none of these

45. Prewired raceway assemblies shall be used only where specifically permitted in the *NEC* for the applicable wiring method.

    (a) True
    (b) False

46. Short sections of raceways used for _____ shall not be required to be installed complete between outlet, junction, or splicing points.

    (a) meter to service enclosure connection
    (b) protection of cables from physical damage
    (c) nipples
    (d) separately derived systems

47. Metal raceways shall not be _____ by welding to the raceway.

    (a) supported
    (b) terminated
    (c) connected
    (d) all of these

48. A vertical run of 4/0 AWG copper shall be supported at intervals not exceeding _____.

    (a) 40 ft
    (b) 80 ft
    (c) 100 ft
    (d) 120 ft

49. Conductors in ferrous metal raceways and enclosures shall be arranged so as to avoid heating the surrounding ferrous metal by alternating-current induction. To accomplish this, the _____ conductor(s) shall be grouped together.

    (a) phase
    (b) grounded
    (c) equipment grounding
    (d) all of these

50. _____ is a nonferrous, nonmagnetic metal that has no heating due to hysteresis heating.

    (a) Steel
    (b) Iron
    (c) Aluminum
    (d) all of these

51. Electrical installations in hollow spaces, vertical shafts, and ventilation or air-handling ducts shall be made so that the possible spread of fire or products of combustion is not _____.

    (a) substantially increased
    (b) allowed
    (c) inherent
    (d) possible

52. Openings around electrical penetrations into or through fire-resistant-rated walls, partitions, floors, or ceilings shall _____ to maintain the fire-resistance rating.

    (a) be documented
    (b) not be permitted
    (c) be firestopped using approved methods
    (d) be enlarged

53. No wiring of any type shall be installed in ducts used to transport _____.

    (a) dust
    (b) flammable vapors
    (c) loose stock
    (d) all of these

54. Equipment and devices shall only be permitted within ducts or plenum chambers specifically fabricated to transport environmental air if necessary for their direct action upon, or sensing of, the _____.

    (a) contained air
    (b) air quality
    (c) air temperature
    (d) none of these

55. The space above a hung ceiling used for environmental air-handling purposes is an example of _____, and the wiring limitations of _____ apply.

    (a) a specifically fabricated duct used for environmental air, 300.22(B)
    (b) other space used for environmental air (plenum), 300.22(C)
    (c) a supply duct used for environmental air, 300.22(B)
    (d) none of these

56. Wiring methods permitted in the ceiling areas used for environmental air include _____.

    (a) electrical metallic tubing
    (b) FMC of any length
    (c) RMC without an overall nonmetallic covering
    (d) all of these

57. Wiring methods and equipment installed behind suspended-ceiling panels shall be arranged and secured to allow access to the electrical equipment.

    (a) True
    (b) False

Article 310. Conductors for General Wiring

1. Conductors shall be permitted for use in any of the wiring methods recognized in Chapter 3 and as permitted in the *NEC*.

    (a) True
    (b) False

2. Insulated conductors used in wet locations shall be _____.

   (a) moisture-impervious metal-sheathed
   (b) MTW, RHW, RHW-2, TW, THW, THW-2, THHW, THWN, THWN-2, XHHW, XHHW-2, or ZW
   (c) listed for wet locations
   (d) any of these

3. In general, the minimum size conductor permitted for use in parallel installations is _____ AWG.

   (a) 10
   (b) 4
   (c) 1
   (d) 1/0

4. Parallel conductors shall have the same _____.

   (a) length
   (b) material
   (c) size in circular mil area
   (d) all of these

5. Where conductors in parallel are run in separate raceways, the raceways shall have the same electrical characteristics.

   (a) True
   (b) False

6. No conductor shall be used where its operating temperature exceeds that designated for the type of insulated conductor involved.

   (a) True
   (b) False

7. The _____ rating of a conductor is the maximum temperature, at any location along its length, which the conductor can withstand over a prolonged period of time without serious degradation.

   (a) ambient
   (b) temperature
   (c) maximum withstand
   (d) short-circuit

8. There are four principal determinants of conductor operating temperature, one of which is _____ generated internally in the conductor as the result of load current flow, including fundamental and harmonic currents.

   (a) friction
   (b) magnetism
   (c) heat
   (d) none of these

9. The ampacities listed in 310.15 do not take _____ into consideration.

   (a) continuous loads
   (b) voltage drop
   (c) insulation
   (d) wet locations

10. The ampacity of a conductor can be different along the length of the conductor. The higher ampacity can be used beyond the point of transition for a distance of no more than _____ ft, or no more than _____ percent of the circuit length figured at the higher ampacity, whichever is less.

    (a) 10, 10
    (b) 10, 20
    (c) 15, 15
    (d) 20, 10

11. Each current-carrying conductor of a paralleled set of conductors shall be counted as a current-carrying conductor for the purpose of applying the adjustment factors of 310.15(B)(3)(a).

    (a) True
    (b) False

12. Where six current-carrying conductors are run in the same conduit or cable, the ampacity of each conductor shall be adjusted by a factor of _____ percent.

    (a) 40
    (b) 60
    (c) 80
    (d) 90

13. Conductor adjustment factors shall not apply to conductors in raceways having a length not exceeding _____ in.

    (a) 12
    (b) 24
    (c) 36
    (d) 48

14. The ampacity adjustment factors of Table 310.15(B)(3)(a) do not apply to Type AC or Type MC cable without an overall outer jacket, if which of the following conditions are met?

    (a) Each cable has not more than three current-carrying conductors.
    (b) The conductors are 12 AWG copper.
    (c) No more than 20 current-carrying conductors are installed without maintaining spacing.
    (d) all of these

15. THWN insulated conductors are rated _____.

    (a) 75°C
    (b) for wet locations
    (c) a and b
    (d) not enough information

16. THW insulation has a _____ rating when installed within electric-discharge lighting equipment, such as through fluorescent luminaires.

    (a) 60°C
    (b) 75°C
    (c) 90°C
    (d) 105°C

17. Which conductor type has an insulation temperature rating of 90°C?

    (a) THWN
    (b) RHW
    (c) THHN
    (d) TW

18. The minimum size conductor permitted for branch circuits under 600V is _____ AWG.

    (a) 14
    (b) 12
    (c) 10
    (d) 8

19. Where installed in raceways, conductors _____ AWG and larger shall be stranded.

    (a) 10
    (b) 8
    (c) 6
    (d) 4

Article 312. Cabinets

1. Surface-type cabinets, cutout boxes, and meter socket enclosures in damp or wet locations shall be mounted so there is at least _____ in. airspace between the enclosure and the wall or supporting surface.

   (a) $\frac{1}{16}$
   (b) ¼
   (c) 1¼
   (d) 6

2. Cabinets, cutout boxes, and meter socket enclosures installed in wet locations shall be _____.

   (a) waterproof
   (b) raintight
   (c) weatherproof
   (d) watertight

3. Where raceways or cables enter above the level of uninsulated live parts of cabinets, cutout boxes, and meter socket enclosures in a wet location, a(n) _____ shall be used.

   (a) fitting listed for wet locations
   (b) explosionproof seal
   (c) fitting listed for damp locations
   (d) insulated fitting

4. In walls constructed of wood or other _____ material, electrical cabinets shall be flush with the finished surface or project there from.

    (a) nonconductive
    (b) porous
    (c) fibrous
    (d) combustible

5. Noncombustible surfaces that are broken or incomplete shall be repaired so there will be no gaps or open spaces greater than _____ in. at the edge of a cabinet or cutout box employing a flush-type cover.

    (a) 1/32
    (b) 1/16
    (c) 1/8
    (d) 1/4

6. Openings in cabinets, cutout boxes, and meter socket enclosures through which conductors enter shall be _____.

    (a) closed in an approved manner
    (b) made using concentric knockouts only
    (c) centered in the cabinet wall
    (d) identified

7. Each cable entering a cutout box _____.

    (a) shall be secured to the cutout box
    (b) can be sleeved through a chase
    (c) shall have a maximum of two cables per connector
    (d) all of these

8. Nonmetallic cables can enter the top of surface-mounted cabinets, cutout boxes, and meter socket enclosures through nonflexible raceways not less than 18 in. or more than _____ ft in length if all of the required conditions are met.

    (a) 3
    (b) 10
    (c) 25
    (d) 100

9. Enclosures for switches or overcurrent devices are allowed to have conductors feeding through where the wiring space at any cross section is not filled to more than _____ percent of the cross-sectional area of the space.

    (a) 20
    (b) 30
    (c) 40
    (d) 60

10. Cabinets, cutout boxes, and meter socket enclosures can be used for conductors feeding through, spliced, or tapping off to other enclosures, switches, or overcurrent devices where _____.

    (a) the total area of the conductors at any cross section doesn't exceed 40 percent of the cross-sectional area of the space
    (b) the total area of conductors, splices, and taps installed at any cross section doesn't exceed 75 percent of the cross-sectional area of that space
    (c) a warning label on the enclosure identifies the closest disconnecting means for any feed-through conductors
    (d) all of these

Article 314. Outlet, Device, Pull and Junction Boxes; Conduit Bodies; and Handhole Enclosures

1. Nonmetallic boxes can be used with _____.

    (a) nonmetallic sheaths
    (b) nonmetallic raceways
    (c) flexible cords
    (d) all of these

2. Metal boxes shall be _____ in accordance with Article 250.

    (a) grounded
    (b) bonded
    (c) a and b
    (d) none of these

3. Boxes, conduit bodies, and fittings installed in wet locations shall be required to be listed for use in wet locations.

    (a) True
    (b) False

4. Surface-mounted outlet boxes shall be _____.

    (a) rigidly and securely fastened in place
    (b) supported by cables that protrude from the box
    (c) supported by cable entries from the top and permitted to rest against the supporting surface
    (d) none of these

5. _____ can be used to fasten boxes to a structural member using brackets on the outside of the enclosure.

    (a) Nails
    (b) Screws
    (c) Bolts
    (d) a and b

6. A wood brace used for supporting a box for structural mounting shall have a cross-section not less than nominal _____.

    (a) 1 in. x 2 in.
    (b) 2 in. x 2 in.
    (c) 2 in. x 3 in.
    (d) 2 in. x 4 in.

7. Enclosures not over 100 cu in. having threaded entries and not containing a device shall be considered to be adequately supported where _____ or more conduits are threaded wrenchtight into the enclosure and each conduit is secured within 3 ft of the enclosure.

    (a) one
    (b) two
    (c) three
    (d) none of these

8. In straight pulls, the length of the box or conduit body shall not be less than _____ times the trade size of the largest raceway.

    (a) six
    (b) eight
    (c) twelve
    (d) none of these

9. Where angle or U pulls are made, the distance between each raceway entry inside the box or conduit body and the opposite wall of the box or conduit body shall not be less than _____ times the trade size of the largest raceway in a row plus the sum of the trade sizes of the remaining raceways in the same wall and row .

    (a) six
    (b) eight
    (c) twelve
    (d) none of these

10. Pull boxes or junction boxes with any dimension over _____ ft shall have all conductors cabled or racked in an approved manner.

    (a) 3
    (b) 6
    (c) 9
    (d) 12

11. Power distribution blocks shall be permitted in pull and junction boxes over 100 cubic inches when they comply with the provisions of 314.28(E)(1) through (5).

    (a) True
    (b) False

12. Power distribution blocks shall be permitted in pull and junction boxes over 100 cubic inches when _____.

    (a) they are listed as a power distribution block.
    (b) they are installed in a box not smaller than required by the installation instructions of the power distribution block.
    (c) the junction box is sized so that the wire-bending space requirements of 312.6 can be met.
    (d) all of these

13. Exposed live parts on the power distribution block are allowed when the junction box cover is removed.

    (a) True
    (b) False

14. Where the junction box contains a power distribution block, and it has conductors that don't terminate on the power distribution block(s), the through conductors must be arranged so the power distribution block terminals are _____ following installation.

    (a) unobstructed
    (b) above the through conductors
    (c) visible
    (d) labeled

15. _____ shall be installed so that the wiring contained in them can be rendered accessible without removing any part of the building or structure or, in underground circuits, without excavating sidewalks, paving, or earth.

    (a) Boxes
    (b) Conduit bodies
    (c) Handhole enclosures
    (d) all of these

16. Listed boxes and handhole enclosures designed for underground installation can be directly buried when covered by _____, if their location is effectively identified and accessible.

    (a) concrete
    (b) gravel
    (c) noncohesive granulated soil
    (d) b or c

17. Handhole enclosures shall be designed and installed to withstand _____.

    (a) 600 lb
    (b) 3,000 lb
    (c) 6,000 lb
    (d) all loads likely to be imposed

18. Underground raceways and cable assemblies entering a handhole enclosure shall extend into the enclosure, but they are not required to be _____.

    (a) bonded
    (b) insulated
    (c) mechanically connected to the handhole enclosure
    (d) below minimum cover requirements after leaving the handhole

19. Conductors, splices or terminations in a handhole enclosure shall be listed as suitable for _____.

    (a) wet locations
    (b) damp locations
    (c) direct burial in the earth
    (d) none of these

20. Handhole enclosure covers shall have an identifying _____ that prominently identifies the function of the enclosure, such as "electric."

    (a) mark
    (b) logo
    (c) manual
    (d) a or b

21. Handhole enclosure covers shall require the use of tools to open, or they shall weigh over _____.

    (a) 45 lb
    (b) 70 lb
    (c) 100 lb
    (d) 200 lb

Article 320. Armored Cable (Type AC)

1. Type _____ cable is a fabricated assembly of insulated conductors in a flexible interlocked metallic armor.

    (a) AC
    (b) MC
    (c) NM
    (d) b and c

2. Type AC cable is permitted in _____ installations.

    (a) wet
    (b) cable trays
    (c) exposed
    (d) b and c

3. Armored cable shall not be installed _____.

    (a) in damp or wet locations
    (b) where subject to physical damage
    (c) where exposed to corrosive conditions
    (d) all of these

4. Exposed runs of Type AC cable can be installed on the underside of joists where supported at each joist and located so it is not subject to physical damage.

    (a) True
    (b) False

5. Type AC cable installed through, or parallel to, framing members shall be protected against physical damage from penetration by screws or nails.

    (a) True
    (b) False

6. When Type AC cable is run across the top of a floor joist in an attic without permanent ladders or stairs, guard strips within _____ of the scuttle hole or attic entrance shall protect the cable.

    (a) 3 ft
    (b) 4 ft
    (c) 5 ft
    (d) 6 ft

7. When armored cable is run parallel to the sides of rafters, studs, or floor joists in an accessible attic, the cable shall be protected with running boards.

    (a) True
    (b) False

8. The radius of the curve of the inner edge of any bend shall not be less than _____ for Type AC cable.

    (a) five times the largest conductor within the cable
    (b) three times the diameter of the cable
    (c) five times the diameter of the cable
    (d) six times the outside diameter of the conductors

9. Type AC cable shall be supported and secured by _____.

    (a) staples
    (b) cable ties
    (c) straps
    (d) any of these

10. Type AC cable shall be secured at intervals not exceeding 4½ ft and within _____ in. of every outlet box, cabinet, conduit body, or fitting.

    (a) 6
    (b) 8
    (c) 10
    (d) 12

11. Type AC cable installed horizontally through wooden or metal framing members is considered supported where support doesn't exceed _____ ft intervals.

    (a) 2
    (b) 3
    (c) 4½
    (d) 6

12. At Type AC cable terminations, a(n) _____ shall be provided.

    (a) fitting (or box design) that protects the conductors from abrasion
    (b) insulating bushing between the conductors and the cable armor
    (c) a and b
    (d) none of these

13. Type AC cable installed in thermal insulation shall have conductors that are rated at 90°C. The ampacity of the cable in this application shall not exceed that of a _____ rated conductor.

    (a) 60°C
    (b) 75°C
    (c) 90°C
    (d) none of these

Article 330. Metal-Clad Cable (Type MC)

1. Type _____ cable is a factory assembly of insulated circuit conductors within an armor of interlocking metal tape, or a smooth or corrugated metallic sheath.

    (a) AC
    (b) MC
    (c) NM
    (d) b and c

2. Type MC cable shall not be _____ unless the metallic sheath or armor is resistant to the conditions, or is protected by material resistant to the conditions.

    (a) used for direct burial in the earth
    (b) embedded in concrete
    (c) exposed to cinder fill
    (d) all of these

3. Type MC cable installed through, or parallel to, framing members shall be protected against physical damage from penetration by screws or nails by 1¼ in. separation or protected by a suitable metal plate.

    (a) True
    (b) False

4. Smooth-sheath Type MC cable with an external diameter not greater than ¾ in. shall have a bending radius not more than _____ times the cable external diameter.

    (a) five
    (b) 10
    (c) 12
    (d) 13

5. Bends made in interlocked or corrugated sheath Type MC cable shall have a radius of at least _____ times the external diameter of the metallic sheath.

    (a) 5
    (b) 7
    (c) 10
    (d) 12

6. Type MC cable containing four or fewer conductors, sized no larger than 10 AWG, shall be secured within _____ in. of every box, cabinet, fitting, or other cable termination.

    (a) 8
    (b) 12
    (c) 18
    (d) 24

7. Type MC cable shall be secured at intervals not exceeding _____ ft.

    (a) 3
    (b) 4
    (c) 6
    (d) 8

8. Type MC cable installed horizontally through wooden or metal framing members are considered secured and supported where such support doesn't exceed _____ ft intervals.

    (a) 3
    (b) 4
    (c) 6
    (d) 8

9. Fittings used for connecting Type MC cable to boxes, cabinets, or other equipment shall _____.

    (a) be nonmetallic only
    (b) be listed and identified for such use
    (c) be listed and identified as weatherproof
    (d) include anti-shorting bushings

Article 338. Service-Entrance Cable (Types SE and USE)

1. Type _____ cable is an assembly primarily used for services.

    (a) NM
    (b) TC
    (c) SE
    (d) none of these

2. Type _____ is a multiconductor cable identified for use as underground service-entrance cable.

    (a) SE
    (b) NM
    (c) UF
    (d) USE

3. Type SE cable shall be permitted to be used as _____ in wiring systems where all of the circuit conductors of the cable are of the thermoset or thermoplastic type.

    (a) branch circuits
    (b) feeders
    (c) a or b
    (d) neither a or b

4. Type SE cables shall be permitted to be used for branch circuits or feeders where the insulated conductors are used for circuit wiring and the uninsulated conductor is used only for _____ purposes.

    (a) grounded connection
    (b) equipment grounding
    (c) remote control and signaling
    (d) none of these

5. Type SE cable can be used for interior wiring as long as it complies with the installation requirements of Part II of Article 334, excluding 334.80.

    (a) True
    (b) False

6. Type USE cable is not permitted for _____ wiring.

    (a) underground
    (b) interior
    (c) a or b
    (d) a and b

7. Type USE cable used for service laterals shall be permitted to emerge from the ground if terminated in an enclosure at an outside location and protected in accordance with 300.5(D).

    (a) True
    (b) False

8. The radius of the curve of the inner edge of any bend, during or after installation, shall not be less than _____ times the diameter of Type USE or SE cable.

   (a) five
   (b) seven
   (c) 10
   (d) 12

Article 340. Underground Feeder and Branch-Circuit Cable (Type UF)

1. Type _____ cable is a factory assembly of conductors with an overall covering of nonmetallic material suitable for direct burial in the earth.

   (a) NM
   (b) UF
   (c) SE
   (d) TC

2. Type UF cable is permitted to be used for inside wiring.

   (a) True
   (b) False

3. Type UF cable can be used for service conductors.

   (a) True
   (b) False

4. Type UF cable can be used in commercial garages.

   (a) True
   (b) False

5. Type UF cable shall not be used in _____.

   (a) motion picture studios
   (b) storage battery rooms
   (c) hoistways
   (d) all of these

6. Type UF cable shall not be used _____.

   (a) in any hazardous (classified) location except as otherwise permitted in this *Code*
   (b) embedded in poured cement, concrete, or aggregate
   (c) where exposed to direct rays of the sun, unless identified as sunlight resistant
   (d) all of these

7. Type UF cable shall not be used where subject to physical damage.

   (a) True
   (b) False

8. The ampacity of Type UF cable shall be that of _____ conductors in accordance with 310.15.

   (a) 60°C
   (b) 75°C
   (c) 90°C
   (d) 105°C

Article 342. Intermediate Metal Conduit (Type IMC)

1. IMC can be installed in or under cinder fill subject to permanent moisture _____.

   (a) where the conduit is not less than 18 in. under the fill
   (b) when protected on all sides by 2 in. of noncinder concrete
   (c) where protected by corrosion protection and judged suitable for the condition
   (d) any of these

2. Materials such as straps, bolts, screws, and so forth, which are associated with the installation of IMC in wet locations shall be _____.

   (a) weatherproof
   (b) weathertight
   (c) corrosion resistant
   (d) none of these

3. Where practicable, contact of dissimilar metals shall be avoided in an IMC raceway installation to prevent _____.

   (a) corrosion
   (b) galvanic action
   (c) shorts
   (d) none of these

4. A run of IMC shall not contain more than the equivalent of _____ quarter bend(s) between pull points such as conduit bodies and boxes.

   (a) one
   (b) two
   (c) three
   (d) four

5. When IMC is cut in the field, reaming is required to remove the burrs and rough edges.

   (a) True
   (b) False

6. IMC must be secured _____.

   (a) by fastening within 3 ft of each outlet box, junction box, device box, cabinet, conduit body, or other conduit termination
   (b) within 5 ft of a box or termination fitting when structural members don't permit the raceway to be secured within 3 ft of the termination
   (c) except when the IMC is within 3 ft of the service head for an above-the-roof termination of a mast
   (d) any of these

7. Trade size 1 IMC shall be supported at intervals not exceeding _____ ft.

   (a) 8
   (b) 10
   (c) 12
   (d) 14

8. Horizontal runs of IMC supported by openings through framing members at intervals not exceeding 10 ft and securely fastened within 3 ft of terminations shall be permitted.

   (a) True
   (b) False

9. Threadless couplings and connectors used on threaded IMC ends shall be listed for the purpose.

   (a) True
   (b) False

10. Threadless couplings approved for use with IMC in wet locations shall be _____.

    (a) rainproof
    (b) listed for wet locations
    (c) moistureproof
    (d) concrete-tight

11. Running threads shall not be used on IMC for connection at couplings.

    (a) True
    (b) False

12. Where IMC enters a box, fitting, or other enclosure, _____ shall be provided to protect the wire from abrasion unless the design of the box, fitting, or enclosure affords equivalent protection.

    (a) a bushing
    (b) duct seal
    (c) electrical tape
    (d) seal fittings

Article 344. Rigid Metal Conduit (Type RMC)

1. Galvanized steel, stainless steel and red brass RMC can be installed in concrete, in direct contact with the earth, or in areas subject to severe corrosive influences when protected by _____ and judged suitable for the condition.

    (a) ceramic
    (b) corrosion protection
    (c) backfill
    (d) a natural barrier

2. Galvanized steel, stainless steel, and red brass RMC shall be permitted in or under cinder fill subject to permanent moisture, when protected on all sides by a layer of non-cinder concrete not less than _____ in. thick.

    (a) 2
    (b) 4
    (c) 6
    (d) 18

3. Materials such as straps, bolts, and so forth., associated with the installation of RMC in wet locations shall be _____.

    (a) weatherproof
    (b) weathertight
    (c) corrosion resistant
    (d) none of these

4. Aluminum fittings and enclosures can be used with _____ conduit where not subject to severe corrosive influences.

    (a) steel rigid metal
    (b) aluminum rigid metal
    (c) PVC-coated rigid conduit only
    (d) a and b

5. The minimum radius of a field bend on trade size 1¼ RMC is _____ in.

    (a) 7
    (b) 8
    (c) 10
    (d) 14

6. A run of RMC shall not contain more than the equivalent of _____ quarter bend(s) between pull points such as conduit bodies and boxes.

    (a) one
    (b) two
    (c) three
    (d) four

7. Cut ends of RMC shall be _____ or otherwise finished to remove rough edges.

    (a) threaded
    (b) reamed
    (c) painted
    (d) galvanized

8. Horizontal runs of RMC supported by openings through _____ at intervals not exceeding 10 ft and securely fastened within 3 ft of termination points shall be permitted.

    (a) walls
    (b) trusses
    (c) rafters
    (d) framing members

9. Threadless couplings and connectors used with RMC in wet locations shall be _____.

    (a) listed for wet locations
    (b) listed for damp locations
    (c) nonabsorbent
    (d) weatherproof

10. Threadless couplings and connectors used with RMC buried in masonry or concrete shall be the _____ type.

    (a) raintight
    (b) wet and damp location
    (c) nonabsorbent
    (d) concrete tight

11. Running threads shall not be used on RMC for connection at _____.

    (a) boxes
    (b) cabinets
    (c) couplings
    (d) meter sockets

12. Where RMC enters a box, fitting, or other enclosure, _____ shall be provided to protect the wire from abrasion, unless the design of the box, fitting, or enclosure affords equivalent protection.

    (a) a bushing
    (b) duct seal
    (c) electrical tape
    (d) seal fittings

13. The standard length of RMC shall _____.

    (a) be 10 ft
    (b) include a coupling on each length
    (c) be threaded on each end
    (d) all of these

Article 348. Flexible Metal Conduit (Type FMC)

1. _____ is a raceway of circular cross section made of a helically wound, formed, interlocked metal strip.

    (a) Type MC cable
    (b) Type AC Cable
    (c) LFMC
    (d) FMC

2. FMC shall not be installed _____.

    (a) in wet locations
    (b) embedded in poured concrete
    (c) where subject to physical damage
    (d) all of these

3. FMC can be installed exposed or concealed where not subject to physical damage.

    (a) True
    (b) False

4. Bends in FMC shall be made so that the conduit is not damaged and the internal diameter of the conduit is _____.

    (a) larger than ⅜ in.
    (b) not effectively reduced
    (c) increased
    (d) larger than 1 in.

5. Bends in FMC _____ between pull points.

    (a) shall not be made
    (b) need not be limited (in degrees)
    (c) shall not exceed 360 degrees
    (d) shall not exceed 180 degrees

6. Cut ends of FMC shall be trimmed or otherwise finished to remove rough edges, except where fittings _____.

    (a) are the crimp-on type
    (b) thread into the convolutions
    (c) contain insulated throats
    (d) are listed for grounding

7. FMC shall be supported and secured _____.

    (a) at intervals not exceeding 4½ ft
    (b) within 8 in. on each side of a box where fished
    (c) where fished
    (d) at intervals not exceeding 6 ft

8. Flexible metal conduit must be securely fastened by a means approved by the authority having jurisdiction within _____ of termination.

    (a) 6 in.
    (b) 10 in.
    (c) 1 ft
    (d) 10 ft

9. Flexible metal conduit shall not be required to be _____ where fished between access points through concealed spaces in finished buildings or structures and supporting is impracticable.

    (a) secured
    (b) supported
    (c) complete
    (d) a and b

10. For flexible metal conduit, if flexibility is necessary after installation, unsecured lengths from the last point the raceway is securely fastened must not exceed _____

    (a) 3 ft for trade sizes ½ through 1¼
    (b) 4 ft for trade sizes 1½ through 2
    (c) 5 ft for trade sizes 2½ and larger
    (d) all of these

11. FMC to a luminaire or electrical equipment within an accessible ceiling is permitted to be unsupported for not more than 6 ft from the last point where the raceway is securely fastened, including securing by listed FMC fittings.

    (a) True
    (b) False

12. In an FMC installation, _____ connectors shall not be concealed.

    (a) straight
    (b) angle
    (c) grounding-type
    (d) none of these

13. When FMC is used where flexibility is necessary to minimize the transmission of vibration from equipment or to provide flexibility for equipment that requires movement after installation, _____ shall be installed.

    (a) an equipment grounding conductor
    (b) an expansion fitting
    (c) flexible nonmetallic connectors
    (d) none of these

Article 350. Liquidtight Flexible Metal Conduit (Type LFMC)

1. _____ is a raceway of circular cross section having an outer liquidtight, nonmetallic, sunlight-resistant jacket over an inner flexible metal core.

    (a) FMC
    (b) LFNMC
    (c) LFMC
    (d) none of these

2. The use of LFMC shall be permitted for _____.

    (a) direct burial where listed and marked for the purpose
    (b) exposed work
    (c) concealed work
    (d) all of these

3. Liquidtight flexible metal conduit must be securely fastened by a means approved by the authority having jurisdiction within _____ of termination.

    (a) 6 in.
    (b) 10 in.
    (c) 1 ft
    (d) 10 ft

4. LFMC shall be supported and secured _____.

    (a) at intervals not exceeding 4½ ft
    (b) within 8 in. on each side of a box where fished
    (c) where fished
    (d) at intervals not exceeding 6 ft

5. LFMC shall not be required to be secured or supported where fished between access points through _____ spaces in finished buildings or structures and supporting is impractical.

    (a) concealed
    (b) exposed
    (c) hazardous
    (d) completed

6. For liquidtight flexible metal conduit, if flexibility is necessary after installation, unsecured lengths from the last point the raceway is securely fastened must not exceed _____.

    (a) 3 ft for trade sizes ½ through 1¼
    (b) 4 ft for trade sizes 1½ through 2
    (c) 5 ft for trade sizes 2½ and larger
    (d) all of these

7. _____ connectors shall not be concealed when used in installations of LFMC.

    (a) Straight
    (b) Angle
    (c) Grounding-type
    (d) none of these

8. When LFMC is used to connect equipment where flexibility is necessary to minimize the transmission of vibration from equipment of for equipment requiring movement after installation, a(n) _____ conductor shall be installed.

    (a) main bonding
    (b) grounded
    (c) equipment grounding
    (d) none of these

9. Where flexibility _____, liquidtight flexible metal conduit shall be permitted to be used as an equipment grounding conductor when installed in accordance with 250.118(6).

    (a) is required after installation
    (b) is not required after installation
    (c) either a or d
    (d) is optional

Article 352. Rigid Polyvinyl Chloride Conduit (Type PVC)

1. Extreme _____ may cause PVC conduit to become brittle, and therefore more susceptible to damage from physical contact.

    (a) sunlight
    (b) corrosive conditions
    (c) heat
    (d) cold

2. PVC conduit shall be permitted for exposed work where subject to physical damage if identified for such use.

    (a) True
    (b) False

3. PVC conduit can support nonmetallic conduit bodies not larger than the largest entering raceway, but the conduit bodies shall not contain devices, luminaires, or other equipment.

    (a) True
    (b) False

4. Conductors rated at a temperature _____ than the listed temperature rating of PVC conduit shall be permitted to be installed in PVC conduit, provided the conductors are not operated at a temperature above the raceway's listed temperature rating.

    (a) lower
    (b) the same as
    (c) higher
    (d) a or b

5. PVC conduit shall not be used _____, unless specifically permitted.

    (a) in hazardous (classified) locations
    (b) for the support of luminaires or other equipment
    (c) where subject to physical damage unless identified for such use
    (d) all of these

6. The number of conductors permitted in PVC conduit shall not exceed the percentage fill specified in _____.

   (a) Chapter 9, Table 1
   (b) Table 250.66
   (c) Table 310.15(B)(16)
   (d) 240.6

7. Bends in PVC conduit shall be made only _____.

   (a) by hand forming the bend
   (b) with bending equipment identified for the purpose
   (c) with a truck exhaust pipe
   (d) by use of an open flame torch

8. Bends in PVC conduit shall _____ between pull points.

   (a) not be made
   (b) not be limited in degrees
   (c) be limited to 360 degrees
   (d) be limited to 180 degrees

9. The cut ends of PVC conduit must be trimmed to remove the burrs and rough edges.

   (a) True
   (b) False

10. PVC conduit shall be securely fastened within _____ in. of each box.

    (a) 6
    (b) 12
    (c) 24
    (d) 36

11. Where PVC conduit enters a box, fitting, or other enclosure, a bushing or adapter shall be provided to protect the conductor from abrasion unless the design of the box, fitting, or enclosure affords equivalent protection.

    (a) True
    (b) False

12. Joints between PVC conduit, couplings, fittings, and boxes shall be made by _____.

    (a) the authority having jurisdiction
    (b) set screw fittings
    (c) an approved method
    (d) expansion fittings

Article 358. Electrical Metallic Tubing (Type EMT)

1. _____ is a listed thin-wall, metallic tubing of circular cross section used for the installation and physical protection of electrical conductors when joined together with listed fittings.

   (a) LFNC
   (b) EMT
   (c) NUCC
   (d) RTRC

2. EMT, elbows, couplings, and fittings can be installed in concrete, in direct contact with the earth, or in areas subject to severe corrosive influences if _____.

   (a) protected by corrosion protection
   (b) approved as suitable for the condition
   (c) a and b
   (d) list for wet locations

3. When EMT is installed in wet locations, all supports, bolts, straps, and screws shall be _____.

   (a) of corrosion-resistant materials
   (b) protected against corrosion
   (c) a or b
   (d) of nonmetallic materials only

4. EMT shall not be used where _____.

   (a) subject to severe physical damage
   (b) protected from corrosion only by enamel
   (c) used for the support of luminaires
   (d) any of these

5. EMT shall not be threaded.

   (a) True
   (b) False

6. EMT couplings and connectors shall be made up _____.

   (a) of metal
   (b) in accordance with industry standards
   (c) tight
   (d) none of these

Article 376. Metal Wireways

1. Metal wireways are sheet metal troughs with _____ for housing and protecting electric conductors and cable.

   (a) removable covers
   (b) hinged covers
   (c) a or b
   (d) none of these

2. Wireways shall be permitted for _____.

   (a) exposed work
   (b) totally concealed work
   (c) wet locations if listed for the purpose
   (d) a and c

3. Wireways can pass transversely through a wall _____.

   (a) if the length passing through the wall is unbroken
   (b) if the wall is of fire-rated construction
   (c) in hazardous (classified) locations
   (d) if the wall is not of fire-rated construction

4. Conductors larger than that for which the wireway is designed can be installed in any wireway.

   (a) True
   (b) False

5. The sum of the cross-sectional areas of all contained conductors at any cross-section of a metal wireway shall not exceed _____ percent.

   (a) 50
   (b) 20
   (c) 25
   (d) 80

6. The ampacity adjustment factors in 310.15(B)(3)(a) shall be applied to a metal wireway only where the number of current-carrying conductors in any cross section of the wireway exceeds _____.

   (a) 30
   (b) 40
   (c) 50
   (d) 60

7. Where insulated conductors are deflected within a metal wireway, the wireway shall be sized to meet the bending requirements corresponding to _____ wire per terminal in Table 312.6(A).

   (a) one
   (b) two
   (c) three
   (d) four

8. Power distribution blocks installed in metal wireways on the line side of the service equipment shall be listed for the purpose.

   (a) True
   (b) False

9. Power distribution blocks installed in metal wireways shall _____.

   (a) allow for sufficient wire-bending space at terminals
   (b) not have uninsulated exposed live parts
   (c) a or b
   (d) a and b

Article 392. Cable Trays

1. A cable tray is a unit or assembly of units or sections and associated fittings forming a _____ system used to securely fasten or support cables and raceways.

   (a) structural
   (b) flexible
   (c) movable
   (d) secure

2. Cable trays can be used as a support system for _____.

   (a) service conductors, feeders, and branch circuits
   (b) communications circuits
   (c) control and signaling circuits
   (d) all of these

3. Where exposed to the direct rays of the sun, insulated conductors and jacketed cables installed in cable trays shall be _____ as being sunlight resistant.

   (a) listed
   (b) approved
   (c) identified
   (d) none of these

4. Cable trays and their associated fittings shall be _____ for the intended use.

   (a) listed
   (b) approved
   (c) identified
   (d) none of these

5. _____ wiring methods can be installed in a cable tray.

   (a) Metal raceway
   (b) Nonmetallic raceway
   (c) Cable
   (d) all of these

6. Cable tray systems shall not be used _____.

   (a) in hoistways
   (b) where subject to severe physical damage
   (c) in hazardous (classified) locations
   (d) a or b

7. Each run of cable tray shall be _____ before the installation of cables.

   (a) tested for 25 ohms resistance
   (b) insulated
   (c) completed
   (d) all of these

8. Cable trays shall be _____ except as permitted by 392.10(D).

   (a) exposed
   (b) accessible
   (c) concealed
   (d) a and b

9. In industrial facilities where conditions of maintenance and supervision ensure that only qualified persons will service the installation, cable tray systems can be used to support _____.

   (a) raceways
   (b) cables
   (c) boxes and conduit bodies
   (d) all of these

10. For raceways terminating at a cable tray, a(n) _____ cable tray clamp or adapter shall be used to securely fasten the raceway to the cable tray system.

    (a) listed
    (b) approved
    (c) identified
    (d) none of these

11. Where single conductor cables comprising each phase, neutral, or grounded conductor of a circuit are connected in parallel in a cable tray, the conductors shall be installed _____, to prevent current unbalance in the paralleled conductors due to inductive reactance.

    (a) in groups consisting of not more than three conductors per phase or neutral
    (b) in groups consisting of not more than one conductor per phase or neutral
    (c) as individual conductors securely bound to the cable tray
    (d) in separate groups

12. Cable trays shall be supported at intervals in accordance with the installation instructions.

    (a) True
    (b) False

13. A box shall not be required where cables or conductors from cable trays are installed in bushed conduit and tubing used as support or for protection against _____.

    (a) abuse
    (b) unauthorized access
    (c) physical damage
    (d) tampering

14. Cable _____ made and insulated by approved methods can be located within a cable tray provided they are accessible, and do not project above the side rails where the splices are subject to physical damage.

    (a) connections
    (b) jumpers
    (c) splices
    (d) conductors

15. Metal cable trays containing only non-power conductors (such as communication, data, and signal conductors and cables) must be electrically continuous through approved connections or the use of a(n) _____.

    (a) grounding electrode conductor
    (b) bonding jumper
    (c) equipment grounding conductor
    (d) grounded conductor

16. Steel or aluminum cable tray systems shall be permitted to be used as an equipment grounding conductor, provided the cable tray sections and fittings are identified as _____, among other requirements.

    (a) an equipment grounding conductor
    (b) special
    (c) industrial
    (d) all of these

17. The conductor ampacity adjustment factors only apply to the number of current-carrying conductors in the cable and not to the number of conductors in the cable tray.

    (a) True
    (b) False

Notes

Mike Holt's Illustrated Guide to Understanding NEC Requirements for Solar Photovoltaic Systems

CHAPTER 4

EQUIPMENT FOR GENERAL USE

Introduction to Chapter 4—Equipment for General Use

The final chapter in the *NEC* necessary for building a solid foundation in general work is Chapter 4. This chapter helps you apply the first three to installations involving general equipment. The first four chapters of the *Code* follow a natural sequential progression. Each of the next four chapters—5, 6, 7, and 8—build upon these, but in no particular order. You need to understand all of the first four chapters to properly apply any of those that follow.

As in the preceding chapters, Chapter 4 is also arranged logically. Here are the groupings:

- Flexible cords and cables
- Switches
- Switchboards and panelboards
- Batteries, capacitors, and other components

This logical arrangement of the *NEC* is something to keep in mind when you're searching for a particular item. You know, for example, that transformers are general equipment. So you'll find the *Code* requirements for them in Chapter 4. You know they're wound devices, so you'll find transformer requirements located somewhere near motor requirements.

This textbook, with its focus on PV systems, only covers four of the 21 articles in Chapter 4 of the *NEC*. They are:

- **Article 404—Switches.** The requirements of Article 404 apply to switches of all types. These include snap (toggle) switches, dimmer switches, fan switches, knife switches, circuit breakers used as switches, and automatic switches such as time clocks, timers, and switches and circuit breakers used for disconnecting means.

- **Article 408—Switchboards and Panelboards.** Article 408 covers specific requirements for switchboards, panelboards, and distribution boards that supply lighting and power circuits.

- **Article 450—Transformers.** This article covers the installation of transformers.

- **Article 480—Batteries.** Article 480 covers stationary installations of storage batteries.

Notes

ARTICLE 404

SWITCHES

Introduction to Article 404—Switches

The requirements of Article 404 apply to switches of all types, including snap (toggle) switches, dimmer switches, fan switches, knife switches, circuit breakers used as switches, and automatic switches, such as time clocks and timers.

404.1 Scope

The requirements of Article 404 apply to all types of switches, switching devices, and circuit breakers used as switches. Figure 404–1

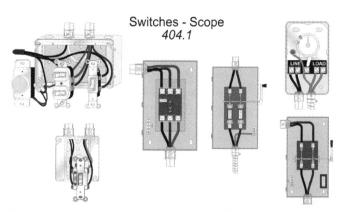

Switches - Scope
404.1

The requirements of Article 404 apply to all types of switches, such as snap (toggle) switches, knife switches, circuit breakers used as switches, and automatic switches such as time clocks.

Copyright 2014, www.MikeHolt.com

Figure 404–1

404.3 Switch Enclosures

(A) General. Switches and circuit breakers used as switches must be of the externally operable type mounted in an enclosure listed for the intended use.

(B) Used for Raceways or Splices. Switch or circuit-breaker enclosures can contain splices and taps if the splices and/or taps don't fill the wiring space at any cross section to more than 75 percent.

Switch or circuit-breaker enclosures can have conductors feed through them if the wiring doesn't fill the wiring space at any cross section to more than 40 percent in accordance with 312.8.

404.4 Damp or Wet Locations

(A) Surface-Mounted Switches or Circuit Breakers. Surface-mounted switches and circuit breakers in a damp or wet location must be installed in a weatherproof enclosure. The enclosure must be installed so not less than ¼ in. of airspace is provided between the enclosure and the wall or other supporting surface [312.2]. Figure 404–2

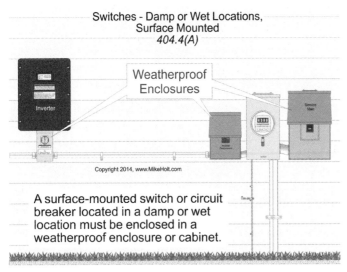

Switches - Damp or Wet Locations,
Surface Mounted
404.4(A)

Weatherproof
Enclosures

Inverter

Copyright 2014, www.MikeHolt.com

A surface-mounted switch or circuit
breaker located in a damp or wet
location must be enclosed in a
weatherproof enclosure or cabinet.

Figure 404–2

(B) Flush-Mounted Switches or Circuit Breakers. A flush-mounted switch or circuit breaker in a damp or wet location must have a weatherproof cover.

404.6 Position of Knife Switches

(A) Single-Throw Knife Switch. Single-throw knife switches must be installed so gravity won't tend to close them.

(C) Connection of Switches. Single-throw knife switches, molded case switches, and circuit breakers used as switches must have the terminals supplying the load deenergize when the switch is in the open position.

Exception: The blades and terminals supplying the load can be energized when the switch is in the open position if connected to circuits or equipment inherently capable of providing a back-feed source of power. For such installations, a permanent label that isn't <u>handwritten and of sufficient durability to withstand the environment involved</u> *[110.21(B)] must on the switch enclosure or immediately adjacent to open switches and is required to read:*

**WARNING—LOAD SIDE TERMINALS MAY
BE ENERGIZED BY BACKFEED.**

404.7 Indicating

General-use switches and circuit breakers must be marked to indicate the "on" or "off" position; when operated vertically, the "up" position must be the "on" position [240.81]. Figure 404–3

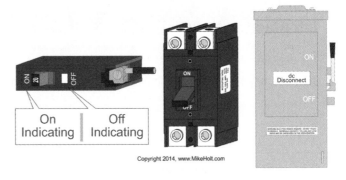

General-Use Switches and Circuit Breakers
404.7

On
Indicating

Off
Indicating

dc
Disconnect

Copyright 2014, www.MikeHolt.com

Must be marked to indicate the "on" or "off" position, and when operated vertically, the "up" position must be the "on" position.

Figure 404–3

404.8 Accessibility and Grouping

(A) Location. Switches and circuit breakers used as switches must be capable of being operated from a readily accessible location. They must also be installed so the center of the grip of the operating handle of the switch or circuit breaker, when in its highest position, isn't more than 6 ft 7 in. above the floor or working platform [240.24(A)]. Figure 404–4

Ex 2: Switches and circuit breakers used as switches can be mounted above 6 ft 7 in. if they're next to the equipment they supply, and are accessible by portable means [240.24(A)(4)].

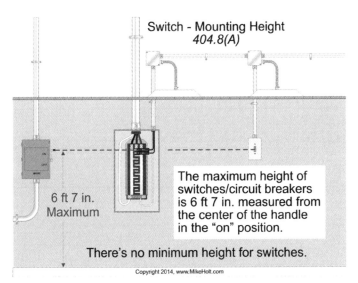

Switch - Mounting Height
404.8(A)

6 ft 7 in.
Maximum

The maximum height of switches/circuit breakers is 6 ft 7 in. measured from the center of the handle in the "on" position.

There's no minimum height for switches.

Copyright 2014, www.MikeHolt.com

Figure 404–4

404.11 Circuit Breakers Used as Switches

A manually operable circuit breaker used as a switch must show when it's in the "on" (closed) or "off" (open) position [404.7]. Figure 404–5

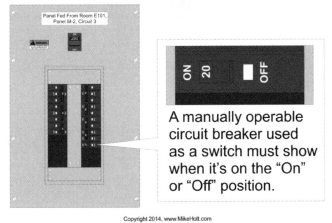

Circuit Breakers Used as Switches
404.11

Panel Fed From Room E101,
Panel M-2, Circuit 3

A manually operable circuit breaker used as a switch must show when it's on the "On" or "Off" position.

Copyright 2014, www.MikeHolt.com

Figure 404–5

404.12 Grounding of Enclosures

Metal enclosures for switches and circuit breakers used as switches must be connected to an equipment grounding conductor of a type recognized in 250.118 [250.4(A)(3)]. Nonmetallic boxes for switches must be installed using a wiring method that includes an equipment grounding conductor.

404.15 Switch Marking

(A) Markings. Switches must be marked with the current, voltage, and if horsepower rated, the maximum rating for which they're designed.

(B) Off Indication. If in the off position, a switching device with a marked "off" position must completely disconnect all ungrounded conductors of the load it controls.

ARTICLE 408 SWITCHBOARDS AND PANELBOARDS

Introduction to Article 408—Switchboards and Panelboards

Article 408 covers the specific requirements for switchboards and panelboards that control power and lighting circuits. Some key points to remember:

- One objective of Article 408 is that the installation prevents contact between current-carrying conductors and people or equipment.
- The circuit directory of a panelboard must clearly identify the purpose or use of each circuit that originates in the panelboard.
- You must understand the detailed grounding and overcurrent protection requirements for panelboards.

Part I. General

408.1 Scope

Article 408 covers the specific requirements for switchboards and panelboards that control power and lighting circuits. Figure 408–1

408.4 Field Identification

(A) Circuit Directory or Circuit Identification. All circuits, and circuit modifications, must be legibly identified as to their clear, evident, and specific purpose. Spare positions that contain unused overcurrent devices must also be identified. Identification must include <u>an approved amount of detail to allow</u> each circuit to be distinguished from all others, and the identification must be on a circuit directory located on the face or inside of the door of the panelboard. See 110.22. Figure 408–2

Switchboards and Panelboards
408.1

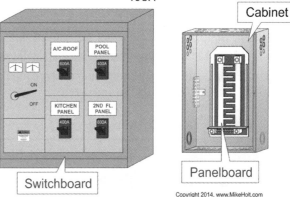

Article 408 contains the requirements for switchboards and panelboards for light and power.

Figure 408–1

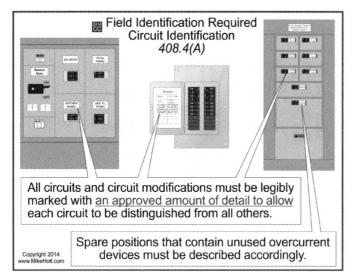

Figure 408–2

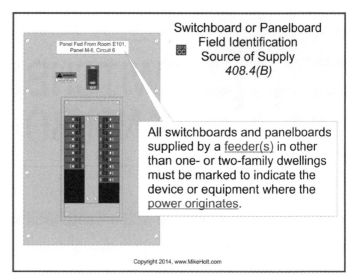

Figure 408–3

2014 CHANGE ANALYSIS: The *NEC* Style Manual contains a list of terms that shouldn't be used in the *Code*. The term "sufficient" is on the naughty list, so proposals were made throughout the *NEC* to remove it where possible. "Approved" is the term now used, which is clearly defined and not subject to as much debate (maybe).

(B) Source of Supply. All switchboards and panelboards supplied by a feeder(s) in other than one- or two-family dwellings must be marked as to the device or equipment where the power originates. Figure 408–3

408.5 Clearance for Conductors Entering Bus Enclosures

If raceways enter a switchboard, floor-standing panelboard, or similar enclosure, the raceways, including end fittings, must not rise more than 3 in. above the bottom of the enclosure.

408.7 Unused Openings

Unused openings for circuit breakers and switches must be closed using identified closures, or other means approved by the authority having jurisdiction, that provide protection substantially equivalent to the wall of the enclosure. Figure 408–4

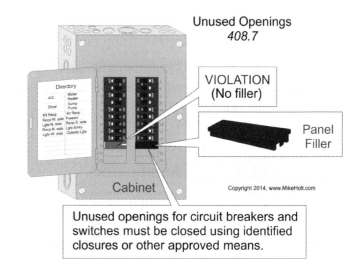

Figure 408–4

Part III. Panelboards

408.36 Overcurrent Protection of Panelboards

Each panelboard must be provided with overcurrent protection located within, or at any point on the supply side of, the panelboard. The overcurrent device must have a rating not greater than that of the panelboard, and it can be located within or on the supply side of the panelboard. Figure 408–5

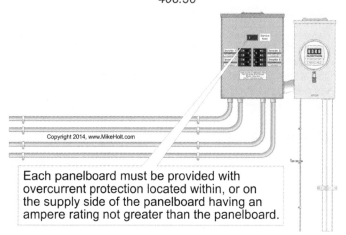

Panelboard Overcurrent Protection
408.36

Each panelboard must be provided with overcurrent protection located within, or on the supply side of the panelboard having an ampere rating not greater than the panelboard.

Figure 408–5

Ex 1: Individual overcurrent protection isn't required for panelboards used as service equipment in accordance with 230.71.

(D) Back-Fed Devices. Plug-in circuit breakers that are back-fed from field-installed conductors must be secured in place by an additional fastener that requires other than a pull to release the breaker from the panelboard. Figure 408–6

Author's Comment:

- The purpose of the breaker fastener is to prevent the circuit breaker from being accidentally removed from the panelboard while energized, thereby exposing someone to dangerous voltage.

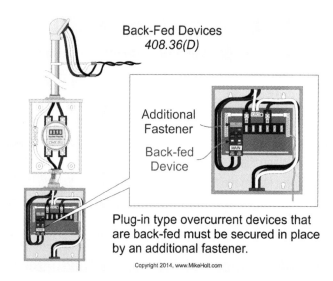

Back-Fed Devices
408.36(D)

Additional Fastener

Back-fed Device

Plug-in type overcurrent devices that are back-fed must be secured in place by an additional fastener.

Copyright 2014, www.MikeHolt.com

Figure 408–6

- For PV systems, conductors from the PV ac inverter are permitted to backfeed dedicated circuit breakers that aren't marked "Line" and "Load," and aren't required to be secured in place by an additional fastener that requires other than a pull to release the breaker from the panelboard [705.12(D)(5)]. Figure 408–7

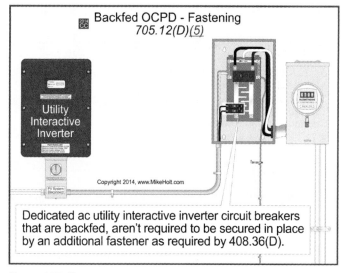

Backfed OCPD - Fastening
705.12(D)(5)

Utility Interactive Inverter

Copyright 2014, www.MikeHolt.com

Dedicated ac utility interactive inverter circuit breakers that are backfed, aren't required to be secured in place by an additional fastener as required by 408.36(D).

Figure 408–7

408.37 Panelboards in Damp or Wet Locations

The enclosures (cabinets) for panelboards must prevent moisture or water from entering or accumulating within the enclosure, and they must be weatherproof when located in a wet location. When the enclosure is surface mounted in a wet location, the enclosure must be mounted with not less than ¼ in. air space between it and the mounting surface [312.2].

408.40 Equipment Grounding Conductor

Metal panelboard cabinets and frames must be connected to an equipment grounding conductor of a type recognized in 250.118 [215.6 and 250.4(A)(3)]. Where a panelboard cabinet contains equipment grounding conductors, a terminal bar for the equipment grounding conductors must be bonded to the metal cabinet or be connected to the feeder equipment grounding conductor. Figure 408–8

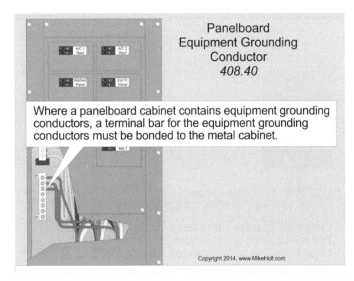

Panelboard
Equipment Grounding
Conductor
408.40

Where a panelboard cabinet contains equipment grounding conductors, a terminal bar for the equipment grounding conductors must be bonded to the metal cabinet.

Copyright 2014, www.MikeHolt.com

Figure 408–8

Equipment grounding conductors aren't permitted to terminate on the neutral terminal bar, and neutral conductors aren't permitted to terminate on the equipment grounding terminal bar, except as permitted by 250.142 for services and separately derived systems. Figure 408–9

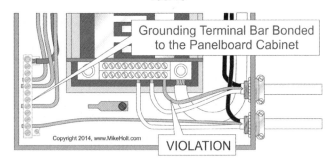

Panelboard - Equipment Grounding Conductor
408.40

Grounding Terminal Bar Bonded
to the Panelboard Cabinet

Copyright 2014, www.MikeHolt.com

VIOLATION

Equipment grounding conductors must not terminate on the same terminal bar with the neutral conductor, except as permitted by 250.142 for services and separately derived systems.

Figure 408–9

408.41 Neutral Conductor Terminations

Each neutral conductor within a panelboard must terminate to an individual terminal. Figure 408–10

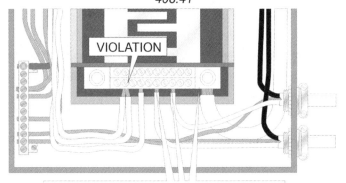

Neutral Conductor Terminations
408.41

VIOLATION

Each neutral conductor must terminate
to an individual terminal in the panelboard.

Copyright 2014, www.MikeHolt.com

Figure 408–10

ARTICLE 450

TRANSFORMERS

Introduction to Article 450—Transformers

Article 450 opens by saying, "This article covers the installation of all transformers." Then it lists eight exceptions. So what does Article 450 really cover? Essentially, it covers power transformers and most kinds of lighting transformers.

A major concern with transformers is preventing overheating. The *Code* doesn't completely address this issue. Article 90 explains that the *NEC* isn't a design manual, and it assumes that the person using the *Code* has a certain level of expertise. Proper transformer selection is an important part of preventing it from overheating.

The *NEC* assumes you've already selected a transformer suitable to the load characteristics. For the *Code* to tell you how to do that would push it into the realm of a design manual. Article 450 then takes you to the next logical step—providing overcurrent protection and the proper connections. But this article doesn't stop there; 450.9 provides ventilation requirements, and 450.13 contains accessibility requirements.

Part I of Article 450 contains the general requirements such as guarding, marking, and accessibility, Part II contains the requirements for different types of transformers, and Part III covers transformer vaults.

Part I. General

450.1 Scope

Article 450 covers the installation requirements of transformers and transformer vaults. Figure 450–1

450.3 Overcurrent Protection

(B) Overcurrent Protection for Transformers Not Over 1,000V. The primary winding of a transformer must be protected against overcurrent in accordance with the percentages listed in Table 450.3(B) and all applicable notes.

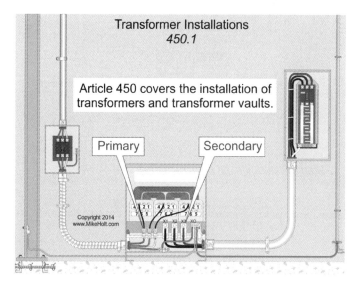

Transformer Installations
450.1

Article 450 covers the installation of transformers and transformer vaults.

Primary   Secondary

Copyright 2014
www.MikeHolt.com

Figure 450–1

Table 450.3(B) Primary Protection Only

Primary Current Rating	Maximum Protection
9A or More	125%, see Table Note 1
Less Than 9A	167%
Less Than 2A	300%

Note 1. If 125 percent of the primary current doesn't correspond to a standard rating of a fuse or nonadjustable circuit breaker, the next higher rating is permitted [240.6(A)].

Question: *What's the primary overcurrent device rating and conductor size required for a 45 kVA, three-phase, 480V transformer that's fully loaded? The terminals are rated 75°C.* Figure 450–2

(a) 8 AWG, 40A   (b) 6 AWG, 50A

(c) 6 AWG, 60A   (d) 4 AWG, 70A

Answer: *(d) 4 AWG, 70A*

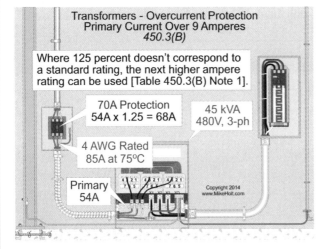

Figure 450–2

Step 1: *Determine the primary current:*

$$I = VA/(E \times 1.732)$$

$$I = 45,000 \ VA/(480V \times 1.732)$$

$$I = 54A$$

Step 2: *Determine the primary overcurrent device rating [240.6(A)]:*

54A x 1.25 = 68A, next size up 70A,
   Table 450.3(B), Table Note 1

Step 3: *The primary conductor must be sized to carry 54A continuously (54A x 1.25 = 68A) [215.2(A)(1)] and be protected by a 70A overcurrent device [240.4(B)]. A 4 AWG conductor rated 85A at 75°C meets all of the requirements [110.14(C)(1) and 310.15(B)(16)].*

450.9 Ventilation

Transformers must be installed in accordance with the manufacturer's instructions, and their ventilating openings must not be blocked [110.3(B)].

Note 2: Transformers can become excessively heated above their rating because nonlinear loads can increase heat in a transformer without operating its overcurrent protective device [450.3 Note].

450.10 Grounding and Bonding

(A) Dry-Type Transformer Enclosures. Where separate equipment grounding conductors and supply-side bonding jumpers are installed, a terminal bar for these conductors must be installed inside the enclosure. The terminal bar must not cover any ventilation openings. Figure 450–3

Exception: Where a dry-type transformer is equipped with wire-type connections (leads), the terminal bar isn't required.

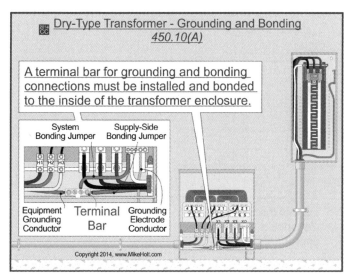

Figure 450–3

2014 CHANGE ANALYSIS: When you consider the number of green and bare wires that are typically found in a transformer, it's really a wonder that this rule hasn't been in the *Code* for 100 years. The primary conductors supplying the transformer will usually contain an equipment grounding conductor. The secondary conductors will include a supply-side bonding jumper. There will (typically) be a system bonding jumper inside the transformer. There will also be (typically) a grounding electrode conductor in the transformer. Wouldn't it be nice if there was a place to terminate these wires?

450.11 Marking

(B) Source Marking. A transformer can be supplied at the secondary voltage if allowed by the manufacturer's instructions.

2014 CHANGE ANALYSIS: New to this *Code* edition is the text regarding secondary voltage-supplied transformers. Many people don't realize that transformers are only suitable to be supplied at the secondary voltage if the transformer is marked for this application. For example, a transformer that's marked as 480V primary, 208V secondary can't be wired with a 208V primary and 480V secondary. According to UL 1561, only transformers marked in this manner can be installed this way.

450.13 Transformer Accessibility

Transformers must be readily accessible to qualified personnel for inspection and maintenance, except as permitted by (A) or (B).

(A) Open Installations. Dry-type transformers can be located in the open on walls, columns, or structures. Figure 450–4

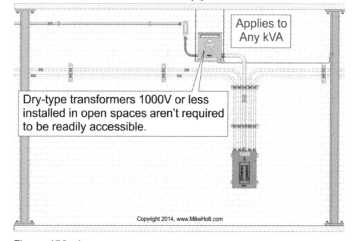

Figure 450–4

(B) Suspended Ceilings. Dry-type transformers, rated not more than 50 kVA, are permitted above suspended ceilings or in hollow spaces of buildings, if not permanently closed in by the structure. Figure 450–5

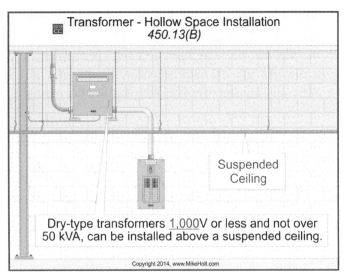

Figure 450–5

Author's Comment:

■ Dry-type transformers not exceeding 50 kVA with a metal enclosure can be installed above a suspended-ceiling space used for environmental air-handling purposes (plenum) [300.22(C)(3)].

450.14 Disconnecting Means

A disconnect is required to disconnect all transformer ungrounded primary conductors, unless the transformer is Class 2 or Class 3. Figure 450–6

The disconnect must be located within sight of the transformer, unless the location of the disconnect is field marked on the transformer and the disconnect is lockable, as described in 110.25. Figure 450–7

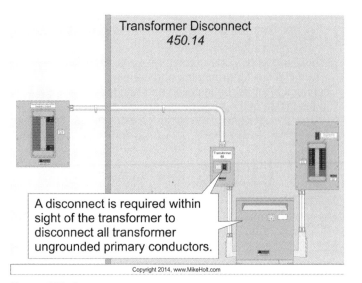

Figure 450–6

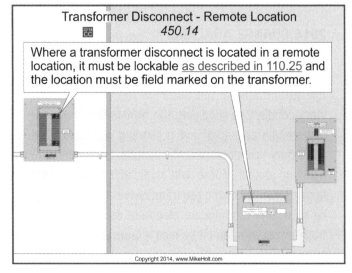

Figure 450–7

Author's Comment:

■ Within sight means that it's visible and not more than 50 ft from one to the other [Article 100].

2014 CHANGE ANALYSIS: In an effort to create a consistent *Code*, a new section 110.25 was added. This section contains the rules for disconnecting means that aren't within sight of their equipment. By referring to it, we no longer have different rules that cover the same thing spread throughout the *NEC*.

ARTICLE 480

STORAGE BATTERIES

Introduction to Article 480—Storage Batteries

The stationary battery is the heart of any uninterruptible power supply. Article 480 addresses stationary batteries for commercial and industrial grade power supplies, not the small, "point of use," UPS boxes.

Stationary batteries are also used in other applications, such as emergency power systems. Regardless of the application, if it uses stationary batteries, Article 480 applies.

Lead-acid stationary batteries fall into two general categories: flooded, and valve regulated (VRLA). These differ markedly in such ways as maintainability, total cost of ownership, and scalability. The *NEC* doesn't address these differences, as they're engineering issues and not fire safety or electrical safety matters [90.1].

The *Code* doesn't address such design issues as optimum tier height, distance between tiers, determination of charging voltage, or string configuration. Nor does it address battery testing, monitoring, or maintenance. All of these involve highly specialized areas of knowledge, and are required for optimizing operational efficiency. Standards other than the *NEC* address these topics.

What the *Code* does address, in Article 480, are issues related to preventing electrocution and the ignition of the gases that all stationary batteries (even "sealed" ones) emit.

480.1 Scope

The provisions of Article 480 apply to stationary storage battery installations.

Note: The following standards are frequently referenced for the installation of stationary batteries:

(1) IEEE 484, *Recommended Practice for Installation Design and Installation of Vented Lead-Acid Batteries for Stationary Applications.*

(2) IEEE 485, *Recommended Practice for Sizing Vented Lead-Acid Storage Batteries for Stationary Applications.*

(3) IEEE 1145, *Recommended Practice for Installation and Maintenance of Nickel-Cadmium Batteries for Photovoltaic (PV) Systems.*

(4) IEEE 1187, *Recommended Practice for Installation Design, and Installation of Valve-Regulated Lead-Acid Batteries for Stationary Applications.*

(5) IEEE 1375, *IEEE Guide for the Protection of Stationary Battery Systems.*

(6) IEEE 1578, *Recommended Practice for Stationary Battery Spill Containment and Management.*

(7) IEEE 1635/ASHRAE 21, *Guide for the Ventilation and Thermal Management of Stationary Battery Installations.*

2014 CHANGE ANALYSIS: PV installations often use storage batteries, making them much more commonplace than ever before. Several notes have been added to let *Code* users know of other resources that can be consulted. These resources include several IEEE documents having to do with issues such as venting, spill containment, and the various types of batteries that are available. It's worth remembering that these notes aren't enforceable [90.5(C)], and are intended only to provide assistance.

480.2 Definitions

Cell. The basic electrochemical unit, consisting of an anode and a cathode, which receives, stores, and delivers electrical energy.

Author's Comment:

- A battery is made up of one or more cells.

Container. An object that holds the elements of a single unit in a battery.

Note: Containers can be single-cell or multi-cell and are often called "jars."

Intercell Connector. A conductive bar or cable that connects adjacent cells.

Intertier Connector. An electrical conductor that connects two cells on different tiers of the same rack, or different shelves of the same rack.

Nominal Voltage (Battery or Cell). The value assigned to a cell or battery for conveniently designating the voltage class. The operating voltage of the cell or battery can be higher or lower than the nominal voltage.

Note: The most common nominal cell voltages are 2V per cell for lead-acid, 1.20V per cell for alkali, and 3.60V to 3.80V per cell for lithium-ion. Figure 480–1

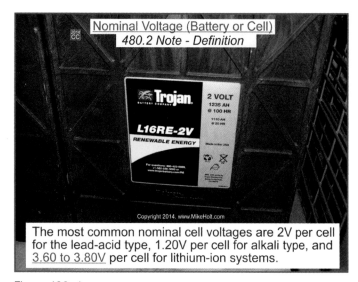

Nominal Voltage (Battery or Cell)
480.2 Note - Definition

The most common nominal cell voltages are 2V per cell for the lead-acid type, 1.20V per cell for alkali type, and 3.60 to 3.80V per cell for lithium-ion systems.

Figure 480–1

Author's Comment:

- The voltage of a battery will decrease below the nominal voltage while it's being used (discharged) and the actual voltage will often be higher than nominal when the battery is fully charged.

Sealed Cell or Battery. A cell or battery with no provision for the routine addition of water or electrolyte.

Storage Battery. A battery consisting of one or more rechargeable cells.

2014 CHANGE ANALYSIS: With the growing popularity of storage batteries, this article is now receiving the attention that it's probably deserved for quite some time. Many definitions in this article were revised, some were removed, and several new ones have appeared.

The definitions of "Cell" and "Container" have been added, due to the fact that the *Code* uses these terms in the article but previously didn't define them. The definitions come from the IEEE stationary battery committee.

"Intercell Connector" and "Intertier Connector" are two new terms and also came from the IEEE stationary battery committee. They weren't used in previous editions of Article 480, but are now discussed in the new 480.3. The definition of "Nominal Voltage" was revised for clarity, and the old text that was in the definition is now part of an Informational Note, which is probably a better location.

2014 CHANGE ANALYSIS: When dissimilar metals are in contact with each other, corrosion can occur as a result of galvanic action. This is typically prevented by using connections that are identified for the purpose, as required in 110.14, although this section (480.3) seems to allow for the usage of antioxidant material instead. The best approach is to always avoid contact between dissimilar materials, but when that isn't possible an identified means of connection should be used. Interestingly, even if you're using identified fittings, this new rule requires that you also use an antioxidant compound (unlike the general rule in 110.14).

The sizing of intercell and intertier connections and conductors are now discussed in the *Code*. This requirement doesn't provide any real prescriptive requirements on sizing, but rather leaves it to the performance requirement of "thou shalt not allow the wire to melt." How does one achieve this? I'm not sure, but hopefully the IEEE 1375, referenced in the new Note, gives a little more information.

480.3 Battery and Cell Terminations

(A) Dissimilar Metals. Where connections between dissimilar metals occur, antioxidant material must be used.

Note: The manufacturer's instructions may have guidance for acceptable materials.

(B) Intercell and Intertier Conductors and Connections. The ampacity of field-assembled intercell and intertier connectors and conductors must be sized so that the temperature rise under maximum load conditions and at maximum ambient temperature doesn't exceed the safe operating temperature of the conductor insulation.

Note: IEEE 1375, *Guide for the Protection of Stationary Battery Systems* provides guidance for overcurrent protection and associated cable sizing. Typical voltage-drop considerations for ac circuits might not be adequate for battery systems.

480.4 Wiring and Equipment Supplied from Batteries

Wiring and equipment supplied from storage batteries must be in accordance with Chapters 1 through 4 unless otherwise permitted by 480.5.

480.8 Racks and Trays

Racks and trays must be:

(A) Racks. Racks (rigid frames designed to support battery cells or trays) must be made of one of the following: Figure 480–2

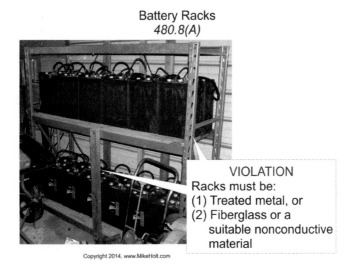

Battery Racks
480.8(A)

VIOLATION
Racks must be:
(1) Treated metal, or
(2) Fiberglass or a
    suitable nonconductive
    material

Copyright 2014, www.MikeHolt.com

Figure 480–2

(1)   Metal, treated to be resistant to deteriorating action by the electrolyte and provided with nonconducting or continuous insulating material members directly supporting the cells.

(2)   Fiberglass or other suitable nonconductive materials.

(B) Trays. Trays (boxes of nonconductive material) must be constructed or treated so as to be resistant to deteriorating action by the electrolyte. Figure 480–3

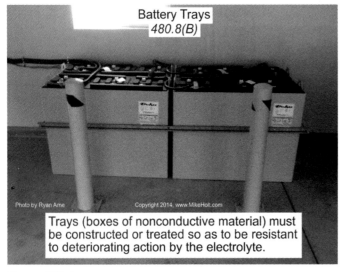

Battery Trays
480.8(B)

Photo by Ryan Arne   Copyright 2014, www.MikeHolt.com

Trays (boxes of nonconductive material) must be constructed or treated so as to be resistant to deteriorating action by the electrolyte.

Figure 480–3

(C) Accessible. The terminals of all cells or multi-cell units must be readily accessible for readings, inspection, and cleaning as necessary. Transparent battery containers must have one side of the container readily accessible for inspection of the internal components.

2014 CHANGE ANALYSIS: Measuring the voltage of a battery or battery system requires personnel to work with live parts. It's only fair to the person doing the measuring to ensure that he or she can do that task safely by providing requirements for access to the terminals of the batteries or cells.

When transparent battery containers are used they must be installed in such a manner that one can take advantage of the transparency by locating at least one side of the container in a manner that allows for visual inspection.

480.9 Battery Locations

(A) Ventilation. Provisions must permit sufficient diffusion and ventilation of battery gases to prevent the accumulation of an explosive mixture. Figure 480–4

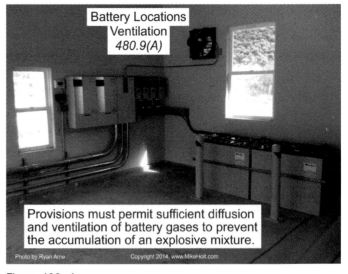

Battery Locations
Ventilation
480.9(A)

Provisions must permit sufficient diffusion and ventilation of battery gases to prevent the accumulation of an explosive mixture.

Photo by Ryan Arne   Copyright 2014, www.MikeHolt.com

Figure 480–4

(B) Live Parts. Live parts of battery systems must be protected in accordance with 110.27.

Author's Comment:

- According to 110.27, electrical equipment must not be installed where subject to physical damage, unless enclosures or guards are arranged and of such strength as to prevent damage [110.27(B)]. In addition, entrances to rooms and other guarded locations containing exposed live parts must be marked with conspicuous signs forbidding unqualified persons to enter [110.27(C)].

(C) Working Space for Battery Racks. A minimum clearance of 1 in. is required between a cell container and any wall or structure on the side not requiring access for maintenance. Battery stands can make contact with adjacent walls or structures.

Note: Additional space is often needed to accommodate battery hoisting equipment, tray removal, or spill containment.

(D) Top Terminal Batteries. Where top terminal batteries are installed on tiered racks, working space in accordance with the battery manufacturer's instructions must be provided between the highest point on a cell and the row or ceiling above that point.

Note: Battery manufacturer's installation instructions typically define how much top working space is necessary for a particular battery model.

(E) Egress. A personnel door(s) intended for entrance to, and egress from, rooms designated as battery rooms must open in the direction of egress and be equipped with listed panic hardware.

(F) Piping in Battery Rooms. Gas piping isn't permitted in a dedicated battery room.

(G) Illumination. The working space must have illumination that isn't controlled by automatic means only and that doesn't:

(1) Expose personnel to energized battery components while performing maintenance on the luminaires; or

(2) Create a hazard to the battery upon failure of the luminaire.

2014 CHANGE ANALYSIS: Measuring the voltage of a battery or battery system requires personnel to work with live parts. It's only fair to the person doing the measuring to ensure that he or she can do that task safely by providing requirements for access to the terminals of the batteries or cells.

When transparent battery containers are used they must be installed in such a manner that one can take advantage of the transparency by locating at least one side of the container in a manner that allows for visual inspection.

CHAPTER 4 PRACTICE QUESTIONS

Please use the 2014 *Code* book to answer the following questions.

Article 404. Switches

1. Surface-mounted switches or circuit breakers in a damp or wet location shall be enclosed in a _____ enclosure or cabinet that complies with 312.2.

    (a) weatherproof
    (b) rainproof
    (c) watertight
    (d) raintight

2. Single-throw knife switches shall be installed so that gravity will tend to close the switch.

    (a) True
    (b) False

3. Which of the following switches must indicate whether they are in the open (off) or closed (on) position?

    (a) General-use switches
    (b) Motor-circuit switches
    (c) Circuit breakers
    (d) all of these

4. Switches and circuit breakers used as switches shall be installed so that they may be operated from a readily accessible place.

    (a) True
    (b) False

5. Switches and circuit breakers used as switches can be mounted _____ if they are installed adjacent to motors, appliances, or other equipment that they supply and are accessible by portable means.

    (a) not higher than 6 ft 7 in.
    (b) higher than 6 ft 7 in.
    (c) in the mechanical equipment room
    (d) up to 8 ft high

6. Nonmetallic boxes for switches shall be installed with a wiring method that provides or includes _____.

    (a) a grounded conductor
    (b) an equipment grounding conductor
    (c) an inductive balance
    (d) none of these

7. Metal enclosures for switches or circuit breakers shall be connected to the circuit _____.

    (a) grounded conductor
    (b) grounding conductor
    (c) equipment grounding conductor
    (d) any of these

8. Switches shall be marked with _____.

    (a) current
    (b) voltage
    (c) maximum horsepower, if horsepower rated
    (d) all of these

9. A switching device with a marked OFF position shall completely disconnect all _____ conductors of the load it controls.

    (a) grounded
    (b) ungrounded
    (c) grounding
    (d) all of these

Article 408. Switchboards and Panelboards

1. In switchboards and panelboards, load terminals for field wiring shall be so located that it is not necessary to reach across or beyond a(n) _____ ungrounded line bus in order to make connections.

    (a) insulated
    (b) uninsulated
    (c) grounded
    (d) high impedance

2. Panelboards supplied by a three-phase, 4-wire, delta-connected system shall have the phase with higher voltage-to-ground (high-leg) connected to the _____ phase.

    (a) A
    (b) B
    (c) C
    (d) any of these

3. Circuit directories can include labels that depend on transient conditions of occupancy.

    (a) True
    (b) False

4. The purpose or use of panelboard circuits and circuit _____, including spare positions, shall be legibly identified on a circuit directory located on the face or inside of the door of a panelboard, and at each switch or circuit breaker on a switchboard.

    (a) manufacturers
    (b) conductors
    (c) feeders
    (d) modifications

5. All switchboards and panelboards supplied by a feeder in _____ shall be marked as to the device or equipment where the power supply originates.

    (a) other than one- or two-family dwellings
    (b) all dwelling units
    (c) all non dwelling units
    (d) b and c

6. Noninsulated busbars shall have a minimum space of _____ in. between the bottom of a switchboard enclosure and busbars or other obstructions.

    (a) 6
    (b) 8
    (c) 10
    (d) 12

7. Conduits and raceways, including end fittings, shall not rise more than _____ in. above the bottom of a switchboard enclosure.

    (a) 3
    (b) 4
    (c) 5
    (d) 6

8. Unused openings for circuit breakers and switches in switchboards and panelboards shall be closed using _____ or other approved means that provide protection substantially equivalent to the wall of the enclosure.

(a) duct seal and tape
(b) identified closures
(c) exothermic welding
(d) sheet metal

9. A panelboard shall be protected by an overcurrent device within the panelboard, or at any point on the _____ side of the panelboard.

(a) load
(b) supply
(c) a or b
(d) none of these

10. Plug-in-type circuit breakers that are backfed shall be _____ by an additional fastener that requires more than a pull to release.

(a) grounded
(b) secured in place
(c) shunt tripped
(d) none of these

11. When separate equipment grounding conductors are provided in panelboards, a _____ shall be secured inside the cabinet.

(a) grounded conductor
(b) terminal lug
(c) terminal bar
(d) none of these

Article 450. Transformers

1. The primary overcurrent protection for a transformer rated 1,000V, nominal, or less, with no secondary protection and having a primary current rating of over 9A must be set at not more than _____ percent.

(a) 125
(b) 167
(c) 200
(d) 300

2. Transformers with ventilating openings shall be installed so that the ventilating openings are _____.

(a) a minimum 18 in. above the floor
(b) not blocked by walls or obstructions
(c) aesthetically located
(d) vented to the exterior of the building

3. Transformers and transformer vaults shall be readily accessible to qualified personnel for inspection and maintenance, except _____.

(a) dry-type transformers 1,000V or less, located in the open on walls, columns, or structures
(b) dry-type transformers rated not more than 50 kVA/1,000V installed in hollow spaces of buildings not permanently closed in by structure
(c) a or b
(d) none of these

4. For transformers, other than Class 2 and Class 3, a means is required to disconnect all transformer ungrounded primary conductors. The disconnecting means must be located within sight of the transformer unless the disconnect _____.

(a) location is field marked on the transformer
(b) is lockable in accordance with 110.25
(c) is nonfusible
(d) a and b

Article 480. Storage Batteries

1. The provisions of Article _____ apply to stationary storage battery installations.

   (a) 450
   (b) 460
   (c) 470
   (d) 480

2. Nominal battery voltage, as it relates to storage batteries, is the value of a(n) _____ of a given voltage class for convenient designation.

   (a) cell or battery
   (b) container
   (c) electrolyte
   (d) intertier connector

3. Nominal battery voltage is typically _____.

   (a) 2V per cell for lead-acid systems
   (b) 1.20V for per cell for alkali systems
   (c) 3.60 to 3.80V per cell for Li-ion systems
   (d) all of these

4. Wiring and equipment supplied from storage batteries must be in accordance with Chapters 1 through 4 of the *NEC* unless otherwise permitted by 480.5.

   (a) True
   (b) False

5. A disconnecting means is required within sight of the storage battery for all ungrounded battery system conductors operating at over _____ nominal.

   (a) 20V
   (b) 30V
   (c) 40V
   (d) 50V

6. A(n) _____ disconnecting means is required within sight of the storage battery for all ungrounded battery system conductors operating at over 50V nominal.

   (a) accessible
   (b) readily accessible
   (c) safety
   (d) all of these

7. Provisions appropriate to the battery technology shall be made for sufficient diffusion and ventilation of the gases from a storage battery to prevent the accumulation of a(n) _____ mixture.

   (a) corrosive
   (b) explosive
   (c) toxic
   (d) all of these

8. The required working space for battery systems is measured from the edge of the battery _____.

   (a) terminals
   (b) enclosure
   (c) rack or cabinet
   (d) any of these

9. Each vented cell of a battery, as it relates to storage batteries, shall be equipped with _____ that is(are) designed to prevent destruction of the cell due to ignition of gases within the cell by an external spark or flame under normal operating conditions.

   (a) pressure relief
   (b) a flame arrester
   (c) fluid level indicators
   (d) none of these

Notes

Mike Holt's Illustrated Guide to Understanding NEC Requirements for Solar Photovoltaic Systems

CHAPTER 6

SPECIAL EQUIPMENT

Introduction to Chapter 6—Special Equipment

Chapter 6, which covers special equipment, is the second of three *NEC* chapters that deal with special topics. Chapters 5 and 7 focus on special occupancies, and special conditions respectively. Remember, the first four chapters of the *Code* are sequential and form a foundation for each of the subsequent three. Chapter 8 covers communications systems and isn't subject to the requirements of Chapters 1 through 7 except where the requirements are specifically referenced in Chapter 8 [90.3].

What exactly is "Special Equipment?" It's equipment that, by the nature of its use, construction, or by its unique nature creates a need for additional measures to ensure the "safeguarding of people and property" mission of the *NEC*, as stated in Article 90.

- ■ **Article 690—Solar Photovoltaic (PV) Systems.** This is the only Chapter 6 article that we'll cover in this textbook.

Mike Holt's Illustrated Guide to Understanding NEC Requirements for Solar Photovoltaic Systems

ARTICLE 690

SOLAR PHOTOVOLTAIC (PV) SYSTEMS

Introduction to Article 690—Solar Photovoltaic (PV) Systems

You've seen, or maybe own, photocell-powered devices such as night lights, car coolers, and toys. These generally consist of a small solar module and a small light or motor. Typically, these run on less than 10V dc and draw only a fraction of an ampere. These kinds of devices are very different from a system that can power a house or interconnect with a utility to offset a building's energy consumption.

Consider the sheer size and weight of solar modules for providing electrical power to a building. You're looking at mechanical and site selection issues that may require specialized expertise. Structural and architectural issues must also be addressed. In summary, these installations are complicated and require expertise in several nonelectrical areas, which the *NEC* doesn't address.

Article 690 focuses on reducing the electrical hazards that may arise from installing and operating a PV system, to the point where it can be considered safe for property and people.

This article consists of eight Parts and the general requirements of Chapters 1 through 4 apply to these installations, except as specifically modified by Article 690.

Part I. General

690.1 Scope

Article 690 applies to PV electrical energy systems, array circuit(s), inverter(s), and charge controller(s) for PV systems. These systems may be interactive with other electrical power sources (electric utility, wind, generator) or stand-alone with or without energy storage (batteries). Figure 690–1

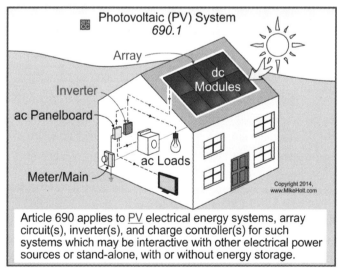

Article 690 applies to PV electrical energy systems, array circuit(s), inverter(s), and charge controller(s) for such systems which may be interactive with other electrical power sources or stand-alone, with or without energy storage.

Figure 690–1

690.2 Definitions

Alternating-Current PV Module. A PV module unit consisting of solar cells, and an integral micro-inverter that changes dc power to ac power when exposed to sunlight. Figure 690–2

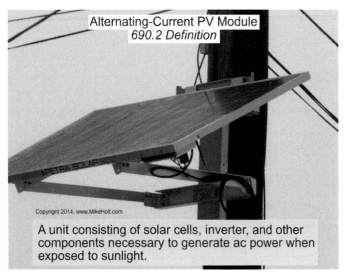

A unit consisting of solar cells, inverter, and other components necessary to generate ac power when exposed to sunlight.

Figure 690–2

Author's Comment:

- A module is only an ac module if it's listed as such.

- According to the UL White Book, ac modules provide single-phase power at 50/60 Hz when exposed to sunlight. Alternating-current modules are connected in parallel with each other and are intended to operate interactively with an electric utility supply. They've been evaluated to de-energize their output upon loss of utility power.

    Alternating-current modules are marked with the maximum size of the dedicated branch circuit on which they may be installed and the maximum number of modules which may be connected to each circuit.

Array. An electrical, mechanically integrated assembly of PV modules or panels with a support structure and foundation, tracker, and other components that form a dc power-producing unit. Figure 690–3

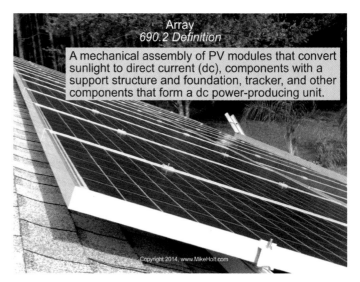

Array
690.2 Definition

A mechanical assembly of PV modules that convert sunlight to direct current (dc), components with a support structure and foundation, tracker, and other components that form a dc power-producing unit.

Figure 690–3

Bipolar Photovoltaic Array. A PV array that has two outputs, each having opposite polarity to a common reference point or center tap.

Building Integrated Photovoltaics. PV cells, devices, modules, or modular materials designed to integrate into the outer surface or structure of a building. Figure 690–4

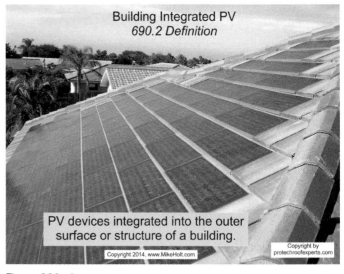

PV devices integrated into the outer surface or structure of a building.

Figure 690–4

Author's Comment:

- An example of building integrated photovoltaic would be roof shingles that are the actual modules.

Direct Current (dc) Combiner. A device that combines two or more dc circuit inputs and provides one dc circuit output. Figure 690–5

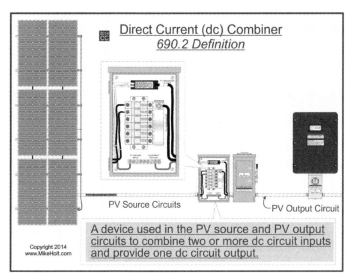

Figure 690–5

DC-to-DC Converter. A device installed in the PV source circuit or PV output circuit that provides output dc voltage and current at a higher or lower value than the input dc voltage and current. Figure 690–6

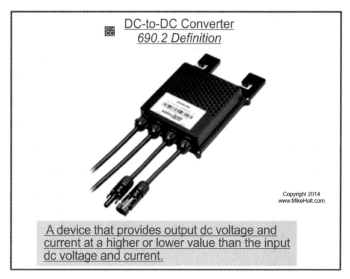

Figure 690–6

Author's Comment:

- The dc combiner connects multiple PV source circuit conductors of PV modules together in parallel. DC combiners can also combine two or more output circuits together into another "output circuit." These "array combiners" are used on large inverter systems where there are several tiers of combiners.

Author's Comment:

- These are components that are intended to maximize the output of independent modules and reduce losses due to variances between modules' outputs. They're directly wired to each module and are bolted to the module frame or the PV rack.

2014 CHANGE ANALYSIS: Because slang terms are often used that mean different things to different people, the *NEC* has been modified to include this new term. The terms "dc combiner," "source circuit combiners," "recombiners," "subcombiners," "string combiner," and "array combiner" are often used in the industry to describe the same piece of equipment. Due to this inconsistency, the term "dc combiner" is now defined, and will hopefully eliminate the other ones.

2014 CHANGE ANALYSIS: A dc-to-dc converter is a piece of equipment that optimizes the PV system by providing a more consistent voltage throughout the system. As with so many other things in the PV industry, these converters are becoming more and more popular as technologies advance. This is a new definition for a fairly new product that you'll be certain to see in new PV installations.

Interactive System. A <u>PV</u> system that operates in parallel (interactive) with electrical utility power (or other power source, such as a generator or wind system) through a utility-interactive inverter. Figure 690–7

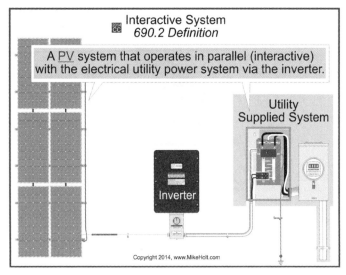

Figure 690–7

Author's Comment:

■ Listed utility-interactive inverters automatically stop exporting ac power upon loss of the utility (or other source) power, and they automatically resume exporting ac power to the utility source once it's been restored for at least five minutes [705.40 Ex].

Inverter. Electrical equipment that changes dc power from the PV system to grid-interactive ac power. Figure 690–8

Author's Comment:

■ Inverters change direct current produced by the PV modules or batteries into alternating current. Grid-tied inverters synchronize the ac output current with the utility's ac frequency, thus allowing the PV system to transfer unused PV system current to the utility grid. Battery-based inverters for stand-alone systems often include a charge controller, which is capable of charging a battery bank from a generator during cloudy weather.

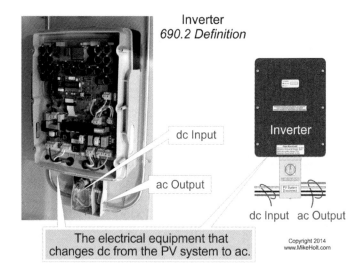

Figure 690–8

Inverter Input Circuit. The dc conductors between the battery and inverter of stand-alone systems or PV output circuits and an inverter for a utility-interactive system. Figures 690–9 and 690–10

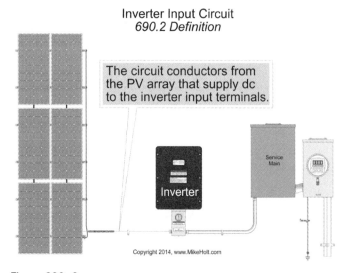

Figure 690–9

Inverter Output Circuit. The ac circuit conductors from the inverter output terminals that supply ac power to premises wiring, including conductors from ac modules [690.6(B)]. Figure 690–11

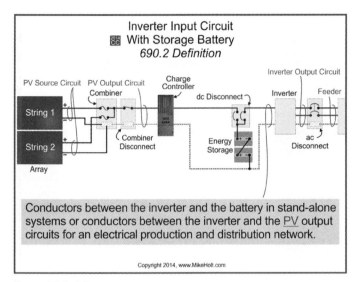

Figure 690–10

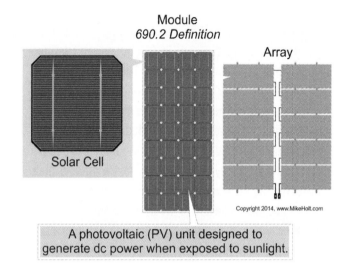

Figure 690–12

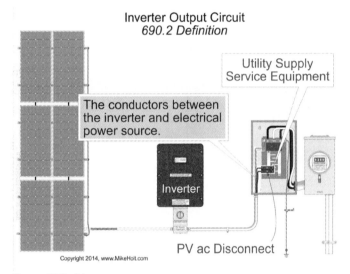

Figure 690–11

Module. A PV unit designed to generate dc power when exposed to sunlight. Figure 690–12

Author's Comment:

- PV modules use sunlight to make direct current (dc) electricity by using light (photons) to move electrons in a circuit. This is known as the "photovoltaic effect."

Monopole Subarray. A PV subarray that has two conductors in the output circuit, one positive (+) and one negative (–). Two monopole PV subarrays are used to form a bipolar PV array.

Author's Comment:

- Every module is monopole (two wires).

Multimode Inverter. An inverter that has the capabilities of both stand-alone and utility-interactive systems. Figure 690–13

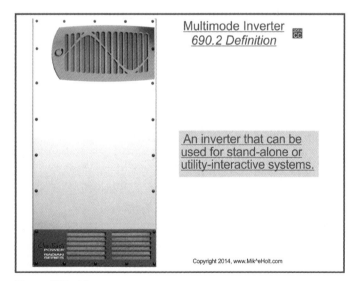

Figure 690–13

2014 CHANGE ANALYSIS: Multimode inverters are discussed in this article, and in 705, but weren't defined in previous editions of the *Code*. These inverters can be used for either stand-alone or utility-interactive systems, as they have the capabilities for both. Multimode inverters address a serious drawback that people have with PV systems. Many customers believe that putting a PV system on their roof will allow their lights to stay on when the utility power goes out. With a typical utility-interactive inverter this isn't the case, because when the "other" power sources (normally utility power but it could be a generator or wind) shuts off, so does the inverter. A multimode inverter solves this concern because, under normal conditions, it acts just like a standard utility-interactive inverter. When the "other" power source shuts off, the inverter automatically switches modes, and signals a relay in the inverter to break connection to the other source. This acts as a sort of transfer switch in the effect it has of proving safety to utility workers who are anticipating working on a de-energized line. Due to this, optional standby power can now be provided in a system that's also utility-interactive. Many people in the industry are looking at these inverters as a real "game changer" in the way we use PV systems.

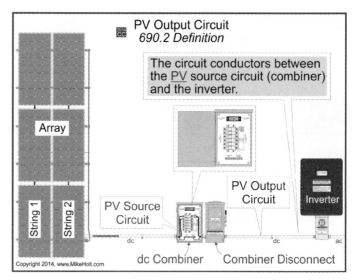

Figure 690–14

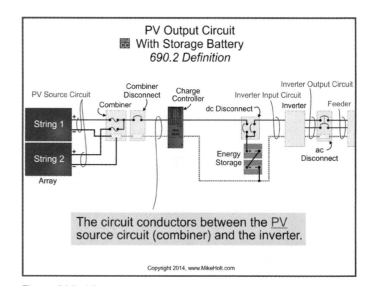

Figure 690–15

PV Output Circuit. Circuit conductors between the dc combiner and the dc input terminals of the inverter or dc disconnect. Figures 690–14 and 690–15

PV Power Source. One or more arrays of PV modules that generate dc voltage and current power. Figure 690–16

PV Source Circuit. The circuit conductors between the PV modules and the terminals of the dc combiner, or the inverter dc input terminals if no dc combiner is used. Figures 690–17 and 690–18

PV Power Source
690.2 Definition

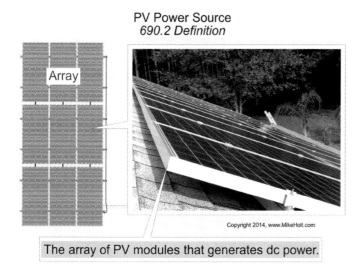

The array of PV modules that generates dc power.

Figure 690–16

PV Source Circuit - With Combiner
690.2 Definition

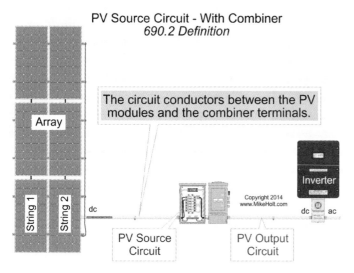

The circuit conductors between the PV modules and the combiner terminals.

Figure 690–17

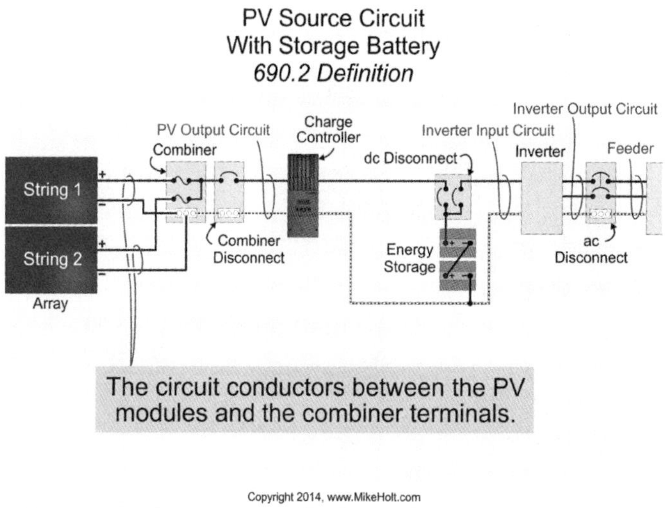

PV Source Circuit With Storage Battery
690.2 Definition

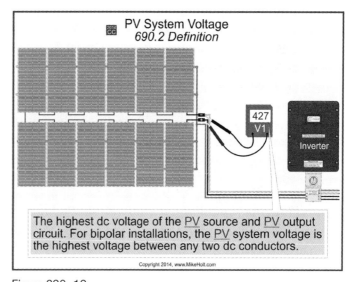

The circuit conductors between the PV modules and the combiner terminals.

Figure 690–18

PV System Voltage
690.2 Definition

The highest dc voltage of the PV source and PV output circuit. For bipolar installations, the PV system voltage is the highest voltage between any two dc conductors.

Figure 690–19

Author's Comment:

■ PV Source Circuits are often called "strings."

PV System Voltage. The direct current (dc) voltage of any PV source or PV output circuit. For multiwire installations, the PV system voltage is the highest voltage between any two dc conductors. Figure 690–19

Solar Cell. The basic building block of PV modules that generates dc power when exposed to sunlight. Figure 690–20

Stand-Alone System. A PV system that supplies power without an interconnection to another electric power source. Figure 690–21

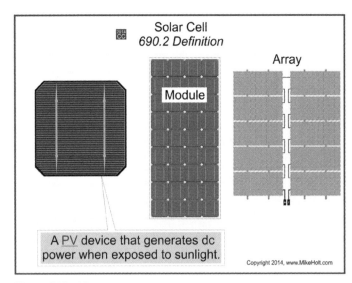

Figure 690–20

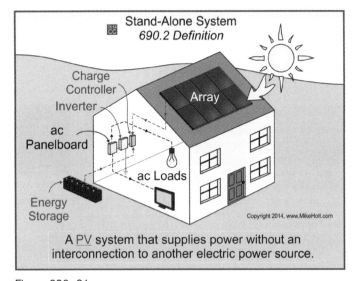

Figure 690–21

690.3 Other Articles

All of the requirements contained in Chapters 1 through 4 apply to PV installations, except where supplemented or modified by this article.

690.4 General Requirements

(A) PV Systems. A PV system is permitted to supply power to a building in addition to any other <u>electrical</u> supply system(s).

(B) Listed Equipment. Equipment for PV systems such as inverters, <u>PV</u> modules, <u>dc combiners, dc-to-dc converters,</u> and charge controllers must be <u>listed</u> for <u>PV</u> application. Figure 690–22

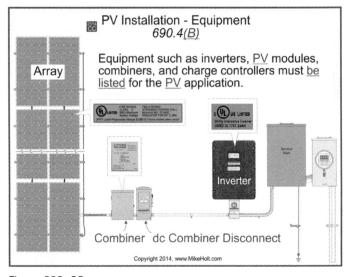

Figure 690–22

Author's Comment:

■ Listing means that the equipment is in a list published by a testing laboratory acceptable to the authority having jurisdiction [Article 100].

(C) Qualified Persons. <u>PV systems, associated wiring, and interconnections must be installed by a qualified person.</u> Figure 690–23

Note: A qualified person has the knowledge related to construction and operation of PV equipment and installations; along with safety training to recognize and avoid hazards to persons and property [Article 100].

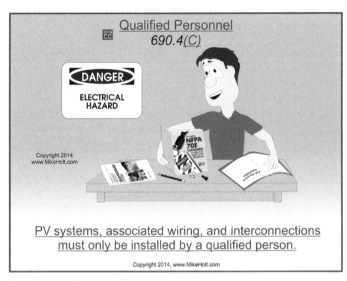

Figure 690–23

(D) Multiple Inverters. Where multiple utility-interactive inverters are located remote from each other, a directory is required at each dc PV system disconnecting means, ac disconnecting means for mini- and micro-inverters, and service disconnecting means showing the location of all dc and ac PV system disconnecting means in the building/structure [705.10].

Ex: A directory isn't required where all PV system disconnecting means are grouped at the service disconnecting means.

2014 CHANGE ANALYSIS: Article 690 might be the most difficult article in the entire *Code* book through which to navigate. For several years, the requirements in this article didn't really change that much, then a huge influx of changes occurred due to the sudden popularity of these systems. When a massive volume of changes occur to one article the end result will almost certainly be confusing, with requirements in sections that don't seem to make much sense. This section is a perfect example of this. Circuit routing and connection requirements were found here in 2011, but are those really "general requirements?" These changes may seem insignificant, but they make this article much easier to use, and therefore were certainly worth making.

One technical change that occurred to this section can be found in 690.4(B), which addressed the listing of PV system equipment. Keeping up with new products and technologies is a very difficult task when updating the *NEC*, so you can expect *Code* changes every time new products come out. The example here is dc combiners and dc-to-dc converters. By adding them to the list of equipment in 690.4(B) they must be listed.

There are several changes in Article 690 that are simple relocations. These certainly make the *NEC* a better document. Examples of this include 690.13 and 690.14 which were condensed into just 690.13 (covering the rules for disconnecting means). Previous editions of the *Code* had 690.13 covering disconnects, then 690.14 covering "additional provisions" for disconnecting means!

690.5 Ground-Fault Protection

Grounded dc PV arrays must be provided with dc ground-fault protection meeting the requirements of 690.5(A) through (C) to reduce fire hazards. Figure 690–24

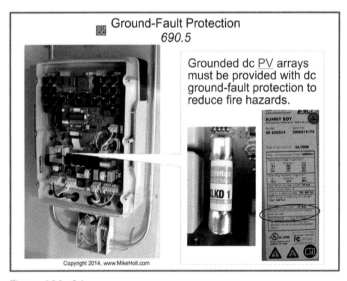

Figure 690–24

Ungrounded dc <u>PV</u> arrays must be provided with dc ground-fault protection in accordance with 690.35(C).

Ex: Ground-fault detection isn't required for ground- or pole-mounted PV arrays with not more than two source circuits isolated from buildings. Figure 690–25

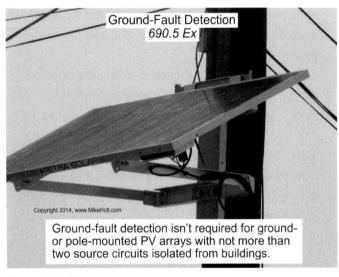

Figure 690–25

(A) Ground-Fault Detection and Interruption (GFDI). The ground fault protection must:

(1) <u>Be capable of detecting a ground fault in the PV array dc current-carrying conductors and components, including any intentionally grounded conductors,</u>

(2) <u>Interrupt the flow of fault current,</u>

(3) <u>Provide an indication of the fault, and,</u>

(4) <u>Be listed for providing PV ground-fault protection.</u>

(C) Labels and Markings. A warning label <u>that isn't handwritten and is of sufficient durability to withstand the environment involved, must be permanently affixed [110.21(B)]</u> on the utility-interactive inverter at a visible location at PV system batteries stating the following: Figure 690–26

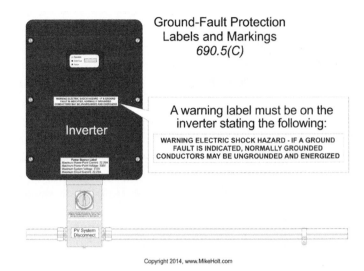

Figure 690–26

WARNING: ELECTRIC SHOCK HAZARD—IF A GROUND FAULT IS INDICATED, NORMALLY GROUNDED CONDUCTORS MAY BE UNGROUNDED AND ENERGIZED

2014 CHANGE ANALYSIS: Two changes were made in this section, which covers ground-fault detection and interruption, although neither is likely to really affect the installer. New to this edition of the *NEC* is that the grounded conductor must now be provided with ground-fault protection, whereas in 2011 it was permitted but not required. This change will force manufacturers to revise their products. The other change is to 690.5(C), which simply refers the *Code* user back to the general rule of 110.21(B) for the requirements of signs. These requirements include suitability for the environment involved, as well as a prohibition on hand written warnings. This is of little consequence in this context, because this sign is almost always provided by the manufacturer.

690.6 Alternating-Current Modules

(A) PV Source Circuits. Article 690 requirements pertaining to dc PV circuits don't apply to ac PV modules since ac PV modules don't have a dc source or output circuit. Figure 690–27

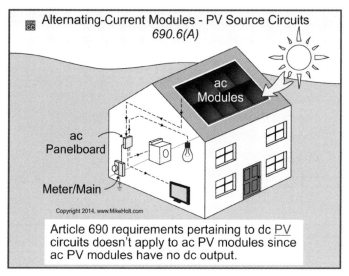

Figure 690–27

(B) Inverter Output Circuit. The output circuit conductors of an ac module are considered an "Inverter Output Circuit" as defined in 690.2. Figure 690–28

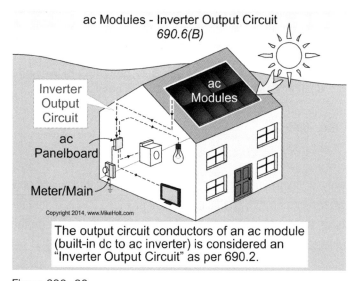

Figure 690–28

Part II. Circuit Requirements

690.7 Maximum Voltage

(A) Maximum PV System Voltage. For dc circuits, the maximum PV system voltage for that circuit is equal to the rated open-circuit voltage (Voc) of the series-connected PV modules, as corrected for the lowest expected ambient temperature. This voltage is used to determine the voltage rating of conductors and equipment for the dc circuits. Figure 690–29

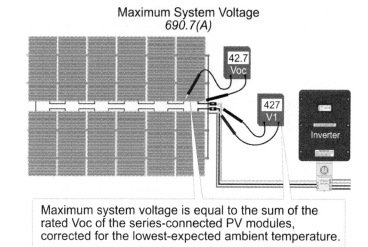

Figure 690–29

Author's Comment:

- Open circuit voltage (Voc) is the voltage when there's no load on the system.

When open-circuit voltage temperature coefficients are supplied by the manufacturer as part of the installation instructions for listed PV modules, they must be used to calculate the maximum PV system voltage instead of using Table 690.7, as required by 110.3(B).

Note: One source for lowest-expected ambient temperature is the Extreme Annual Mean Minimum Design Dry Bulb Temperature found in the *ASHRAE Handbook—Fundamentals*. See www.solarabcs.org/permitting/map.

Author's Comment:

- PV module voltage has an inverse relationship with temperature, which means that at lower temperatures, the PV modules' voltage increases; at higher temperatures, the PV modules' voltage decreases from the manufacturers nameplate Voc values.

PV System Voltage Based on Manufacturer Temperature Coefficient %/°C

Example: Using the manufacturer's temperature coefficient of -0.36%/°C, what's the maximum PV source circuit voltage for twelve modules each rated Voc 38.30, at a temperature of -7°C? Figure 690–30

$$PV\ Voc = Rated\ Voc \times \{1 + [(Temp.\ °C - 25°C) \times Module\ Coefficient\ \%/°C]\} \times \#\ Modules\ per\ Series\ String$$

Module Voc = 38.30 Voc × {1+ [(-7°C - 25°C) × -0.36%/°C]}

Module Voc = 38.30 Voc × {1 + [-32°C × -0.36%/°C]}

Module Voc = 38.30 Voc × {1 + 11.52%}

Module Voc = 38.30 Voc × 1.1152

Module Voc = 42.71V

PV Voltage = 42.71 x 12

PV Voltage = 513V

PV System Voltage Based on Manufacturer Temperature Coefficient V/°C

Example: Using the manufacturer's temperature coefficient of -0.137V/°C, what's the maximum PV source circuit voltage for twenty-three modules each rated Voc 38.30, at a temperature of -7°C? Figure 690–31

$$PV\ Voc\ (V/°C) = \{Rated\ Voc + [(Temp.\ °C - 25°C) \times Module\ Coefficient\ V/°C]\} \times \#\ Modules\ per\ Series\ String$$

Module Voc = {38.30V + [(-7°C - 25°C) × -0.137V/°C]}

Module Voc = {38.30V + [-32°C × -0.137V/°C))

Module Voc = (38.30V + 4.384V)

Module Voc = 42.68V

PV Voc = 42.68V x 12

PV Voc = 512V

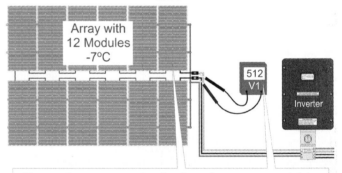

Maximum System Voltage - V/°C
690.7

The maximum source circuit voltage for an array containing twelve modules, each 38.30 Voc, temperature coefficient of -0.137V/°C, at a temperature of -7°C will be 512 Voc.

Figure 690–31

Only for crystalline and multicrystalline silicon modules, and only where temperature coefficients aren't provided by the manufacturer, the rated open-circuit voltage must be multiplied by the correction factor provided in Table 690.7.

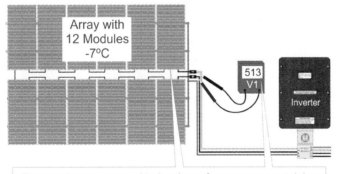

Maximum System Voltage -%/°C
Table 690.7

The maximum source circuit voltage for an array containing twelve modules, each 38.30 Voc, temperature coefficient of -0.36%/°C, at a temperature of -7°C will be 513 Voc.

Figure 690–30

Table 690.7 Voltage Correction Factors

Lowest-Expected Ambient Temperature °C	°F	Temperature Correction Factor
4 to 0	40 to 32	1.10
-5 to -1	31 to 23	1.12
-10 to -6	22 to 14	1.14
-15 to -11	13 to 5	1.16
-20 to -16	-4 to 4	1.18
-25 to -21	-13 to -5	1.20
-30 to -26	-22 to -14	1.21
-35 to -31	-31 to -23	1.23
-40 to -36	-40 to -32	1.25

PV System Voltage Based on Table 690.7 Temperature Correction

Example: Using Table 690.7, what's the maximum PV source circuit voltage for twelve modules each rated Voc 38.30, at a temperature of -7°C? Figure 690–33

> *String Voc Table 690.7 = Module Voc × Table 690.7 Correction Factor × # Modules per Series String*

Module Voc = 38.30 Voc × 1.14
Module Voc = 43.66V

PV Voc = 43.66V × 12 modules
PV Voc = 524V

CAUTION: *Illumination at dawn, dusk, heavy overcast, and even on rainy days is sufficient to produce dangerous voltage.* Figure 690–32

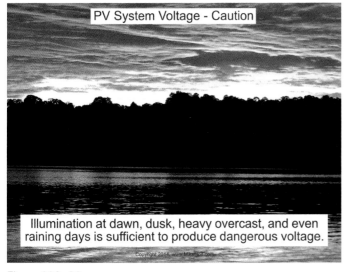

PV System Voltage - Caution

Illumination at dawn, dusk, heavy overcast, and even raining days is sufficient to produce dangerous voltage.

Figure 690–32

Voltage Correction Factors
Table 690.7

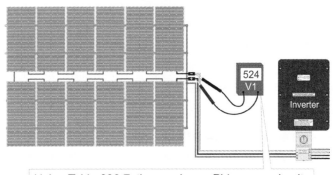

Using Table 690.7, the maximum PV source circuit voltage (Voc) for 12 modules each rated 38.30 Voc, at temperature of -7°C is 524 Voc.

Copyright 2014, www.MikeHolt.com

Figure 690–33

(C) Maximum PV System Voltage One- and Two-Family Dwellings. For one- and two-family dwellings, the maximum PV system dc voltage is limited to 600V, which is equal to the standard voltage insulation of electrical conductors. Figure 690–34

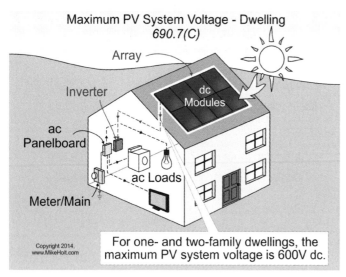

Maximum PV System Voltage - Dwelling
690.7(C)

For one- and two-family dwellings, the maximum PV system voltage is 600V dc.

Figure 690–34

Author's Comment:

- The maximum PV system dc voltage for other than one- and two-family dwelling units is permitted to be up to 1,000V, but the working space, the voltage rating of conductor insulation, and equipment (such as disconnects and fuses), must be based on the maximum PV dc system voltage of 1,000V.

2014 CHANGE ANALYSIS: *Code* users that are experienced in Article 690 will notice that the voltages discussed in this article have been changed from 600V to 1,000V. These changes were made as a result of a task group for the 2014 *NEC* that wanted to make changes that would result in the *Code* corresponding more closely with the IEC (International Electrotechnical Commission) standard that's used in some other countries. By changing the voltage threshold in the *NEC*, it allows products that are manufactured for IEC compliance to be used in *NEC* installations, with no real safety concerns being added. It's interesting to note that the original proposal to this section wanted to allow for 1,000V installations at dwelling units, but that portion of the proposal was rejected. It will interesting to see if this changes in future editions of the *Code*, as many people are already a bit put off by having 600V systems at dwelling units!

(E) Bipolar Circuits. For a 2-wire circuit connected to bipolar systems, the maximum system voltage of the circuit is the highest voltage between the conductors of the 2-wire circuit if all of the following conditions apply:

(1) One conductor of the 2-wire circuit is solidly grounded.

(2) Each 2-wire circuit is connected to a separate subarray.

(3) Bipolar equipment must have a permanently affixed label that isn't handwritten and is of sufficient durability to withstand the environment involved [110.21(B)] with the following wording:

> **WARNING—BIPOLAR PV ARRAY. DISCONNECTION OF NEUTRAL OR GROUNDED CONDUCTORS MAY RESULT IN OVERVOLTAGE ON ARRAY OR INVERTER.**

690.8 Circuit Current and Circuit Sizing

 Scan this QR code for a video of this *Code* rule. See page xiii for information on how to use the QR codes.

(A) Calculating Maximum Circuit Current.

(1) Maximum PV Source Circuit Current. The maximum PV source circuit current is calculated by multiplying the module nameplate short-circuit current rating (Isc) by 125 percent. Figure 690–35

Maximum PV Source Circuit Current (Isc)
690.8(A)(1)

ELECTRICAL CHARACTERISTICS	
Maximum Power (Pmax)*	250 W
Tolerance of Pmax	+5%/-0%
PTC Rating	223.6 W
Type of Cell	Polycrystalline silicon
Cell Configuration	60 in series
Open Circuit Voltage (Voc)	38.3 V
Maximum Power Voltage (Vpm)	29.8 V
Short Circuit Current (Isc)	8.90 A
Maximum Power Current (Ipm)	8.40 A
Module Efficiency (%)	15.3%
Maximum System (DC) Voltage	600 V (UL)/1000V (IEC)
Series Fuse Rating	15 A
NOCT	47.5°C
Temperature Coefficient (Pmax)	-0.485%/°C
Temperature Coefficient (Voc)	-0.36%/°C
Temperature Coefficient (Isc)	0.053%/°C

*Illumination of 1 kW/m² (1 sun) at spectral distribution of AM 1.5 (ASTM E892 global spectral irradiance) at a cell temperature of 25°C.

Maximum PV source circuit current is calculated by multiplying the module nameplate Isc by 125 percent.

Figure 690–35

Author's Comment:

- The 125% current multiplier is due to the module's ability to produce more current than its rated value based on the intensity of the sunlight, which can be affected by altitude, reflection due to snow or other buildings, or even the dryness of the air.

- The PV source circuit consists of the circuit conductors between the PV modules and the terminals of the dc combiner or inverter dc input terminals if no dc combiner is used [690.2].

Maximum PV Source Circuit Current

Example: *What's the maximum PV source circuit current for 12 series connected dc modules having a nameplate Isc of 8.90A?* Figure 690–36

Maximum PV Source Circuit Current =
Module Isc × 1.25

Maximum PV Source Circuit Current = 8.90A × 1.25
Maximum PV Source Circuit Current = 11.13A

---

(2) Maximum PV Output Circuit Current. The maximum PV output circuit current is equal to the sum of parallel PV maximum source circuit currents as calculated in 690.8(A)(1).

Author's Comment:

- The PV output circuit consists of circuit conductors between the PV source circuit (dc combiner) and the dc input terminals of the inverter or dc disconnect.

Maximum PV Output Circuit Current

Example: *What's the maximum PV output circuit current for two PV source circuits (strings), each containing 12 dc modules having a nameplate Isc of 8.90A?* Figure 690–37

Maximum PV Output Circuit Current =
(Module Isc × 1.25)* × Number of Strings

Maximum PV Output Circuit Current = (8.90A × 1.25)* × 2
Maximum PV Output Circuit Current = 11.13A × 2
Maximum PV Output Circuit Current = 22.26A
*690.8(A)(1)

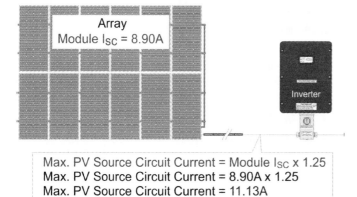

Maximum PV Source Circuit Current
690.8(A)(1)

Array
Module I_{SC} = 8.90A

Inverter

Max. PV Source Circuit Current = Module I_{SC} x 1.25
Max. PV Source Circuit Current = 8.90A x 1.25
Max. PV Source Circuit Current = 11.13A

Copyright 2014, www.MikeHolt.com

Figure 690–36

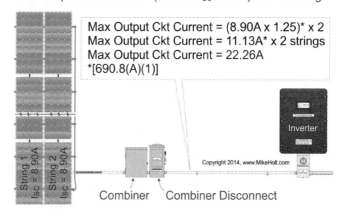

Maximum Output Circuit Current
690.8(A)(2)

Max Output Ckt Current = (Module I_{SC} x 1.25)* x # of Strings

Max Output Ckt Current = (8.90A x 1.25)* x 2
Max Output Ckt Current = 11.13A* x 2 strings
Max Output Ckt Current = 22.26A
*[690.8(A)(1)]

Inverter

String 1
Isc = 8.90A

String 2
Isc = 8.90A

Combiner   Combiner Disconnect

Copyright 2014, www.MikeHolt.com

Figure 690–37

---

(3) Maximum Inverter Output Circuit Current. The maximum inverter output current is equal to the continuous output current marked on the inverter nameplate or installation manual. Figure 690–38

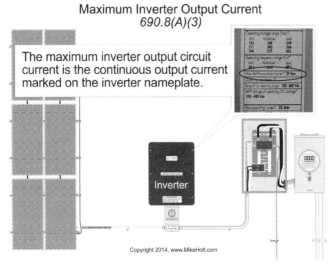

Figure 690–38

Author's Comment:

■ The inverter output circuit consists of the circuit conductors from the inverter output terminals or ac modules [690.6(B)] to ac premises wiring.

■ The instruction manual should be used because the inverter output current can change based on the input voltage. Regardless of the modules, conductors and overcurrent devices are based on the output current, whether there's one module or one million modules.

(5) DC-to-DC Converter Output Current. The maximum output current for a dc-to-dc converter is the converter continuous output current rating. Figure 690–39

(B) Conductor Ampacity Sizing. PV circuit conductors must be sized to the larger of 690.8(B)(1) or 690.8(B)(2).

(1) Before Ampacity Correction or Adjustment. PV circuit conductors must have an ampacity of not less than 125 percent of 690.8(A) current before the application of conductor

DC-to-DC Output Current
690.8(A)(5)

The maximum output current for a dc-to-dc converter is the converter continuous output current rating (100%).

Figure 690–39

ampacity correction [310.15(B)(2)(a) and 310.15(B)(3)(c)] and adjustment [310.15(B)(3)(a)]. Figure 690–40

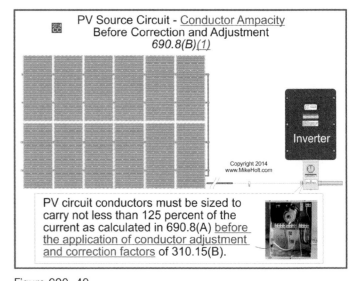

Figure 690–40

Author's Comment:

■ Conductors terminating on terminals rated 75°C are sized in accordance with the ampacities listed in the 75°C temperature column of Table 310.15(B)(16) [110.14(C)(1)(a)(3)], if the conductor insulation temperature rating is 75°C or 90°C.

PV Source Circuit Ampacity before Correction and Adjustment

Example: *What's the minimum PV source circuit conductor ampacity before the application of conductor correction or adjustment for the PV source circuit (string) conductors having a short-circuit current rating of 8.90A; assuming all terminals are rated 75°C?* Figure 690–41

Conductor Ampacity = (Module Isc × 1.25)* × 1.25

Conductor Ampacity = (8.90A × 1.25)* × 1.25
Conductor Ampacity = (11.13A)* × 1.25
Conductor Ampacity = 13.91A
Conductor Ampacity = 14 AWG rated 20A at 75ºC
[Table 310.15(B)(16)]
*690.8(A)(1)

PV Output Circuit Ampacity before Correction and Adjustment

Example: *What's the minimum PV output circuit conductor ampacity, before the application of conductor correction or adjustment, supplied by two PV source circuits, each having a short-circuit current rating of 8.90A; if all terminals are rated 75°C?* Figure 690–42

Conductor Ampacity = (Module Isc × 1.25 × Number of Source Circuits)* × 1.25

Conductor Ampacity = (8.90A × 1.25 × 2 strings)* × 1.25
Conductor Ampacity = 22.26A* × 1.25
Conductor Ampacity = 27.83A
Conductor Ampacity = 10 AWG rated 35A at 75ºC
[Table 310.15(B)(16)]
*690.8(A)(2)

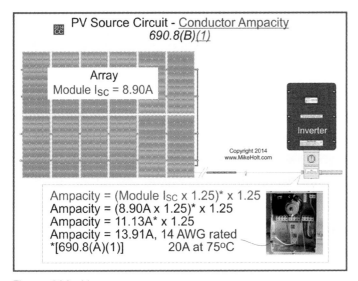

Figure 690–41

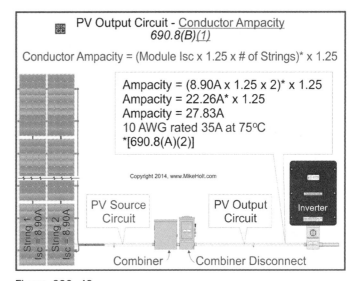

Figure 690–42

Inverter Output Circuit Ampacity before Correction and Adjustment

Example: *What's the minimum inverter ac output circuit conductor ampacity, before the application of conductor correction or adjustment factors, if the maximum continuous nameplate ac rating of the inverter is 24A; if all terminals are rated 75°C?* Figure 690–43

> *Conductor Ampacity =*
> *Inverter Nameplate Rating* × 1.25*

Conductor Ampacity = 24A* × 1.25

Conductor Ampacity = 30A

Conductor Ampacity = 10 AWG rated 35A at 75°C
  [310.15(B)(16)]

*690.8(A)(3)

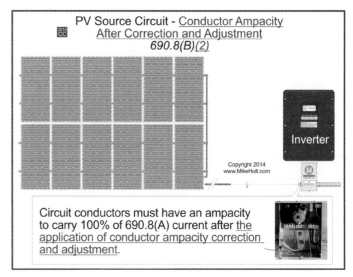

Figure 690–44

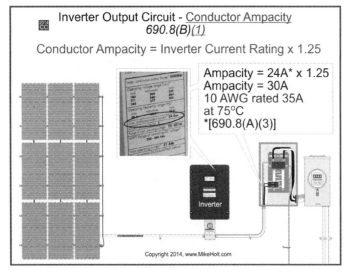

Figure 690–43

(2) After Ampacity Correction or Adjustment. Circuit conductors must have an ampacity to carry 100% of 690.8(A) current after the application of conductor ampacity correction [310.15(B)(2)(a) and 310.15(B)(3)(c)] and adjustment [310.15(B)(3)(a)]. Figure 690–44

Author's Comment:

■ When performing conductor ampacity correction and adjustment calculations, use the conductor ampacity listed in the 90°C column of Table 310.15(B)(16) for RHH/RHW-2/USE-2 [310.15(B)] and PV wire at 90°C [110.14(C)(1)(b)(2)]. Figure 690–45

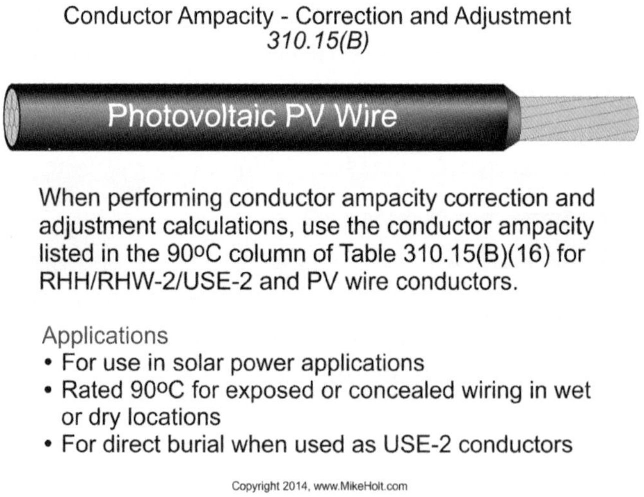

Conductor Ampacity - Correction and Adjustment
310.15(B)

Photovoltaic PV Wire

When performing conductor ampacity correction and adjustment calculations, use the conductor ampacity listed in the 90ºC column of Table 310.15(B)(16) for RHH/RHW-2/USE-2 and PV wire conductors.

Applications
• For use in solar power applications
• Rated 90ºC for exposed or concealed wiring in wet or dry locations
• For direct burial when used as USE-2 conductors

Copyright 2014, www.MikeHolt.com

Figure 690–45

PV Source Circuit Ampacity after Correction and Adjustment

Example: *What's the conductor ampacity after temperature correction for two current-carrying size 14 RHH/ RHW-2/USE-2 or PV wires rated 90°C in a raceway or cable on the roof, where the ambient temperature is 90°F with 60°F added in accordance with Table 310.15(B)(3)(c), supplying modules having a nameplate Isc rating of 8.90A?* Figure 690–46

> ***Conductor Ampacity = Table 310.15(B)(16) Ampacity at 90°C Column x Temperature Correction***

Temperature Correction = 0.58, Table 310.15(B)(2)(a)
  based on 150°F (ambient plus 60°F roof temperature adder)

Conductor Ampacity = 25A x 0.58
Conductor Ampacity = 14.50A, which has sufficient ampacity after correction and adjustment to supply the PV source circuit current of 11.13A (8.90A x 1.25) [690.8(A)(1)].

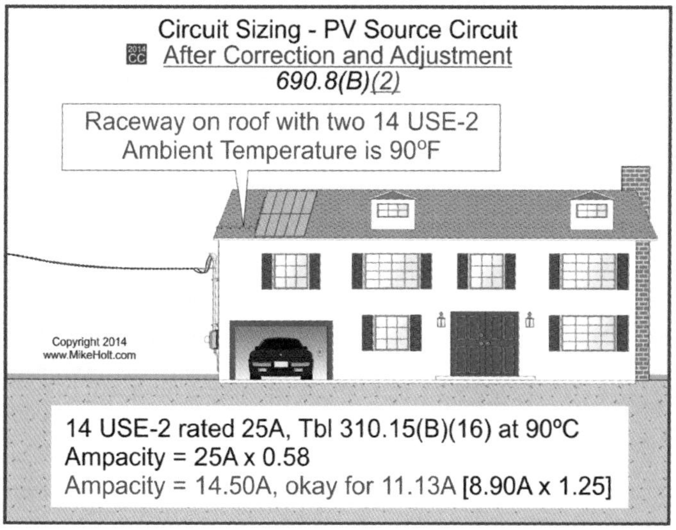

PV Source Circuit after Correction and Adjustment

Example: *What's the conductor ampacity after temperature correction and adjustment for four current-carrying size 14 RHH/RHW-2/USE-2 or PV wires rated 90°C in a raceway or cable on the roof, where the ambient temperature is 90°F with 60°F added in accordance with Table 310.15(B)(3)(c), supplying modules having a nameplate Isc rating of 8.90A for each circuit?* Figure 690–47

> ***Conductor Ampacity = Table 310.15(B) (16) Ampacity at 90°C Column x Temperature Correction x Adjustment***

Temperature Correction = 0.58, Table 310.15(B)(2)(a)
  based on 150°F (ambient plus 60°F roof temperature adder)
Adjustment = 0.80, Table 310.15(B)(3)(a), based on four current-carrying conductors in a raceway or cable
Conductor Ampacity = 25A x 0.58 x 0.80
Conductor Ampacity = 11.60A, which has sufficient ampacity after correction and adjustment to supply the PV source circuit current of 11.13A [8.90A x 1.25, 690.8(A)(1)].

Circuit Sizing - PV Source Circuit
After Correction and Adjustment
690.8(B)(2)

Raceway on roof with two 14 USE-2 Ambient Temperature is 90°F

Copyright 2014
www.MikeHolt.com

14 USE-2 rated 25A, Tbl 310.15(B)(16) at 90°C
Ampacity = 25A x 0.58
Ampacity = 14.50A, okay for 11.13A [8.90A x 1.25]

Figure 690–46

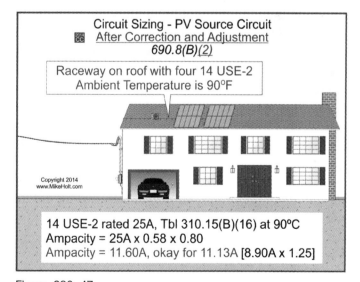

Circuit Sizing - PV Source Circuit
After Correction and Adjustment
690.8(B)(2)

Raceway on roof with four 14 USE-2 Ambient Temperature is 90°F

Copyright 2014
www.MikeHolt.com

14 USE-2 rated 25A, Tbl 310.15(B)(16) at 90°C
Ampacity = 25A x 0.58 x 0.80
Ampacity = 11.60A, okay for 11.13A [8.90A x 1.25]

Figure 690–47

Inverter ac Output Circuit after Correction and Adjustment

Example: *What's the conductor ampacity after temperature correction for two current-carrying size 10 RHH/RHW-2/USE-2 or PV wires rated 90°C installed at a location where the ambient temperature is 90°F, supplying a 24A inverter output circuit? Figure 690–48*

Conductor Ampacity = Table 310.15(B)(16) Ampacity at 90°C Column x Temperature Correction

Temperature Correction = 0.96, Table 310.15(B)(2)(a) based on 90°F ambient temperature
Conductor Ampacity = 40A x 0.96 [Table 310.15(B)(2)(a)]
Conductor Ampacity = 38.40A, which has sufficient ampacity after correction to supply the inverter ac output circuit current of 24A [690.8(A)(3)].

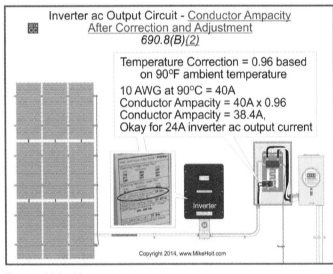

Figure 690–48

690.9 Overcurrent Protection

(A) Circuits and Equipment. PV source circuits, PV output circuits, inverter output circuits, and storage battery circuits and equipment must have overcurrent protection in accordance with Article 240. Figure 690–49

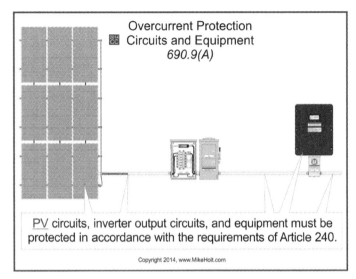

Figure 690–49

Overcurrent devices for PV source circuits (strings) and PV output circuits must comply with (A) through (E). Circuits that are connected to both a power limited supply (such as a PV module) and another supply that has high available fault current (such as an utility) must be protected against overcurrent from both systems.

Author's Comment:

■ For an ungrounded system [690.35], both the positive and negative conductor must have overcurrent protection; for grounded systems, only the ungrounded conductor requires overcurrent protection [240.15].

Ex: Overcurrent protection isn't required for PV dc circuits where:

(a) There are no external sources such as parallel-connected source circuits, batteries, or backfeed from inverters.

(b) The short-circuit currents (Isc) from all sources don't exceed the ampacity of the PV circuit conductors or the maximum overcurrent device size specified on the PV module nameplate. Figure 690–50

Author's Comment:

■ This occurs when the PV source or PV output circuits consist of no more than two circuits and the inverter isn't capable of being backfed to the PV array. When

Overcurrent Protection
Circuits and Equipment
690.9(A) Ex

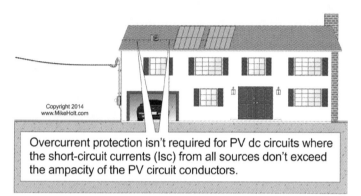

Overcurrent protection isn't required for PV dc circuits where the short-circuit currents (Isc) from all sources don't exceed the ampacity of the PV circuit conductors.

Figure 690–50

more than two circuits are connected, the total of all available circuits (minus the faulted circuit) must be calculated to determine if the conductors and module overcurrent protection device (OCPD) ratings are observed. When the current exceeds the conductor ampacity or module OCPD rating, an OCPD is generally required for each PV source circuit (string) conductor at the location where the circuits are combined.

2014 CHANGE ANALYSIS: The revision in (A) isn't exactly new, but now a person can read it and actually understand what the intent of the rule is. Interrupting ratings of overcurrent devices are often forgotten in a PV installation, because the available fault current is limited by the modules. When the PV system is also connected to a utility, for example, the available fault current could be in the tens of thousands of amperes! Installing a properly sized (ampere rating) fuse or breaker will protect the system and components from overloads and from ground faults and short circuits from the PV system, but an improperly sized interrupting rating on the system could result in a tragedy if the fault is from the utility. It's important to remember that when a system is connected to multiple sources, we need protection from both systems.

(B) Overcurrent Devices. Where conductor overcurrent protection is required [690.9], it must be sized no less than 125 percent of the maximum circuit currents in accordance with 690.8(A).

Author's Comment:

■ PV source circuit current—module nameplate short-circuit current rating (Isc) times 125 percent [690.8(A)(1)].

■ PV output circuit current—sum of the parallel PV source circuit currents (module nameplate short-circuit current rating (Isc) times 125 percent) [690.8(A)(2)].

■ Inverter ac output circuit current—ac output current marked on the inverter nameplate or installation manual [690.8(A)(3)].

PV Source Circuit Overcurrent Protection Size

Example: *Size the OCPD for a string of modules having a nameplate short-circuit current (Isc) rating of 8.90A.* Figure 690–51

$$OCPD = (Module\ Isc \times 1.25)^* \times 1.25$$

$OCPD = (8.90A \times 1.25)^* \times 1.25$
$OCPD = (11.30A)^* \times 1.25$
$OCPD = 13.91A$
$OCPD = 15A\ [240.6(A)]$
*690.8(A)(1)

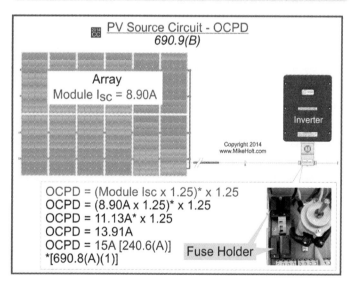

PV Source Circuit - OCPD
690.9(B)

Array
Module I_{SC} = 8.90A

Inverter

OCPD = (Module Isc x 1.25)* x 1.25
OCPD = (8.90A x 1.25)* x 1.25
OCPD = 11.13A* x 1.25
OCPD = 13.91A
OCPD = 15A [240.6(A)]
*[690.8(A)(1)]

Fuse Holder

Figure 690–51

Author's Comment:

- The PV source circuit OCPD isn't permitted to exceed the maximum overcurrent rating marked on the PV module nameplate [110.3(B)]. Figure 690–52

Inverter Output Circuit - OCPD
690.9(B)

OCPD = Inverter ac Output Current Rating x 1.25

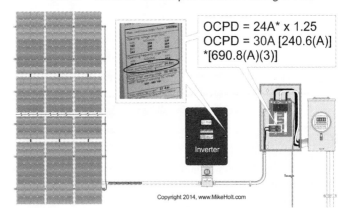

OCPD = 24A* x 1.25
OCPD = 30A [240.6(A)]
*[690.8(A)(3)]

Figure 690–53

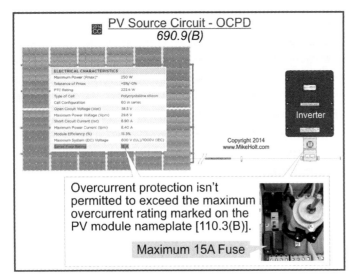

Figure 690–52

Inverter Output Circuit Overcurrent Protection Size

Example: *What size OCPD is required for an inverter output circuit having a maximum inverter continuous ac output nameplate current rating of 24A?* Figure 690–53

OCPD = Inverter ac Output Current Rating* × 1.25

OCPD = 24A × 1.25*
OCPD = 30A
OCPD = 30A circuit breaker [240.6(A)]
*690.8(A)(3)

Summary Circuit Sizing and Overcurrent Protection

Conductor Ampacity Before Correction and Adjustment: PV circuit conductors must have an ampacity of not less than 125 percent of 690.8(A) current before the application of conductor ampacity correction and adjustment [690.8(B)(1)].

Conductor Ampacity After Correction and Adjustment. Circuit conductors must have an ampacity of not less than 100% of 690.8(A) current after the application of conductor ampacity correction and adjustment [690.8(B)(2)].

Overcurrent Protection Sizing. Where conductor overcurrent protection is required [690.9], it must be sized no less than 125 percent of the maximum circuit currents in accordance with 690.8(A) [690.9(B)].

Conductor Overcurrent Protection. The overcurrent protection device must be sized to protect the conductor after the application of conductor ampacity correction and adjustment in accordance with 240.4.

PV Source Circuit

Example: *What's the PV source circuit conductor ampacity after temperature correction for two current-carrying size 14 RHH/RHW-2/USE-2 or PV wires rated 90°C in a raceway or cable on the roof, where the ambient temperature is 90°F with 60°F added in accordance with Table 310.15(B)(3)(c), supplying modules having a nameplate Isc rating of 8.90A?* Figure 690–54

> *Conductor Ampacity = Table 310.15(B)(16) Ampacity at 90°C Column x Temperature Correction*

Temperature Correction = 0.58, Table 310.15(B)(2)(a)
*   based on 150°F (ambient plus 60°F roof temperature*
*   adder)*
Conductor Ampacity = 25A [14 AWG at 90°C, Table
*   310.15(B)(16)] x 0.58*
Conductor Ampacity = 14.50A, which has sufficient
*   ampacity after correction and adjustment to supply*
*   the PV source circuit current of 11.30A (8.90A x 1.25)*
*   [690.8(A)(1)].*

> *OCPD = (Module Isc × 1.25)* × 1.25*

OCPD = (8.90A × 1.25)* × 1.25
OCPD = (11.30A)* × 1.25
OCPD = 13.91A
OCPD = 15A [240.6(A)], which will protect the 14.50A
*   conductors [240.4]*
*690.8(A)(1)

(C) Direct-Current Rating. Fuses or circuit breakers used for PV systems must be listed.

⚠️ **CAUTION:** *PV systems operating at 1,000V dc must use protection devices listed for 1,000V dc [110.3(B)].* Figure 690–55

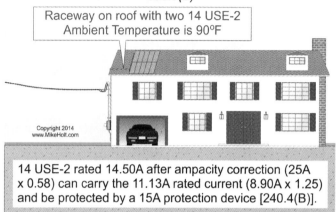

Circuit Sizing and Protection
PV Source Circuit
690.9(B)

Raceway on roof with two 14 USE-2
Ambient Temperature is 90°F

Copyright 2014
www.MikeHolt.com

14 USE-2 rated 14.50A after ampacity correction (25A x 0.58) can carry the 11.13A rated current (8.90A x 1.25) and be protected by a 15A protection device [240.4(B)].

Figure 690–54

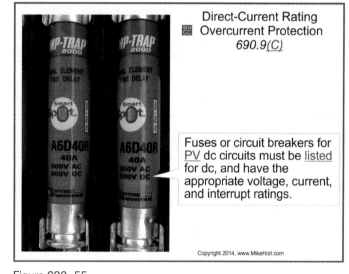

Direct-Current Rating
Overcurrent Protection
690.9(C)

Fuses or circuit breakers for PV dc circuits must be listed for dc, and have the appropriate voltage, current, and interrupt ratings.

Copyright 2014, www.MikeHolt.com

Figure 690–55

(D) PV Source and Output Circuits. Overcurrent protection devices for PV source and PV output circuits aren't required to be readily accessible, but they must be accessible. Figure 690–56

(E) Series Overcurrent Protection. Where overcurrent protection is required [690.9(A)] for a grounded PV source circuit, a single OCPD must be used to protect the PV modules and interconnecting conductors.

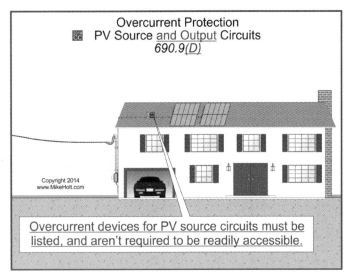

Figure 690–56

In ungrounded PV source circuits complying with 690.35, an overcurrent protection device, where required, must be installed in each ungrounded circuit conductor to protect the PV modules and interconnecting conductors.

690.10 Stand-Alone Systems

(A) Inverter Output. The ac current output from stand-alone inverter(s) must be no less than the rating of the largest single load connected to the system.

(B) Sizing and Protection. Inverter ac output circuit conductors must be sized to the output rating of the inverter and have overcurrent protection in accordance with Article 240. The inverter ac output circuit overcurrent protection device must be located at the output of the inverter.

(C) Single 120V Supply. The inverter output of a stand-alone PV system is permitted to supply a 120V single-phase, 3-wire, 120/240V distribution panelboard; however, 240V outlets or multiwire branch circuits aren't permitted. The stand-alone PV system equipment must be permanently marked with the following words or equivalent with a label that isn't handwritten and is of sufficient durability to withstand the environment involved [110.21(B)]:

WARNING—SINGLE 120-VOLT SUPPLY. DO NOT CONNECT MULTIWIRE BRANCH CIRCUITS!

(D) Energy Storage or Backup Power. Stand-alone PV systems aren't required to have energy storage power supplies.

(E) Backfed Circuit Breakers. Circuit breakers that are back-fed must be secured in place by a fastener that requires other than a pull to release the breaker from the panelboard, if they're fed from a stand-alone or multimode inverter output in a stand-alone system. Circuit breakers marked "line" and "load" aren't suitable for backfeed or reverse current. Figures 690–57 and 690–58

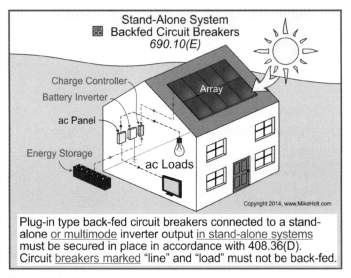

Figure 690–57

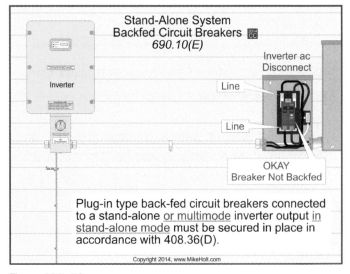

Figure 690–58

Author's Comment:

- The purpose of the breaker fastener is to prevent the circuit breaker from being accidentally removed from the panelboard while energized, thereby exposing persons to dangerous voltage.

2014 CHANGE ANALYSIS: The rules found in this section and in 705.12 seemed to contradict each other in the 2011 *NEC*. There was actually no contradiction, but the *Code* user really had to put their brains to work in order to realize it. Because the rule was so hard for many people to grasp, this change was made, which does make for a better *NEC*. When installed grid-direct (utility interactive, with no battery backup or bimodal), there's no need to secure a backfed breaker because, even when backfed, it isn't energized when it's disconnected from the utility power. Due to this, there's no hazard and therefore no reason to secure the breaker. Multimode inverters are now included in this section as well, due to the fact that the plug-in breaker could be removed and remain energized.

690.11 Arc-Fault Circuit Protection (Direct Current)

PV dc source and output circuits with a PV system voltage of 80V or greater must be protected by a listed PV dc arc-fault circuit interrupter (AFCI) that:

(1) Detects and interrupts arcing faults from a failure in the conductor, connection, module, or other dc system component.

(2) Disables the inverter and requires a manual restart process to resume system operation.

(3) Has visual indication that the AFCI has operated.

Author's Comment:

- The listing standard for certification of PV AFCI devices is UL Subject 1699B, *Photovoltaic (PV) DC Arc-Fault Circuit Protection,* which requires PV AFCI devices to behave according to the requirements of 2011 *NEC* Section 690.11. UL Subject 1699B stipulates that a PV AFCI device must detect an electric arc of 300W or more, and interrupt it within a maximum time period of two seconds.

2014 CHANGE ANALYSIS: The fact that an arcing fault can cause a fire doesn't change whether the fault is located indoors or outdoors. By removing the "on or penetrating buildings" portion of this rule, all dc conductors in a PV system that operate at over 80V must now be protected by an AFCI device that's listed for use on dc systems.

690.12 Rapid Shutdown of PV Systems on Buildings

 Scan this QR code for a video of this *Code* rule. See page xiii for information on how to use the QR codes.

PV dc circuits installed on or in buildings must include a rapid shutdown function as follows: Figure 690–59

(1) The rapid shutdown system only applies to PV dc conductors more than 5 ft in length inside of a building and PV dc conductors more than 10 ft from the array.

(2) The rapid shutdown system must reduce the PV dc circuit voltage and power to no more than 30V and 240VA as measured between any conductors and/or between any conductor and the equipment grounding conductor within 10 seconds of rapid shutdown initiation.

(3) Voltage and power must be measured between any two conductors and between any conductor and the metal parts of the system.

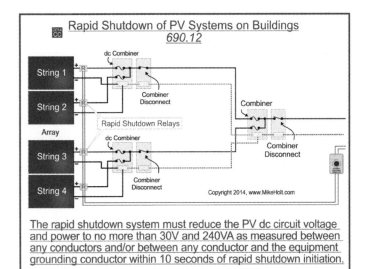

Rapid Shutdown of PV Systems on Buildings
690.12

The rapid shutdown system must reduce the PV dc circuit voltage and power to no more than 30V and 240VA as measured between any conductors and/or between any conductor and the equipment grounding conductor within 10 seconds of rapid shutdown initiation.

Figure 690–59

(4) The rapid shutdown equipment must be labeled in accordance with 690.56(B).

(5) The rapid shutdown equipment must be listed and identified for such use.

2014 CHANGE ANALYSIS: Among the many things that should cause alarm for a firefighter, a PV system has to be fairly high on the list. Because the only way to de-energize a PV system is to turn off the sun (or otherwise cover the modules), firefighters are at particular risk when dealing with these systems. Few will argue that nobody deserves to be forced to deal with energized components, especially in a high risk, high stress environment such as while fighting a structure fire. With these safety concerns in mind, this new requirement was added to the *Code* for one reason only: to decrease the risk to fire fighters. Some opponents of this change agreed with the idea of providing the increased safety, but wanted an effective date of three years in the future in order to allow manufacturers to come up to speed on the new requirement. Without the effective date, manufacturers will be scrambling to accommodate those areas that adopt the new *NEC* in 2014. Because the equipment is required to be listed, they will need to get to work on this immediately.

When a utility-interactive inverter is used, this rule is met simply by having the inverter within 10 ft of the array. Turning off the service disconnect also turns off the inverter, so nothing else is required.

Even though the location of the rapid shutdown equipment isn't addressed in the *Code*, considering the intent of this rule, it should probably be located near the service equipment.

Part III. Disconnecting Means

690.13 Building Supplied by a PV System

A dc disconnecting means for the PV system is required to open all ungrounded dc conductors. Figure 690–60

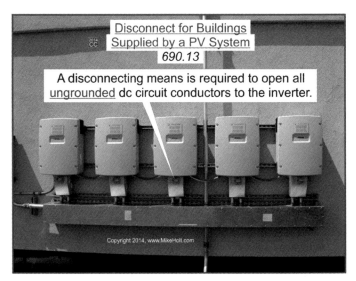

Figure 690–60

(A) Location. Each dc PV system building disconnect must be located at a readily accessible location either outside the building, or inside nearest the point of dc PV system conductor entry. Figure 690–61

Ex: Where the dc PV system building disconnect(s) isn't located at the point of entry, the dc PV conductors must be installed in a metal raceway, Type MC cable, or metal enclosure [690.31(G)]. Figure 690–62

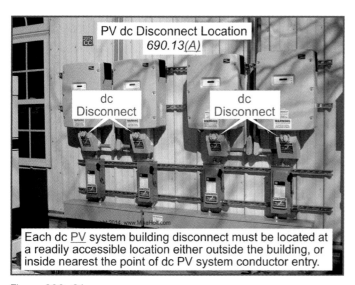

Figure 690–61

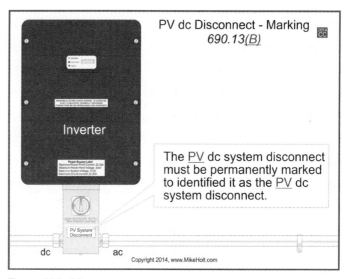

Figure 690–63

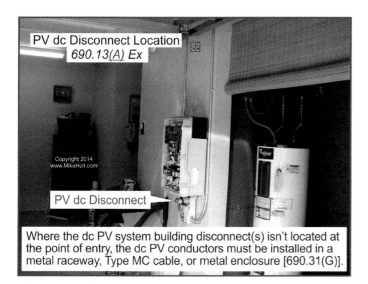

Figure 690–62

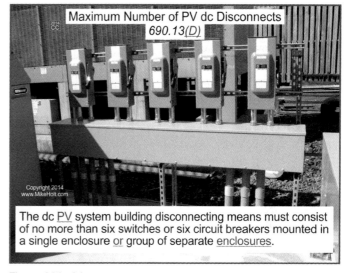

Figure 690–64

(B) Marking. Each dc PV system building disconnect must be permanently marked to identify it as the PV system disconnect. Figure 690–63

(C) Suitable for Use. The dc PV system building disconnect isn't required to be listed as suitable for use as service equipment.

(D) Maximum Number of Disconnects. The dc PV system building disconnecting means must consist of no more than six switches or six circuit breakers mounted in a single or group of separate enclosures. Figure 690–64

(E) Grouping. The dc PV system building disconnect(s) must be grouped together in accordance with 690.13(D). A PV dc disconnect isn't required at the array location, but they are permitted [690.15(B)]. Figure 690–65

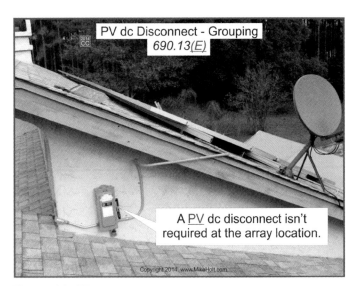

Figure 690–65

690.15 PV Equipment Disconnect

PV equipment such as inverters, batteries, and charge controllers must have a disconnecting means that opens all ungrounded circuit conductors from all sources of power. Figure 690–66

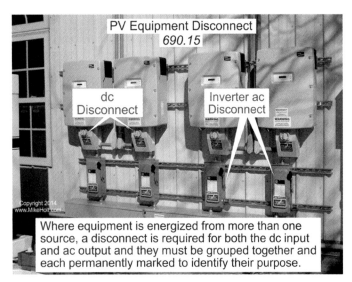

Figure 690–66

Where equipment is energized from more than one source, such as an inverter supplied by dc current input from the array and

ac current output to the utility source, a disconnecting means is required for both the dc input and ac output and they must be grouped and permanently marked and identified as to their purpose. Figure 690–67

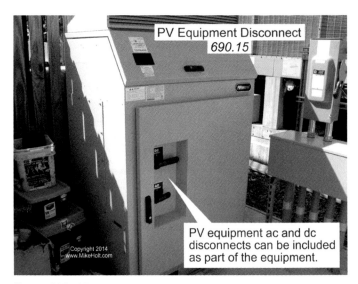

Figure 690–67

A single disconnecting means in accordance with 690.17 is permitted for the combined ac output of one or more inverters or ac modules in an interactive system.

(A) Utility Interactive Inverters Not Readily Accessible. Utility interactive inverters installed outdoors that aren't readily accessible must comply with the following:

(1) The inverter dc input circuit disconnect must be within sight of and not more than 50 ft away from the inverter.

(2) The inverter ac output circuit disconnect must be within sight of the inverter and not more than 50 ft away from the inverter.

(3) A disconnect for the inverter dc input circuit must be located either outside the building, or inside nearest the point of dc input circuit conductor entry at a readily accessible location [690.13(A)].

(4) A permanent directory must be installed denoting all electric power sources on or in the premises at service equipment and all inverter ac output circuit disconnect(s) in accordance with 705.10.

(B) Equipment. PV source circuit isolating switches, overcurrent protection devices, and dc combiners are permitted on the PV side of the PV system dc disconnect. Figure 690–68

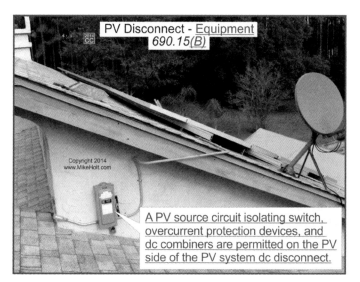

Figure 690–68

(C) DC Combiner Disconnect. DC combiners mounted on roofs must have a load break disconnecting means located in or within 6 ft of the dc combiner. Figures 690–69 and 690–70

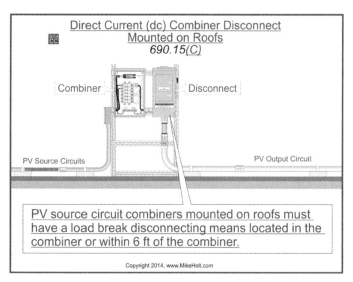

Figure 690–69

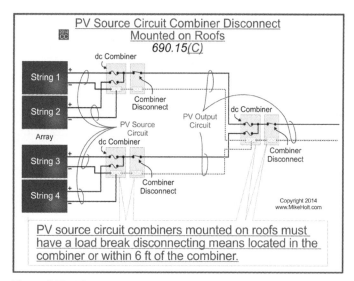

Figure 690–70

690.16 Disconnecting Means for Fuses

(A) Disconnecting Means. A means must be provided to disconnect each PV circuit fuse if energized from both directions. Figure 690–71

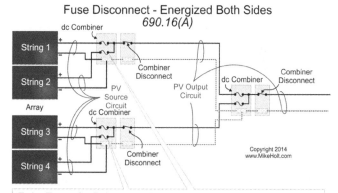

Figure 690–71

Fuses for PV source circuits must be capable of being disconnected independently of fuses in other PV source circuits. Figure 690–72

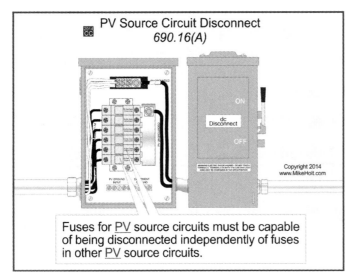

Figure 690–72

Author's Comment:

■ Tilt-out fuse holders meet the requirement for de-energizing the fuse as long as a load break switch is available at the PV source circuit combiner in accordance with 690.15(C).

(B) PV Output Circuit Fuse Disconnect. Where fuses for output circuits can't be isolated from energized circuits, a disconnect that complies with 690.17 must be located within sight of, or integral with, the PV output circuit fuse holder. Figure 690–73

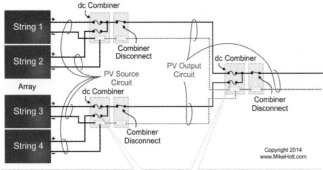

Where fuses for output circuit can't be isolated from energized circuits, a disconnect located within sight of or integral with the PV output circuit fuse holder must be installed.

Figure 690–73

Where the output circuit fuse disconnect is located more than 6 ft from the fuses, a directory showing the location of each PV output circuit fuse disconnect must be installed at the fuse location.

Non-load-break-rated fuse disconnecting means must be marked "Do not open under load." Figure 690–74

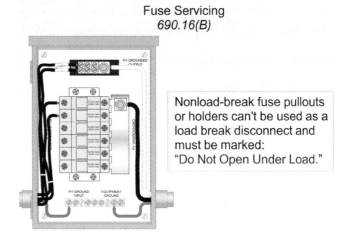

Nonload-break fuse pullouts or holders can't be used as a load break disconnect and must be marked: "Do Not Open Under Load."

Figure 690–74

690.17 Disconnect Type (dc)

(A) Manually Operable. The disconnecting means for ungrounded PV dc circuit conductors must be one of the following listed products: Figure 690–75

(1) A PV industrial control switch marked for use in PV systems

(2) A PV molded-case circuit breaker marked for use in PV systems

(3) A PV molded-case switch marked for use in PV systems

(4) A PV enclosed switch marked for use in PV systems

(5) A PV open-type switch marked for use in PV systems

(6) A dc-rated molded-case circuit breaker suitable for back-feed operation

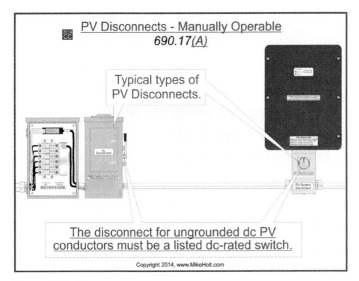

Figure 690–75

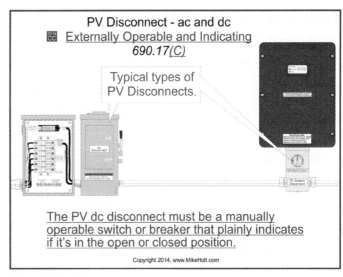

Figure 690–76

(7) A dc-rated, molded-case switch suitable for backfeed operation

(8) A dc-rated enclosed switch

(9) A dc-rated open-type switch

(10) A dc-rated low-voltage power circuit breaker

Note: Devices marked with "line" and "load" aren't suitable for backfeed or reverse current.

(B) Simultaneous Disconnect. The PV dc disconnect must simultaneously disconnect all ungrounded conductors within the circuit.

(C) Externally Operable and Indicating. The PV dc disconnect must be externally operable without exposing live parts and indicate whether in the open (off) or closed (on) position. Figure 690–76

(D) Disconnection of Grounded Conductor. The grounded PV dc conductor isn't permitted to be opened by a switch, circuit breaker, or other device if the operation of the device(s) leaves the marked, grounded conductor in an ungrounded and energized state.

Ex 2: The grounded PV dc conductor is permitted to be opened by a disconnect switch if it's: Figure 690–77

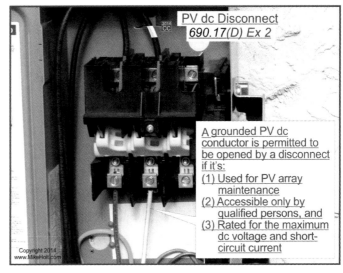

Figure 690–77

(1) Only used for array maintenance,

(2) Accessible only to qualified persons, and

(3) Rated for the maximum dc voltage and dc short-circuit current.

(E) Interrupting Rating. The PV system building dc disconnect must have an interrupting rating sufficient for the maximum circuit voltage and current that's available at the line terminals of the equipment.

Where line and load conductor terminals of the dc disconnect may be energized in the open (off) position, a permanently installed warning label that isn't handwritten, and is of sufficient durability to withstand the environment involved [110.21(B)] must be mounted on or adjacent to the dc disconnect with the following words or equivalent: Figure 690–78

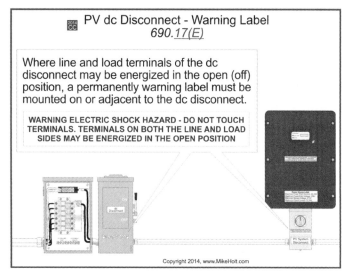

Figure 690–78

WARNING: ELECTRIC SHOCK HAZARD DO NOT TOUCH TERMINALS. TERMINALS ON BOTH THE LINE AND LOAD SIDES MAY BE ENERGIZED IN THE OPEN POSITION.

Ex: Plug connectors meeting the requirements of 690.33(C) can be used as the required ac and dc disconnect if listed and identified for this use. Figures 690–79 *and* 690–80

Author's Comment:

■ Micro-inverters, mini-inverters, and ac modules are the most common applications where plug connectors are used as the required disconnecting means for both dc and ac conductors.

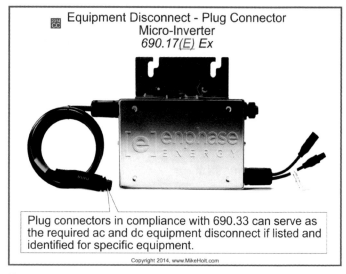

Figure 690–79

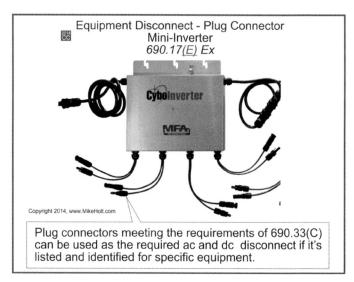

Figure 690–80

690.18 Installation and Service

Open circuiting, short circuiting, or opaque covering must be used to disable an array or portions of an array for installation and service. Figure 690–81

Note: The interconnecting cables for PV modules are energized whenever the module is exposed to light, including heavy overcast and rainy days! Figure 690–82

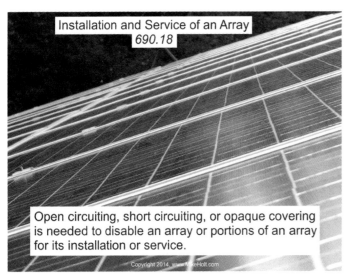

Figure 690–81

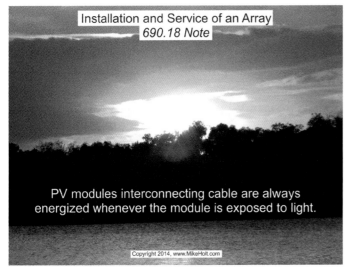

Figure 690–82

Author's Comment:

- Open-circuiting of modules is the most common method used to disable an array for installation and service.

Part IV. Wiring Methods

690.31 Wiring Methods

(A) Wiring Systems. Wiring methods permitted for PV systems include any Chapter 3 wiring method, wiring listed for PV use, and wiring that's part of a listed system. Figure 690–83

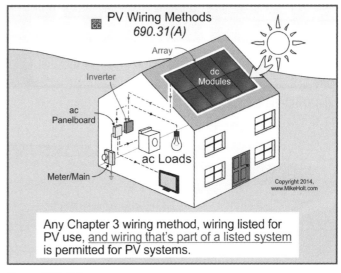

Figure 690–83

Author's Comment:

- Wiring that's part of a listed system includes the wiring harness of a micro- or mini-inverter.

Readily accessible exposed PV source or output circuit conductors operating at over 30V must be installed in a raceway or be guarded. Figure 690–84

Note: PV modules operate at elevated temperatures when exposed to high ambient temperatures and bright sunlight. Module interconnection conductors are available with insulation rated for wet locations and a temperature rating of 90°C or greater. Figure 690–85

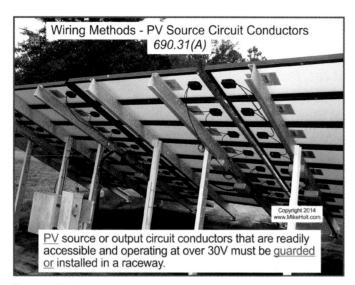

Figure 690–84

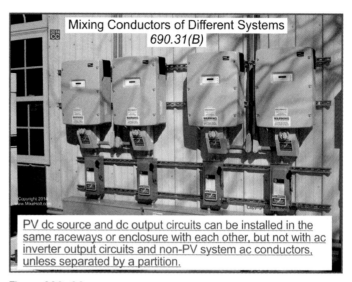

Figure 690–86

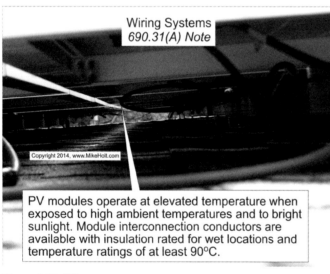

Figure 690–85

(B) Identification and Grouping. PV source and output circuits can be installed in the same raceways or enclosure with each other, but not with non-PV system conductors, unless separated by a partition. Figure 690–86

PV system conductors must be identified and grouped by color coding, marking, tagging, or other approved means as follows:

(1) PV Source Circuits. Identified at points of termination, connection, and splices.

(2) PV Output and Inverter Circuits. Identified at points of termination, connection, and splices.

(3) Conductors of Multiple Systems. Where the conductors of more than one PV system occupy the same junction box, raceway, or equipment, the conductors of each system must be identified at all termination, connection, and splice points. Figure 690–87

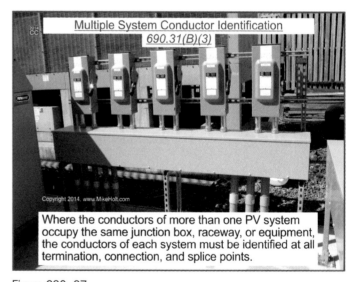

Figure 690–87

Ex: Identification of different systems isn't required where conductor identification is evident by spacing or arrangement.

(4) Grouping. Where the conductors of more than one PV system occupy the same junction box or raceway with a removable cover, the ac and dc conductors of each system must be grouped separately by cable ties, and then grouped at intervals not to exceed 6 ft. Figure 690–88

Figure 690–88

Ex: Grouping isn't required if the PV circuit enters from a cable or raceway unique to the circuit that makes the grouping obvious.

(C) Single-Conductor Cable.

(1) General. Single-conductor Type USE-2 or listed PV wire can be run exposed within the PV array where not readily accessible [690.31(A)].

Ex: Single-conductor PV circuits must be installed in a raceway when not guarded or readily accessible; see 690.31(A).

(2) Cable Tray. Single-conductor PV wire of any size can be installed in cable trays outdoors, provided the cables are supported at intervals not exceeding 12 in. and are secured at intervals not exceeding 4½ ft.

> **Note:** PV wire raceway fill is based on the actual area of the conductor (see manufacturer's specifications) in conjunction with Table 1 of Chapter 9, see 300.17.

2014 CHANGE ANALYSIS: There's a debate that occurs among *Code* users about the applicability of the 1/0 AWG rule in cable trays [392.10(B)] as it relates to PV systems. By adding this new language it's very clear these rules modify the general requirements of 392.10 by allowing any size of PV wire in a cable tray, provided that it meets the securing and supporting requirements. These securing and supporting requirements mirror those found in 320.30 and 334.30 for AC and NM cables, respectively.

(D) Multi-Conductor Cable. Type TC-ER or USE-2 can be used outdoors for PV inverter ac output circuits for a utility-interactive inverter that isn't readily accessible. The cable must be secured at intervals not exceeding 6 ft.

Author's Comment:

- TC-ER cable is tray cable (TC) that's listed for use in exposed runs (ER). The product standards require better crush and impact performance for a cable that contains the ER rating.

(E) Flexible Cords and Cables. Flexible cords used to connect the moving parts of tracking PV modules must be identified as a hard service cord or portable power cable suitable for extra-hard usage, listed for outdoor use, water resistant, sunlight resistant, and comply Article 400.

Author's Comment:

- According to note 9 of Table 400.4, a "W" in the suffix of the cord type indicates that the cord is suitable for use in wet locations, and is weather, sunlight, and water, and sunlight resistant.

(G) Circuits On or Inside Buildings. Where PV dc source and output conductors are run inside a building, they must be contained in a metal raceway, Type MC cable, or a metal enclosure, and must comply with (1) through (4). Figure 690–89

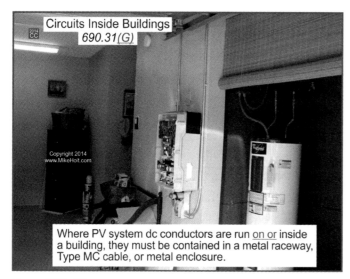

Figure 690–89

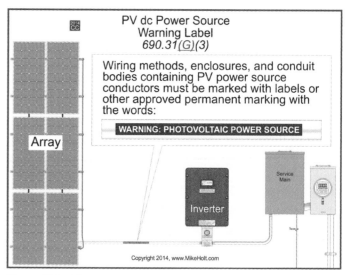

Figure 690–90

(1) Embedded in Building Surfaces. PV dc circuits embedded in built-up, laminate, or membrane roofing materials in roof areas that aren't covered by a PV module and associated equipment, must have the location be clearly marked in a manner that's suitable for continuous exposure to sunlight and weather.

(2) Flexible Wiring Methods. Flexible metal conduit smaller than trade size ¾ or Type MC Cable smaller than 1 in. in diameter containing PV dc circuit conductors installed across ceilings or floor joists must be protected by substantial guard strips that are at least as high as the wiring method.

Where flexible metal conduit smaller than trade size ¾ or Type MC cable smaller than 1 in. in diameter containing PV dc circuit conductors are run exposed, other than within 6 ft of their connection to equipment, the wiring methods must closely follow the building surface or be protected from physical damage by an approved means.

(3) PV dc Power Source Warning Label. Exposed wiring methods and enclosures containing PV dc power source conductors must be marked with labels or other approved permanent marking with the words: Figure 690–90

WARNING: PHOTOVOLTAIC POWER SOURCE

(4) Marking/Labeling Methods. The PV dc power source warning marking required by 690.31(G)(3) must be visible after installation and appear on every section of the wiring system separated by enclosures, walls, partitions, ceilings, or floors. The PV dc power source warning label must be reflective, having white text in capital letters not smaller than ⅜ in. on a red background. Spacing between PV dc power source labels must not be more than 10 ft, and labels must be suitable for the environment. Figures 690–91 and 690–92

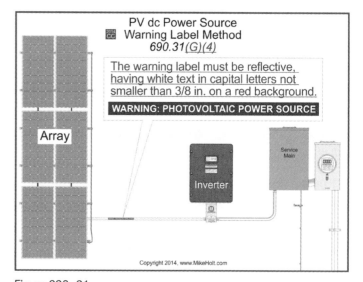

Figure 690–91

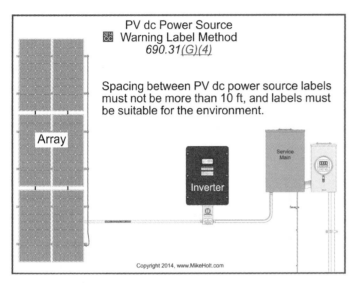

PV dc Power Source
CC Warning Label Method
690.31(G)(4)

Spacing between PV dc power source labels must not be more than 10 ft, and labels must be suitable for the environment.

Array

Inverter

Service Main

Copyright 2014, www.MikeHolt.com

Figure 690–92

(H) Flexible, Fine-Stranded Conductors. Flexible, fine-stranded conductors must terminate in terminals, lugs, devices, or connectors identified and listed for fine-stranded conductors in accordance with 110.14. Figure 690–93

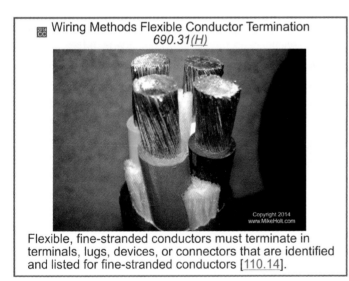

CC Wiring Methods Flexible Conductor Termination
690.31(H)

Copyright 2014
www.MikeHolt.com

Flexible, fine-stranded conductors must terminate in terminals, lugs, devices, or connectors that are identified and listed for fine-stranded conductors [110.14].

Figure 690–93

(I) Bipolar Photovoltaic Systems. Where the sum, without consideration of polarity, of the PV system voltages of the two monopole subarrays exceeds the rating of the conductors and connected equipment, monopole subarrays must be physically separated, and the electrical output circuits from each monopole subarray must be installed in separate raceways until connected to the inverter. The disconnecting means and overcurrent devices for each monopole subarray output must be in separate enclosures. Bipolar PV systems must be clearly marked with a permanent, legible warning notice indicating that the disconnection of the grounded conductor(s) may result in overvoltage on the equipment.

Ex: Listed switchgear for bipolar systems rated for the maximum voltage between circuits with a physical barrier separating the disconnecting means for each monopole subarray can be used instead of disconnecting means in separate enclosures.

(J) Module Connection Arrangement. The connection to a module must be arranged so that removal of a module from a PV source circuit doesn't interrupt a grounded conductor connection to other PV source circuits.

690.33 Connectors

The connectors permitted by Article 690 must comply with the following: Figure 690–94

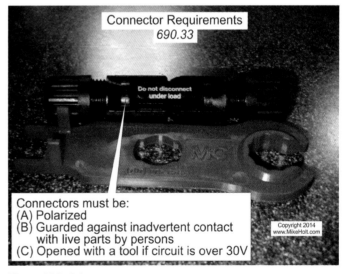

Connector Requirements
690.33

Do not disconnect
under load

Copyright 2014
www.MikeHolt.com

Connectors must be:
(A) Polarized
(B) Guarded against inadvertent contact with live parts by persons
(C) Opened with a tool if circuit is over 30V

Figure 690–94

(A) Configuration. Connectors must be polarized.

(B) Guarding. Connectors must be designed and installed so that they guard against inadvertent contact with live parts by persons.

(C) Type. Connectors for circuits operating at over 30V, nominal, must require a tool for opening.

(D) Grounding Member. The grounding member must be the first to make and the last to break contact with the mating connector.

(E) Interruption of Circuit. Connectors must be either: Figure 690–95

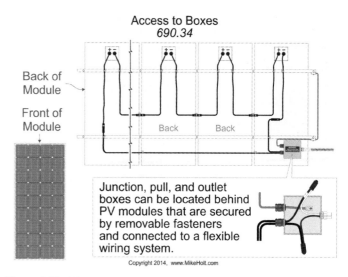

Access to Boxes
690.34

Figure 690–96

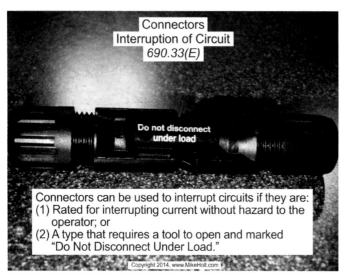

Figure 690–95

(1) Rated to interrupt current without hazard to the operator.

(2) Require a tool to open and be marked "Do Not Disconnect Under Load" or "Not for Current Interrupting."

690.34 Access to Boxes

Junction, pull, and outlet boxes can be located behind PV modules that are secured by removable fasteners and connected by a flexible wiring system. Figure 690–96

690.35 Ungrounded Systems

PV power systems are permitted to be ungrounded if:

(A) Disconnects. The PV source and output circuit conductors have a disconnecting means in accordance with Part III of Article 690.

(B) Overcurrent Protection. All ungrounded conductors have overcurrent protection in accordance with 690.9.

(C) Ground-Fault Protection. All PV source and output circuits are provided with a ground-fault protection device or system that:

(1) Detects ground fault(s) in the PV array dc current-carrying conductors and components

(2) Indicates a ground fault has occurred

(3) Automatically disconnects all conductors or causes the inverter or charge controller connected to the faulted circuit to automatically stop supplying power to output circuits

(4) Is listed for providing PV ground-fault protection.

(D) Conductors. PV source circuit conductors must be one or more of the following:

(1) Installed using metallic or nonmetallic jacketed multiconductor cables

(2) Installed in Raceways

(3) Listed and identified as PV Wire, or

(4) Direct-buried conductors identified for such use.

(F) Markings. The ungrounded PV system must have a permanently affixed warning label that isn't handwritten and is of sufficient durability to withstand the environment involved [110.21(B)] at every junction box and termination point stating:

WARNING—ELECTRIC SHOCK HAZARD.
THE DC CONDUCTORS OF THIS PHOTOVOLTAIC SYSTEM
ARE UNGROUNDED AND MAY BE ENERGIZED.

(G) Listed Equipment. Inverters or charge controllers for ungrounded PV systems must be listed for the purpose [690.4(B)].

Author's Comment:

■ Ungrounded systems are sometimes called "transformerless" or "non-isolating" inverters.

2014 CHANGE ANALYSIS: Item (D)(1) has been revised to allow for metallic jacketed cables, which makes sense as they're probably stronger than their non-metallic equivalents. In addition, item (4) has been added to allow for direct-buried conductors, as there's no real safety reason to prohibit them.

Like many other sections of the *Code*, this one was also revised to refer to the new requirements of 110.21(B), which provides rules for labels.

Part V. Grounding

690.41 System Grounding

PV systems must comply with one of the following:

(1) Ungrounded Systems. Circuit conductors for ungrounded systems aren't required to be grounded to the earth, but they must comply with the requirements of 690.35.

(2) Grounded 2-Wire System. Circuit conductors for grounded 2-wire dc PV systems must have one conductor grounded or impedance grounded to the earth and comply with 690.5. Figure 690–97

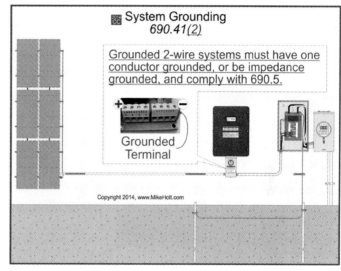

Figure 690–97

(3) Grounded 3-Wire System. Bipolar PV systems must have the reference (center tap) conductor grounded or impedance grounded and comply with 690.5.

2014 CHANGE ANALYSIS: At a glance, it appears that this section was simply formatted into a list instead of the (absurdly) long sentence that used to make up the entire section. While that's mainly true, there are a couple of technical changes, including the mention of impedance grounded systems, and removal of the 50V reference. With this change, systems that operate at less than 50V are now addressed.

690.42 Point of Grounding Connection

For grounded PV systems, the dc system grounding connection required by 690.41 is permitted to be made at any single point on the PV output circuit.

Ex: Systems with a 690.5 ground-fault protection device having the circuit grounding connection made by the inverter manufacturer. Figure 690–98

Circuit Conductor Grounding Point
690.42 Ex

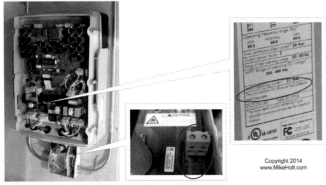

Systems with ground-fault protection have the grounding connection made by the inverter manufacturer.

Figure 690–98

Author's Comment:

- PV dc system grounding is most often established within the inverter by the inverter manufacturer, most frequently as part of a Ground-Fault Detection and Interruption GFDI system [690.5]. Typically it isn't necessary for field electricians to add a new dc system grounding bond, although the location and polarity of the dc system grounding bond should be verified.

690.43 Equipment Grounding (Bonding)

(A) Equipment Grounding (Bonding) Required. Exposed metal parts of PV module frames, electrical equipment, raceways, and enclosures must be connected to an equipment grounding conductor of a type permitted in 250.118 [250.134]. Figure 690–99

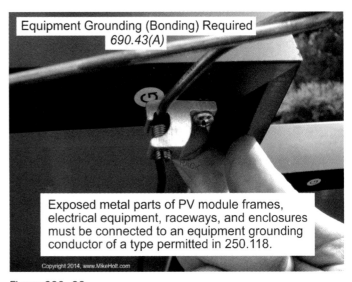

Equipment Grounding (Bonding) Required
690.43(A)

Exposed metal parts of PV module frames, electrical equipment, raceways, and enclosures must be connected to an equipment grounding conductor of a type permitted in 250.118.

Figure 690–99

(B) Equipment Grounding Conductor Required. An equipment grounding conductor is required between a PV array and metal parts of equipment.

(C) Structure as Equipment Grounding Conductor. Devices listed for grounding metallic frames of PV modules and associated equipment can be used to bond exposed metal surfaces of the modules and equipment to metal racks. Figure 690–100

Metallic mounting racks used as an equipment grounding conductor must have identified bonding jumpers or devices between the separate racks, and be connected to an equipment grounding conductor. Figure 690–101

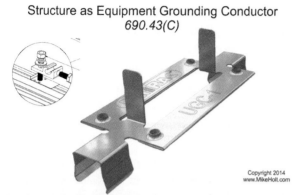

Structure as Equipment Grounding Conductor
690.43(C)

Devices listed and identified for grounding the metallic frames of PV modules and associated equipment can be used to bond the exposed metal surfaces of the modules and equipment to the metal racks.

Figure 690–100

Equipment Grounding
Securing Devices and Systems
690.43(D)

Devices and systems securing PV modules to metal mounting racks that serve as an equipment grounding conductor must be identified for the purpose.

Figure 690–102

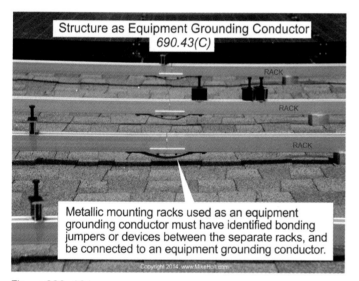

Structure as Equipment Grounding Conductor
690.43(C)

Metallic mounting racks used as an equipment grounding conductor must have identified bonding jumpers or devices between the separate racks, and be connected to an equipment grounding conductor.

Figure 690–101

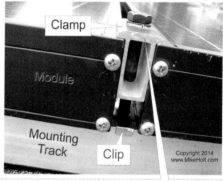

Equipment Grounding - Adjacent Modules
690.43(E)

Clamp
Module
Mounting Track
Clip

Devices identified and listed for bonding metallic frames of PV modules can be used to bond PV modules to the metallic frames of adjacent PV modules.

Figure 690–103

(D) Securing Devices and Systems. Devices and systems securing PV modules to metal mounting racks that serve as an equipment grounding conductor must be identified for such purposes. Figure 690–102

(E) Adjacent Modules. Devices identified and listed for bonding metallic frames of PV modules can be used to bond PV modules to adjacent PV modules. Figure 690–103

(F) Conductors Run Together. All conductors of the PV array, including the equipment grounding conductor, must be installed in the same raceway or cable or run with PV array circuit conductors when they leave the vicinity of the array. Figure 690–104

Conductors Run Together
690.43(F)

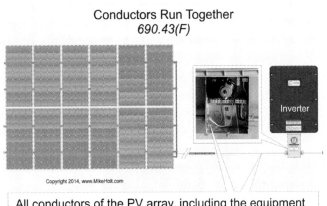

All conductors of the PV array, including the equipment grounding conductor, must be installed in the same raceway or cable or run with PV array circuit conductors when they leave the vicinity of the array.

Figure 690–104

690.45 Size of Equipment Grounding Conductors

For PV dc circuits with overcurrent protection, equipment grounding conductors of the wire type must be sized in accordance with 250.122, based on the rating of the circuit overcurrent device. Figure 690–105

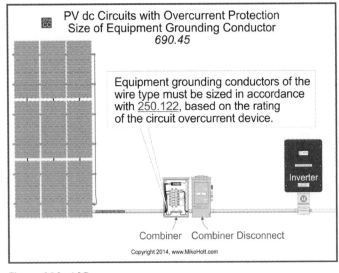

PV dc Circuits with Overcurrent Protection
Size of Equipment Grounding Conductor
690.45

Equipment grounding conductors of the wire type must be sized in accordance with 250.122, based on the rating of the circuit overcurrent device.

Combiner   Combiner Disconnect

Figure 690–105

For PV dc circuits without overcurrent protection [690.9 Ex], the equipment grounding conductors must be sized in accordance with Table 250.122 based on the rating of the PV circuit short-circuit current rating (Isc), times 125 percent, in accordance with 690.8(A). Figure 690–106

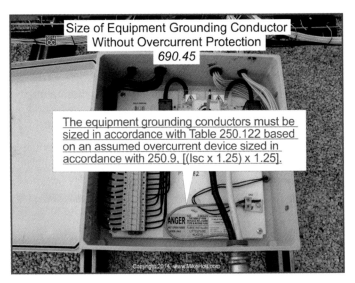

Size of Equipment Grounding Conductor
Without Overcurrent Protection
690.45

The equipment grounding conductors must be sized in accordance with Table 250.122 based on an assumed overcurrent device sized in accordance with 250.9, [(Isc x 1.25) x 1.25].

Figure 690–106

The equipment grounding conductor for dc PV circuits isn't required to be increased in size to accommodate voltage drop. Figure 690–107

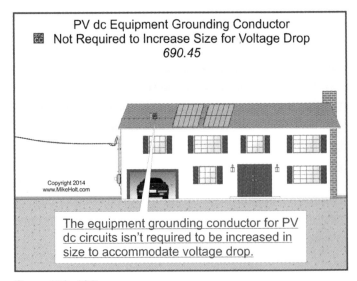

PV dc Equipment Grounding Conductor
Not Required to Increase Size for Voltage Drop
690.45

The equipment grounding conductor for PV dc circuits isn't required to be increased in size to accommodate voltage drop.

Figure 690–107

Table 250.122 Sizing Equipment Grounding Conductor	
Overcurrent Device Rating	Copper Conductor
15A	14 AWG
20A	12 AWG
25A—60A	10 AWG
70A—100A	8 AWG
110A—200A	6 AWG
225A—300A	4 AWG
350A—400A	3 AWG
450A—500A	2 AWG
600A	1 AWG
700A—800A	1/0 AWG
1,000A	2/0 AWG
1,200A	3/0 AWG

2014 CHANGE ANALYSIS: When *NEC* rules refer to other requirements of the *Code*, attention must be paid to whether just the table (Table 250.122) or the entire section (250.122) is referred to. In this instance, the rule refers to all of 250.122, not just the table. Due to this, 250.122(B) would apply, which mandates that the equipment grounding conductor be increased in size if the ungrounded conductors are increased in size. While that makes perfect sense in a traditional ac power system, it's indefensible in a PV system. Remember that we aren't trying to trip a 1,000A breaker here like we may be in an ac system.

690.46 Array Equipment Grounding Conductors

For PV modules, exposed equipment grounding conductors sized 8 AWG and smaller that are subject to physical damage must be installed in a raceway [250.120(C)]. Figure 690–108

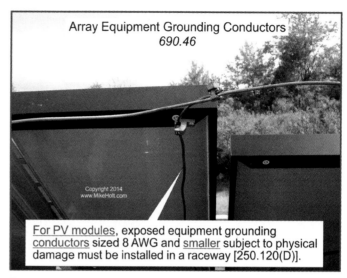

Array Equipment Grounding Conductors
690.46

For PV modules, exposed equipment grounding conductors sized 8 AWG and smaller subject to physical damage must be installed in a raceway [250.120(D)].

Figure 690–108

Equipment grounding conductors and grounding electrode conductors 6 AWG and smaller are permitted to be solid where installed in raceways.

690.47 Grounding Electrode System

 Scan this QR code for a video of this *Code* rule. See page xiii for information on how to use the QR codes.

(A) Alternating-Current PV System Grounding Requirements. For ac PV systems, a grounding electrode system must be provided in accordance with 250.50 through 250.60, with the ac grounding electrode conductor installed in accordance with 250.64. Figure 690–109

(B) Direct-Current PV System Grounding Requirements. For dc PV systems, a grounding electrode system in accordance with 250.166 for grounded systems, or 250.169 for ungrounded systems, must be provided. Figure 690–110

A common dc grounding-electrode conductor can service multiple inverters. Section 250.166 is used to size the common grounding electrode and the tap conductors. The tap conductors must be connected to the common grounding-electrode conductor by exothermic welding or with connectors listed as grounding and bonding equipment.

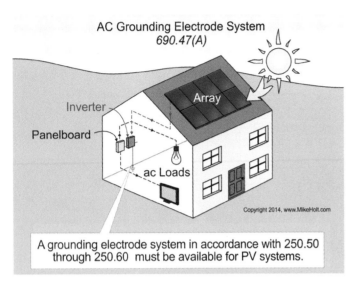

AC Grounding Electrode System
690.47(A)

A grounding electrode system in accordance with 250.50 through 250.60 must be available for PV systems.

Figure 690–109

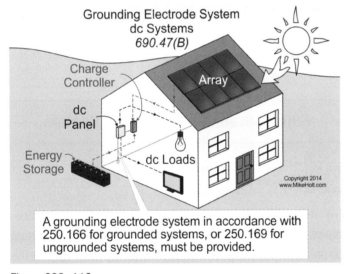

Grounding Electrode System
dc Systems
690.47(B)

A grounding electrode system in accordance with 250.166 for grounded systems, or 250.169 for ungrounded systems, must be provided.

Figure 690–110

The ac grounding electrode system can be used for equipment grounding of inverters and for the ground-fault detection reference for un-grounded PV systems.

(C) PV Grounded System with Alternating-Current Power System. Grounded PV systems constructed of dc modules must have the dc system grounded by one of the following methods:

(1) Separate dc Electrode. A grounding electrode conductor run from the marked dc GEC point at the inverter to the separate dc grounding electrode sized no smaller than the largest ungrounded dc conductor, but no smaller than 8 AWG

[250.166(B)]. The dc grounding electrode must be bonded to the ac grounding electrode with a bonding jumper sized to the larger of the dc grounding electrode conductor [250.166] or ac grounding electrode conductor [250.66]. Figure 690–111

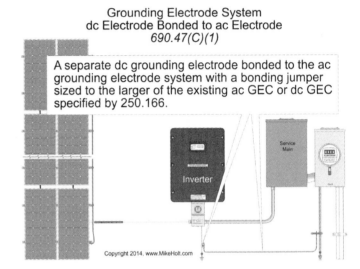

Grounding Electrode System
dc Electrode Bonded to ac Electrode
690.47(C)(1)

A separate dc grounding electrode bonded to the ac grounding electrode system with a bonding jumper sized to the larger of the existing ac GEC or dc GEC specified by 250.166.

Figure 690–111

(2) Alternating-Current Grounding Electrode. A grounding electrode conductor sized in accordance with 250.166 must be run from the marked dc GEC point at the inverter to the ac grounding electrode. Figure 690–112

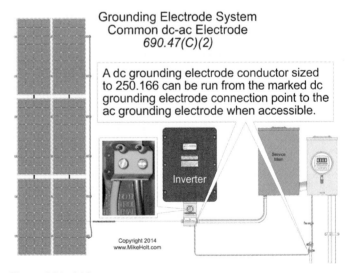

Grounding Electrode System
Common dc-ac Electrode
690.47(C)(2)

A dc grounding electrode conductor sized to 250.166 can be run from the marked dc grounding electrode connection point to the ac grounding electrode when accessible.

Figure 690–112

Where an ac grounding electrode isn't accessible, the dc grounding electrode conductor must terminate to the ac grounding electrode conductor with a connector listed as grounding and bonding equipment. Figure 690–113

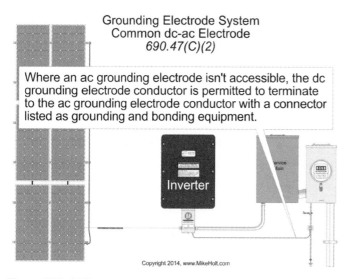

Grounding Electrode System
Common dc-ac Electrode
690.47(C)(2)

Where an ac grounding electrode isn't accessible, the dc grounding electrode conductor is permitted to terminate to the ac grounding electrode conductor with a connector listed as grounding and bonding equipment.

Figure 690–113

(3) Combination ac Equipment Grounding Conductor/dc Grounding Electrode Conductor. For grounded PV Systems, the ac equipment grounding conductor sized to the larger of 250.122 or 250.166 can serve as both the ac circuit equipment grounding conductor and dc grounding electrode conductor. Figure 690–114

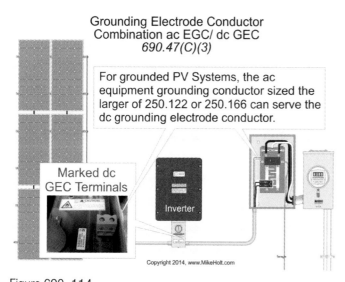

Grounding Electrode Conductor
Combination ac EGC/ dc GEC
690.47(C)(3)

For grounded PV Systems, the ac equipment grounding conductor sized the larger of 250.122 or 250.166 can serve the dc grounding electrode conductor.

Marked dc
GEC Terminals

Figure 690–114

Author's Comment:

- The ac equipment grounding conductor is sized in accordance with 250.122 based on the rating of the ac circuit overcurrent protection device; the dc grounding electrode conductor is sized no smaller than 8 AWG and no smaller than the dc circuit conductors [250.166(B)].

Question: What size EGC/GEC is required for a grounded PV system, where the inverter dc input circuit conductors are 14 AWG and the inverter ac output circuit conductors are 10 AWG protected by a 30A breaker? Figure 690–115

Answer: Table 250.122 requires the ac EGC to be sized no smaller than 10 AWG, and 250.166(B) requires the dc grounding electrode conductor to be no smaller than the largest dc circuit conductors, but no smaller than 8 AWG. In this case, the combined EGC/GEC must be no smaller than 8 AWG.

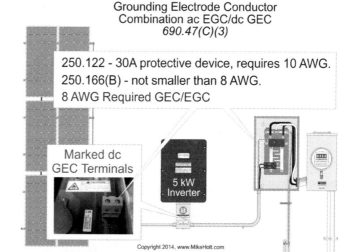

Grounding Electrode Conductor
Combination ac EGC/dc GEC
690.47(C)(3)

250.122 - 30A protective device, requires 10 AWG.
250.166(B) - not smaller than 8 AWG.
8 AWG Required GEC/EGC

Marked dc
GEC Terminals

5 kW
Inverter

Figure 690–115

For ungrounded systems, the ac equipment grounding conductor sized no smaller than required by 250.122 based on the rating of the ac circuit overcurrent protection device can serve as both the ac circuit equipment grounding conductor and dc grounding electrode conductor. Figure 690–116

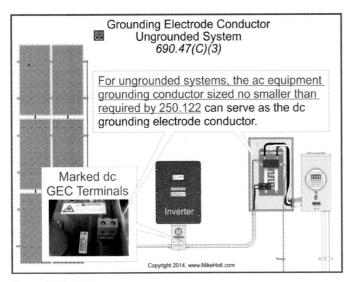

Figure 690–116

Ex No. 1: An array grounding electrode(s) isn't required where the load served by the array is integral with the array.

Ex No. 2: An additional array grounding electrode(s) isn't required if located within 6 ft of the premises wiring electrode.

Author's Comment:

■ Auxiliary electrodes have no *NEC* requirements since they serve no useful purpose relating to electrical safety, yet are permitted. If an auxiliary electrode is installed, it isn't required to be bonded to the building grounding electrode system, required to have the grounding conductor sized to 250.66, or to comply with the 25-ohm requirement of 250.53(A)(2) Ex [250.54].

⚠ **CAUTION:** *An auxiliary electrode typically serves no useful purpose, and in some cases it may actually cause equipment failures by providing a path for lightning to travel through electronic equipment.* Figure 690–118

(D) Auxiliary Electrode for Array. A dc grounding electrode conductor from the array structure sized in accordance with 250.166 must be connected to a grounding electrode that complies with 250.52 and 250.54.

The metal structure of a ground- or pole-mounted PV array can serve as the grounding electrode if it complies with 250.52.

Roof-mounted PV arrays can use the metal frame of a building or structure as the electrode if it meets 250.52(A)(2). Figure 690–117

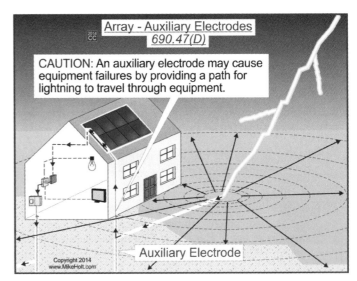

Figure 690–118

Figure 690–117

2014 CHANGE ANALYSIS: The requirements for grounding the PV array were included in the 2008 *Code*, but disappeared in the 2011 edition. Due to the fact that there was no technical substantiation in either the report on proposals or the report on comments to remove it from the 2011 edition, it was inserted back into the 2014 *Code* without substantiation.

690.48 Continuity of Equipment Grounding

Where the removal of equipment opens the grounding connection, a bonding jumper is required to maintain the connection while the equipment is removed.

690.49 Continuity of System Grounding

Where the removal of equipment opens the grounding electrode conductor connection required by 690.47, a bonding jumper is required to maintain the connection while the equipment is removed.

Part VI. Marking

690.53 PV dc Power Source Label

A permanent label must be applied at the PV dc disconnect indicating the: Figure 690–119

(1) Maximum rated power-point current (Imp x number of combined paralleled source circuits).*

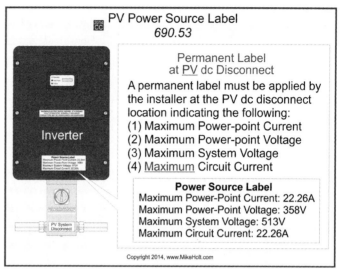

Figure 690–119

(2) Maximum rated power-point voltage (Vpm x number of modules in each source circuit).*

(3) Maximum rated system voltage (Voc).*

Note: See 690.7(A) on the calculations for maximum rated PV system voltage.

(4) Maximum rated circuit current (Isc* x 1.25).

Note: See 690.8(A)(1) for maximum rated circuit current calculation.

*The maximum rated power-point current (Imp), power-point voltage (Vpm), open circuit voltage (Voc), and short-circuit current (Isc) are contained in the manufacturer's specifications sheet for the modules used.

(5) Maximum rated output current of the charge controller (if installed)

PV dc Power Source Label

Example: *Determine the information needed for the PV dc power source label for an array that consists of two source circuits (strings) of ten 250W modules, each rated 8.40 Imp, 29.80 Vpm, 38.30 Voc (at -7°C), 8.90 Isc. The manufacturer's temperature coefficient is -0.36%/°C.*

(1) Maximum Power-Point Current (Imp), Information from manufacturer

Imp = Module Rated Imp × Number of Strings in Parallel

Imp = 8.40A × 2
Imp = 16.80A

(2) Maximum Power-Point Voltage (Vpm), Information from manufacturer

Vpm = Module Vpm × Number of Modules per String

Vpm = 29.8V × 12 = 358V

(3) Maximum System Voltage (Voc), Information from manufacturer

PV Voc = Rated Voc × {1 + [(Temp. °C - 25°C) × Module Coefficient %/°C]} × # Modules per Series String

Module Voc = 38.30 Voc × {1+ [(-7°C - 25°C) × -0.36%/°C]}
Module Voc = 38.30 Voc × {1 + [-32°C × -0.36%/°C]}
Module Voc = 38.30 Voc × {1 + 11.52%}
Module Voc = 38.30 Voc × 1.1152
Module Voc = 42.71V
PV Voltage = 42.71 x 12
PV Voltage = 513V

(4) Maximum Circuit Current (Isc x 1.25), 690.8(A)(1)

Isc = Module Isc × 1.25 × Number of Strings in Parallel

Isc = (8.90A × 1.25) × 2
Isc = 11.13A × 2
Isc = 22.26A

690.54 Interactive System

The point of connection of the PV system to other systems must be marked at an accessible location at the ac disconnecting means with the inverter ac output current and nominal ac voltage. Figure 690–120

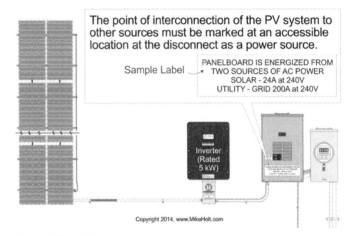

Interactive Point of Interconnection
690.54

The point of interconnection of the PV system to other sources must be marked at an accessible location at the disconnect as a power source.

Sample Label → PANELBOARD IS ENERGIZED FROM TWO SOURCES OF AC POWER
SOLAR - 24A at 240V
UTILITY - GRID 200A at 240V

Inverter (Rated 5 kW)

Copyright 2014, www.MikeHolt.com

Figure 690–120

690.55 PV Systems with Energy Storage

PV systems having energy storage must be marked with the maximum operating voltage, equalization voltage, and polarity of the grounded circuit conductor.

690.56 Identification of Power Sources

(A) Facilities with Stand-Alone Systems. Any building with a stand-alone PV system (not connected to a utility power source) must have a permanent plaque placed on the exterior of the building at a readily visible location that's acceptable to the authority having jurisdiction. The plaque must indicate the location of the stand-alone PV system disconnecting means and that the structure contains a stand-alone electrical power system. Figure 690–121

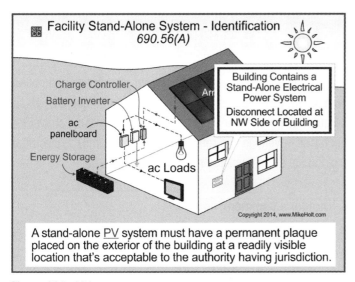

Figure 690–121

(B) Facilities with Utility Power and PV Systems. Buildings containing utility power and a PV system must have a plaque permanently affixed that isn't handwritten, and is of sufficient durability to withstand the environment involved [110.21(B)], placed at the service and PV system dc disconnecting means. The plaque must identify the location of the other system(s) if not located at the same location. Figure 690–122

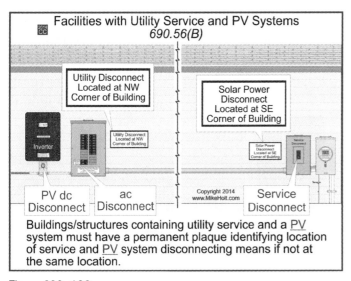

Figure 690–122

Authors' Comment:

- This requirement is better described in 705.10.

(C) Facilities with Rapid Shutdown. Buildings with both utility and PV systems with a rapid shutdown system [690.12] must have a permanent plaque with the words:

PHOTOVOLTAIC SYSTEM EQUIPPED
WITH RAPID SHUTDOWN

The plaque or directory must be reflective, be written with capital letters not less than ⅜ in. high, and be white with a red background. Figure 690–123

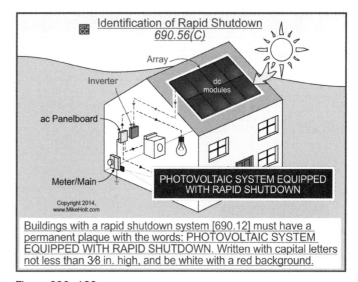

Figure 690–123

Author's Comment:

- While the *Code* doesn't specifically state where this label should be applied, the most sensible place to put it is at the service disconnect(s) for the building.

2014 CHANGE ANALYSIS: Every time I read Article 690, I find myself humming that old song by Five Man Electrical Band (signs, signs, everywhere signs…). Yes, there are a lot of signs required in this article, and at first glance this change seems like just another sign rule. When you stop and consider it, however, you might agree that this is an important sign. If you're a fire fighter responding to a building fire, and see PV modules on that building, you might be hesitant to proceed in the same manner as you would with a structure without those modules. Knowing that there's a mechanism in place that will make it safer for you to do your job is something you need to know.

Part VII. Connection to Other Sources

690.60 Interactive Systems

Only inverters and ac PV modules listed as interactive can be used with other power sources. Figure 690–124

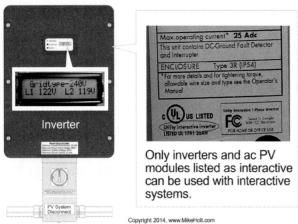

Identified Interactive Equipment
690.60

Only inverters and ac PV modules listed as interactive can be used with interactive systems.

Copyright 2014, www.MikeHolt.com

Figure 690–124

690.61 Loss of Interactive System Power

An inverter or an ac module connected to a building supplied with other power sources must automatically de-energize its ac output voltage and current to the connected electrical system upon loss of voltage and remain de-energized until the electrical distribution system voltage has been restored.

Author's Comment:

- This requirement is met if the inverter is listed as a utility-interactive inverter in accordance with UL Standard 1741—*Equipment for Use with Distributed Energy Resources.*

690.63 Unbalanced Interconnections

Unbalanced connections must be in accordance with 705.100.

690.64 Point of Connection

The output of a utility-interactive inverter must be connected to the premises wiring in accordance with 705.12. Figure 690–125

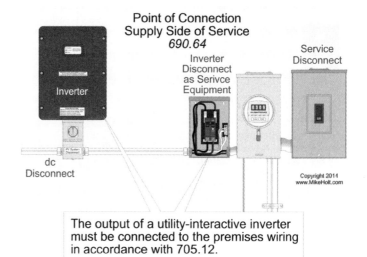

Point of Connection
Supply Side of Service
690.64

The output of a utility-interactive inverter must be connected to the premises wiring in accordance with 705.12.

Figure 690–125

Part VIII. Storage Batteries

690.71 Storage Battery Installation

(A) General. Batteries for PV systems must be installed in accordance with Article 480.

(B) Dwellings.

(1) Operating Voltage. For dwellings, battery cells must be series connected so as to operate at 50V, nominal or less.

(2) Guarding of Live Parts. Live parts of battery systems for dwellings must be guarded to prevent accidental contact by persons or objects regardless of voltage. Figure 690–126

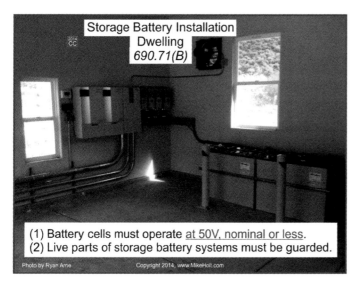

(1) Battery cells must operate at 50V, nominal or less.
(2) Live parts of storage battery systems must be guarded.

Figure 690–126

Note: Batteries require maintenance, such as checking electrolyte and cleaning connections.

(C) Current Limiting. Listed current-limiting overcurrent devices must be installed at the batteries where the available short-circuit current from a battery or battery bank exceeds the interrupting or withstand ratings of equipment it supplies.

(H) Disconnect and Overcurrent Protection. Where battery terminals are more than 5 ft from connected equipment, or conductors pass through a wall or partition, the installation must comply with the following: Figure 690–127

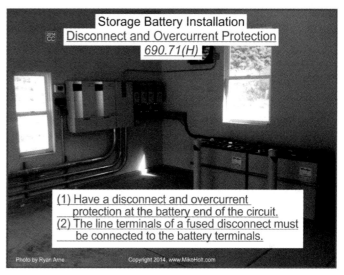

(1) Have a disconnect and overcurrent protection at the battery end of the circuit.
(2) The line terminals of a fused disconnect must be connected to the battery terminals.

Figure 690–127

(1) Disconnect and overcurrent protection must be provided at the battery end of the circuit.

(2) Where fused disconnecting means are used, the line terminals of the disconnecting means must be connected to the battery terminals.

(3) Overcurrent devices and disconnects aren't permitted in the battery enclosure.

(4) A second disconnect is required at connected equipment if the disconnect required by 690.71(H)(1) isn't within sight of connected equipment.

(5) Where the battery disconnect isn't within sight of the PV dc disconnecting means, a directory must be installed at the locations of all disconnecting means indicating the location of all disconnecting means.

690.72 Charge Control

(A) General. Charge control must be provided for a battery system unless the PV source circuit matches the voltage and charge current requirements of the interconnected battery cells.

690.74 Battery Interconnections

Connectors and terminals for conductors more finely stranded than Class B and Class C, as shown in Table 10 of Chapter 9, must be identified for the use of finely stranded conductors [110.14]. Figure 690–128

Finely Stranded Flexible Conductor Termination
690.74

Connectors and terminations for conductors more finely stranded than Class B and Class C stranding must be identified for the conductor class [Chapter 9, Table 10].

Figure 690–128

Part X. Electric Vehicle Charging

690.90 General

Photovoltaic systems used directly to charge electric vehicles shall comply with Article 625 in addition to the requirements of this article.

690.91 Charging Equipment

Electric vehicle couplers shall comply with 625.10. Personnel protection systems in accordance with 625.22 and automatic de-energization of cables in accordance with 625.19 aren't required for PV systems with maximum system voltages of less than 80V dc.

CHAPTER 6 PRACTICE QUESTIONS

Please use the 2014 *Code* book to answer the following questions.

Article 690. Solar Photovoltaic (PV) Systems

1. The provisions of Article 690 apply to _____ systems, including inverter(s), array circuit(s), and controller(s) for such systems.

    (a) solar photoconductive
    (b) solar PV
    (c) solar photogenic
    (d) solar photosynthesis

2. An alternating-current photovoltaic module is designed to generate ac power when exposed to _____.

    (a) electromagnetic induction
    (b) heat
    (c) sunlight
    (d) hysteresis

3. A mechanically integrated assembly of PV modules or panels with a support structure and foundation, tracker, and other components, as required, to form a dc power-producing unit, is known as a(n) _____.

    (a) pulse width modulator
    (b) array
    (c) capacitive supply bank
    (d) alternating-current photovoltaic module

4. _____ include photovoltaic cells, devices, modules, or modular materials that are integrated into the outer surface or structure of a building and serve as the outer protective surface of that building.

    (a) Protective photovoltaics
    (b) Building integrated photovoltaics
    (c) Bipolar photovoltaic arrays
    (d) Bipolar photoconductive arrays

5. For PV systems, a(n) _____ is a device that changes direct-current input to an alternating-current output.

    (a) diode
    (b) rectifier
    (c) transistor
    (d) inverter

6. The conductors between the inverter and the battery in a stand-alone system or the conductors between the inverter and the PV output circuits for an electrical production and distribution network are part of the _____.

    (a) branch circuit
    (b) feeder
    (c) inverter input circuit
    (d) inverter output circuit

7. For PV systems, the conductors between the inverter and an alternating-current panelboard for stand-alone systems, or the conductors between the inverter and the service equipment or another electric power production source, such as a utility, for an electrical production and distribution network, are part of the _____.

(a) bipolar photovoltaic array
(b) monopole subarray
(c) emergency standby power
(d) inverter output circuit

8. A(n) _____ is a complete, environmentally protected unit consisting of solar cells, and other components, exclusive of tracker, designed to generate direct-current power when exposed to sunlight.

(a) interface
(b) battery
(c) module
(d) cell bank

9. The circuit conductors between the inverter or direct-current utilization equipment and the PV source circuit(s) is part of the _____.

(a) photovoltaic output circuit
(b) photovoltaic input circuit
(c) inverter input circuit
(d) inverter output circuit

10. A single array or aggregate of arrays that generates direct-current power at system voltage and current is the photovoltaic _____.

(a) output source
(b) source circuit
(c) power source
(d) array source

11. For PV systems, the circuit(s) between modules and from modules to the common connection point(s) of the direct-current system is known as the _____.

(a) photovoltaic source circuit
(b) photovoltaic array circuit
(c) photovoltaic input circuit
(d) photovoltaic output circuit

12. The photovoltaic system voltage is the direct-current voltage of any PV source or PV output circuit.

(a) True
(b) False

13. The _____ is the basic PV device that generates electricity when exposed to light.

(a) solar battery
(b) solar cell
(c) solar atom
(d) solar ray

14. A stand-alone PV system supplies power in conjunction with and to supplement an electrical production and distribution network.

(a) True
(b) False

15. PV systems are permitted to supply a building or other structure in addition to any other _____ supply system(s).

(a) electrical
(b) telephone
(c) plumbing
(d) none of these

16. All equipment intended for use in PV power systems shall be _____ for the PV application.

(a) identified
(b) listed
(c) approved
(d) a and b

17. Where multiple utility-interactive inverters are remotely located from each other, a directory must be provided at each dc PV system disconnecting means, each ac disconnecting means, and at the main service disconnecting means showing the location of all ac and dc PV system disconnecting means in the building/structure.

    (a) True
    (b) False

18. Grounded dc PV arrays must be provided with direct-current _____ meeting the requirements of 690.5(a) through (c) to reduce fire hazards.

    (a) arc-fault protection
    (b) rectifier protection
    (c) ground-fault monitors
    (d) ground-fault protection

19. A warning label on the utility-interactive inverter or applied by the _____ must be on the PV utility-interactive inverter stating the following: WARNING ELECTRIC SHOCK HAZARD—IF A GROUND FAULT IS INDICATED, NORMALLY GROUNDED CONDUCTORS MAY BE UNGROUNDED AND ENERGIZED

    (a) homeowner
    (b) inspector
    (c) installer
    (d) power company

20. Article 690 requirements pertaining to dc PV source circuits do not apply to ac PV modules since ac PV modules have no dc output. The PV source circuit, conductors and inverters are considered as internal wiring of an ac module.

    (a) True
    (b) False

21. The output of an ac module is considered an _____ output circuit as defined in 690.2.

    (a) inverter
    (b) module
    (c) PV
    (d) subarray

22. The _____ of a dc PV source circuit or output circuit is used to calculate as the sum of the rated open-circuit voltage of the series-connected PV modules multiplied by the correction factor provided in Table 690.7.

    (a) minimum allowable ampacity of conductors
    (b) maximum allowable ampacity of conductors
    (c) minimum photovoltaic system voltage
    (d) maximum photovoltaic system voltage

23. For PV systems, one source for lowest-expected ambient temperature is the "Extreme Annual Mean Minimum Design Dry Bulb Temperature" found in the *ASHRAE Handbook Fundamentals*.

    (a) True
    (b) False

24. For one- and two-family dwellings, the maximum voltage for PV source or PV circuits is _____.

    (a) 24V
    (b) 48V
    (c) 250V
    (d) 600V

25. For PV systems, in one- and two-family dwellings, live parts over 150V to ground must not be accessible to an _____ while energized.

    (a) inspector
    (b) electrician
    (c) unqualified person
    (d) all of these

26. The PV source circuit current is calculated by multiplying the sum of the parallel module nameplate short-circuit current ratings (Isc) by 125 percent.

    (a) True
    (b) False

27. The PV output circuit current is equal to the sum of parallel PV source circuit maximum currents as calculated in _____.

    (a) 690.8(A)(1)
    (b) 690.8(A)(2)
    (c) 690.8(A)(3)
    (d) none of these

28. The maximum PV inverter output circuit current is equal to the _____ output current rating.

    (a) average
    (b) peak
    (c) continuous
    (d) intermittent

29. Currents of PV systems are to be considered _____.

    (a) safe
    (b) continuous
    (c) noncontinuous
    (d) inverted

30. Overcurrent devices for PV systems shall be rated to carry not less than _____ percent of the maximum currents calculated in 690.8(A).

    (a) 80
    (b) 100
    (c) 125
    (d) 250

31. Fuses or circuit breakers for PV dc circuits must be _____ for use in dc circuits and shall have the appropriate voltage, current, and interrupt ratings.

    (a) identified
    (b) approved
    (c) recognized
    (d) listed

32. Overcurrent devices for PV source circuits must be readily accessible.

    (a) True
    (b) False

33. In grounded PV source circuits, one overcurrent protection device is not permitted to protect the PV modules and the interconnecting conductors.

    (a) True
    (b) False

34. For stand-alone PV systems, the ac current output from a stand-alone inverter(s) can be _____ than the calculated load connected to the disconnect, but not less than the largest single utilization equipment connected to the system.

    (a) less
    (b) more
    (c) greater
    (d) any of these

35. For stand-alone PV systems, energy storage or backup power supplies are required.

    (a) True
    (b) False

36. Plug-in type backfed circuit breakers for a stand-alone or multimode inverter connected to a stand-alone PV system are not required to be secured in place by an additional fastener that requires other than a pull to release the breaker from the panelboard.

    (a) True
    (b) False

37. For stand-alone PV systems, circuit breakers that are marked "Line" and "Load" can be backfed.

    (a) True
    (b) False

38. A disconnecting means is required to open ungrounded dc circuit conductors of the PV system.

    (a) True
    (b) False

39. The ungrounded PV system dc disconnect must be placed at a readily accessible location _____ of a building or structure to disconnect the ungrounded PV system dc circuit conductors.

    (a) outside
    (b) inside, nearest the point of entrance
    (c) anywhere inside
    (d) a or b

40. The PV system disconnecting means must be _____ to identify it as a photovoltaic system disconnect.

    (a) listed
    (b) approved
    (c) permanently marked
    (d) temporarily marked

41. For PV systems, means must be provided to disconnect equipment, such as batteries, inverters, charge controllers, and the like, from all ungrounded conductors of all sources.

    (a) True
    (b) False

42. Disconnecting means must be provided to disconnect a fuse from all sources of supply if energized from both directions and shall be capable of being disconnected independently of fuses in other PV source circuits.

    (a) True
    (b) False

43. Disconnecting means must be installed for PV output circuits where fuses that must be serviced can't be isolated from energized circuits. The disconnect must be within sight and accessible to the fuse or integral with the fuse holder, be externally operable without exposing the operator to contact with live parts, and plainly indicating whether in the open or closed position [690.17(C)]. Where the disconnecting means is located more than _____ ft from the fuse, a directory showing the location of each fuse disconnect must be installed at the fuse location.

    (a) 3
    (b) 6
    (c) 10
    (d) 12

44. Non-load-break-rated disconnecting means for PV output circuits must be marked "Do not open under load."

    (a) True
    (b) False

45. The PV disconnecting means shall be externally operable without exposing the operator to contact with live parts and shall indicate whether in the open or closed position.

    (a) True
    (b) False

46. A disconnecting switch is permitted to open the grounded dc conductor of a PV system when the switch is _____.

    (a) used only for PV array maintenance
    (b) accessible only by qualified persons
    (c) rated for the maximum dc voltage and current, including ground-fault conditions
    (d) all of these

47. For PV systems, where all terminals of a disconnecting means may be energized when the switch is in the open position, a warning sign must be placed on or adjacent to the disconnecting means. The sign shall be similar to: WARNING ELECTRIC SHOCK HAZARD. DO NOT TOUCH TERMINALS. TERMINALS ON BOTH THE LINE AND LOAD SIDES MAY BE ENERGIZED IN THE OPEN POSITION.

    (a) True
    (b) False

48. _____ must be used to disable a PV array or portions of an array for installation and service.

    (a) Open circuiting
    (b) Short circuiting
    (c) Opaque covering
    (d) any of these

49. All raceway and cable wiring methods included in this *Code*, other wiring systems and fittings specifically listed for use on PV arrays, and wiring as part of a listed system shall be permitted.

    (a) True
    (b) False

50. Where PV source and output circuits operating at greater than _____ are installed in a(n) _____ location, the circuit conductors must be guarded or installed in a Chapter 3 wiring method.

    (a) 30V, accessible
    (b) 30V, readily accessible
    (c) 60V, accessible
    (d) 60V, readily accessible

51. PV source circuits and PV output circuits are not permitted to be contained in the same raceway, cable tray, cable, outlet box, junction box, or similar fitting, with non-PV systems unless the two systems are separated by a partition.

    (a) True
    (b) False

52. PV system conductors shall be identified by separate color coding, marking tape, tagging, or other approved means.

    (a) True
    (b) False

53. PV source circuits shall be identified at all points of termination, connection, and splices.

    (a) True
    (b) False

54. The conductors of PV output circuits and inverter input and output circuits shall be identified at all points of termination, connection, and splices.

    (a) True
    (b) False

55. Where the conductors of more than one PV system occupy the same junction box, raceway, or equipment, the conductors of each system shall be identified at all termination, connection, and splice points.

    (a) True
    (b) False

56. Where the conductors of more than one PV system occupy the same junction box or raceway with removable cover(s), the ac and dc conductors of each system shall be grouped separately by cable ties or similar means at least once, and then shall be grouped at intervals not to exceed _____.

    (a) 6 in.
    (b) 12 in.
    (c) 36 in.
    (d) 6 ft

57. The requirement for grouping PV source and output circuits is not required if the circuit enters from a cable or raceway unique to the circuit that makes the grouping obvious.

    (a) True
    (b) False

58. Single-conductor Type USE-2 and single conductor cable _____ as PV wire can be run exposed at outdoor locations for PV source circuits for PV module interconnections within the PV array.

    (a) approved
    (b) listed or labeled
    (c) listed and labeled
    (d) none of the above

59. Where the source circuit operates at over 30V, single-conductor Type USE-2 or listed and labeled PV wires installed in a readily accessible location must be installed in a raceway

    (a) True
    (b) False

60. Where dc PV source or output circuits are run inside a building or structure, they must be contained in _____.

    (a) metal raceways
    (b) Type MC cables
    (c) metal enclosures
    (d) any of these

61. The location of PV source and output conductors embedded in built-up, laminate, or membrane roofing materials in areas not covered by PV modules and associated equipment must be clearly marked.

    (a) True
    (b) False

62. Labels or markings of PV system raceways and enclosures must be suitable for the environment and be placed with a maximum of _____ ft of spacing.

    (a) 5
    (b) 10
    (c) 20
    (d) 25

63. Photovoltaic wiring methods containing _____ must be terminated only with terminals, lugs, devices, or connectors that are identified and listed for such use.

    (a) flexible, fine-stranded cables
    (b) solid conductors
    (c) flexible raceways
    (d) all of these

64. Monopole subarrays in a bipolar PV system shall be physically _____ where the sum of the PV system voltages, without consideration of polarity, of the two monopole subarrays exceeds the rating of the conductors and connected equipment.

    (a) separated
    (b) connected
    (c) joined
    (d) together

65. The connection to a _____ shall be arranged so that removal of either from a PV source circuit does not interrupt a grounded conductor connection to other PV source circuits.

    (a) panelboard or switchboard
    (b) bus or lug
    (c) module or panel
    (d) array or subarray

66. The connectors permitted by Article 690 shall _____.

    (a) be polarized
    (b) guard against inadvertent contact with live parts by persons
    (c) require a tool for opening if the circuit operates at over 30V nominal maximum dc or 30V ac
    (d) all of these

67. Junction, pull, and outlet boxes can be located behind PV modules that are secured by removable fasteners.

    (a) True
    (b) False

68. A grounded ____-wire PV system must have one conductor grounded or be impedance grounded, and comply with 690.5.

    (a) 2
    (b) 3
    (c) 4
    (d) any of these

69. The direct-current system grounding connection must be made at any ____ point(s) on the PV output circuit.

    (a) single
    (b) two
    (c) three
    (d) four

70. A(n) ____ must be installed between a photovoltaic array and other equipment.

    (a) grounded conductor
    (b) main bonding jumper
    (c) equipment grounding conductor
    (d) system bonding jumper

71. Devices ____ for grounding the metallic frames of PV modules and other equipment can be used to bond the exposed metal surfaces of the modules and equipment to the mounting structures.

    (a) identified
    (b) approved
    (c) listed
    (d) a and c

72. For PV systems, metallic mounting structures used for grounding purposes must be ____ as equipment grounding conductors or have ____ bonding jumpers or devices connected between the separate metallic sections and be bonded to the grounding system.

    (a) listed/labeled
    (b) labeled/listed
    (c) identified/Identified
    (d) a and b

73. Devices and systems used for mounting PV modules that also provide grounding of the module frames must be ____ for the purpose of grounding PV modules.

    (a) listed
    (b) labeled
    (c) identified
    (d) a and b

74. Devices ____ for bonding the metallic frames of PV modules shall be permitted to bond the exposed metallic frames of PV modules to the metallic frames of adjacent PV modules.

    (a) listed/labeled
    (b) labeled/listed
    (c) identified/identified
    (d) a and c

75. All conductors of a circuit, including the equipment grounding conductor, must be installed in the same raceway or cable, or otherwise run with the PV array circuit conductors when they leave the vicinity of the PV array.

    (a) True
    (b) False

76. Equipment grounding conductors for PV circuits having overcurrent protection must be sized in accordance with ____.

    (a) 250.122
    (b) 250.66
    (c) Table 250.122
    (d) Table 250.66

77. Where no overcurrent protection is provided for the PV circuit, an assumed overcurrent device rated at the PV maximum circuit current must be used to size the equipment grounding conductor in accordance with ____.

    (a) 250.122
    (b) 250.66
    (c) Table 250.122
    (d) Table 250.66

78. Where exposed and subject to physical damage, PV array equipment grounding conductors smaller than 4 AWG must be protected by raceway or cable armor.

    (a) True
    (b) False

79. A common dc grounding electrode conductor of a PV system is permitted to serve multiple inverters with the size of the common grounding electrode and the tap conductors in accordance with 250.166. The tap conductors must be connected to the common grounding electrode conductor in such a manner that the common grounding electrode conductor remains _____.

    (a) without a splice or joint
    (b) inside inverter enclosures
    (c) inside a raceway
    (d) supported on insulators

80. PV systems having no direct connection between the dc grounded conductor and ac grounded conductor shall have a(n) _____ grounding system which shall be bonded to the ac grounding system.

    (a) ac
    (b) dc
    (c) separately derived
    (d) none of these

81. PV systems with dc modules having no direct connection between the dc grounded conductor and ac grounded conductor must be bonded to the ac grounding system by a(n) _____.

    (a) separate dc grounding electrode bonded to the ac grounding electrode system with a bonding jumper
    (b) dc grounding electrode conductor sized to 250.166 run from the marked dc grounding electrode connection point to the ac grounding electrode
    (c) unspliced, or irreversibly spliced, combined grounding conductor run from the marked dc grounding electrode connection point along with the ac circuit conductors to the grounding busbar in the associated ac equipment
    (d) any of these

82. Where the removal of equipment opens the bonding connection between the _____ and exposed conducting surfaces in the PV source or output circuit equipment, a bonding jumper shall be installed while the equipment is removed.

    (a) equipment grounding conductor
    (b) grounded conductor
    (c) grounding electrode conductor
    (d) ungrounded conductor

83. Where the removal of the utility-interactive inverter or other equipment disconnects the bonding connection between the grounding electrode conductor and the PV source and/or PV output circuit grounded conductor, a _____ shall be installed to maintain the system grounding while the inverter or other equipment is removed.

    (a) grounding electrode conductor
    (b) fuse
    (c) bonding jumper
    (d) overcurrent device

84. A permanent label must be applied by the installer at the PV dc power source disconnect indicating the _____.

    (a) rated maximum power-point current and voltage
    (b) maximum system voltage and circuit current
    (c) maximum rated output current of the charge controller (if installed)
    (d) all of these

85. The point of interconnection of the PV system power source to other sources must be marked at an accessible location at the _____ as a power source and with the rated ac output current and nominal operating ac voltage.

    (a) disconnecting means
    (b) array
    (c) inverter
    (d) none of the above

86. Any building or structure with a stand-alone PV system (not connected to a utility service source) must have a permanent _____ installed on the exterior of the building or structure at a readily visible location acceptable to the authority having jurisdiction. The _____ must indicate the location of the stand-alone PV system disconnecting means and that the structure contains a stand-alone electrical power system.

    (a) plaque
    (b) directory
    (c) a and b
    (d) a or b

87. Buildings/structures containing both utility service and a PV system must have a permanent _____ placed at the service disconnecting means and the PV system disconnecting means identifying the location of the other system if they are not located at the same location.

    (a) plaque
    (b) directory
    (c) a and b
    (d) a or b

88. Only inverters and ac PV modules listed and identified as interactive can be used with interactive systems.

    (a) True
    (b) False

89. An inverter or an ac module in an interactive PV system must automatically de-energize its output to the connected electrical distribution system upon _____ of voltage and remain de-energized until the electrical distribution system voltage has been restored.

    (a) surge
    (b) spike
    (c) loss
    (d) unbalance

90. In dwellings, battery cells for PV systems must be connected so as to operate at _____, nominal, or less.

    (a) 20V
    (b) 30V
    (c) 40V
    (d) 50V

91. Live parts of PV storage battery systems for dwellings shall be _____ to prevent accidental contact by persons or objects regardless of voltage.

    (a) isolated
    (b) grounded
    (c) insulated
    (d) guarded

92. For PV systems, a listed current-limiting overcurrent device must be installed where the available short-circuit current from the battery bank exceeds the interrupting or _____ ratings of equipment it supplies.

    (a) short-circuit
    (b) withstand
    (c) ground-fault current
    (d) none of these

93. For PV systems, where used for battery interconnections, flexible cables listed for hard-service use and identified as moisture resistant in Article 400, must be a minimum size of _____ AWG.

    (a) 1/0
    (b) 2/0
    (c) 3/0
    (d) 4/0

94. For PV systems, where flexible cables are installed, they are only permitted between the battery terminals to a nearby junction box where they must connect to an approved wiring method, or between batteries and cells within the battery enclosure.

    (a) True
    (b) False

95. For PV systems, where used for battery interconnections, flexible, fine-stranded cables must terminate in terminals, lugs, devices, or connectors that are _____ for fine-stranded conductors.

    (a) identified
    (b) listed
    (c) a or b
    (d) a and b

Mike Holt's Illustrated Guide to Understanding NEC Requirements for Solar Photovoltaic Systems

SPECIAL CONDITIONS

Introduction to Chapter 7—Special Conditions

Chapter 7, which covers special conditions, is the third of the *NEC* chapters that deal with special topics. Remember, the first four chapters of the *NEC* are sequential and form a foundation for each of the subsequent three chapters. What exactly is a "Special Condition?" It's a situation that doesn't fall under the category of special occupancies or special equipment, but creates a need for additional measures to ensure the "safe-guarding of people and property" mission of the *NEC*, as stated in 90.1(A).

The *Code* groups these logically, as you might expect. Here are the general groupings:

- Backup power systems—Articles 700, 701, and 702. Article 700 addresses emergency systems, Article 701 applies to legally required standby systems, and Article 702 covers optional standby systems.
- Interconnected power sources—Article 705. Primarily used for PV and wind generators systems.
- Low-voltage, limited energy systems—Articles 725 through 770. Examples include control, signaling, instrumentation, fire alarm systems, and optical fiber installations.

This textbook, with its focus on PV systems, only covers Article 705.

- **Article 705-Interconnected Electric Power Production Sources.** Article 705 relates to power sources that operate in parallel with a primary source. Typically, a primary source is the utility supply, but it can be an on-site source instead. For instance, in addition to the requirements of Article 690, provisions of this article apply to solar photovoltaic systems that also use another source of energy, such as the electric utility.

Notes

Mike Holt's Illustrated Guide to Understanding NEC Requirements for Solar Photovoltaic Systems

ARTICLE 705

INTERCONNECTED ELECTRIC POWER PRODUCTION SOURCES

Introduction to Article 705—Interconnected Electric Power Production Sources

Anytime there's more than one source of power production at the same building or structure, safety issues arise. In cases where a power production source such as a generator is used strictly for backup power, the *NEC* requires transfer switches and other safety considerations as covered in Articles 700, 701, or 702 depending on whether the backup power is an emergency system, or a legally required or optional standby system. When interactive electrical power production sources, such as wind powered generators, solar PV systems, or fuel cells are present, there usually isn't a transfer switch. In fact, it can be expected that there'll be more than one source of electrical supply connected simultaneously. This can raise many questions regarding how to maintain a satisfactory level of safety when more than one power source is present.

Article 705 answers these and other questions related to power sources that operate in parallel with a primary source. Typically, a primary source is the utility supply, but it can be an on-site source instead.

Part I. General

705.1 Scope

Article 705 covers the installation of electric power production sources such as Solar PV systems, wind powered generators, micro-hydro generators, or fuel cells that operate in parallel with a primary source of electricity (such as an electric utility). Figure 705–1

Note: Primary sources of electricity include a utility supply.

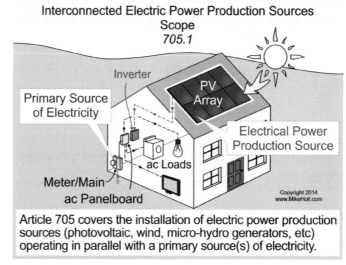

Interconnected Electric Power Production Sources
Scope
705.1

Article 705 covers the installation of electric power production sources (photovoltaic, wind, micro-hydro generators, etc) operating in parallel with a primary source(s) of electricity.

Figure 705–1

705.2 Definitions

Power Production Equipment. The generating source, and all associated distribution equipment, that generates electricity from a source other than a utility supplied service. Figure 705–2

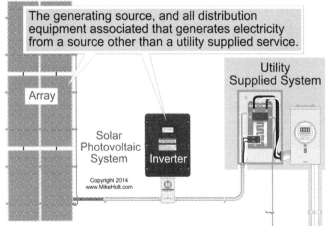

Figure 705–2

Author's Comment:

■ For this textbook, the power production equipment is a Solar PV system. The "other" source is the electric utility.

705.6 Qualified Persons

The installation of PV systems operating in parallel with an electric utility must be installed by a qualified person. Figure 705–3

Note: A qualified person has the knowledge related to construction and operation of PV equipment and installations; along with safety training to recognize and avoid hazards to persons and property [Article 100].

PV systems operating in parallel with a primary source(s) of electricity must be installed only by qualified persons.

Figure 705–3

705.10 Directory of Power Sources

A directory is required at each dc PV system disconnecting means, ac disconnecting means for mini- and micro-inverters, and service disconnecting means showing the location of all dc and ac PV system disconnecting means in the building/structure. Figure 705–4

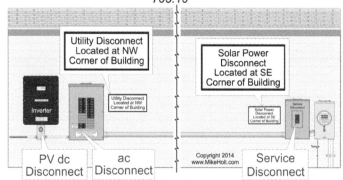

Buildings/structures containing utility service and a PV system must have a permanent plaque identifying location of service and PV system disconnecting means if not at the same location.

Figure 705–4

705.12 Point of Connection

 Scan this QR code for a video of this *Code* rule. See page xxiii for information on how to use the QR codes.

(A) Supply Side. The PV system can be connected to the supply side of the service disconnecting means in accordance with 230.82(6). Figure 705–5

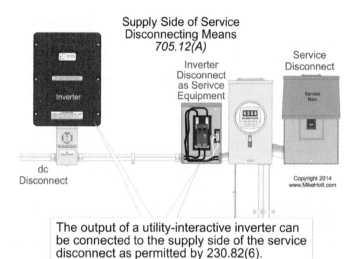

Supply Side of Service Disconnecting Means
705.12(A)

The output of a utility-interactive inverter can be connected to the supply side of the service disconnect as permitted by 230.82(6).

Figure 705–5

Where the PV system is connected to the supply side of the service disconnecting means, the sum of the ratings of the inverter ac inverter overcurrent protection device(s) must not exceed the rating of the utility service. Figure 705–6

Author's Comment:

■ When determining the number of disconnects per service in accordance with 230.71(A), don't count the PV disconnect(s) connected on the supply side of service equipment, since it's not a service disconnect as defined in Article 100. Figure 705–7

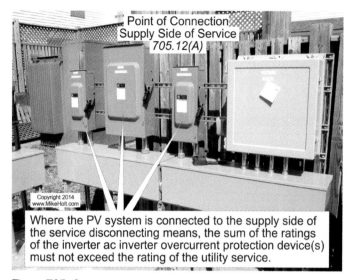

Point of Connection Supply Side of Service *705.12(A)*

Where the PV system is connected to the supply side of the service disconnecting means, the sum of the ratings of the inverter ac inverter overcurrent protection device(s) must not exceed the rating of the utility service.

Figure 705–6

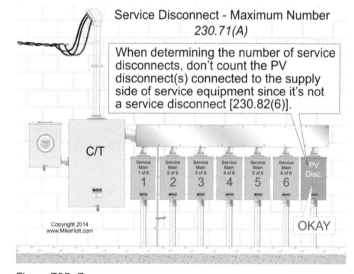

Service Disconnect - Maximum Number
230.71(A)

When determining the number of service disconnects, don't count the PV disconnect(s) connected to the supply side of service equipment since it's not a service disconnect [230.82(6)].

Figure 705–7

■ The neutral conductor on the supply side of service equipment must be bonded to the PV disconnect in accordance with 250.24(C). Figure 705–8

■ Raceways and enclosures containing service conductors [250.92(A)] must be bonded in accordance with 250.92(B). Figure 705–9

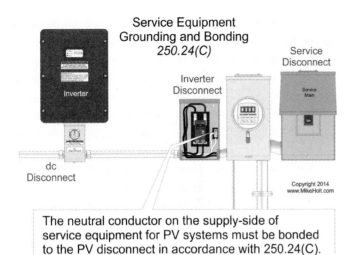

Figure 705–8

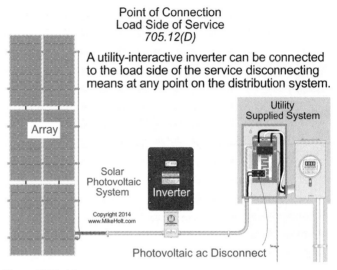

Figure 705–10

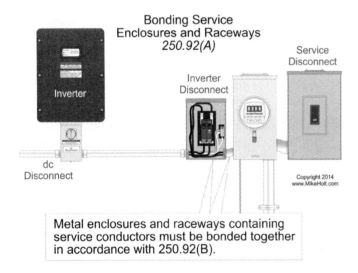

Figure 705–9

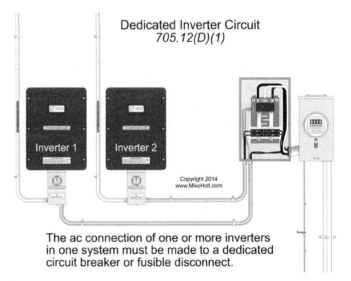

Figure 705–11

(D) Load Side. The output of a utility-interactive inverter can be connected to the load side of the service disconnecting means at any distribution equipment on the premises. Figure 705–10

The interconnecting provisions must comply with 705.12(D)(1) through (D)(6) if the distribution equipment is supplied by a primary source of electricity (utility) and a utility-interactive inverter(s), and is capable of supplying branch circuits or feeders, or both.

(1) Dedicated Circuit. The ac connection of one or more inverters in one system must be made to a dedicated circuit breaker or fusible disconnect. Figure 705–11

(2) Feeder Conductor and Panelboard Bus Ampere Rating.

(1) Feeder Conductor Ampere Rating. Where the inverter ac output connection isn't made at the opposite end of the feeder overcurrent protection device, that portion of the feeder on the load side of the inverter ac output connection must be protected by one of the following methods:

(a) The feeder conductor on the load side of the inverter ac output connection must have an ampacity not less than the feeder overcurrent protection device, plus 125 percent of the inverter output ac circuit current rating. Figure 705–12

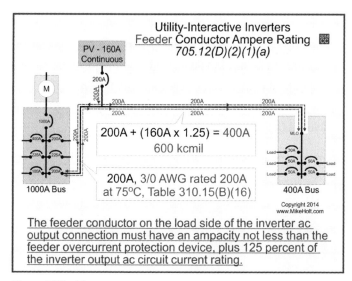

Figure 705–12

(b) The feeder conductor on the load side of the inverter ac output connection must have overcurrent protection on the load side of the inverter output ac connection sized not greater than the ampacity of the feeder. Figure 705–13

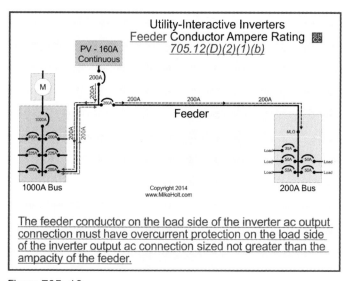

Figure 705–13

(2) Feeder Tap Ampere Rating. Feeder tap conductors between the feeder overcurrent protection device and the inverter ac output protection device, must have an ampacity not less than the feeder overcurrent protection device, plus 125 percent of the inverter output ac circuit current rating in accordance with 240.21(B).

Author's Comment:

■ According to 240.2, a tap conductor is a conductor, other than a service conductor, that has overcurrent protection rated more than the ampacity of a conductor.

Feeder Tap—10-foot Rule

Example: *What size feeder tap conductor (not longer than 10 ft) will be required for a tap to a 100A overcurrent device made between a feeder overcurrent protection device rated 200A and an inverter with ac output current rated 160A? Figure 705–14*

(a) 100A　　(b) 120A　　(c) 160A　　(d) 200A

Answer: *(a) 100A. Feeder tap conductors must have an ampacity no less than 1/10 the ampacity of the 200A feeder protection and 160A inverter ac output current rating, 200A + (160A x 1.25) = 400A x 0.10 = 40A [240.21(B)(2)(1)], and not less than the rating of the termination of the tap overcurrent protection device of 100A [240.21(B)(1)(4)].*

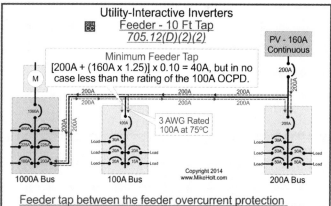

Figure 705–14

Feeder Tap—25-foot Rule

Example: *What size feeder tap conductor (longer than 10 ft but not over 25 ft) will be required for a tap to a 100A overcurrent device made between a feeder overcurrent protection device rated 200A and an inverter with ac output current rated 160A?* Figure 705–15

(a) 112A   (b) 133A   (c) 150A   (d) 182A

Answer: *(b) 133A. Feeder tap conductors must have an ampacity no less than ⅓ the ampacity of the 200A feeder protection and 160A inverter ac output current rating, 200A + (160A x 1.25) = 400A x 0.3333 = 133A [240.21(B)(2)(1)], and not less than the rating of the termination of the tap overcurrent protection device of 100A [240.21(B)(2)(1)].*

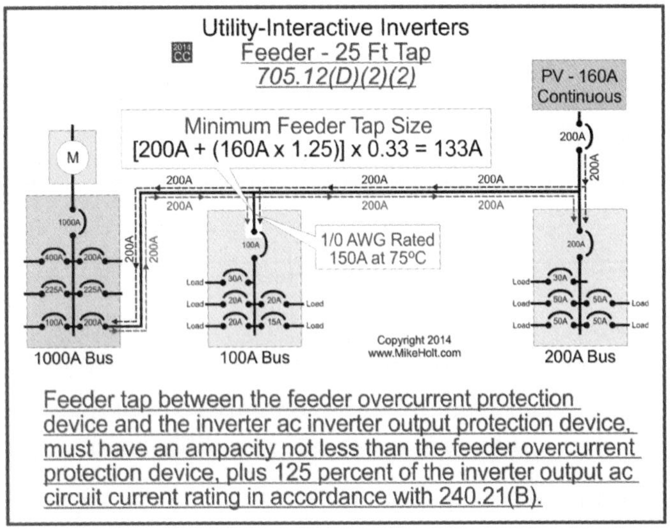

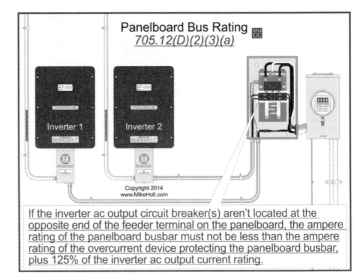

Utility-Interactive Inverters
Feeder - 25 Ft Tap
705.12(D)(2)(2)

Minimum Feeder Tap Size
[200A + (160A x 1.25)] x 0.33 = 133A

1/0 AWG Rated
150A at 75°C

PV - 160A Continuous

1000A Bus   100A Bus   200A Bus

Copyright 2014
www.MikeHolt.com

Feeder tap between the feeder overcurrent protection device and the inverter ac inverter output protection device, must have an ampacity not less than the feeder overcurrent protection device, plus 125 percent of the inverter output ac circuit current rating in accordance with 240.21(B).

Figure 705–15

(3) Panelboard Busbar Ampere Rating. The ampacity of the panelboard busbar must comply with one of the following:

Author's Comment:

- Only one of the four methods (a) through (d) is used to determine the busbar ampacity based on the specific condition.

(a) If the inverter ac output circuit breaker(s) aren't located at the opposite end of the feeder terminal on the panelboard, the ampere rating of the panelboard busbar must not be less than the ampere rating of the overcurrent device protecting the panelboard busbar, plus 125% of the inverter ac output current ratings. Figures 705–16 and 705–17

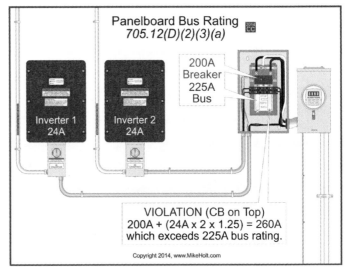

Panelboard Bus Rating
705.12(D)(2)(3)(a)

Inverter 1   Inverter 2

Copyright 2014
www.MikeHolt.com

If the inverter ac output circuit breaker(s) aren't located at the opposite end of the feeder terminal on the panelboard, the ampere rating of the panelboard busbar must not be less than the ampere rating of the overcurrent device protecting the panelboard busbar, plus 125% of the inverter ac output current rating.

Figure 705–16

Panelboard Bus Rating
705.12(D)(2)(3)(a)

200A Breaker
225A Bus

Inverter 1
24A   Inverter 2
24A

VIOLATION (CB on Top)
200A + (24A x 2 x 1.25) = 260A
which exceeds 225A bus rating.

Copyright 2014, www.MikeHolt.com

Figure 705–17

Note: Under this condition [705.12(D)(3)(a)], the inverter ac output circuit breaker(s) can be located anywhere in the panelboard.

(b) If the inverter ac output circuit breaker(s) are located at the opposite end of the feeder termination on the panelboard busbar, the ampere rating of the overcurrent device protecting the panelboard busbar, plus 125% of the inverter output ac current rating must not exceed 120% of the ampere rating of the panelboard busbar. Figure 705–18

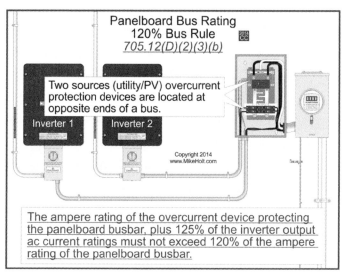

Figure 705–18

Panelboard Busbar Ampere Rating— Opposite Feeder Termination

Example 1: *A panelboard having a 200A rated busbar, protected by a 200A overcurrent device can be supplied by two inverters each having an output ac current rating of 24A.* Figure 705–19

(a) True   (b) False

Answer: *(b) False*

> *Busbar Ampere Rating x 1.20 => Panelboard Overcurrent + (Inverter Output Current x 1.25)*

200A x 1.20 => 200A + (24A x 1.25 x 2)
240A => 200A + 30A + 30A
240A => 260A

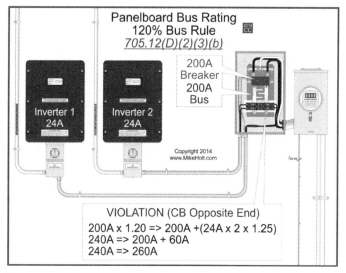

Figure 705–19

Panelboard Busbar Ampere Rating— Opposite Feeder Termination

Example 2: *A panelboard having a 200A rated busbar, protected by a 175A overcurrent device can be supplied by two inverters each having an output ac current rating of 24A.* Figure 705–20

(a) True   (b) False

Answer: *(a) True*

> *Busbar Ampere Rating x 1.20 => Panelboard Overcurrent + (Inverter Output Current x 1.25)*

200A x 1.20 => 175A + (24A x 1.25 x 2)
240A => 175A + 30A + 30A
240A => 235A

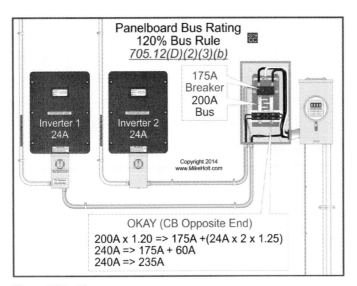

Figure 705–20

Where the inverter ac output circuit breaker(s) are located at the opposite end of the feeder termination on the panelboard busbar, a permanently affixed warning label that isn't handwritten and with sufficient durability to withstand the environment involved [110.21(B)], must be applied adjacent to the back-fed inverter ac output circuit breaker with the following or equivalent wording: Figure 705–21

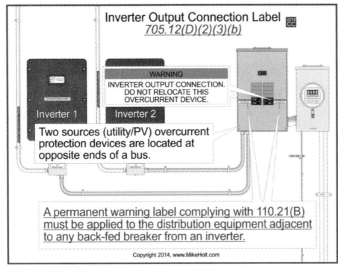

Figure 705–21

WARNING: INVERTER OUTPUT CONNECTION; DO NOT RELOCATE THIS OVERCURRENT DEVICE.

(c) A panelboard is permitted to have any number of circuit breakers as long as the total ampere ratings of all of the circuit breakers, excluding the rating of the overcurrent device protecting the busbar, don't exceed the ampere rating of the busbar. Figure 705–22

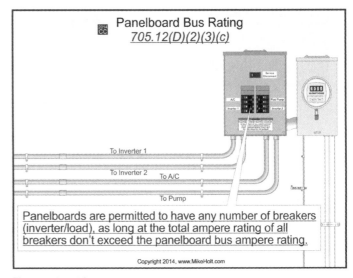

Figure 705–22

Author's Comment:

- Under this condition [705.12(D)(3)(c)], the inverter ac output circuit breaker(s) can be located anywhere in the panelboard.

**Panelboard Busbar Ampere Rating—Breakers
Not to Exceed Busbar Ampere Rating**

Example 1: *What's the minimum busbar ampere rating for a panelboard containing two 30A, two-pole, 240V circuit breakers and six 20A, 240V two-pole circuit breaker? Figure 705–23*

(a) 180A   (b) 240A   (c) 320A   (d) 400A

Answer: *(a) 180A*

	Line 1	Line 2
Inverter 1, 240V	*30A*	*30A*
Inverter 2, 240V	*30A*	*30A*
Six 20A, 240V	*120A*	*120A*
Total Per Phase	*180A*	*180A*

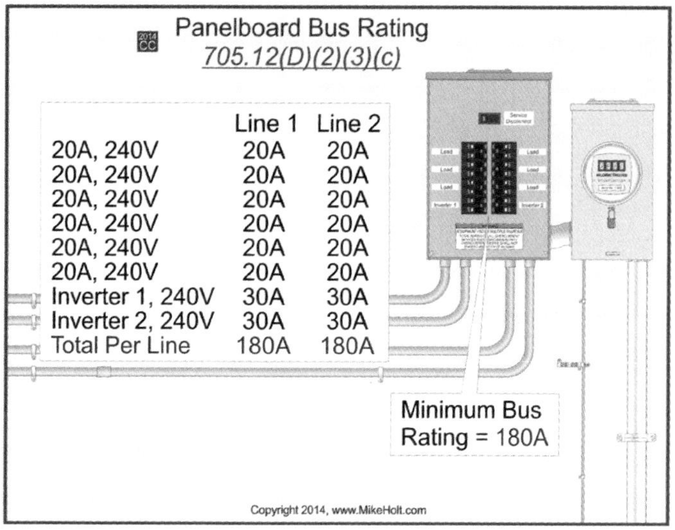

Panelboard Bus Rating
705.12(D)(2)(3)(c)

	Line 1	Line 2
20A, 240V	20A	20A
20A, 240V	20A	20A
20A, 240V	20A	20A
20A, 240V	20A	20A
20A, 240V	20A	20A
20A, 240V	20A	20A
Inverter 1, 240V	30A	30A
Inverter 2, 240V	30A	30A
Total Per Line	180A	180A

Minimum Bus Rating = 180A

Copyright 2014, www.MikeHolt.com

Figure 705–23

**Panelboard Busbar Ampere Rating—Breakers
Not to Exceed Busbar Ampere Rating**

Example 2: *What's the minimum busbar ampere rating for a panelboard containing six 30A, two-pole, 240V circuit breakers and one 20A, 120V one-pole circuit breaker? Figure 705–24*

(a) 120A   (b) 180A   (c) 200A   (d) 220A

Answer: *(a) 120A*

	Line 1	Line 2
Inverter 1, 240V	*30A*	*30A*
Inverter 2, 240V	*30A*	*30A*
Inverter 3, 240V	*30A*	*30A*
Inverter 4, 240V	*30A*	*30A*
Inverter 5, 240V	*30A*	*30A*
Inverter 6, 240V	*30A*	*30A*
One 20A, 120V	*20A*	*00A*
Total Per Phase	*200A*	*180A*

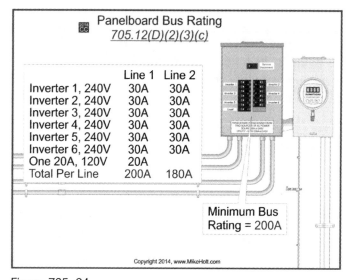

Panelboard Bus Rating
705.12(D)(2)(3)(c)

	Line 1	Line 2
Inverter 1, 240V	30A	30A
Inverter 2, 240V	30A	30A
Inverter 3, 240V	30A	30A
Inverter 4, 240V	30A	30A
Inverter 5, 240V	30A	30A
Inverter 6, 240V	30A	30A
One 20A, 120V	20A	
Total Per Line	200A	180A

Minimum Bus Rating = 200A

Copyright 2014, www.MikeHolt.com

Figure 705–24

Under this condition, a permanently affixed warning label that isn't handwritten, and of sufficient durability to withstand the environment involved [110.21(B)] must be applied to distribution equipment with the following or equivalent: Figure 705–25

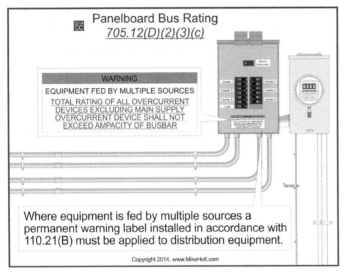

Figure 705–25

WARNING: THIS EQUIPMENT FED BY MULTIPLE SOURCES. TOTAL RATING OF ALL OVERCURRENT DEVICES, EXCLUDING MAIN SUPPLY OVERCURRENT DEVICE, SHALL NOT EXCEED AMPACITY OF BUSBAR.

(d) Connections are permitted on multiple-ampacity busbars or center-fed panelboards where designed under engineering supervision that includes fault studies and busbar load calculations.

2014 CHANGE ANALYSIS: Although the 2011 *NEC* had provisions about the ampacity of the busbars and conductors in this section, it was very lacking. Unfortunately, there's no simple way to handle this concept, so sometimes the only way to deal with it is break it up into bite-sized pieces and attack each circumstance individually. The new version of these rules break up the rules for feeders, taps, and busbars into their own subsections for ease of reading (yes, I know it still isn't

easy, but is easier). Pay close attention to the text in this textbook and in the *Code*, and pay especially close attention to the graphics in this textbook to help you understand the rules. You may need to read it several times and you'll certainly need to be focused if you want to really understand these rules.

(3) Marking. Panelboards containing ac inverter circuit breakers must be field marked to indicate the presence of multiple ac power sources. Figure 705–26

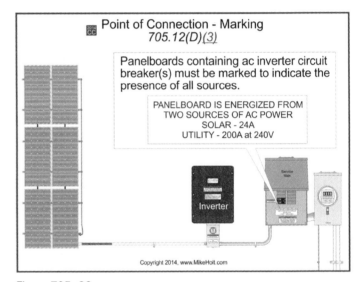

Figure 705–26

(4) Suitable for Backfeed. Conductors can backfeed circuit breakers that aren't marked "Line" and "Load." Figure 705–27

Note: Fused disconnects are suitable for backfeeding, unless otherwise marked.

(5) Fastening. Circuit breakers for utility-interactive inverters that are backfed aren't required to be secured in place by an additional fastener as required by 408.36(D). Figure 705–28

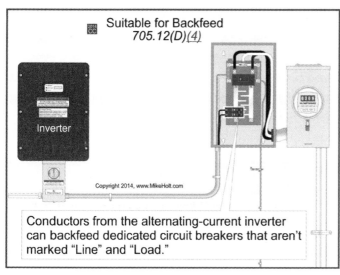

Figure 705–27

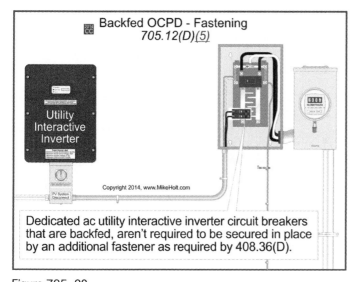

Figure 705–28

Author's Comment:

■ Once the dedicated ac inverter circuit breaker has been removed from the panelboard, the listed interactive inverter automatically powers down and turns off output ac power generation from the inverter.

(6) Wire Harness Arc-Fault Protection. Utility-interactive inverter(s) that have a wire harness or cable output circuit rated 240V, 30A or less must be provided with an AFCI protection device, unless the harness or conductors are installed in a raceway.

Author's Comment:

■ This rule applies to micro-inverters.

2014 CHANGE ANALYSIS: All conductors and equipment will degrade over time, but when they're exposed to the weather (and rodents, birds, humans, and so on), the degradation increases rapidly. When this occurs, series and parallel arcing is often the result, which can lead to obvious safety concerns. Due to this, a new requirement for AFCI protection has been added to the 2014 edition of the *Code*. Because this damage isn't likely to happen to conductors installed in a raceway, they're exempt from this new requirement.

705.31 Location of Overcurrent Protection

Conductors for utility-interactive inverter(s) on the supply side of the service disconnect must have overcurrent protection within 10 ft of the point where the conductors are connected to the service conductors. Figure 705–29

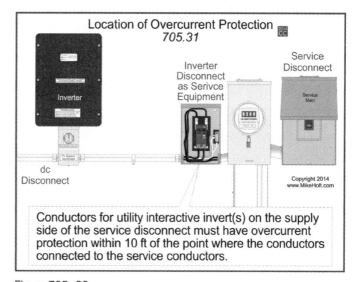

Figure 705–29

2014 CHANGE ANALYSIS: This new section provides protection of the alternate source (PV system) from short circuits that may occur on the primary power source. In the event of a short circuit on the primary side, huge amounts of current will be present, and could cause significant damage to the interconnected power source equipment.

705.32 Ground-Fault Protection

Where ground-fault protection of equipment is installed [230.95], the output of the interactive system must be connected to the supply side of the ground-fault protection.

Exception: The connection can be made to the load side if ground-fault protection for equipment is provided to protect from all ground-fault current sources.

Author's Comment:

- This rule means that you must connect the PV system to the supply side of the GFPE breaker (a breaker 480V, 1,000A or more). If not, you must provide GFPE protection of the PV system independently.

705.40 Loss of Primary Source

Upon loss of the utility source power, an electric power production source must be automatically disconnected from all ungrounded conductors of the utility source and not reconnected until the utility source has been restored.

Ex: A listed utility-interactive inverter can automatically cease exporting power upon loss of utility source power and isn't required to automatically disconnect all ungrounded conductors from the utility source power. A listed utility-interactive inverter can automatically resume exporting power to the utility source once the utility source has been restored.

Part II. Utility-Interactive Inverters

705.100 Voltage Unbalanced (Imbalanced) Interconnections

(A) Single Phase. Single-phase inverters connected to a three-phase utility power source must not increase utility unbalanced system voltage by more than 3 percent.

Note: See ANSI/C84.1, *Electric Power Systems and Equipment— Voltage Ratings (60 Hertz).*

Author's Comment:

- ANSI C84.1 recommends that "electric supply systems should be designed to limit the maximum voltage unbalance to 3 percent when measured at the electric-utility revenue meter under no-load conditions." Improperly connecting single-phase inverters to a three-phase system can result in a significant increase in unbalanced system voltage. That causes three-phase motors to run hotter because unbalanced voltage results in unbalanced magnetic fields created by the windings working against each other.

The NEMA formula to determine maximum unbalanced voltage is:

$$\textit{Maximum Unbalanced Voltage} = 100 \times \textit{Maximum Deviation from Average Voltage/Average Voltage.}$$

Existing Installation

Example: *If we connect two single-phase PV systems to lines B – C and this causes the B – C voltage to increase from 200V to 201V because of a decrease in loading, the maximum unbalanced system voltage for the following line voltages: A – B 206V, B–C 201V, and A – C 204V will be _____ percent.*

Maximum Unbalanced Voltage = Maximum Deviation Volts from Average Voltage/ Average Voltage x 100 (for Percent)

Average Voltage = (206V + 200V + 204V)/3 lines
    = 203.33V

Maximum Deviation from Average = 206V – 203.33
    = 2.67V

Maximum Unbalanced Voltage = 2.67V/203.33V x 100
    = 1.31%

Example: *If we connect two single-phase PV systems to lines B – C and this results in B – C voltage to rise from 200V to 201V because of a decrease in loading, the maximum unbalanced system voltage for the following line voltages: A – B 206V, B – C 201V, and A – C 204V will be _____%.*

Maximum Unbalanced Voltage = Maximum Deviation from Average Voltage/ Average Voltage x 100 (for Percent)

Average Voltage = (206V + 201V + 204V)/3 lines
    = 203.66V

Maximum Deviation from Average = 206V – 203.66V
    = 2.34V

Maximum Unbalanced Voltage = 2.34V/203.66V x 100
    = 1.15%

Example: *If we connect two single-phase PV systems to lines A – B and this causes the A – B voltage to increase from 206V to 208V because of a decrease in loading, the maximum unbalanced system voltage for the following line voltages: A – B 208V, B – C 200V, and A – C 204V will be _____ percent.*

Maximum Unbalanced Voltage = Maximum Deviation from Average Voltage/ Average Voltage x 100 (for Percent)

Average Voltage = (208V + 200V + 204V)/3 lines = 204V
Maximum Deviation from Average = 208V - 204V = 4V
Maximum Unbalanced Voltage = 4V/204V x 100 = 1.96%

2014 CHANGE ANALYSIS: Previous editions of the *Code* addressed unbalanced interconnections, but only required that "significant unbalanced voltages" didn't occur. What did "significant" mean? Your guess was as good as mine, but now we no longer have to guess. Three percent is now the limit.

CHAPTER 7 PRACTICE QUESTIONS

Please use the 2014 *Code* book to answer the following questions.

Article 705. Interconnected Electric Power Production Sources

1. Article _____ covers the installation of electric power production sources operating in parallel with a primary source(s) of electricity.

    (a) 700
    (b) 701
    (c) 702
    (d) 705

2. For interconnected electric power production sources, the generating source and all distribution equipment associated with it that generates electricity from a source other than a utility supplied service is called _____.

    (a) a service drop
    (b) power production equipment
    (c) the service point
    (d) utilization equipment

3. For interconnected electric power production sources, installation of one or more electrical power production sources operating in parallel with a primary source(s) of electricity must be installed only by _____.

    (a) qualified persons
    (b) a utility company
    (c) the authority having jurisdiction
    (d) b or c

4. For interconnected electric power production sources, a permanent _____, denoting all electric power sources on or in the premises, must be installed at each service equipment location and all interconnected electric power production sources.

    (a) label
    (b) plaque
    (c) directory
    (d) b or c

5. For interconnected electric power production sources, an electric power production source is permitted to be connected to the supply side of the service disconnecting means.

    (a) True
    (b) False

6. For interconnected electric power production sources, the sum of the ratings of all overcurrent devices connected to power production sources are permitted to exceed the rating of the service.

    (a) True
    (b) False

7. For interconnected electric power production sources, the output of a utility-interactive inverter can be connected to the load side of the service disconnecting means at any distribution equipment on the premises.

   (a) True
   (b) False

8. The source interconnection of one or more inverters installed in one system shall be made at a dedicated circuit breaker or fusible disconnecting means.

   (a) True
   (b) False

9. In accordance with Article 705, where two sources, one a utility and the other an inverter, are located at opposite ends of a busbar that contains loads, a permanent warning label must be applied to the panelboard to warn others that the inverter output connection circuit breaker must not be relocated.

   (a) True
   (b) False

10. For interconnected electric power production sources, panelboards containing ac inverter circuit breakers must be field marked to indicate the presence of multiple ac power sources.

    (a) True
    (b) False

11. For interconnected electric power production sources, _____, unless otherwise marked, are suitable for backfeeding.

    (a) circuit breakers
    (b) PV system overcurrent devices
    (c) utility-interactive inverters
    (d) fused disconnects

12. For interconnected electric power production sources, dedicated ac inverter circuit breakers that are backfed must be secured in place by an additional fastener as required by 408.36(D).

    (a) True
    (b) False

13. For interconnected electric power production sources, upon loss of utility source power, an electric power production source must be manually disconnected from all ungrounded conductors of the utility source and must not be reconnected until the utility source has been restored.

    (a) True
    (b) False

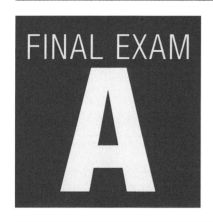

FINAL EXAM A FOR SOLAR PHOTOVOLTAIC SYSTEMS

Please use the 2014 *Code* book to answer the following questions.

1. If the circuit's overcurrent device exceeds _____, the conductor ampacity must have a rating not less than the rating of the overcurrent device.

   (a) 800A
   (b) 1,000A
   (c) 1,200A
   (d) 2,000A

2. Nominal battery voltage is typically _____.

   (a) 2V per cell for lead-acid systems
   (b) 1.20V for per cell for alkali systems
   (c) 3.60V to 3.80V per cell for Li-ion systems
   (d) all of these

3. Direct-buried service conductors that are not encased in concrete and that are buried 18 in. or more below grade shall have their location identified by a warning ribbon placed in the trench at least _____ in. above the underground installation.

   (a) 6
   (b) 10
   (c) 12
   (d) 18

4. Connection by means of wire-binding screws, studs, or nuts having upturned lugs or the equivalent shall be permitted for _____ or smaller conductors.

   (a) 12 AWG
   (b) 10 AWG
   (c) 8 AWG
   (d) 6 AWG

5. In order for a metal underground water pipe to be used as a grounding electrode, it shall be in direct contact with the earth for _____.

   (a) 5 ft
   (b) 10 ft or more
   (c) less than 10 ft
   (d) 20 ft or more

6. Flexible metal conduit must be securely fastened by a means approved by the authority having jurisdiction within _____ of termination.

   (a) 6 in.
   (b) 10 in.
   (c) 1 ft
   (d) 10 ft

7. Liquidtight flexible metal conduit must be securely fastened by a means approved by the authority having jurisdiction within _____ of termination.

    (a) 6 in.
    (b) 10 in.
    (c) 1 ft
    (d) 10 ft

8. The ampacity of a conductor can be different along the length of the conductor. The higher ampacity can be used beyond the point of transition for a distance of no more than _____ ft, or no more than _____ percent of the circuit length figured at the higher ampacity, whichever is less.

    (a) 10, 10
    (b) 10, 20
    (c) 15, 15
    (d) 20, 10

9. PVC conduit shall be securely fastened within _____ in. of each box.

    (a) 6
    (b) 12
    (c) 24
    (d) 36

10. When installing PVC conduit underground without concrete cover, there shall be a minimum of _____ in. of cover.

    (a) 6
    (b) 12
    (c) 18
    (d) 22

11. What is the minimum size copper equipment bonding jumper for a 40A rated circuit?

    (a) 14 AWG
    (b) 12 AWG
    (c) 10 AWG
    (d) 8 AWG

12. Where used outside, aluminum or copper-clad aluminum grounding electrode conductors shall not be terminated within _____ of the earth.

    (a) 6 in.
    (b) 12 in.
    (c) 15 in.
    (d) 18 in.

13. A bare 4 AWG copper conductor installed horizontally near the bottom or vertically, and within that portion of a concrete foundation or footing that is in direct contact with the earth can be used as a grounding electrode when the conductor is at least _____ ft in length.

    (a) 10
    (b) 15
    (c) 20
    (d) 25

14. The sum of the cross-sectional areas of all contained conductors at any cross-section of a metal wireway shall not exceed _____ percent.

    (a) 50
    (b) 20
    (c) 25
    (d) 80

15. Within sight means visible and not more than _____ ft distant from the equipment.

    (a) 10
    (b) 20
    (c) 25
    (d) 50

16. Conductor adjustment factors shall not apply to conductors in raceways having a length not exceeding _____ in.

    (a) 12
    (b) 24
    (c) 36
    (d) 48

17. Enclosures for switches or overcurrent devices are allowed to have conductors feeding through where the wiring space at any cross section is not filled to more than _____ percent of the cross-sectional area of the space.

    (a) 20
    (b) 30
    (c) 40
    (d) 60

18. The working space in front of the electric equipment shall not be less than _____ wide, or the width of the equipment, whichever is greater.

    (a) 15 in.
    (b) 30 in.
    (c) 40 in.
    (d) 60 in.

19. Where rock bottom is encountered when driving a ground rod at an angle up to 45 degrees, the electrode can be buried in a trench that is at least _____ deep.

    (a) 18 in.
    (b) 30 in.
    (c) 4 ft
    (d) 8 ft

20. A disconnecting means is required within sight of the storage battery for all ungrounded battery system conductors operating at over _____ nominal.

    (a) 20V
    (b) 30V
    (c) 40V
    (d) 50V

21. What is the minimum size copper supply-side bonding jumper for a service raceway containing 4/0 THHN aluminum conductors?

    (a) 6 AWG aluminum
    (b) 4 AWG aluminum
    (c) 4 AWG copper
    (d) 3 AWG copper

22. Overcurrent devices shall be readily accessible and installed so the center of the grip of the operating handle of the switch or circuit breaker, when in its highest position, is not more than _____ above the floor or working platform.

    (a) 2 ft
    (b) 4 ft 6 in.
    (c) 5 ft
    (d) 6 ft 7 in.

23. For flexible metal conduit, if flexibility is necessary after installation, unsecured lengths from the last point the raceway is securely fastened must not exceed _____

    (a) 3 ft for trade sizes ½ through 1¼
    (b) 4 ft for trade sizes 1½ through 2
    (c) 5 ft for trade sizes 2½ and larger
    (d) all of these

24. For liquidtight flexible metal conduit, if flexibility is necessary after installation, unsecured lengths from the last point the raceway is securely fastened must not exceed _____.

    (a) 3 ft for trade sizes ½ through ¼
    (b) 4 ft for trade sizes 1½ through 2
    (c) 5 ft for trade sizes 2½ and larger
    (d) all of these

25. The ampacity adjustment factors in 310.15(B)(3)(a) shall be applied to a metal wireway only where the number of current-carrying conductors in any cross section of the wireway exceeds _____.

    (a) 30
    (b) 40
    (c) 50
    (d) 60

26. The provisions of Article _____ apply to stationary storage battery installations.

    (a) 450
    (b) 460
    (c) 470
    (d) 480

27. Where direct-buried conductors and cables emerge from grade, they shall be protected by enclosures or raceways to a point at least _____ ft above finished grade.

    (a) 3
    (b) 6
    (c) 8
    (d) 10

28. Where six current-carrying conductors are run in the same conduit or cable, the ampacity of each conductor shall be adjusted by a factor of _____ percent.

    (a) 40
    (b) 60
    (c) 80
    (d) 90

29. Grounded conductors _____ and larger can be identified by distinctive white or gray markings at their terminations.

    (a) 10 AWG
    (b) 8 AWG
    (c) 6 AWG
    (d) 4 AWG

30. Grounding electrode conductors _____ and larger that are not subject to physical damage can be run exposed along the surface of the building construction if securely fastened to the construction.

    (a) 10 AWG
    (b) 8 AWG
    (c) 6 AWG
    (d) 4 AWG

31. Ground rod electrodes shall be installed so that at least _____ of the length is in contact with the soil.

    (a) 5 ft
    (b) 8 ft
    (c) ½
    (d) 80 percent

32. Each vented cell of a battery, as it relates to storage batteries, shall be equipped with _____ that is(are) designed to prevent destruction of the cell due to ignition of gases within the cell by an external spark or flame under normal operating conditions.

    (a) pressure relief
    (b) a flame arrester
    (c) fluid level indicators
    (d) none of these

33. Many terminations and equipment are either marked with _____, or have that information included in the product's installation instructions.

    (a) an etching tool
    (b) a removable label
    (c) a tightening torque
    (d) the manufacturer's initials

34. Electrical equipment rooms or enclosures housing electrical apparatus that are controlled by a lock(s) shall be considered _____ to qualified persons.

    (a) readily accessible
    (b) accessible
    (c) available
    (d) none of these

35. Overcurrent devices shall be _____.

    (a) accessible (as applied to wiring methods)
    (b) accessible (as applied to equipment)
    (c) readily accessible
    (d) inaccessible to unauthorized personnel

36. Capable of being reached quickly for operation, renewal, or inspections without resorting to portable ladders or the use of tools is known as _____.

    (a) accessible (as applied to equipment)
    (b) accessible (as applied to wiring methods)
    (c) accessible, readily
    (d) all of these

37. Electrical equipment such as switchboards, switchgear, panelboards, industrial control panels, meter socket enclosures, and motor control centers, that are in other than dwelling units, and are likely to require _____ while energized, shall be field or factory marked to warn qualified persons of potential electric arc-flash hazards.

    (a) examination
    (b) adjustment
    (c) servicing or maintenance
    (d) any of these

38. All switchboards and panelboards supplied by a feeder in _____ shall be marked as to the device or equipment where the power supply originates.

    (a) other than one- or two-family dwellings
    (b) all dwelling units
    (c) all nondwelling units
    (d) b and c

39. Electrical installations in hollow spaces, vertical shafts, and ventilation or air-handling ducts shall be made so that the possible spread of fire or products of combustion is not _____.

    (a) substantially increased
    (b) allowed
    (c) inherent
    (d) possible

40. _____ shall not be used as grounding electrodes.

    (a) Metal underground gas piping systems
    (b) Aluminum
    (c) Metal well casings
    (d) a and b

41. The next higher standard rating overcurrent device above the ampacity of the ungrounded conductors being protected shall be permitted to be used, provided the _____.

    (a) conductors are not part of a branch circuit supplying more than one receptacle for cord-and-plug-connected portable loads
    (b) ampacity of the conductors doesn't correspond with the standard ampere rating of a fuse or circuit breaker
    (c) next higher standard rating selected doesn't exceed 800A
    (d) all of these

42. Compliance with the provisions of the *NEC* will result in _____.

    (a) good electrical service
    (b) an efficient electrical system
    (c) an electrical system essentially free from hazard
    (d) all of these

43. Conductor terminal and splicing devices must be _____ for the conductor material and they must be properly installed and used.

    (a) listed
    (b) approved
    (c) identified
    (d) all of these

44. An arc-fault circuit interrupter is a device intended to de-energize the circuit when it recognizes characteristics unique to _____.

    (a) overcurrent
    (b) arcing
    (c) a ground fault
    (d) harmonic fundamentals

45. Metal or nonmetallic raceways, cable armors, and cable sheaths _____ between cabinets, boxes, fittings, or other enclosures or outlets.

    (a) can be attached with electrical tape
    (b) are allowed gaps for expansion
    (c) shall be continuous
    (d) none of these

46. Nonmandatory Informative Annexes contained in the back of the *Code* book _____.

    (a) are for information only
    (b) aren't enforceable as a requirement of the *Code*
    (c) are enforceable as a requirement of the *Code*
    (d) a and b

47. Factory-installed _____ wiring of listed equipment need not be inspected at the time of installation of the equipment, except to detect alterations or damage.

    (a) external
    (b) associated
    (c) internal
    (d) all of these

48. An electrode encased by at least 2 in. of concrete, located horizontally near the bottom or vertically and within that portion of a concrete foundation or footing that is in direct contact with the earth, shall be permitted as a grounding electrode when it consists of _____.

    (a) at least 20 ft of ½ in. or larger steel reinforcing bars or rods
    (b) at least 20 ft of bare copper conductor of 4 AWG or larger
    (c) a or b
    (d) none of these

49. The _____ has the responsibility for deciding on the approval of equipment and materials.

    (a) manufacturer
    (b) authority having jurisdiction
    (c) testing agency
    (d) none of these

50. Bare aluminum or copper-clad aluminum grounding electrode conductors shall not be used where in direct contact with _____ or where subject to corrosive conditions.

    (a) masonry or the earth
    (b) bare copper conductors
    (c) wooden framing members
    (d) all of these

51. Each direct-buried single-conductor cable must be located _____ in the trench to the other single-conductor cables in the same parallel set of conductors, including equipment grounding conductors.

    (a) perpendicular
    (b) bundled together
    (c) in close proximity
    (d) spaced apart

52. All conductors of the same circuit, including the grounded and equipment grounding conductors, shall be contained within the same _____, unless otherwise permitted elsewhere in the *Code*.

    (a) raceway
    (b) cable
    (c) trench
    (d) all of these

53. Access and _____ shall be provided and maintained about all electrical equipment to permit ready and safe operation and maintenance of such equipment.

    (a) ventilation
    (b) cleanliness
    (c) circulation
    (d) working space

54. A conductor used to connect the system grounded conductor or the equipment to a grounding electrode or to a point on the grounding electrode system is called the "_____ conductor."

    (a) main grounding
    (b) common main
    (c) equipment grounding
    (d) grounding electrode

55. The temperature rating associated with the ampacity of a _____ shall be selected and coordinated so as not to exceed the lowest temperature rating of any connected termination, conductor, or device.

    (a) terminal
    (b) conductor
    (c) device
    (d) all of these

56. The purpose or use of panelboard circuits and circuit _____, including spare positions, shall be legibly identified on a circuit directory located on the face or inside of the door of a panelboard, and at each switch or circuit breaker on a switchboard.

    (a) manufacturers
    (b) conductors
    (c) feeders
    (d) modifications

57. _____ shall be installed so that the wiring contained in them can be rendered accessible without removing any part of the building or structure or, in underground circuits, without excavating sidewalks, paving, or earth.

    (a) Boxes
    (b) Conduit bodies
    (c) Handhole enclosures
    (d) all of these

58. In grounded systems, normally noncurrent-carrying electrically conductive materials that are likely to become energized shall be _____ in a manner that establishes an effective ground-fault current path.

    (a) connected together
    (b) connected to the electrical supply source
    (c) connected to the closest grounded conductor
    (d) a and b

59. Nominal battery voltage, as it relates to storage batteries, is the value of a(n) _____ of a given voltage class for convenient designation.

    (a) cell or battery
    (b) container
    (c) electrolyte
    (d) intertier connector

60. The *Code* contains provisions considered necessary for safety, which will not necessarily result in _____.

    (a) efficient use
    (b) convenience
    (c) good service or future expansion of electrical use
    (d) all of these

61. Extreme _____ may cause PVC conduit to become brittle, and therefore more susceptible to damage from physical contact.

    (a) sunlight
    (b) corrosive conditions
    (c) heat
    (d) cold

62. _____ is defined as the area between the top of direct-burial cable and the top surface of the finished grade.

    (a) Notch
    (b) Cover
    (c) Gap
    (d) none of these

63. The authority having jurisdiction has the responsibility for _____.

    (a) making interpretations of rules
    (b) deciding upon the approval of equipment and materials
    (c) waiving specific requirements in the *Code* and permitting alternate methods and material if safety is maintained
    (d) all of these

64. Equipment or materials included in a list published by a testing laboratory acceptable to the authority having jurisdiction is said to be "_____."

    (a) book
    (b) digest
    (c) manifest
    (d) listed

65. Overcurrent devices aren't permitted to be located in the bathrooms of _____.

    (a) dwelling units
    (b) dormitories
    (c) guest rooms or guest suites of hotels or motels
    (d) all of these

66. The interior of underground raceways shall be considered a _____ location.

    (a) wet
    (b) dry
    (c) damp
    (d) corrosive

67. An effective ground-fault current path is an intentionally con-structed, low-impedance electrically conductive path designed and intended to carry current under ground-fault conditions from the point of a ground fault on a wiring system to _____.

    (a) ground
    (b) earth
    (c) the electrical supply source
    (d) none of these

68. For grounded systems, electrical equipment and electri-cally conductive material likely to become energized, shall be installed in a manner that creates a low-impedance circuit capable of safely carrying the maximum ground-fault current likely to be imposed on it from where a ground fault may occur to the _____.

    (a) ground
    (b) earth
    (c) electrical supply source
    (d) none of these

69. For grounded systems, normally noncurrent-carrying conductive materials enclosing electrical conductors or equipment, or form-ing part of such equipment, shall be connected together and to the _____ to establish an effective ground-fault current path.

    (a) ground
    (b) earth
    (c) electrical supply source
    (d) none of these

70. For ungrounded systems, noncurrent-carrying conductive materials enclosing electrical conductors or equipment shall be connected to the _____ in a manner that will limit the volt-age imposed by lightning or unintentional contact with higher-voltage lines.

    (a) ground
    (b) earth
    (c) electrical supply source
    (d) none of these

71. Only wiring methods recognized as _____ are included in this *Code*.

    (a) expensive
    (b) efficient
    (c) suitable
    (d) cost-effective

72. In straight pulls, the length of the box or conduit body shall not be less than _____ times the trade size of the largest raceway.

    (a) six
    (b) eight
    (c) twelve
    (d) none of these

73. Where angle or U pulls are made, the distance between each raceway entry inside the box or conduit body and the oppo-site wall of the box or conduit body shall not be less than _____ times the trade size of the largest raceway in a row plus the sum of the trade sizes of the remaining raceways in the same wall and row .

    (a) six
    (b) eight
    (c) twelve
    (d) none of these

74. This *Code* covers the installation of _____ for public and private premises, including buildings, structures, mobile homes, recre-ational vehicles, and floating buildings.

    (a) optical fiber cables
    (b) electrical equipment
    (c) raceways
    (d) all of these

75. Wiring methods permitted for service-entrance conductors include _____.

    (a) rigid metal conduit
    (b) electrical metallic tubing
    (c) PVC conduit
    (d) all of these

76. A(n) _____ is a device, or group of devices, by which the conductors of a circuit can be disconnected from their source of supply.

    (a) feeder
    (b) enclosure
    (c) disconnecting means
    (d) conductor interrupter

77. The required working space for battery systems is measured from the edge of the battery _____.

    (a) terminals
    (b) enclosure
    (c) rack or cabinet
    (d) any of these

78. A connection between equipment grounding conductors and a metal box shall be by _____.

    (a) a grounding screw used for no other purpose
    (b) equipment listed for grounding
    (c) a listed grounding device
    (d) any of these

79. The grounding conductor connection to the grounding electrode shall be made by _____.

    (a) listed lugs
    (b) exothermic welding
    (c) listed pressure connectors
    (d) any of these

80. Provisions appropriate to the battery technology shall be made for sufficient diffusion and ventilation of the gases from a storage battery to prevent the accumulation of a(n) _____ mixture.

    (a) corrosive
    (b) explosive
    (c) toxic
    (d) all of these

81. Unless identified for use in the operating environment, no conductors or equipment shall be _____ having a deteriorating effect on the conductors or equipment.

    (a) located in damp or wet locations
    (b) exposed to fumes, vapors, liquids, or gases
    (c) exposed to excessive temperatures
    (d) all of these

82. Premises wiring includes _____ wiring from the service point or power source to the outlets.

    (a) interior
    (b) exterior
    (c) underground
    (d) a and b

83. A battery system includes storage batteries and battery chargers, and can include inverters, converters, and associated electrical equipment.

    (a) True
    (b) False

84. A grounding electrode conductor shall be permitted to be run to any convenient grounding electrode available in the grounding electrode system where the other electrode(s), if any, is (are) connected by bonding jumpers in accordance with 250.53(C).

    (a) True
    (b) False

85. A hybrid system includes the utility power system.

    (a) True
    (b) False

86. An encased or buried connection to a concrete-encased, driven, or buried grounding electrode shall be accessible.

    (a) True
    (b) False

87. An important consideration for limiting imposed voltage on electrical systems is to remember that bonding and grounding electrode conductors shouldn't be any longer than necessary and unnecessary bends and loops should be avoided.

    (a) True
    (b) False

88. Boxes, conduit bodies, and fittings installed in wet locations shall be required to be listed for use in wet locations.

    (a) True
    (b) False

89. By special permission, the authority having jurisdiction may waive specific requirements in this *Code* where it is assured that equivalent objectives can be achieved by establishing and maintaining effective safety.

    (a) True
    (b) False

90. Circuit directories can include labels that depend on transient conditions of occupancy.

    (a) True
    (b) False

91. Direct-buried conductors or cables can be spliced or tapped without the use of splice boxes when the splice or tap is made in accordance with 110.14(B).

    (a) True
    (b) False

92. Equipment intended to interrupt current at fault levels shall have an interrupting rating at nominal circuit voltage sufficient for the current that is available at the line terminals of the equipment.

    (a) True
    (b) False

93. Explanatory material, such as references to other standards, references to related sections of the *NEC*, or information related to a *Code* rule, are included in the form of Informational Notes.

    (a) True
    (b) False

94. Ferrous metal raceways and enclosures for grounding electrode conductors shall be electrically continuous from the point of attachment to cabinets or equipment to the grounding electrode.

    (a) True
    (b) False

95. Fittings and connectors shall be used only with the specific wiring methods for which they are designed and listed.

    (a) True
    (b) False

96. For grounded systems, normally noncurrent-carrying conductive materials enclosing electrical conductors or equipment shall be connected to earth so as to limit the voltage-to-ground on these materials.

    (a) True
    (b) False

97. For grounded systems, the earth is considered an effective ground-fault current path.

    (a) True
    (b) False

98. For indoor installations, heating, cooling, or ventilating equipment shall not be installed in the dedicated space above a panelboard or switchboard.

    (a) True
    (b) False

99. No conductor shall be used where its operating temperature exceeds that designated for the type of insulated conductor involved.

    (a) True
    (b) False

100. Power distribution blocks installed in metal wireways on the line side of the service equipment shall be listed for the purpose.

     (a) True
     (b) False

Please use the 2014 *Code* book to answer the following questions.

1. _____ include photovoltaic cells, devices, modules, or modular materials that are integrated into the outer surface or structure of a building and serve as the outer protective surface of that building.

   (a) Protective photovoltaics
   (b) Building integrated photovoltaics
   (c) Bipolar photovoltaic arrays
   (d) Bipolar photoconductive arrays

2. _____ must be used to disable a PV array or portions of an array for installation and service.

   (a) Open circuiting
   (b) Short circuiting
   (c) Opaque covering
   (d) Any of these

3. A common dc grounding electrode conductor of a PV system is permitted to serve multiple inverters with the size of the common grounding electrode and the tap conductors in accordance with 250.166. The tap conductors must be connected to the common grounding electrode conductor in such a manner that the common grounding electrode conductor remains _____.

   (a) without a splice or joint
   (b) inside inverter enclosures
   (c) inside a raceway
   (d) supported on insulators

4. A disconnecting means is required to open ungrounded dc circuit conductors of the PV system.

   (a) True
   (b) False

5. A disconnecting switch is permitted to open the grounded dc conductor of a PV system when the switch is _____.

   (a) used only for PV array maintenance
   (b) accessible only by qualified persons
   (c) rated for the maximum dc voltage and current, including ground-fault conditions
   (d) all of these

6. A grounded _____-wire PV system must have one conductor grounded or be impedance grounded, and comply with 690.5.

   (a) 2
   (b) 3
   (c) 4
   (d) any of these

7. A mechanically integrated assembly of PV modules or panels with a support structure and foundation, tracker, and other components, as required, to form a dc power-producing unit, is known as a(n) _____.

(a) pulse width modulator
(b) array
(c) capacitive supply bank
(d) alternating-current photovoltaic module

8. A permanent label must be applied by the installer at the PV dc power source disconnect indicating the _____.

(a) rated maximum power-point current and voltage
(b) maximum system voltage and circuit current
(c) maximum rated output current of the charge controller (if installed)
(d) all of these

9. A single array or aggregate of arrays that generates direct-current power at system voltage and current is the photovoltaic _____.

(a) output source
(b) source circuit
(c) power source
(d) array source

10. A stand-alone PV system supplies power in conjunction with and to supplement an electrical production and distribution network.

(a) True
(b) False

11. A warning label on the utility-interactive inverter or applied by the _____ must be on the PV utility-interactive inverter stating the following: WARNING ELECTRIC SHOCK HAZARD—IF A GROUND FAULT IS INDICATED, NORMALLY GROUNDED CONDUCTORS MAY BE UNGROUNDED AND ENERGIZED

(a) homeowner
(b) inspector
(c) installer
(d) power company

12. A(n) _____ is a complete, environmentally protected unit consisting of solar cells, and other components, exclusive of tracker, designed to generate direct-current power when exposed to sunlight.

(a) interface
(b) battery
(c) module
(d) cell bank

13. A(n) _____ must be installed between a photovoltaic array and other equipment.

(a) grounded conductor
(b) main bonding jumper
(c) equipment grounding conductor
(d) system bonding jumper

14. All conductors of a circuit, including the equipment grounding conductor, must be installed in the same raceway or cable, or otherwise run with the PV array circuit conductors when they leave the vicinity of the PV array.

(a) True
(b) False

15. All equipment intended for use in PV power systems shall be _____ for the PV application.

(a) identified
(b) listed
(c) approved
(d) a and b

16. All raceway and cable wiring methods included in this *Code*, other wiring systems and fittings specifically listed for use on PV arrays, and wiring as part of a listed system shall be permitted.

(a) True
(b) False

17. An alternating-current photovoltaic module is designed to generate ac power when exposed to _____.

(a) electromagnetic induction
(b) heat
(c) sunlight
(d) hysteresis

18. An inverter or an ac module in an interactive PV system must automatically de-energize its output to the connected electrical distribution system upon _____ of voltage and remain de-energized until the electrical distribution system voltage has been restored.

    (a) surge
    (b) spike
    (c) loss
    (d) unbalance

19. Any building or structure with a stand-alone PV system (not connected to a utility service source) must have a permanent _____ installed on the exterior of the building or structure at a readily visible location acceptable to the authority having jurisdiction. The _____ must indicate the location of the stand-alone PV system disconnecting means and that the structure contains a stand-alone electrical power system.

    (a) plaque
    (b) directory
    (c) a and b
    (d) a or b

20. Article _____ covers the installation of electric power production sources operating in parallel with a primary source(s) of electricity.

    (a) 700
    (b) 701
    (c) 702
    (d) 705

21. Article 690 requirements pertaining to dc PV source circuits do not apply to ac PV modules since ac PV modules have no dc output. The PV source circuit, conductors and inverters are considered as internal wiring of an ac module.

    (a) True
    (b) False

22. Buildings/structures containing both utility service and a PV system must have a permanent _____ placed at the service disconnecting means and the PV system disconnecting means identifying the location of the other system if they are not located at the same location.

    (a) plaque
    (b) directory
    (c) a and b
    (d) a or b

23. Currents of PV systems are to be considered _____.

    (a) safe
    (b) continuous
    (c) noncontiguous
    (d) inverted

24. Devices _____ for bonding the metallic frames of PV modules shall be permitted to bond the exposed metallic frames of PV modules to the metallic frames of adjacent PV modules.

    (a) listed
    (b) labeled
    (c) identified
    (d) a and c

25. Devices _____ for grounding the metallic frames of PV modules and other equipment can be used to bond the exposed metal surfaces of the modules and equipment to the mounting structures.

    (a) identified
    (b) approved
    (c) listed
    (d) a and c

26. Devices and systems used for mounting PV modules that also provide grounding of the module frames must be _____ for the purpose of grounding PV modules.

    (a) listed
    (b) labeled
    (c) identified
    (d) a and b

27. Disconnecting means must be installed for PV output circuits where fuses that must be serviced can't be isolated from energized circuits. The disconnect must be within sight and accessible to the fuse or integral with the fuse holder, be externally operable without exposing the operator to contact with live parts, and plainly indicating whether in the open or closed position [690.17(C)]. Where the disconnecting means is located more than _____ ft from the fuse, a directory showing the location of each fuse disconnect must be installed at the fuse location.

    (a) 3
    (b) 6
    (c) 10
    (d) 12

28. Disconnecting means must be provided to disconnect a fuse from all sources of supply if energized from both directions and shall be capable of being disconnected independently of fuses in other PV source circuits.

    (a) True
    (b) False

29. Equipment grounding conductors for PV circuits having overcurrent protection must be sized in accordance with _____.

    (a) 250.122
    (b) 250.66
    (c) Table 250.122
    (d) Table 250.66

30. For interconnected electric power production sources, _____, unless otherwise marked, are suitable for backfeeding.

    (a) circuit breakers
    (b) PV system overcurrent devices
    (c) utility-interactive inverters
    (d) fused disconnects

31. For interconnected electric power production sources, a permanent _____, denoting all electric power sources on or in the premises, must be installed at each service equipment location and all interconnected electric power production sources.

    (a) label
    (b) plaque
    (c) directory
    (d) b or c

32. For interconnected electric power production sources, an electric power production source is permitted to be connected to the supply side of the service disconnecting means.

    (a) True
    (b) False

33. For interconnected electric power production sources, dedicated ac inverter circuit breakers that are backfed must be secured in place by an additional fastener as required by 408.36(D).

    (a) True
    (b) False

34. For interconnected electric power production sources, installation of one or more electrical power production source(s) operating in parallel with a primary source(s) of electricity must be installed only by _____.

    (a) qualified persons
    (b) a utility company
    (c) the authority having jurisdiction
    (d) b or c

35. For interconnected electric power production sources, panelboards containing ac inverter circuit breakers must be field marked to indicate the presence of multiple ac power sources.

    (a) True
    (b) False

36. For interconnected electric power production sources, the generating source and all distribution equipment associated with it that generates electricity from a source other than a utility supplied service is called _____.

    (a) a service drop
    (b) power production equipment
    (c) the service point
    (d) utilization equipment

37. For interconnected electric power production sources, the output of a utility-interactive inverter can be connected to the load side of the service disconnecting means at any distribution equipment on the premises.

    (a) True
    (b) False

38. For interconnected electric power production sources, the sum of the ratings of all overcurrent devices connected to power production sources are permitted to exceed the rating of the service.

    (a) True
    (b) False

39. For interconnected electric power production sources, upon loss of utility source power, an electric power production source must be manually disconnected from all ungrounded conductors of the utility source and must not be reconnected until the utility source has been restored.

    (a) True
    (b) False

40. For one- and two-family dwellings, the maximum voltage for PV source or PV circuits is _____.

    (a) 24V
    (b) 48V
    (c) 250V
    (d) 600V

41. For PV systems, a listed current-limiting overcurrent device must be installed where the available short-circuit current from the battery bank exceeds the interrupting or _____ ratings of equipment it supplies.

    (a) short-circuit
    (b) withstand
    (c) ground-fault current
    (d) none of these

42. For PV systems, a(n) _____ is a device that changes direct-current input to an alternating-current output.

    (a) diode
    (b) rectifier
    (c) transistor
    (d) inverter

43. For PV systems, in one- and two-family dwellings, live parts over 150V to ground must not be accessible to an _____ while energized.

    (a) inspector
    (b) electrician
    (c) unqualified person
    (d) all of these

44. For PV systems, means must be provided to disconnect equipment, such as batteries, inverters, charge controllers, and the like, from all ungrounded conductors of all sources.

    (a) True
    (b) False

45. For PV systems, metallic mounting structures used for grounding purposes must be _____ as equipment grounding conductors or have _____ bonding jumpers or devices connected between the separate metallic sections and be bonded to the grounding system.

    (a) listed/labeled
    (b) labeled/listed
    (c) identified/identified
    (d) none of these

46. For PV systems, one source for lowest-expected ambient temperature is the "Extreme Annual Mean Minimum Design Dry Bulb Temperature" found in the *ASHRAE Handbook Fundamentals*.

    (a) True
    (b) False

47. For PV systems, the circuit(s) between modules and from modules to the common connection point(s) of the direct-current system is known as the _____.

    (a) photovoltaic source circuit
    (b) photovoltaic array circuit
    (c) photovoltaic input circuit
    (d) photovoltaic output circuit

48. For PV systems, the conductors between the inverter and an alternating-current panelboard for stand-alone systems, or the conductors between the inverter and the service equipment or another electric power production source, such as a utility, for an electrical production and distribution network, are part of the ____.

    (a) bipolar photovoltaic array
    (b) monopole subarray
    (c) emergency standby power
    (d) inverter output circuit

49. For PV systems, where all terminals of a disconnecting means may be energized when the switch is in the open position, a warning sign must be placed on or adjacent to the disconnecting means. The sign shall be similar to: WARNING ELECTRIC SHOCK HAZARD. DO NOT TOUCH TERMINALS. TERMINALS ON BOTH THE LINE AND LOAD SIDES MAY BE ENERGIZED IN THE OPEN POSITION.

    (a) True
    (b) False

50. For PV systems, where flexible cables are installed, they are only permitted between the battery terminals to a nearby junction box where they must connect to an approved wiring method, or between batteries and cells within the battery enclosure.

    (a) True
    (b) False

51. For PV systems, where used for battery interconnections, flexible cables listed for hard-service use and identified as moisture resistant in Article 400, must be a minimum size of ____ AWG.

    (a) 1/0
    (b) 2/0
    (c) 3/0
    (d) 4/0

52. For PV systems, where used for battery interconnections, flexible, fine-stranded cables must terminate in terminals, lugs, devices, or connectors that are ____ for fine-stranded conductors.

    (a) identified
    (b) listed
    (c) a or b
    (d) a and b

53. For stand-alone PV systems, circuit breakers that are marked "Line" and "Load" can be backfed.

    (a) True
    (b) False

54. For stand-alone PV systems, energy storage or backup power supplies are required.

    (a) True
    (b) False

55. For stand-alone PV systems, the ac current output from a stand-alone inverter(s) can be ____ than the calculated load connected to the disconnect, but not less than the largest single utilization equipment connected to the system.

    (a) less
    (b) more
    (c) greater
    (d) any of these

56. Fuses or circuit breakers for PV dc circuits must be ____ for use in dc circuits and shall have the appropriate voltage, current, and interrupt ratings.

    (a) identified
    (b) approved
    (c) recognized
    (d) listed

57. Grounded dc PV arrays must be provided with direct-current ____ meeting the requirements of 690.5(a) through (c) to reduce fire hazards.

    (a) arc-fault protection
    (b) rectifier protection
    (c) ground-fault monitors
    (d) ground-fault protection

58. In accordance with Article 705, where two sources, one a utility and the other an inverter, are located at opposite ends of a busbar that contains loads, a permanent warning label must be applied to the panelboard to warn others that the inverter output connection circuit breaker must not be relocated.

    (a) True
    (b) False

59. In dwellings, battery cells for PV systems must be connected so as to operate at _____, nominal, or less.

    (a) 20V
    (b) 30V
    (c) 40V
    (d) 50V

60. In grounded PV source circuits, one overcurrent protection device is not permitted to protect the PV modules and the interconnecting conductors.

    (a) True
    (b) False

61. Junction, pull, and outlet boxes can be located behind PV modules that are secured by removable fasteners.

    (a) True
    (b) False

62. Labels or markings of PV system raceways and enclosures must be suitable for the environment and be placed with a maximum of _____ ft of spacing.

    (a) 5
    (b) 10
    (c) 20
    (d) 25

63. Live parts of PV storage battery systems for dwellings shall be _____ to prevent accidental contact by persons or objects regardless of voltage.

    (a) isolated
    (b) grounded
    (c) insulated
    (d) guarded

64. Monopole subarrays in a bipolar PV system shall be physically _____ where the sum of the PV system voltages, without consideration of polarity, of the two monopole subarrays exceeds the rating of the conductors and connected equipment.

    (a) separated
    (b) connected
    (c) joined
    (d) together

65. Non-load-break-rated disconnecting means for PV output circuits must be marked "Do not open under load."

    (a) True
    (b) False

66. Only inverters and ac PV modules listed and identified as interactive can be used with interactive systems.

    (a) True
    (b) False

67. Overcurrent devices for PV source circuits must be readily accessible.

    (a) True
    (b) False

68. Overcurrent devices for PV systems shall be rated to carry not less than _____ percent of the maximum currents calculated in 690.8(A).

    (a) 80
    (b) 100
    (c) 125
    (d) 250

69. Photovoltaic wiring methods containing _____ must be terminated only with terminals, lugs, devices, or connectors that are identified and listed for such use.

    (a) flexible, fine-stranded cables
    (b) solid conductors
    (c) flexible raceways
    (d) all of these

70. Plug-in type backfed circuit breakers for a stand-alone or multimode inverter connected to a stand-alone PV system are not required to be secured in place by an additional fastener that requires other than a pull to release the breaker from the panelboard.

    (a) True
    (b) False

71. PV source circuits and PV output circuits are not permitted to be contained in the same raceway, cable tray, cable, outlet box, junction box, or similar fitting, with non-PV systems unless the two systems are separated by a partition.

    (a) True
    (b) False

72. PV source circuits shall be identified at all points of termination, connection, and splices.

    (a) True
    (b) False

73. PV system conductors shall be identified by separate color coding, marking tape, tagging, or other approved means.

    (a) True
    (b) False

74. PV systems are permitted to supply a building or other structure in addition to any other _____ supply system(s).

    (a) electrical
    (b) telephone
    (c) plumbing
    (d) none of these

75. PV systems having no direct connection between the dc grounded conductor and ac grounded conductor shall have a(n) _____ grounding system which shall be bonded to the ac grounding system.

    (a) ac
    (b) dc
    (c) separately derived
    (d) none of these

76. PV systems with dc modules having no direct connection between the dc grounded conductor and ac grounded conductor must be bonded to the ac grounding system by a(n) _____.

    (a) separate dc grounding electrode bonded to the ac grounding electrode system with a bonding jumper
    (b) dc grounding electrode conductor sized to 250.166 run from the marked dc grounding electrode connection point to the ac grounding electrode
    (c) unspliced, or irreversibly spliced, combined grounding conductor run from the marked dc grounding electrode connection point along with the ac circuit conductors to the grounding busbar in the associated ac equipment
    (d) any of these

77. Single-conductor Type USE-2 and single-conductor cable _____ as PV wire can be run exposed at outdoor locations for PV source circuits for PV module interconnections within the PV array.

    (a) approved
    (b) listed or labeled
    (c) listed and labeled
    (d) none of the above

78. The _____ is the basic PV device that generates electricity when exposed to light.

    (a) solar battery
    (b) solar cell
    (c) solar atom
    (d) solar ray

79. The _____ of a dc PV source circuit or output circuit is used to calculate the sum of the rated open-circuit voltage of the series-connected PV modules multiplied by the correction factor provided in Table 690.7.

    (a) minimum allowable ampacity of conductors
    (b) maximum allowable ampacity of conductors
    (c) minimum photovoltaic system voltage
    (d) maximum photovoltaic system voltage

80. The circuit conductors between the inverter or direct-current utilization equipment and the PV source circuit(s) is part of the ____.

    (a) photovoltaic output circuit
    (b) photovoltaic input circuit
    (c) inverter input circuit
    (d) inverter output circuit

81. The conductors between the inverter and the battery in a stand-alone system or the conductors between the inverter and the PV output circuits for an electrical production and distribution network are part of the ____.

    (a) branch circuit
    (b) feeder
    (c) inverter input circuit
    (d) inverter output circuit

82. The conductors of PV output circuits and inverter input and output circuits shall be identified at all points of termination, connection, and splices.

    (a) True
    (b) False

83. The connection to a ____ shall be arranged so that removal of either from a PV source circuit does not interrupt a grounded conductor connection to other PV source circuits.

    (a) panelboard or switchboard
    (b) bus or lug
    (c) module or panel
    (d) array or subarray

84. The connectors permitted by Article 690 shall ____.

    (a) be polarized
    (b) guard against inadvertent contact with live parts by persons
    (c) require a tool for opening if the circuit operates at over 30V nominal maximum dc or 30V ac
    (d) all of these

85. The direct-current system grounding connection must be made at any ____ point(s) on the PV output circuit.

    (a) single
    (b) two
    (c) three
    (d) four

86. The location of PV source and output conductors embedded in built-up, laminate, or membrane roofing materials in areas not covered by PV modules and associated equipment must be clearly marked.

    (a) True
    (b) False

87. The maximum PV inverter output circuit current is equal to the ____ output current rating.

    (a) average
    (b) peak
    (c) continuous
    (d) intermittent

88. The output of an ac module is considered an ____ output circuit as defined in 690.2.

    (a) inverter
    (b) module
    (c) PV
    (d) subarray

89. The photovoltaic system voltage is the direct-current voltage of any PV source or PV output circuit.

    (a) True
    (b) False

90. The point of interconnection of the PV system power source to other sources must be marked at an accessible location at the ____ as a power source and with the rated ac output current and nominal operating ac voltage.

    (a) disconnecting means
    (b) array
    (c) inverter
    (d) none of these

91. The provisions of Article 690 apply to _____ systems, including inverter(s), array circuit(s), and controller(s) for such systems.

    (a) solar photoconductive
    (b) solar PV
    (c) solar photogenic
    (d) solar photosynthesis

92. The PV disconnecting means shall be externally operable without exposing the operator to contact with live parts and shall indicate whether in the open or closed position.

    (a) True
    (b) False

93. The PV output circuit current is equal to the sum of parallel PV source circuit maximum currents as calculated in _____.

    (a) 690.8(A)(1)
    (b) 690.8(A)(2)
    (c) 690.8(A)(3)
    (d) none of these

94. The PV source circuit current is calculated by multiplying the sum of the parallel module nameplate short-circuit current ratings (Isc) by 125 percent.

    (a) True
    (b) False

95. The PV system disconnecting means must be _____ to identify it as a photovoltaic system disconnect.

    (a) listed
    (b) approved
    (c) permanently marked
    (d) temporarily marked

96. The requirement for grouping PV source and output circuits is not required if the circuit enters from a cable or raceway unique to the circuit that makes the grouping obvious.

    (a) True
    (b) False

97. The source interconnection of one or more inverters installed in one system shall be made at a dedicated circuit breaker or fusible disconnecting means.

    (a) True
    (b) False

98. The ungrounded PV system dc disconnect must be placed at a readily accessible location _____ of a building or structure to disconnect the ungrounded PV system dc circuit conductors.

    (a) outside
    (b) inside, nearest the point of entrance
    (c) anywhere inside
    (d) a or b

99. Where dc PV source or output circuits are run inside a building or structure, they must be contained in _____.

    (a) metal raceways
    (b) Type MC cables
    (c) metal enclosures
    (d) any of these

100. Where exposed and subject to physical damage, PV array equipment grounding conductors smaller than 4 AWG must be protected by raceway or cable armor.

    (a) True
    (b) False

INDEX

Description	Rule	Page

A

Armored Cable (Type AC)

Bends	320.24	221
Boxes and Fittings	320.40	222
Conductor Ampacity	320.80	222
Construction	320.100	223
Definition	320.2	219
Equipment Grounding Conductor	320.108	223
Exposed Work	320.15	220
In Accessible Attics or Roof Spaces	320.23	221
Scope	320.1	219
Securing and Supporting	320.30	221
Through or Parallel to Framing Members	320.17	220
Uses Not Permitted	320.12	220
Uses Permitted	320.10	220

B

Boxes

Boxes and Conduit Bodies for Conductors 4 AWG and Larger	314.28	214
Conductors That Enter Boxes or Conduit Bodies	314.17	212
Damp or Wet Locations	314.15	212
Handhole Enclosures	314.30	218
Metal Boxes	314.4	212
Nonmetallic Boxes	314.3	211
Scope	314.1	211
Support of Boxes and Conduit Bodies	314.23	213
Wiring to be Accessible	314.29	217

Description	Rule	Page

C

Cabinets

Cabinets With Splices, Taps, and Feed-Through

Conductors	312.8	208
Damp or Wet Locations	312.2	206
Deflection of Conductors	312.6	208
Enclosures	312.5	206
Installed in Walls	312.3	206
Repairing Gaps	312.4	206
Scope	312.1	205

Cable Trays

Ampacity of Conductors	392.80	279
Bushed Raceway	392.46	278
Cable and Conductor Installation	392.20	278
Cable Splices	392.56	278
Cable Tray Installations	392.18	277
Definition	392.2	275
Equipment Grounding Conductor	392.60	278
Number of Conductors or Cables	392.22	278
Scope	392.1	275
Securing and Supporting	392.30	278
Uses Not Permitted	392.12	277
Uses Permitted	392.10	276

Conductors

Conductor Ampacity	310.15	197
Conductor Construction and Application	310.104	202
Conductor Identification	310.110	203
Conductors	310.106	203
Scope	310.1	194
Uses Permitted	310.10	194

Description	Rule	Page
E		
Electrical Metallic Tubing (Type EMT)		
Bends	358.24	267
Couplings and Connectors	358.42	268
Definition	358.2	265
Grounding	358.60	269
Listing Requirement	358.6	265
Number of Bends (360°)	358.26	267
Number of Conductors	358.22	266
Reaming and Threading	358.28	267
Scope	358.1	265
Securing and Supporting	358.30	268
Trade Size	358.20	266
Uses Not Permitted	358.12	266
Uses Permitted	358.10	265
F		
Flexible Metal Conduit (Type FMC)		
Bends	348.24	251
Definition	348.2	249
Fittings	348.42	252
Grounding and Bonding	348.60	252
Listing Requirements	348.6	249
Number of Bends (360°)	348.26	251
Number of Conductors	348.22	250
Scope	348.1	249
Securing and Supporting	348.30	251
Trade Size	348.20	250
Trimming	348.28	251
Uses Not Permitted	348.12	250
Uses Permitted	348.10	249
G		
General Requirements		
Approval of Conductors and Equipment	110.2	33
Arc-Flash Hazard Warning	110.16	46
Boxes or Conduit Bodies	300.15	183
Circuit Impedance, Short-Circuit Current Rating, and Other Characteristics	110.10	37
Code Arrangement	90.3	4
Conductor Sizes	110.6	35
Conductor Termination and Splicing	110.14	40
Conductors	300.3	168
Copper Conductors	110.5	35
Definitions	100	13
Deteriorating Agents	110.11	38
Electrical Continuity	300.10	181
Enclosure Types	110.28	57
Enforcement	90.4	5
Examination of Equipment for Product Safety	90.7	7
Examination, Identification, Installation, and Use of Equipment	110.3	34
Formal Interpretations	90.6	7
Guarding	110.27	56
Identification of Disconnecting Means	110.22	47
Induced Currents in Ferrous Metal Enclosures and Raceways	300.20	187
Inserting Conductors in Raceways	300.18	186
Interrupting Protection Rating	110.9	36
Length of Free Conductors	300.14	182
Lockable Disconnecting Means	110.25	47
Mandatory Requirements and Explanatory Material	90.5	6
Markings	110.21	46
Mechanical Continuity	300.12	181
Mechanical Execution of Work	110.12	38
Mounting and Cooling of Equipment	110.13	40
Not Permitted in Raceways	300.8	180
Panels Designed to Allow Access	300.23	191
Protection Against Corrosion and Deterioration	300.6	177
Protection Against Physical Damage	300.4	169
Purpose of the *NEC*	90.1	2
Raceway Sizing	300.17	184
Raceways Exposed to Different Temperatures	300.7	179
Raceways in Wet Locations Above Grade	300.9	180
Scope	110.1	33
Scope	300.1	167
Scope of the *NEC*	90.2	3
Spaces About Electrical Equipment	110.26	48
Splices and Pigtails	300.13	182
Spread of Fire or Products of Combustion	300.21	188
Suitable Wiring Methods	110.8	36
Supporting Conductors in Vertical Raceways	300.19	186
Underground Installations	300.5	172

Description	Rule	Page
G (continued)		
General Requirements (continued)		
Units of Measurement	90.9	7
Wiring in Ducts Not for Air Handling, Fabricated Ducts for Environmental Air, and Other Spaces for Environmental Air (Plenums)	300.22	189
Wiring Integrity	110.7	35
Grounded Conductor		
Grounded and Neutral Conductor Identification	200.6	73
Grounding and Bonding		
Auxiliary Grounding Electrodes	250.54	121
Bonding Conductors and Jumpers	250.102	132
Bonding Equipment for Services	250.92	128
Bonding Metal Parts Containing Circuits over 150V to Ground	250.97	131
Bonding Other Enclosures	250.96	131
Clean Surfaces	250.12	103
Continuity and Attachment of Equipment Grounding Conductors in Metal Boxes	250.148	142
Cord-and-Plug-Connected Equipment	250.114	134
Cord-and-Plug-Connected Equipment	250.138	142
Equipment Connected by Permanent Wiring Methods	250.134	141
Equipment Considered Grounded	250.136	141
Equipment Grounding Conductor Installation	250.120	139
General	250.90	128
General Requirements for Grounding and Bonding	250.4	99
Grounding Electrode Conductor	250.62	121
Grounding Electrode Conductor Installation	250.64	122
Grounding Electrode Conductor Termination Fittings	250.70	128
Grounding Electrode Installation Requirements	250.53	117
Grounding Electrode System	250.50	113
Grounding Electrode Types	250.52	114
Identification of Equipment Grounding Conductors	250.119	138
Other Enclosures	250.86	128
Protection of Fittings	250.10	103
Scope	250.1	99
Separately Derived Systems (Transformers)— Grounding and Bonding	250.30	108
Service Equipment—Grounding and Bonding	250.24	104
Sizing AC Grounding Electrode Conductor	250.66	125
Sizing Equipment Grounding Conductor	250.122	140
Sizing Grounding Electrode Conductor	250.166	143
Specific Equipment Fastened in Place or Connected by Permanent Wiring Methods	250.112	134
Termination of Grounding and Bonding Conductors	250.8	102
Termination to the Grounding Electrode	250.68	126
Types of Equipment Grounding Conductors	250.118	134
Use of Neutral Conductor for Equipment Grounding	250.142	142
I		
Interconnected Electric Power Production Sources		
Definitions	705.2	398
Directory of Power Sources	705.10	398
Ground-Fault Protection	705.32	408
Location of Overcurrent Protection	705.31	407
Loss of Primary Source	705.40	408
Point of Connection	705.12	399
Qualified Persons	705.6	398
Scope	705.1	397
Voltage Unbalanced (Imbalanced) Interconnections	705.100	408
Intermediate Metal Conduit (Type IMC)		
Bends	342.24	239
Bushings	342.46	241
Couplings and Connectors	342.42	241
Definition	342.2	237
Dissimilar Metals	342.14	238
Listing Requirements	342.6	237
Number of Bends (360°)	342.26	239
Number of Conductors	342.22	238
Reaming	342.28	239
Scope	342.1	237
Securing and Supporting	342.30	239
Trade Size	342.20	238
Uses Permitted	342.10	238

Description	Rule	Page
L		
Liquidtight Flexible Metal Conduit (Type LFMC)		
Bends	350.24	255
Definition	350.2	253
Fittings	350.42	256
Grounding and Bonding	350.60	256
Listing Requirements	350.6	253
Number of Bends (360°)	350.26	255
Number of Conductors	350.22	254
Scope	350.1	253
Securing and Supporting	350.30	255
Trade Size	350.20	254
Uses Not Permitted	350.12	254
Uses Permitted	350.10	253
M		
Metal Wireways		
Conductors—Maximum Size	376.21	272
Definition	376.2	271
Number of Conductors and Ampacity	376.22	272
Scope	376.1	271
Splices, Taps, and Power Distribution Blocks	376.56	273
Supports	376.30	273
Uses Not Permitted	376.12	272
Uses Permitted	376.10	272
Wireway Sizing	376.23	273
Metal-Clad Cable (Type MC)		
Bends	330.24	227
Conductor Ampacities	330.80	229
Definition	330.2	225
Equipment Grounding Conductor	330.108	229
Fittings	330.40	228
In Accessible Attics or Roof Spaces	330.23	227
Scope	330.1	225
Securing and Supporting	330.30	228
Through or Parallel to Framing Members	330.17	227
Uses Not Permitted	330.12	227
Uses Permitted	330.10	226

Description	Rule	Page
O		
Overcurrent Protection		
Classification	240.61	96
Damp or Wet Locations	240.32	95
Definitions	240.2	86
General	240.60	95
Indicating	240.81	96
Location of Overcurrent Devices	240.24	92
Markings	240.83	97
Method of Operation	240.80	96
Nontamperable	240.82	97
Overcurrent Protection Location in Circuit	240.21	89
Protection of Conductors	240.4	87
Scope	240.1	86
Standard Ampere Ratings	240.6	88
Supplementary Overcurrent Protection	240.10	89
Ungrounded Conductors	240.15	89
Vertical Position	240.33	95
P		
Panelboards		
Clearance for Conductors Entering Bus Enclosures	408.5	312
Equipment Grounding Conductor	408.40	314
Field Identification	408.4	311
Neutral Conductor Terminations	408.41	314
Overcurrent Protection of Panelboards	408.36	313
Panelboards in Damp or Wet Locations	408.37	314
Scope	408.1	311
Unused Openings	408.7	312
R		
Rigid Metal Conduit (Type RMC)		
Bends	344.24	245
Bushings	344.46	248
Construction	344.100	248
Couplings and Connectors	344.42	247
Definition	344.2	243
Dissimilar Metals	344.14	244
Listing Requirements	344.6	244
Number of Bends (360°)	344.26	245

Description	Rule	Page

R (continued)

Rigid Metal Conduit (Type RMC) (continued)

Description	Rule	Page
Number of Conductors	344.22	245
Reaming	344.28	245
Scope	344.1	243
Securing and Supporting	344.30	246
Standard Lengths	344.130	248
Trade Size	344.20	244
Uses Permitted	344.10	244

Rigid Polyvinyl Chloride Conduit (Type PVC)

Description	Rule	Page
Bends	352.24	260
Bushings	352.46	262
Definition	352.2	257
Equipment Grounding Conductor	352.60	263
Expansion Fittings	352.44	261
Joints	352.48	263
Number of Bends (360°)	352.26	260
Number of Conductors	352.22	259
Scope	352.1	257
Securing and Supporting	352.30	260
Trade Size	352.20	259
Trimming	352.28	260
Uses Not Permitted	352.12	259
Uses Permitted	352.10	258

S

Service-Entrance Cable (Types SE and USE)

Description	Rule	Page
Bends	338.24	233
Definitions	338.2	231
Scope	338.1	231
Uses Not Permitted	338.12	232
Uses Permitted	338.10	232

Services

Description	Rule	Page
Connected on Supply Side of the Service Disconnect	230.82	83
Connection to Terminals	230.81	83
Disconnect Requirements	230.70	80
Grouping of Disconnects	230.72	82
Indicating	230.77	83
Listed as Suitable for Service Equipment	230.66	79
Location of Overcurrent Protection	230.91	84
Manual or Power Operated	230.76	82
Number of Disconnects	230.71	81
Number of Service-Entrance Conductor Sets	230.40	78
Overload Protection Required	230.90	84
Scope	230.1	78
Spliced Conductors	230.46	79
Wiring Methods	230.43	78

Solar Photovoltaic (PV) Systems

Description	Rule	Page
Access to Boxes	690.34	368
Alternating-Current Modules	690.6	341
Arc-Fault Circuit Protection (Direct Current)	690.11	355
Array Equipment Grounding Conductors	690.46	373
Battery Interconnections	690.74	382
Building Supplied by a PV System	690.13	356
Charge Control	690.72	382
Charging Equipment	690.91	382
Circuit Current and Circuit Sizing	690.8	344
Connectors	690.33	367
Continuity of Equipment Grounding	690.48	377
Continuity of System Grounding	690.49	377
Definitions	690.2	332
Disconnect Type (dc)	690.17	360
Disconnecting Means for Fuses	690.16	359
Equipment Grounding (Bonding)	690.43	370
General	690.90	382
General Requirements	690.4	338
Ground-Fault Protection	690.5	339
Grounding Electrode System	690.47	373
Identification of Power Sources	690.56	378
Installation and Service	690.18	362
Interactive System	690.54	378
Interactive Systems	690.60	380
Loss of Interactive System Power	690.61	380
Maximum Voltage	690.7	341
Other Articles	690.3	338
Overcurrent Protection	690.9	350
Point of Connection	690.64	380
Point of Grounding Connection	690.42	370
PV dc Power Source Label	690.53	377
PV Equipment Disconnect	690.15	358
PV Systems with Energy Storage	690.55	378
Rapid Shutdown of PV Systems on Buildings	690.12	355

Description	Rule	Page
S (continued)		
Solar Photovoltaic (PV) Systems (continued)		
Scope	690.1	331
Size of Equipment Grounding Conductors	690.45	372
Stand-Alone Systems	690.10	354
Storage Battery Installation	690.71	381
System Grounding	690.41	369
Unbalanced Interconnections	690.63	380
Ungrounded Systems	690.35	368
Wiring Methods	690.31	363
Storage Batteries		
Battery and Cell Terminations	480.3	321
Battery Locations	480.9	322
Definitions	480.2	320
Racks and Trays	480.8	321
Scope	480.1	319
Wiring and Equipment Supplied from Batteries	480.4	321
Switches		
Accessibility and Grouping	404.8	308
Circuit Breakers Used as Switches	404.11	309
Damp or Wet Locations	404.4	307
Grounding of Enclosures	404.12	309
Indicating	404.7	308
Position of Knife Switches	404.6	308
Scope	404.1	307
Switch Enclosures	404.3	307
Switch Marking	404.15	309

Description	Rule	Page
T		
Transformers		
Disconnecting Means	450.14	318
Grounding and Bonding	450.10	316
Marking	450.11	317
Overcurrent Protection	450.3	315
Scope	450.1	315
Transformer Accessibility	450.13	317
Ventilation	450.9	316
U		
Underground Feeder and Branch-Circuit Cable (Type UF)		
Ampacity	340.80	236
Bends	340.24	236
Definition	340.2	235
Insulation	340.112	236
Listing Requirements	340.6	236
Scope	340.1	235
Uses Not Permitted	340.12	236
Uses Permitted	340.10	236

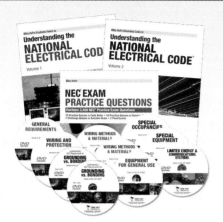

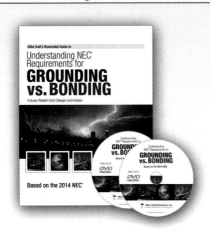